C0-AUJ-733

THE GEOGRAPHICAL LORE OF THE TIME OF THE CRUSADES

THE GEOGRAPHICAL LORE OF THE TIME OF THE CRUSADES

A Study in the History of Medieval Science and Tradition in Western Europe

BY

JOHN KIRTLAND WRIGHT, PH.D.

WITH A NEW INTRODUCTION BY

CLARENCE J. GLACKEN
Department of Geography
University of California at Berkeley

DOVER PUBLICATIONS, INC., NEW YORK

Published in the United Kingdom by Constable and Company, Ltd., 10 Orange Street, London W.C.2.

This Dover edition, first published in 1965, is an unabridged and corrected republication of the work first published by the American Geographical Society in 1925 as Number 15 in the Research Series.
This edition also contains a new Introduction by Clarence J. Glacken, Department of Geography, University of California, Berkeley.

Library of Congress Catalog Card Number: 65-12262

Manufactured in the United States of America

Dover Publications, Inc.
180 Varick Street
New York 14, N.Y.

TO

K. M. W.

INTRODUCTION TO THE DOVER EDITION

The Geographical Lore of the Time of the Crusades is the work of a young man. When John K. Wright completed it in his thirty-fourth year in 1925, medieval studies were well established in America. Henry Charles Lea had already published his impressive works on European religious history, Henry Adams' *Mont Saint-Michel and Chartres* had appeared in 1904, Henry Osborn Taylor's *The Medieval Mind* in 1911, and Lynn Thorndike had started his magistral *History of Magic and Experimental Science*.

Wright was a student of Charles Haskins, a man of deep learning, best known for his full-length studies of the twelfth-century renaissance, the rise of universities, and the history of medieval science, but who also wrote specialized articles on such topics as the Latin literature of sport, and the Emperor Frederick II's treatise on falconry. As a historian trained in the study of medieval science and intellectual history, Wright saw the importance of bringing together in a single work the leading ideas of cosmology and geography of one of the most active, creative, and puzzling periods in the history of Western civilization. This was the age of the Crusades, but it was also a crucial period in the history of Western urbanism, an age of cathedral building, and of the clearing of the woodlands. If one thinks of Richard the Lion-Hearted, one should also think of Suger, abbot of Saint-Denis, and of St. Bernard. A modern writer would not group cosmology with physical and cultural geography, but in the Middle Ages as in classical times, cosmology and cosmogony were firmly linked to geography. They shared the theory of the four elements; at the same time speculations about the macrocosm and the microcosm and astrology encouraged conceptions of an interlocking cosmic order.

The study of medieval geography is inherently intractable. The sources are widely scattered; often they are interminable, repetitious and imitative; meanings may not be clear. Religious or philosophical works omit as unworthy of comment topics about which a modern student would dearly like to know. Unless one is content with cataloguing theories of the size and the shape of the earth or summarizing the compendium-like geography made popular by Pliny and conspicuous in such works as the *Etymologiae* of Isidore of Seville, one is forced to higher hilltops. The materials must be ordered by relating them to broader intellectual themes such as the history of exploration, or of science, or above all to the history of philosophy and theology because it is in these vast repositories of human thought that one finds the fundamental ideas and beliefs regarding the interrelationships of God, man, and nature. One may find sources in the sermons of St. Augustine, the *Summae* of St. Thomas, the works of St. Bernard, or the poetry of *The Romance of the Rose*. Furthermore, the unrelenting Biblical exegesis of the Middle Ages contributed greatly to the clarification of Christian thought regarding these interrelationships. The hexaemeral literature also is a storehouse of physical, cosmological, and geographical thought; the brevity of Genesis 1 and 2, considering the momentous events described, is an invitation to enthusiastic exegesis.

Since the publication of *The Geographical Lore of the Time of the Crusades*, new areas of inquiry of interest to the historian of geography have opened up and earlier breaches have been widened. Of particular interest are the recent works on medieval science, technology, agriculture, grazing and forestry, and the history of Christian philosophy. (See Dr. Wright's note on p. 490 and the bibliographical note at the end of this Introduction.) With the exception, however, of George Kimble's *Geography in the Middle Ages* (1938), no major work of synthesis in the field of medieval geographical thought has appeared. Wright, Kimble, and Kretschmer (*Die physische Erdkunde im christlichen Mittelalter*, 1889) still remain our most reliable guides. In making this statement, I do not wish to slight C. R. Beazley's *The Dawn of Modern Geography*, but it is fair to say that the emphasis of this three-volume work is not on theory or concepts but on the history of medieval travel and exploration.

John K. Wright's book has a secure place in the history of geography and in the history of ideas because it brings order out of a bewildering—and overwhelming—array of theories, speculations, fables, superstitions, and religious and astrological beliefs about men, plants, animals, and inanimate objects; it also throws light on the significance of places even if they are dimly known or legendary. It is distinct from a history of exploration and a history of science, even though it possesses some characteristics of both.

It may be worthwhile, therefore, to mention a few themes that might interest a general reader of this book. First, there is the highly interesting and well-documented story of the classical, Christian, and Muslim contributions to medieval cosmographical and geographical thought. Many old friends whose birthplaces were on the Ionian shore, in Athens, Rome, Alexandria, and Baghdad reappear. The *klimata*, the doctrine of the four elements, the antipodes, Ptolemy's geography, the belief in the macro- and the microcosms play important roles in medieval thought.

Secondly, the meanings one finds in nature and attitudes toward the countryside (pp. 63–65, 235–240) are important because they are based on the philosophy, religion, science, technical arts, and literature of an age. In 1892 Alfred Biese published a short work on the feeling for nature in the Middle Ages and in modern times; this was followed in 1911 by C. V. Langlois' *La connaissance de la nature et du monde au moyen âge* and in 1914 by Wilhelm Ganzenmüller's *Das Naturgefühl im Mittelalter*. Wright has made use of these and other materials and has added interesting observations of his own. Much, however, still remains to be done on this exceedingly important and fascinating subject which is almost invariably linked with the Christian distinction between the Creator and the created: one must love nature because it is a divine creation, but too great a love of its beauties will lead the beholder to worship what has been created and not the Creator.

Other themes emerge from sacred geography and religious thought. In the patristic period, Lactantius, gentle, devout, well-educated, but overly confident, thought it self-evident that human beings could not exist in the antipodes because they would fall away from the earth's lower side (*Divine Institutes*, III, 24). And many later thinkers agreed with him. St. Augustine wrote in *The City of God* (Bk. XVI, ch. 9) that men who thought the antipodes existed were deceived by fables. Belief in the existence of the antipodes, moreover, required an explanation, consistent with Christian doctrine, of the origin of the people living there.

Of more immediate interest are the belief that Jerusalem is the center of the *oikoumene* and the speculations on the nature and location of paradise. A surprising amount of the human geography and anthropology of the Middle Ages is related to these topics (pp. 257–265). The Eden theme influenced geographical thought because of interest not only in the location of the garden, but in its geography and climate as well. Descriptions of Eden often reveal what the author considered to be an ideal environment for human life.

Furthermore, the legend of Prester John became a powerful stimulus to exploration (pp. 283–286). In this period a rudimentary philosophy of history, the idea of a geographical march of civilization from east to west, matured (pp. 233–235); the idea apparently is derived by analogy from the course of the sun, from a reading of ancient history as it was then understood, and from the writings of earlier church fathers and ecclesiastical historians.

A few thinkers of the Middle Ages were interested in theories of environmental influence on man and other forms of life (pp. 231–233). Almost all of them, however, are echoes of classical thought, the most systematic expositions coming a little later in the *De natura locorum* of Albert the Great and St. Thomas Aquinas' *On Kingship, to the King of Cyprus*.

With reference to Wright's discussion of light (pp. 143–144), its function in the creation, and of Robert Grosseteste's theory of its nature, it may be remarked that the idea of light was extremely important in the Middle Ages because it was closely associated with ideas of divine and earthly beauty. As von

Simson has shown in *The Gothic Cathedral*, the luminosity of Gothic architecture was directly related both to the esthetic and metaphysical conception of light. Light gave men insight into cosmic perfection and suggested to them the nature of the Creator. It also suggested radiance, luminosity, and understanding; the power of this idea is still apparent in the *Novum Organum* of Francis Bacon.

Fortunately, some of the works which are discussed in this book have now appeared in well-edited translations in the Columbia University "Records of Civilization" series, among them William of Tyre's *A History of Deeds Done Across the Sea*, Otto, Bishop of Freising's *Two Cities*, and *The Deeds of Frederick Barbarossa*, and Adam of Bremen's *History of the Archbishops of Hamburg-Bremen*. These works, as Wright shows, possess an authenticity and freshness quite out of keeping with popular stereotypes of medieval geographic description and travel. Anyone who has read William of Tyre's *A History of Deeds Done Across the Sea* will not soon forget it. The horror and cruelty of war, the agony of disease, and filth are described unsparingly. The descriptions of natural resources, peoples, towns, and countrysides are straightforward, and in general unadorned.

The extensive documentation of Wright's work is worthy of remark. There is a more vibrant interplay between it and the text than is the case in many scholarly works. The notes with their generous quotations from the original sources often go beyond the peripheral areas of a subject and touch upon other fields, so that one can see clearly how various ideas and concepts are part of a wider body of knowledge and belief. Wright is a superb bibliographer, and his comments on the sources have the same qualities as those of the notes. There is much to be learned from this book regarding innovation and persistence in thought and the transmission of ideas.

The chapter on "Regional Geography" is one of the most revealing in the book, especially if viewed as a study in the persistence and dissemination of ideas. For large areas of Eurasia and parts of Africa the classical authors are still faithful companions, with additions of places made important by Christianity. Wright compares geographical knowledge to areas circumscribed by two concentric circles. The knowledge of the large outer circle is derived from tradition, fable, and speculation, travellers' tales, and similar unreliable sources; that of the smaller inner circle comes from direct observation. An excellent example of this distinction between the material inherited from the past and that acquired from direct and contemporary observation is. Book XV, "On Geography," of *De proprietatibus rerum* by Bartholomew of England. The entry on Paris suggests that Bartholomew had seen what he describes; many other entries are taken from Isidore of Seville, whose ultimate sources are in classical and Christian geography.

The contrast between the geography of tradition and that of observation may be further illustrated by comparing the information about Asia derived from various sources (some going back to Herodotus) with that which men of Western Europe acquired personally from their participation in the Crusades. More concrete and reliable information was gathered by such men (William of Tyre is an outstanding example), and Wright may well be correct in suggesting an important mechanism by which the new knowledge of foreign lands was diffused throughout Europe. "Before the Crusades communities throughout the greater part of Europe had lived very much to themselves, in limited contact with the outside world; but by the year 1200 it is safe to infer that practically every town and village of France, England, Germany, and Italy held someone who had visited the East and was not unready to tell about what he had seen there and on his way out and back" (p. 293).

When John K. Wright finished *The Geographical Lore of the Time of the Crusades*, he left the Middle Ages, and has not returned to them; but as a historian of geography, he has not lost the interest in ideas which is so conspicuous in this work. His association with George Sarton, his book reviews in *Isis* during Sarton's editorship, his essays, "A Plea for the History of Geography" (*Isis*, February, 1925), and "Terrae Incognitae: The Place of the Imagination in Geography" (*Annals of the*

Association of American Geographers, March, 1947), and his volume on the history of the American Geographical Society show how stimulated he has been, through his long and productive life, by the history of ideas and how also he has communicated this enthusiasm to others.

Bibliographical Note

In addition to those mentioned by Dr. Wright, the following recent works may be of interest to the reader of this book:

Bark, William C., *Origins of the Medieval World.* Anchor Books (Garden City, N.Y.: Doubleday & Co., Inc., 1960).

Drew, Katherine Fischer and Lear, Floyd Seyward, eds., *Perspectives in Medieval History.* Rice University Semicentennial Series (Chicago: University of Chicago Press, 1963). Contains articles by A. C. Crombie, Gaines Post, E. Dwight Salmon, S. Harrison Thomson, and Lynn White, Jr.

Gilson, Étienne, *History of Christian Philosophy in the Middle Ages.* (New York: Random House, 1955.)

Grand, Roger and Delatouche, Raymond, *L'agriculture au moyen âge de la fin de l'empire romain au XVIe siècle.* (Paris: E. De Boccard, 1950.)

Singer, Charles, *et al.*, eds., *A History of Technology. Vol. II, The Mediterranean Civilizations and the Middle Ages.* (New York and London: Oxford University Press, 1956.)

Clarence J. Glacken

Berkeley, California
1965

PREFACE TO THE DOVER EDITION

Originally published in a small edition, this book has been out of print and almost unobtainable in second-hand bookstores for many years. Hence I am grateful indeed to Dover Publications, Inc., for republishing it. I also deeply appreciate the kindness of my friend, Professor Clarence J. Glacken, in contributing the Introduction for the new edition.

Although I have maintained an enduring interest in the history of geography since I wrote the book, my interest has shifted to more modern times, and, except for a small work on a fifteenth-century map and some reviews and notes, I have neither published anything new on ancient or medieval geography nor tried to keep up with the flow of "literature" on those subjects. However, for the guidance of those who may wish to pursue further studies in this field, I have contributed to this edition a brief Note on page 490. That Note, the Introduction, this new Preface, a small substitution on page 414, and the correction of minor errors are the only changes that have been made in the new edition, in which the pagination is the same as in the edition of 1925.

JOHN KIRTLAND WRIGHT

Lyme, N. H.
March 14, 1964

PREFACE TO THE FIRST EDITION

When viewed historically, geographical concepts are seen to have come from an immense variety of sources. They have sprung partly from activities that cause men to travel over the surface of the earth: war, commerce, pilgrimage, diplomacy, pleasure. They have also sprung from the accumulated learning and lore of preceding ages and to no small extent from unfettered flights of the imagination. The history of geography, therefore, leads its students into many fields, affording them a key by means of which they may gain a sounder understanding of the extensive ranges of human activity and of the evolution of important phases of intellectual life.

This book is an attempt to illustrate and trace the origins of the most characteristic geographical ideas current in Western Europe at the height of the Middle Ages. Historians of geography have tended to neglect this period partly because of the dramatic appeal of the great Age of Discovery which was immediately to follow. It should be remembered, however, that, small as the known world was during the Middle Ages and naïve as may have been men's conceptions of it, medieval learning was none the less the central element in the scholarly background of the Age of Discovery. The Renaissance brought no sudden and complete emancipation from old modes of thought. While medieval science persisted and some of its errors may have restricted subsequent progress, on the whole the positive achievements of the fifteenth and sixteenth centuries would have been impossible had it not been for the enlightenment transferred from the centuries that went before.

C. R. Beazley in the second volume of his great work, *The Dawn of Modern Geography* (1901), adequately treats of the travels and explorations of the twelfth and early thirteenth centuries, but to the more theoretical aspects of geographical knowledge in this age he gives but meager space. Konrad Kretschmer in a monograph, *Die physische Erdkunde im christlichen Mittelalter* (1889), deals systematically with the physical geography of the entire Middle Ages but necessarily slights or wholly neglects many of the more interesting writings of the century and a half to which the present book is devoted. Other, lesser studies of the geographical conceptions of this period have to do exclusively with points of detail. The present writer ventures to hope, therefore, that there is place for a book in which the geographical lore of the time of the Crusades is discussed with greater fullness and at the same time with an orientation differing in many particulars from that of any work hitherto devoted to the subject.

Except as regards a few minor points (especially in Chapter X) he makes no claim to having based his work upon hitherto unpublished manuscript sources. The main part of the study, however (that dealing with the time of the Crusades, Chapters IV–XIII), is founded essentially upon printed editions of the primary sources for the history of civilization in the period. The first three chapters, on the other hand, relating as they do to the background of medieval geography and covering an enormous field, of necessity have to a large degree been written with the aid of the secondary works of modern scholars.

The volume is an enlargement of a thesis submitted in 1922 in partial fulfillment of the requirements for the degree of Doctor of Philosophy in history at Harvard University. Some of the research was pursued in Europe in 1919–1920, during which academic year the writer held the Woodbury Lowery Fellowship from Harvard. Subsequently the American Geographical Society has generously permitted him, while acting as Librarian of the Society, to devote much time to the revision of the manuscript.

The writer owes a special debt of gratitude to Professor C. H. Haskins, largely as a result of whose advice the particular period dealt with was selected. Helpful suggestions and the occasional receipt from Professor Haskins of a photograph or transcript of a manuscript bearing upon an apposite topic have been a constant stimulus. Useful suggestions have also been made by Professor R. P. Blake of Harvard and by Monsieur Charles de La Roncière of the Bibliothèque Nationale in Paris.

Dr. Charles Singer of the University of London courteously permitted the use of Plate VIII from his *Scientific Views and Visions of St. Hildegard* (1917) as a basis for Figure 5 of the present volume. The writer is indebted to Mr. W. L. G. Joerg, the editor, from whose editorial skill, experience, and tireless care the book has greatly profited. He also wishes to thank Mr. George W. Robinson, Secretary of the Harvard Graduate School of Arts and Sciences, Miss Genevieve R. Fallon, formerly of Radcliffe College, and Mr. Arthur A. Brooks and members of the library staff of the American Geographical Society for their painstaking aid with manuscript and proof.

New York
October 7, 1924

CONTENTS

CHAPTER PAGE

Part II

The Substance and Character of the Geographical Lore of the Time of the Crusades

LIST OF ILLUSTRATIONS

GEOGRAPHICAL LORE OF THE TIME OF THE CRUSADES

INTRODUCTION

The Time of the Crusades

The time of the Crusades, like all great constructive epochs in the history of civilization, was an age of contrasts. A succession of crises marked the progress of conflict between the ideals of Papacy and of Empire. The feudalism of an earlier day was giving place in Western Europe to centralized monarchy, in Italy to the growth of city states. Though faith swayed the masses of men to the undertaking of immense coöperative enterprises—cathedral building and crusades—the time, none the less, was one of questioning and doubt: faith sometimes gave place to heresy hunting. Keener intellects were not afraid to probe deep at the very foundations of established theological doctrine. A profound and widespread enthusiasm for scholarship expressed itself in many forms. The writings of older authorities were ransacked for the wisdom which they contained, and from them erudite and forbidding tomes were compiled. But wandering students and poets were abroad who hated the musty learning of the monastic cell and frankly rejoiced in the beauty of the world around them. For some time historians have been in the habit of speaking of a "twelfth-century renaissance." This expression is not wholly apt if used in a narrow sense to imply merely a rebirth of interest in the Greek and Latin classics. If taken to mean a re-stirring of the vital forces of civilization, the twelfth and thirteenth centuries were an age of renaissance indeed.

The purpose of this book is to illustrate a limited aspect of the intellectual activity of the time of the Crusades, but an aspect that is sufficiently broad to reveal to us something of the contrasting forces of this age.

Scope of the Term "Geographical Lore"

By "geographical lore" we mean what was known, believed, and felt about the origins, present condition, and distribution of the geographical elements of the earth. This covers a wider field than most definitions of geography. It comprises theories of the creation of the earth, of its size, shape, and movements, and of its relations to the heavenly bodies; of the zones of its atmosphere and the varied physiographic features of air, water, and land; finally, it comprises theories of the regions of the earth's surface. Because many of these theories were false they are no less deserving of attention. The errors of an age are as characteristic as the accurate knowledge which it possesses—and often more so. Moreover, in addition to formulated beliefs, whether true or false, our definition of geographical lore covers man's spiritual and esthetic attitude toward the various geographical facts, as revealed—often unconsciously—in descriptions of regions or of landscapes.

The historian of geology or the theologian may complain that we trespass on their domains in discussing theories of the Creation in a book devoted to the history of geography. Yet this is justifiable if we hold with most modern geographers that some explanation of the immediate causes of existing terrestrial conditions is an essential part of geography. These causes, it was the opinion of medieval thinkers, were to be sought for in the processes of the Creation. No man had the vaguest conception of the countless eons that have elapsed during which air, sea, and land have been in evolution. The good Christian thought that the world was made by God in the course of the six days of Genesis and that it then assumed practically the identical geographical appearance it has preserved ever since. In the Middle Ages geology, geography, and theology were inextricably interwoven.

Then again, the geographical lore of the Middle Ages involves a wider range of subjects in space, as well as in time, than is now included in geography. If medieval man had no knowledge of the age of the earth, he also had but the feeblest understanding of the immensity of the universe. To him, earth, stellar bodies, and celestial spheres were all part of a unified system of which the earth formed the core and most important member. Cosmology, astronomy, astrology, theology all dealt with this unified, geocentric, cosmic system; the interrelations between them were immediate and intimate. We cannot avoid some discussion of the matters in which these allied sciences bore directly on geography.

Origins of the Geographical Lore of the Time of the Crusades

Whence came the geographical lore of the time of the Crusades?

Some of it came from books of earlier ages, some of it from contemporary observation. A sharp distinction may be made between the geography of the scholar and churchman, drawn largely from antiquity, and the geography of the merchant, soldier, and pilgrim, who learned of the world by travel and exploration. It was exceptional when the philosopher or theologian incorporated in his book the reports of recent travels. Indeed, we are almost startled to come across a bit of "up-to-date" geography in the philosophical or theological treatises. Even the histories and chronicles of contemporary events, though perforce containing more new geography than works of deeper learning, tended to appeal to ancient authorities in explaining the course of rivers or the relation of provinces or mountain chains to each other.

Any consideration of the state of medieval geography inevitably presupposes some acquaintance with the earlier accumulation of geographical lore from which it borrowed.

This was derived for the most part from two fountainheads of original observation and thought: (1) the writings of Greek historians and philosophers and (2) the Bible. Greek geography was the main source whence Latin writers of the Roman Empire and Moslems of the eighth, ninth, and tenth centuries of our era found their inspiration and facts. The Bible, as interpreted in the exegetical works of the Church Fathers, stimulated thought on geographical problems. The scholar of our period had at his disposal many Latin writings, both classical and patristic, and a somewhat more limited number of Arabic books and translations from the Arabic.

Organization of the Present Work

The aim of the first three chapters of our study is to give an estimate in broad outline of the contributions of classical, patristic, and Oriental geography to the medieval West. The purpose is to show the kind of geographical ideas which a reader of the twelfth or thirteenth century might have gathered from older works in the libraries and to reveal something of the evolution of these ideas. No attempt is made to discuss works not well known in the Occident. The writings of famous Greek geographers like Herodotus, Pausanias, Strabo, Eratosthenes, Hipparchus, and Ptolemy receive only scant attention, and their contents are noted only in so far as they became familiar to Western Christendom through Latin media. Similarly the Greek Fathers of the Church and most of the more important Moslem geographers are overlooked because they exerted almost no influence on Western thought. Nor within the period itself that forms the subject of our investigation is much space given to writers like the Moslem Edrisi or the Greek Michael Psellos, whose researches did not contribute materially to the formation of Western science.

After a fourth chapter, on the literary and cartographic sources which date from the time of the Crusades and upon which our estimate of the geographical lore of this age is based, and a fifth, on the place of geography in the medieval scheme of learning, there follows the main part of this book. The attempt is here made to illustrate from representative sources geographical lore of all kinds, whether original or borrowed, to emphasize evidences of originality where they are apparent, and to trace a few significant borrowed theories to their origins. Though the period under consideration lasted a century and a half, there was not much change during this time in the quantity of geographical information available or in the quality of geographical thinking. Hence it will be more convenient and enlightening to adopt a topical and regional arrangement for the main portion of our treatment than to try to arrange the material chronologically.

By no means all the geographical knowledge and thought of the Crusading age could be stated and discussed in a volume of even many times the size of this. It is the writer's hope that the materials selected are sufficiently diverse to give a rounded and just, though it be necessarily far from complete, understanding of the geographical lore of a significant period in the history of science and of civilization.

PART I

ORIGINS, SOURCES, AND PLACE IN THE CLASSIFICATION OF KNOWLEDGE OF THE GEOGRAPHICAL LORE OF THE TIME OF THE CRUSADES

CHAPTER I

THE CONTRIBUTION OF THE ANCIENT WORLD

SOURCES

The Pythagoreans, Plato, and Aristotle

The earliest writers who dealt with geographical matters in a more or less scientific spirit were the Greeks of Ionia and the Pythagorean philosophers of Magna Graecia. Though their theories exerted no direct influence on the formation of medieval geography, they should not be entirely overlooked. Ionic geography gave many ideas to the later Greeks; Pythagorean thought brought to bear a strong influence on the Platonic cosmology, which reached the Middle Ages through the Latin translation of Plato's *Timaeus* made by Chalcidius early in the fifth century after Christ, and through the Platonists Martianus Capella and Macrobius. Until the middle of the twelfth century Plato, of all philosophers, held the strongest grip on medieval thought; after that time the influence of Aristotle became more potent in the framing of the scholastic conception of the universe. We must regard Plato and, even more, Aristotle as the indirect sources of most of the cosmological, physiographic, and meteorological knowledge which, elaborated by later writers of antiquity and by the Moslems, reached the Middle Ages at second hand. Among the many writings of Aristotle those which contain the most material of interest to the geographer are the *De caelo* (Περὶ οὐρανοῦ) and the *Meteorology*. The former, in four books, treats of the properties of the heavenly bodies, of the elements, and of the earth. Translations of the *De caelo* in the Middle Ages often went under the title *De caelo et mundo*.[1] * The *Meteorology*, besides a detailed discussion of the phenomena of the atmosphere, includes many speculations on physical geography. Theories of cosmology also found expression in the *Physics* and *De generatione et corruptione*.

* The notes will be found at the back of the book grouped by chapters and consecutively numbered within each chapter.

The scientific genius of the Alexandrian Greeks of the Hellenistic period showed itself in the work of men like Eratosthenes and Hipparchus. By them the mathematical and astronomical aspects of geography were developed with accuracy; but unfortunately, owing to the almost universal ignorance of Greek in the West, the products of their genius had little part in the molding of medieval theories.

Roman Influence on Geography

The Roman conquests tended to discredit scientific investigations and to bring into favor works of a descriptive nature which would appeal to the military chief, the provincial governor, or man of the world—to the practical rather than speculative type of mind. Polybius regarded geography as an important auxiliary science to politics and history. The geographical portions of his history treat of the countries of the known world, their peoples and customs; he is not concerned with the size and shape of the earth nor with the determination of latitudes and longitudes. Strabo, writing at the time of Augustus, represents the culmination of the Polybian method; but his great and comprehensive work, though of first importance in the history of ancient geography, was not read at the time of the Crusades.

Ptolemy

The Greek, or more purely scientific, attitude, however, did not completely succumb. Posidonius[2] in the first century before Christ reverted to the method of Eratosthenes; and with Marinus of Tyre and Claudius Ptolemy, in the reigns of Trajan and Hadrian, there came a revival of mathematical geography which almost, if not quite, equaled the high level reached by the Alexandrians.[3] Ptolemy was the author of two works, both of which were destined profoundly to modify the development of science in later ages. These were the *Mathematical Composition* (or *Almagest,* as the Arabs called it), a treatise on astronomy, knowledge of which reached the medieval West through Moslem channels; and the *Geography,* a work which remained virtually unknown in Europe until the fifteenth century.

LATIN WRITERS: PLINY, SOLINUS, CAPELLA, MACROBIUS

Though the most fertile investigations were made by Greeks, Latin writers naturally influenced more directly medieval thought in the West. Of those who dealt with geographic matters in the strictly classical period Pliny the Elder (23–79 A.D.) and Seneca (3 B.C.–65 A.D.) were the most influential. The *Historia naturalis* of Pliny, an ill-digested compilation of information of all sorts, contained books on geography that were destined to furnish the larger part of the lettered man's geographical ideas during many centuries.[4] Pliny's work was not merely extensively read but was used and plagiarized by other writers of possibly greater popularity. The most significant of these was Solinus,[5] a compiler of fables in the third century after Christ, whose *Collectanea rerum memorabilium* consists almost entirely of borrowings from Pliny or from a book from which Pliny drew.[6] The geographical information in Isidore's *Etymologiae* is largely made up of quotations and paraphrases from Solinus. Seneca's *Quaestiones naturales*[7] was also widely read and formed the source of the bulk of the meteorological lore of the Middle Ages.

Two Latin writers of the late Empire also contributed materially to the evolution of geographical knowledge, Martianus Capella (fourth or fifth century) and Macrobius (fifth century). Capella's encyclopedic *De nuptiis Philologiae et Mercurii* is an elaborate commentary on and exposition of the seven arts; the book dealing with geometry gives the author an opportunity of presenting a résumé of geography, more particularly in its mathematical aspects.[8] That Martianus Capella's treatise enjoyed an immense popularity in the medieval period is indicated by the quantity of manuscripts extant and by the frequency with which we find it listed in the medieval library catalogues[9] that have been preserved. The general sketch of the distribution of land and water on the surface of the globe contained in Macrobius' commentary on the *Somnium Scipionis*[10] of Cicero was often quoted at later periods and formed the basis for some of the extremely crude maps of the world used in the twelfth, thirteenth, and fourteenth centuries.

In the remainder of the present chapter a very general

review will be given of the more important geographic ideas borrowed by the Western world in these centuries from Aristotle, Pliny, Solinus, Seneca, Martianus Capella, Macrobius, and some others, and an attempt will be made to indicate the relationship between the growth of these ideas and the broader evolution of ancient geography as a whole.

THE HISTORY OF THE UNIVERSE

Ancient Cosmogony

Though it is not now regarded as lying strictly within the field of geography, the history of the evolution of theories about the origin of the earth is so closely allied to the history of geography that the two cannot well be dissociated. A marked antagonism inevitably arose between the usual Greek view, which regarded matter as eternal, and the Christian view, which was based on the first chapter of Genesis and conceived of the universe as created at a definite point in time or concurrently with time. The men of the Middle Ages tended to adhere strictly to the Christian opinion, for to have done otherwise would have been heretical. Nevertheless, the ancient theory was well known to Christians and exerted in its various forms no small influence on the development of certain phases of Christian thought.

Celestial Influences

It was a deeply rooted belief of many classical thinkers that the events and conditions on this world and on all the regions below the sphere of the moon's orbit are regulated by the heavenly bodies. Aristotle and his followers taught that the heavenly bodies themselves are made of an imperishable and incorruptible, almost divine, fifth element, ether, which distinguishes them from the four corruptible elements (fire, air, water, and earth) that constitute the immediate world of our senses.[11] By virtue of this semi-divine quality, it was argued, the sun, planets, and stars exert an all-powerful control over the earth around which they revolve—an absolutely determining control over all events both great and small.[12] From this fatalistic belief sprang the science of astrology, a science which throughout antiquity was held in equal esteem with astronomy.

The study of the movements of the celestial bodies revealed the fact that at some time in the distant future, sun, planets, and stars will bear exactly the same relative position one to another that they do at the present moment. Consequently, it was inferred that the influence exerted by them on the sublunar regions will at that time be exactly the same as it now is, and all the phenomena now apparent on the earth's surface will be exactly repeated. They will be repeated not only once but an infinite number of times at periodic intervals in the future; similarly they have been repeated throughout infinite cycles in the past.[13]

Cosmic Cycles: The Great Years

This idea of cosmic cycles, or Great Years, appears to have originated in the Orient, possibly with the Chaldeans.[14] It was firmly established among the Ionian Greeks[15] and Pythagoreans,[16] from whom Plato adopted it. Many and various opinions prevailed about the violence and character of the changes produced by the celestial cycles. The Chaldeans had thought that whenever all the planets come into conjunction on one straight line in the sign of the zodiac Cancer, the entire universe is destroyed by fire but destroyed only to be born again; similarly the world is destroyed by water when the same phenomenon occurs in Capricorn.[17] The theory of a complete and universal birth and rebirth (*palingenesis*) was held by some of the Greek philosophers.[18] Plato and Aristotle, however, seem to have restricted the destructive effects of the celestial influence to the sublunar sphere and maintained that the realms above the moon were eternal.[19] On the whole, belief in periodically recurrent destructions of the earth by water was more widespread and was given greater definition than belief in corresponding destructions by fire.[20] The main reason for this is probably to be looked for in the dissemination among nearly all peoples of legends of a great flood, but it also in no small measure may be attributed to rudimentary geological observations (notably of the presence of shells on high ground) which showed that portions of the earth's surface had at one time lain beneath the waters.[21]

Geographic Application of the Theory of the Great Years

The theory of the Great Years was invoked to explain changes in geographic and climatic conditions on the earth's surface.[22] When the various planets and stars bear a certain relation to one another, a period of dryness and heat, or a Great Summer, is experienced; conversely, when other stellar relationships prevail, there is a period of cold and wetness, or a Great Winter. Even land and sea gradually change places under stellar control. Certain parts of the land, Aristotle observed, had once been covered by the sea, and what is now sea had once been land: like plants and animals, land and sea grow to maturity and old age. If the causes adduced for these changes were not so utterly different from those that are now accepted, we might almost be tempted to think that Aristotle had some conception of climatic cycles and cycles of erosion.

After Plato and Aristotle, as before them, the doctrine of the Great Years, though by no means universal, was very popular in antiquity.[23] The Stoics adopted it in its more extreme form involving successive burnings and liquefactions of the universe.[24] It entered into Neoplatonism and was ultimately taken over by the Jews. It seems to have penetrated to India, where the Greek elaboration of the theory gave precision to ideas that were probably already in existence there. The Indian belief in the recurrent reincarnations of Brahma was brought into connection with Hellenic calculations of the duration of the Great Years.[25] From the Hindus and from the Greeks the conception was transferred to the Arabs and by them to the knowledge of the Latin West.

Duration of the Great Years

Numerous endeavors were made in antiquity to calculate the length of a Great Year.[26] The figure that was adopted by the

Arabs and passed on to the Christian world originated in Hipparchus' discovery of the precession of the equinoxes, or apparent gradual revolution of the fixed stars around the pole of the ecliptic.[27] Ptolemy calculated that the period of this revolution was 36,000 years,[28] a figure which became known to the Hindus and Arabs and ultimately to medieval Christendom.[29] The actual figure is approximately 25,800 years.

SHAPE, MOVEMENTS, AND SIZE OF THE EARTH

Sphericity of the Earth

Nearly all scholars of antiquity after the fifth century before Christ thought that the earth was a globe.[30] The earlier opinion of a disk-shaped earth resting upon the waters, which appears to have been held by Anaximander (although some students have thought that he, too, believed in a spherical earth [31]), was discarded by the Pythagoreans and Plato, and after their time no serious thinkers questioned the theory of sphericity. The Pythagoreans based their opinion on speculative and philosophical grounds rather than on physical and experimental proofs; they thought that since the sphere is the most perfect mathematical form, the earth must therefore be a sphere. The whole tendency of Aristotle's thought, less speculative and less hypothetical than Plato's,[32] led him to look for proofs of sphericity,[33] and these he enunciated with great emphasis. Cleomedes,[34] Pliny,[35] Ptolemy,[36] Martianus Capella,[37] and other ancient writers likewise adduced more or less convincing proofs, which were well known and often cited in the medieval period.

Immobility of the Earth

Though the learned men of the ancient world were almost universally agreed that the earth is a globe, they were not unanimous in the belief that it stands immovable in the center of the universe; yet the various theories which diverged from this orthodox view had no place in the development of medieval cosmology until long after our period.[38] Certain among the Pythagoreans maintained that there is a fire in the heart of the earth.[39] Plato said that the center of the earth, which stands immobile[40] in the center of the universe, is the seat, not of a fire, but of the World Soul.[41] Through its own internal movement the World Soul causes the movement of the universe as a whole. Belief in the World Soul of Plato was extraordinarily tenacious, and it emerges in the writings of more than one Neoplatonist of the Middle Ages. Aristotle, however, though he likewise held fast to the doctrine of the immobility of the earth in the center of the universe, differed both from the Pythagoreans and from Plato in refusing to believe that the center of the universe could be the seat of an incorruptible being of the same substance as the celestial bodies, be it fire or World Soul. Aristotle,[42] Pliny,[43] and Ptolemy[44] also brought forward proofs of varying validity in favor of the immobility of the earth.

Circumference of the Earth

Several figures were given by ancient authors for the circumference of the earth. Aristotle stated it to be 400,000 stades;[45] Eratosthenes determined it to be 252,000 stades according to the testimony of many writers, including Pliny,[46] Vitruvius,[47] Martianus Capella,[48] and Macrobius,[49] although Cleomedes, who gives the most circumstantial account of Eratosthenes' measurement, had said that the latter's figure was 250,000.[50] It is probable that Eratosthenes himself arbitrarily added 2000 stades to his result in order to obtain a figure more easily divisible.[51] Cleomedes quotes Posidonius as giving 240,000 stades,[52] and Strabo says that the latter gave 180,000 stades.[53] The last number was that adopted by Marinus of Tyre and by Ptolemy.

Though we have several distinct figures cited by ancient writers, these assuredly do not indicate that as many distinct processes of measurement were carried out. The circumference given by Aristotle was a mere estimate; Eratosthenes' result was the only one based on accurate measurements and calculations;[54] the two figures given by Posidonius may well have been derived from Eratosthenes, the larger arising from a mistaken interpretation or intentional alteration of the latter's figure, and the smaller from the use of a longer stade.[55]

At all events, so far as we know, only one method was employed by the Greeks for determining the size of the earth. This consisted of finding on the same day of the year the meridian altitudes of the sun at two places supposed to be on the same meridian of longitude, the distance between which was known through itineraries. The angle between the two meridian altitudes was then assumed to bear the same relation to the circumference of the heavens as the distance between the two points of observation bore to the circumference of the earth. Cleomedes [56] and Martianus Capella[57] described how Eratosthenes carried out such observations in Egypt.

The figure determined by Eratosthenes is surprisingly accurate. Whether the stade used by him was 157.50 [58] or 168 [59] meters, as different modern scholars contend, the circumference according to his estimate would be 39,375 or 42,336 kilometers. In either case the error is seen to be very slight, the true circumference of the earth being about 40,000 kilometers.

THE DISTRIBUTION OF HABITABLE REGIONS; ZONES; THE DISTRIBUTION OF LAND AND WATER

We see, then, that the writers of antiquity whose opinions were destined to mold the thought of the medieval period believed that the earth is a sphere, immovably fixed in the center of the universe. We must now examine their theories regarding the distribution of phenomena on the surface of the globe and the interaction of these phenomena. Of prime importance were their views concerning the distribution of habitable areas of land, but these were so closely bound up with the theory of climatic zones that it is absolutely necessary to understand what this theory was before going further, even though the subject of zones might more properly be included in the study of the atmosphere.

Zones

Parmenides may have been the first to conceive of zones upon the earth's surface corresponding to the zones into which the astronomers had divided the heavens. Eratosthenes is said to have been the first to place the theory of terrestrial zones upon a firmly scientific footing, "by determining exactly upon the sphere the position of the fixed circles which mark the limits of each zone" (Thalamas).[60] Ancient geographers set the number of terrestrial zones at five, though they differed as to the character of the climates within them. The general opinion—one which was shared by Aristotle—was that the polar caps and the equatorial regions were incapable of sustaining life, the first on account of cold, the second on account of heat. Despite the fact that the notion of the existence of a fiery belt between the tropics was challenged by Polybius and Posidonius, who had heard reports from expeditions in these regions, this notion persisted in the writings of Martianus Capella, Macrobius, and many others and exerted an extremely restrictive effect on the subsequent development of geographical knowledge and enterprise.

The majority of the ancient writers whose works were read in Christendom before 1300 also thought that the *oikoumene*, or portion of the earth inhabited by men of our kind, is completely surrounded by an ocean. This is a belief common to many early peoples.[61] In the Greek world we can trace it back to the Homeric and Hesiodic Ocean Stream and to the conceptions of early Ionian philosophers, who had gone so far as to maintain that the earth had been created out of water,[62] or at least that it was originally submerged beneath the ocean and had been brought forth through the evaporation of the water by sun and stars.[63] The theory of an encircling ocean was certainly held by Aristotle, Pliny,[64] Seneca, Macrobius, and Martianus Capella.

Crates' Theory of Four Land Masses

The two last-named writers set forth an elaboration of an opinion first held by the Pythagoreans and worked out in detail by Crates of Mallos in the second century before Christ, which gained great ascendancy over the minds of map makers and writers of the Middle Ages. They explained that the *oikoumene* is one of four similar inhabited bodies of land on the surface of the globe. These bodies of land are separated from one another by two oceans which encircle the earth, one running east and west in the fiery equatorial regions, and one running north and south at right angles to the equatorial ocean. This idea, which we shall call the "Cratesian" theory after its foremost expositor, did not pass unchallenged either in antiquity or in the Christian period. Involving as it did the doctrine of the antipodes—people dwelling in quarters absolutely inaccessible to men of our race, eternally cut off from our *oikoumene* by the fires of the equator and the terrors of the meridional ocean—the Cratesian theory provoked the indignation of the Fathers of the Church as containing the seeds of heresy.[65]

Extent of the "Oikoumene"

Aristotle, although he had derived from the Pythagoreans the theory of an uninhabitable torrid belt,[66] believed in a greater southward extension of our *oikoumene* than would be possible in accordance with the Cratesian theory. He harbored no idea of the existence of another *oikoumene* in the same latitude as ours. He says very clearly in the *De caelo*[67] that there is no great distance between India and Spain and hinted at the same opinion in the *Meteorology*.[68] Seneca[69] held similar views.

The opposite theory—which has been called the continental as opposed to the oceanic hypothesis[70]—that Africa and Asia extended unknown distances south and east and that the Atlantic and Indian Oceans, like the Caspian Sea, were enclosed basins—also had its adherents, among them Herodotus, Hipparchus, and, most significant of all, Ptolemy. But Ptolemy's *Geography*, though its content was reflected in Arabic notions of the earth's surface, had almost no readers in the Christian West until the fifteenth century, and the works of Herodotus and Hipparchus were unknown.

PHYSICAL GEOGRAPHY

Aristotle, Seneca, and Pliny

Among the writers of antiquity who dealt with physical geography only three can be said to have influenced twelfth- and early thirteenth-century thought to any marked degree. These were, first and foremost, Aristotle, the substance of whose *De caelo* and *Meteorology* had reached the West before the year 1187 through the borrowings and plagiarisms of later scholars and after that time could be read in translations from the Greek and Arabic. In the second place, Seneca's *Quaestiones naturales* was popular before the direct influence of the *De caelo* and *Meteorology* began to be felt. In the third place, as we have seen, the Elder Pliny's *Historia naturalis* was not only widely read in the original, but also much that it contained was familiar through the intermediary channels of Solinus, Isidore, Martianus Capella, and others. Aristotle, however, was the fundamental authority, for a large portion of the material in the books of the two Latin authors came from his treatises.

The Four Elements

Most ancient authorities believed that the universe is composed of four elements, fire, air, water, and earth, arranged in concentric spheres. Theoretically, according to this view, the sphere of water should entirely enclose the earth. Practical observation shows that it covers the lower levels of the earth's surface only. How to reconcile the theoretical conception with observed facts was a problem which, as we shall see, greatly puzzled geographers and physicists during the later Middle Ages.[71]

According to Aristotle the four elements, under the control of the heavenly bodies and through their interaction upon each other, produce all the physical phenomena of the atmosphere, sea, and earth.[72] Working from this axiom, he, and all the ancient writers who dealt with the subject, attempted to explain winds, tides, earthquakes, and other occurrences of nature; but there was little agreement among them as to the manner in which these interactions were manifested. Though there were many theories, the actual matters under discussion were not very numerous. Only the most striking and unusual happenings—such as tides, earthquakes, and floods—attracted attention, and we find almost no trace of a minute and careful observation or even of a superficial understanding of those imperceptibly slow natural forces which modern geology recognizes as having fashioned mountains, rivers, and seas.

A logical division of the subject matter of physical geography is into three studies: that of the atmosphere, that of the waters, and that of the earth. In each of these there is room for a great deal of hairsplitting about what belongs to geography and what to geology, geophysics, or meteorology. Physical geography merges into the other natural sciences as human geography merges into history, politics, economics, or ethnology. Even at the present day, when the often futile attempt is being made to delimit the domains of the various sciences ever more definitely, it is impossible to distinguish where one begins and another ends, and it would be foolish to set up hard and fast definitions in dealing with the lore of the ancient and medieval worlds, when natural science was as yet inchoate.

Meteorology

The ancients were more interested in meteorology[73] than they were in oceanography and physiography (if such terms can be used for their naïve attempts at explaining the features of ocean and land), perhaps because the phenomena of the air make a deeper impression on men than the phenomena of the sea and earth—tides, earthquakes, and volcanoes excepted. Thunder and lightning, comets, rainbows, balls of fire were looked upon as portents, and complex theories were created to explain them and what they were supposed to foretell. But all this type of meteorological lore, however interesting in itself, is, strictly speaking, not geography. On the other hand, there are certain distinctly geographical aspects of the study of the atmosphere as pursued by the Greeks and Romans that deserve our attention.

The men of antiquity conceived of the interaction of atmosphere and earth in two ways: effects produced by the land upon the atmosphere, and effects produced by the winds upon the land. In connection with the first, Seneca makes a remark which, when taken from its context, would not be out of place in a modern manual of meteorology. He conceived the lower portion of the atmosphere to be extremely variable and inconstant as a result of the proximity of the earth. "The earth is a more important cause than all others . . . for the air's changefulness and inconstancy. The varying positions of the land, facing here this way and there another way, are of great moment in determining the temperature of the air." [74] Nothing is truer than this, but the reasons that Seneca gives for the influence of the atmosphere upon the land are not satisfactory, being based to a large extent on the supposition that winds are produced by vapors. Indeed, by the theory of vapors and exhalations many ancient and medieval thinkers attempted to explain nearly all the phenomena of the atmosphere and heavens as well. Aristotle had pointed out that a dry and smokelike exhalation is caused by the sun to rise from the earth's surface through the air and even to penetrate the zone of fire.[75] While near the earth this exhalation takes the form of wind; when ignited at higher levels it becomes comets and shooting stars. Besides this, Aristotle maintained that a damp and watery vapor is also drawn into the atmosphere by the sun's heat and when cooled turns into cloud or falls in the form of rain and snow.[76] These ideas of Aristotle became known to the Western world of the Middle Ages with translations of the *De caelo* and *Meteorology* and found their expression in the thirteenth-century writings of Albertus Magnus.[77] Seneca, on the other hand, explained that the winds were air in motion and that they might be produced by many and various causes.[78]

Winds

All three of the writers whom we are specially considering,[79] Aristotle, Seneca, and Pliny, had observed that there is a variety of local winds—valley, river, sea, and marsh breezes—taking their origin from the exhalations and vapors arising from these natural features. But even though their explanations of the causes for these winds are now regarded as archaic, the observations they made of their occurrence were not inaccurate.

As to the effects of the winds on the earth, we encounter a theory that sounds most extraordinary in the light of modern science but which corresponds logically to the Aristotelian hypothesis of the elements and to the general ideas current in classical times regarding the structure of the earth. This theory, that the winds are the cause of earthquakes, can better be understood after we have examined the ancient opinions about the physical geography of the water and of the earth.

Another persistent belief, held alike by poets, physicists, and geographers, originated in the Homeric mythology of the calm heights of Olympus, dwelling place of the gods. This was to the effect that the winds are limited to the lower part of the atmosphere,[80] a zone some ten or fifteen stades in thickness.[81] The highest mountains were thought to reach above into a realm of perpetual tranquillity where clouds and dew and frost were unknown and where the ashes of sacrifice would remain undisturbed for a year's time.[82] This idea was transferred to the Middle Ages through the writings of Pomponius Mela, Solinus, and others.

Climatology

As to the climates, it has already been shown that many writers of antiquity divided the earth's surface into zones: fiery, temperate, and frozen. Aristotle, Seneca, and Pliny do not seem to have had that more exact understanding of the distribution of climates which recognizes that two countries in the same latitude may, nevertheless, have different climatic conditions and products.[83] To them, all places on the same parallel were virtually the same from the climatic point of view. In this connection it must be pointed out that the parallel strips, or *climata*, into which Eratosthenes, Hipparchus, Ptolemy, Pliny, and Martianus Capella divided the *oikoumene* were not climatic divisions in our modern sense—implying the prevalence of well-defined conditions of temperature and weather—but, rather, artificial astronomical divisions the boundaries of which were determined by arbitrary means.[84] Nevertheless, true climatic differences were well understood; Seneca describes vividly in more than one place in the *Quaestiones naturales* the intense heat and dryness of southern regions[85] and the cold of the far North; Seneca and Pliny had acquired more detailed knowledge than Aristotle of the northern ice and snows.[86] Pliny made some interesting, if unsound, observations connecting the dark complexions of the Ethiopians with the scorching effects of the sun and foreshadowed a modern theory by asserting that the inhabitants of northern Europe are blonde (and savage) because of the coldness and inclemency of the climate in which they dwell.[87] A brief but striking passage from the *Octavius* of Marcus Minutius Felix explains as follows the warming effect of the western ocean upon the climate of Britain: "God is mindful of our welfare not only universally but locally. Britain is deficient in sunshine, but this deficiency is made good by the warmth of the sea that flows around it."[88]

The Greeks and Romans certainly had no satisfactory understanding of the general circulation of the atmosphere. Only with the maritime voyages since the fifteenth century have we come to know the distribution of belts of prevailing winds and calms. Aristotle said that the etesian, or north, winds blow from the cold countries full of water and snow under the Great Bear; and that the south wind originates at, but not south of, the Tropic of Cancer;[89] this is the nearest he came to giving a theory of atmospheric circulation. Megasthenes had heard of the monsoons of the Indian Ocean; Pliny described the use made of them by sailors in going out to India,[90] but he made no attempt to explain the general areas of westerlies or trades. On the other hand, Aristotle,[91] Seneca,[92] and Pliny [93] all recognized and discussed at considerable length the influences of wind on weather; for example, the fact that the etesians, though they bring clear skies to Italy, deluge Ethiopia and India with rain—a conception which contains a shadow of truth.[94] Auster, the south wind, was supposed to bring rain to Italy.

The Water Element

Since water was one of the four—or, according to Aristotle, five—elements that were supposed to make up the universe, the ancient authorities looked upon the ocean as necessarily as old as the earth itself. Seneca thought that the Nile and the Ister (Danube) are of equal age with the primordial ocean, because of remarkable characteristics which differentiate them from all other streams.[95]

THE SEA: ITS SALINITY, DEPTH, CURRENTS, AND TIDES

We must note what features of the sea interested the Greeks and Romans. These were primarily its saltness, its depth, its currents, and its tides.

The problem of why the sea is salt gave rise to a good deal of theorizing. That the evaporation of the lighter fresh water leaves behind the heavy salt water was well understood, but in the further solution of the problem opinions diverged widely. Aristotle thought that the salt was the result of combustion;[96] that it was an ashlike substance first carried into the air by the exhalations from the earth and then deposited in the sea by rainfall—particularly by the autumn rains that accompany the south winds blowing from hot, dry districts where the process of combustion is most active. Pliny believed that the salt came partly from dry vapors intermingled with the sea waters and partly from the nature of the earth, which tends to impregnate the sea with salt.[97]

Aristotle said [98] that the Pontus (Black Sea) was deeper than the Maeotis (Sea of Azov), the Aegean deeper than the Pontus—except in one place—the Sicilian Sea deeper than the Aegean, and the Sardinian and Tyrrhenian the deepest of all seas. Pliny quotes [99] a certain Fabianus to the effect that the greatest known depth of the sea is fifteen stades, or about 1200 fathoms—not an excessive figure, for parts of the Mediterranean are in fact even deeper. Pliny,[100] following Aristotle,[101] believed that the "Deeps of the Euxine," opposite the shores of the people of the Coraxi, were unfathomable.[102] Aristotle had a very false idea that the Atlantic is made up of shallows and mud banks and that it is calm, an idea shared by the Mohammedans and one that may have contributed to the horror of the Western Ocean which lingered in the minds of Mediterranean peoples throughout antiquity and until the close of the Middle Ages.[103]

The ancient geographers certainly had no clearer understanding of the general circulation of the ocean than of the atmosphere, and for the very same reason: they had not traveled sufficiently. Aristotle thought that there is a flow of water southward from the higher northern part of the earth,[104] and Macrobius explained a series of currents in the oceanic belts which he imagined surrounded the earth.[105] Certain currents of the Mediterranean attracted attention: the constant flow from the Euxine into the Aegean and the fluctuating currents of the Strait of Messina and the Euripus (between Euboea and the mainland). A tradition arose at later times that the death of Aristotle was caused by his disgust at being unable to explain to his satisfaction the currents of the Euripus.[106]

Only with the travels of Pytheas of Marseilles along the North Atlantic coasts, the expedition of Alexander, and Nearchus' voyage and exploration of the mouths of the Indus and coasts of Beluchistan and Mekran did the Greeks gain any adequate knowledge of tidal phenomena; for the tides of the Mediterranean, except in a few places, are so low as to be almost negligible.[107] Eratosthenes thought that the currents through narrows in the Mediterranean are caused by variations in the relative levels of the sea at either end of the channels and that these variations are a response of the sea to fluctuations of the tides in the ocean beyond the Pillars of Hercules.[108] As early as the third century before the Christian era the Greeks had understood the relation of the moon's phases to the ebb and flood, but certainly not much earlier, for Aristotle appears to have been ignorant of it.[109] Posidonius was the first to give a full account of the manner in which the moon and sun regulate the tides.[110] He had accurate knowledge of the diurnal, the monthly, and perhaps the annual tidal periods,[111] a knowledge which formed a bulwark of the structure of his astrology. Pliny also believed that the tides were caused by lunar influence and described the three periods with even greater accuracy than Posidonius.[112] He recognized that the tides must correspond to a lunisolar cycle of one hundred lunations, or eight years, an astronomical cycle that had long been familiar to the Greeks.[113] He included in his account an astute observation that the tides, like everything else on the earth's surface depending on celestial controls, tend to drag behind the time when these controls are exerted.[114] Seneca does not try to explain the tides; he mentions them only incidentally in connection with a graphic description of the terrible deluge that will overwhelm the earth at the end of the Great Winter. Though in some respects like the spring tides at the equinoxes, when the sun and moon are in conjunction, this flood will be bound by no law of nature and will have no curb to its fury.[115] Macrobius' explanation of the tides,[116] which was copied by many later writers, though ingenious, was not founded on actual knowledge or observation. He said that the ebb and flood are caused by the impact of the opposing currents of the two ocean belts which encircle the earth, and, with Eratosthenes, he thought that the tide of the Mediterranean is a repercussion of the ocean tides. Indeed, after the time of Pliny there was no addition to the scientific understanding of tidal phenomena until the eighth century.

Subterranean Channels

Evaporation was given by Aristotle as a reason why the sea does not overflow its bed on account of the constant inflow from the rivers.[117] Another explanation of this puzzling circumstance was found by Pliny [118] in a curious theory that prevailed throughout antiquity and the Middle Ages to the effect that the land is seamed with veins, cavities, and tunnels.[119] Into some of these the air enters; others are the passages for rivers which sink into the ground; through still others the water of the sea finds its way to wells, springs, and fountains, where, made fresh by its passage through the earth, it bursts forth to form rivers which return it to the sea. A continuous circulation of the waters of the earth is thus maintained through passages corresponding to the veins, arteries, and canals of the human body.[120]

The origin of the latter theory is undoubtedly to be sought for partly in the nature of the ground in Greece and the Aegean region and partly in the age-old belief that the interior of the earth is the abode of the dead.

The soluble character of the limestone rocks throughout parts of the Balkan Peninsula has led to the production of what is now known as *karst* topography, so called from the Karst, a plateau between Trieste and Fiume, where it has attained its most typical development. In such regions many streams disappear into hollows of the ground; caverns and underground galleries are extremely common; and the traveler occasionally comes across a full-grown river bursting out of the depths of the earth. The old and persistent story that the river Alpheus of the Peloponnesus passes beneath the Ionian Sea only to gush forth in the well of Arethusa in Syracuse was destined to have a medieval counterpart in the explanation of the subterranean courses of the rivers of Paradise.

Rivers of the Underworld

Among the most famous and sinister of the subterranean streams of antiquity were the dark waters of Cocytus, Acheron, Pyriphlegethon, and Styx.[121] These were the streams of the nether world, the world of the dead. Belief in the subterranean position of the after-world, the Hades of the Greeks, the Inferi of the Italian folk, was widespread and lasting among early Mediterranean peoples. Hellenic mythology placed not only Tartarus, the abyss of torment, but also the Elysian Fields in the depths. Plato taught that within the bowels of the earth are immense caverns, some filled with fire, some with water, others the abode of the shades. To be sure, rationalistic arguments against such doctrines were raised by the incredulous. Aristotle had believed that of all four elements the earth is the most dense and solid and that its position is at the center of the universe. Although the earth might be seamed with small water channels, it would be a reversal of the physical laws of the universe to suppose that within it there could exist caverns large enough to "hold Tartarus, the Elysian Fields, and the infinite multitude of the dead" (Cumont).[122] Hence some would identify the Elysian Fields with the Islands of the Blessed, placing them in the antipodes, and would relegate Tartarus to the lowest hollow of the celestial sphere.[123] But even this explanation could not be reconciled with the more mature cosmography of the Alexandrian age. The Epicureans resorted to out-and-out disbelief in a future life and future dwelling place of the spirit.[124] Others looked for the shades in the atmosphere below the moon's orbit or else treated the whole problem in a lofty vein of allegory. Rationalistic questioning of the subterranean position of the next world, however, did not shake faith in this doctrine as it persisted among the ignorant, and the doctrine was given new life, if in somewhat different forms, by the Neoplatonic movement and the influx of Oriental cults during the waning years of the Western Empire.[125] The Neoplatonists reverted to Plato's theory that the interior of the earth may well include hollows large enough to contain the future abode of men's souls. The religion of Mithras tended to spread throughout the Occident the dualistic cosmology of an eternal conflict between the powers of light and goodness on high and the powers of darkness and evil below. In the words of Franz Cumont, whose truly fascinating study of this subject we are here following: Oriental dualism cut "the abode of the souls into two halves, of which it placed one in the luminous sky and the other in subterranean darkness. This was also the conception which, after some hesitation, became generally accepted by the Church and which for long centuries was to remain the common faith of Christendom."[126] In the period with which it is our special problem to deal, then, we shall find that Hell is almost invariably placed in the heart of the earth.[127]

Origin of Rivers

To return from this digression to the vexed question of the origin of super-terrestrial rivers, we find that the circulation of water from the sea either by underground passages or by rain was not regarded by the majority of ancient thinkers as sufficient to account for the huge volumes of water that rivers constantly pour into the sea. Plato had thought that there were enormous reservoirs in the interior of the earth which served to keep the rivers supplied,[128] but Aristotle rejected this hypothesis.[129] A reservoir as large as the entire earth, he said, would be necessary for the purpose. His explanation was worked out of the theory that one element actually may be transformed into another. In a relatively unscientific age what is more natural than to believe, when one sees soluble substances passing into solution in water, that they actually become water? Or when one sees the condensation of invisible vapor into clouds and of clouds into rain, that the air is actually turning to water? Aristotle, followed by Seneca,[130] argued that the air which penetrates into the internal cavities and recesses of the earth is chilled and liquefied by the cold encountered there, just as air seems to be condensed by cold in the outer atmosphere. Aristotle cited as a proof of this the supposed fact that most great rivers have their sources in mountains.[131] Mountains were to be looked upon as enormous elevated sponges exuding water on all sides. Aristotle concluded likewise that the northern part of the earth must be high and mountainous,[132] because many great rivers originate there. But, if the air is transmutable into water, why, then, was it not perfectly logical to suppose that the earth could also undergo a similar change? This as a theory to explain the origin of some of the water of rivers was clearly expressed by Seneca and, among the early Church Fathers, by Gregory of Nyssa.[133] The faulty character of Seneca's scientific thought is seen in his failure to account satisfactorily for the logical demands of his theory, i. e. for the replacement of the land lost by its liquefaction.

The Nile Flood

One of the natural phenomena most puzzling to the Greeks and Romans was the inundation of the Nile.[134] Herodotus in his famous book on Egypt had given a lengthy account of the Nile and what it meant to Egypt. He had called Egypt the "gift of the Nile," for he understood the alluvial character of the country. His theory as to the cause of the flood—he held that the normal height of the river was its flood height but that the etesian winds, by driving the sun southward out of its course in winter, caused the sun to dry up the headwaters of the stream—was less successful than his description of the features of the flood itself. Seneca also gives a long and extremely picturesque description of the inundation [135] and sets forth various older explanations of its origin, all of which he tries to refute without presenting an opinion of his own. He tells how, starting in the upper reaches of the river, the flood travels downstream and arrives in Egypt about midsummer; how it adds to the fertility of the country by its deposits of silt; and how—here Seneca repeats the crisp phrase of Herodotus—Egypt is the creation of its stream. Among the various theories which he comments upon and refutes it is rather significant to find one which had been propounded by Anaxagoras and which is now recognized, in part at least, as the right explanation: that the high water is caused by the melting of the snows on the Ethiopian mountains. Seneca said that there were twenty proofs available to refute this hypothesis.[136] Another view which Seneca rejected was that the flood was caused by the etesian winds backing up the water, a theory fated to reappear in many medieval books, among them the *Expositio in hexaemeron* of Peter Abelard.[137] Pliny discussed the Nile and its peculiarities.[138] Like Herodotus, he believed that it rises in the western part of Africa and reaches the Sudan and Upper Egypt only after a series of long subterranean journeys. He described the flood, giving statistics of the various heights of the water on the nilometer and explaining which heights meant plenty and which meant famine. He shows a lack of critical sense in his remarks on the causes of the high water; for he held that two theories are equally worthy of credence, the theory of the etesian wind, which we have just examined, and the true explanation that the floods are due to summer rains in Ethiopia.

The Lands

To turn now from water to land. We have already discussed Aristotle's idea of the gradual transposition of continents and oceans under the control of the celestial bodies. Pliny describes a large number of local changes of land and sea:[139] the building of new land by alluvial deposits, the sudden appearance of land and islands out of the depths of the waters, the separation of islands from the mainland, the tying of islands to the shore, the total disappearance of entire countries beneath the sea—Plato's Atlantis is given as an example[140]—the collapse of mountains; but in all this, though he tells where such prodigies took place, he rarely tries to explain how and why they happened.

Earthquakes and Volcanoes

The explanation of the causes of earthquakes and volcanoes, however, was attempted by Plato, Aristotle, Pliny, Seneca, and many other writers of antiquity with no small measure of ingenuity. We have seen that ancient philosophers almost universally were of the opinion that the earth is honeycombed with cavities and subterranean passages. Plato said that some of these cavities were filled with water and air but that others contained mighty swamps and streams of fire, including the immense fiery river Pyriphlegethon. The volcanoes of the earth's surface were outpourings from these internal streams, and their minglings with the atmosphere and strivings to burst forth were the cause of earthquakes.[141] Aristotle, on the other hand, denied the possibility of subterranean fires. According to his scheme of physics the place for fire in the universe was above the sphere of air. He maintained that the dry and smokelike exhalation which causes the winds of the atmosphere not only penetrates into the cavities of the earth from the outside but is generated within the earth's interior [142] and that when this exhalation tries to escape and is opposed by any obstacle—for example, by the sea—there is a tremendous upheaval and the land is shaken. Seneca [143] and Pliny [144] ascribed the cause of earthquakes to the winds. Pliny believed that after a great storm, in which wind is driven down and compressed in the interior of the earth, it frequently strives to come forth and in so doing shakes the earth's surface far and wide. Occasionally, if the pressure is too tremendous to be withstood by the crust of the earth, the winds burst through, accompanied by a violent tempest and a rain of sparks and cinders. Aristotle describes such a volcanic eruption in the Eolian (Lipari) Isles.[145] While this was the explanation of violent eruptions, the quiescent volcanic activity of mountains like Etna was usually attributed to a different cause. Pliny [146] speaks of Etna, Chimaera in Lycia, and various other volcanoes as burning, and it would seem that he connected them with such phenomena as burning naphtha wells and pits of bitumen and sulphur.

Height of Mountains

A word must be said about classical estimates of the height of mountains.[147] Aristotle suggested that these altitudes might be determined by observing the duration of sunlight on the peaks.

He would have us believe that the Caucasus range is illumined by the sun for a third of the night after sunset and for a corresponding time before sunrise. If this were true, these mountains would be from 60 to 180 miles high![148] Less fantastic were the estimates of Dicaearchus and Eratosthenes. The former, Pliny tells us, measured Pelion and found it to be 1250 paces (10 stades) in height.[149] If we are right in our understanding of the length of the pace here employed, this represents 5167 feet[150]—certainly not far short of the actual altitude (5308 feet). We do not know the method used by Dicaearchus in this survey, but his calculation was probably determined from simple triangulation with the aid of a diopter, an instrument for measuring angles.[151] Triangulation as a means of finding the height of trees and buildings was well understood. Eratosthenes probably did not carry out a triangulation of his own but adopted the results obtained by Dicaearchus, asserting that the highest mountains in the world do not exceed 10 stades in elevation. He demonstrated by an ingenious and graphic mathematical proof that the volume of mountains is so utterly insignificant in comparison with the volume of the earth as a whole that the earth can be regarded as essentially a sphere,[152] a conception which became well established in the astronomical thought of antiquity and one which reappeared in the Middle Ages.[153] When the Greeks learned something of the Alps, they were able to correct Eratosthenes' underestimate of the maximum height of mountains. Posidonius argued that 15 instead of 10 stades should be taken as the correct figure and that the maximum depth of the sea was no greater than 15 stades.[154]

MATHEMATICAL GEOGRAPHY AND CARTOGRAPHY

Mathematical geography deals in part with the accurate determination of the location of places and with the accurate representation of the earth's surface on maps.

Mathematical Geography Largely Based on Itineraries

The method almost universally employed by ancient geographers for determining locations was the compilation of itineraries; the position of a place was found, not by accurate surveys, but by reference to other places at so many stades or so many days' journey in such and such a direction. Whatever maps the Romans may have had (for example the great representation of the Empire set up by Agrippa in the Porticus Octaviae in Rome) were probably compiled entirely from route traverses. The greater part of the information which even the most accurate and scientific of the Greek geographers, Eratosthenes, Marinus of Tyre, and Ptolemy, possessed, was drawn from such itineraries and from estimates of sea voyages. The figures for the latitude and the longitude of the large number of places given in Ptolemy's *Geography* are for the most part not the result of astronomical observations, and the tables cannot be regarded as analogous to modern tables of latitudes and longitudes but must be considered rather as guides for the construction of maps.[155]

Other methods besides these simple reckonings of locations were well known, none the less.

Astronomical Determination of Latitude

The determination of latitude has always been a comparatively easy astronomical problem. No complicated instruments are needed to measure either the vertical elevation of the sun on the meridian or of the north celestial pole, and from both of these the latitude of the observer can be calculated with extreme accuracy. The instrument commonly used by the Greeks for measuring the angle of the sun[156] consisted of an hemispherical bowl (*scaphe*) with a vertical rod (*gnomon*) for a radius. The shadow of the rod on the concave interior of the bowl gives the elevation of the sun (with an error of 16′[157]) and thereby the latitude. Eratosthenes, Hipparchus, and Ptolemy were all familiar with the latitudes of several places that had thus been determined.

Astronomical Determination of Longitude

To find longitude by astronomical means is a more difficult matter for people who have neither chronometers nor telegraphs. Eratosthenes, Hipparchus, Pliny, and Ptolemy all understood that it may be found by observing the time of eclipses in different localities.[158] Hipparchus believed that an extensive series of observations should be carried out in order to ascertain, by mathematical and astronomical means alone, latitudes and longitudes of a large number of places.[159] To facilitate such a survey he prepared tables of lunar eclipses and tables to aid in the determination of latitudes, but the practical difficulties of the undertaking were too great and the work was never completed. In fact, throughout antiquity the total number of places whose position had thus been accurately determined probably does not exceed half a dozen, if it is as many.

Pliny gives [160] an account of two different occasions when observations were made of the same eclipse at two different places. He says that at the time of the battle of Arbela the moon was eclipsed at the second hour of the night, when at the same hour it was rising in Sicily. He also speaks of an eclipse of the sun that was seen in Campania between the seventh and eighth hours and in Armenia between the eleventh and twelfth, indicating a difference in longitude of four hours, or 60°. The actual distance is no more than half of this. Ptolemy also cites [161] the eclipse of 331 B. C. as giving the distance between Carthage and Arbela. We shall see later that much greater accuracy was attained by the Arabs in their calculations of longitude and that some of their figures were passed on to the Western world in astronomical tables during the twelfth and thirteenth centuries.

Cartography

Little need be said of the cartography of antiquity,[162] for although medieval maps undoubtedly owe much to classical predecessors, none of the classical maps which were destined directly to influence the cartography of the Middle Ages have come down to us. Indeed we have good copies of only two. These are the maps of Ptolemy and the so-called Tabula Peutingeriana,[163] or Peutinger Table. Ptolemy's maps exerted no influence whatever on the cartography of the age of the Crusades.[164]

The Tabula Peutingeriana is preserved in a manuscript of the twelfth century or earlier and probably was originally copied from a large chart showing the main routes and provinces of the Roman Empire. It is an extremely long and narrow affair in which the geography is woefully distorted. Though in itself hardly representative of the best in the Roman cartographer's art, the original may have been compiled from a contemporary Roman map of the world and adapted through its long and narrow form to the especial purpose of illustrating itineraries. We know that maps of the world were officially drawn in imperial Rome and posted up for the benefit of the public: the one constructed by the order of Agrippa and Augustus in the Porticus Octaviae was the most famous;[165] and others are mentioned in literary sources.[166] Certain medieval maps of the world are possibly related to some of these Roman charts,[167] but unfortunately in the absence of the Roman maps themselves the exact relationships cannot satisfactorily be worked out.

Although the ancient astronomers knew a variety of projections for representing the heavens—stereographic, orthographic, and others [168]—these were not applied to maps of the earth until long after our period. Ptolemy describes several projections, among them the conic, which he may have used; but there is no question of any mathematical projections in the twelfth and thirteenth centuries, and none of the cartographers of that period took account of the fact that they were endeavoring to show a globe on a flat surface.

THE EXPANSION OF REGIONAL KNOWLEDGE

We have seen what the geographers of antiquity thought about the general distribution of land and water and about the physical processes of the earth's surface. We now must study a subject which is less concerned with what they thought than with what they actually knew—however vague and inexact this knowledge was. Though the heritage of knowledge which antiquity left to the Middle Ages of the countries and regions of the *oikoumene* was vast, much had been lost and much garbled in the process of transmission. Hence it would be beside the point to discuss the details of topographic information contained in the works of Strabo, Pliny, and Ptolemy; our aim is merely to indicate in a broad way the limits of the regional knowledge of the ancient world. This can best be done by sketching the various stages in which the horizon of geography was expanded until it reached the Shetlands and Scandinavia in the north, China in the east, and, perhaps, the Central African mountains in the south.

Expansion of Greek Regional Knowledge

Homer's geographical horizon was limited by the Mediterranean—one might almost say Aegean—shores; Italy, Sicily, and everything to the west was a realm of fable, and his acquaintance with the Black Sea coasts was little better. The colonizing movement of the eighth to the sixth centuries before Christ brought Greek settlers to these coasts; and through them there was gained some acquaintance with the country behind them, which found expression in the writings of Hecataeus at the close of the sixth century. With this writer ancient geography begins to assume its familiar classical form. He shows some slight knowledge of Central Asia beyond the Caspian Sea and is even aware of the existence of India—or at least of the northwestern portions of that peninsula. The great struggle with Persia brought the Greeks into much closer relations with Asia, and a corresponding increase in geographical knowledge ensued. This was summed up by Herodotus. Much of his geography is fabulous and legendary, but much of it is of surprising detail and accuracy. The voyage of Scylax of Caryanda from the Indus to the Persian Gulf had brought the Indian Ocean within Greek ken. Herodotus also describes the rivers of Scythia and of Central Asia and displays detailed familiarity with Egypt and northeastern Africa; he knew less of the West, although at about this same time the voyages of the Carthaginian Hanno in the Atlantic Ocean extended the horizon at least as far as the Canaries, which were destined to remain on the limits of the known world in that direction for many centuries to come. Shortly after Herodotus, Ctesias, who had lived seventeen years at the Persian court, wrote his *Persica* and *Indica*, in which we find collected together many of the fabulous and marvelous tales of Oriental animals and monsters which were later to figure so strikingly in the *Historia naturalis* of Pliny, in the medieval encyclopedias, and in the *Physiologus*, a collection of animal lore widely read in the Middle Ages. Further detail regarding the local features of Mesopotamia and Armenia was learned from the expedition of Cyrus and preserved for the future in Xenophon's *Anabasis*. But the events which did most to expand the regional knowledge of the ancients were those connected with Alexander's conquests and with the reigns of his successors. Alexander's march in itself opened to Greek eyes wide territories that had been unknown before; it brought Greek armies and, after them, Greek merchants into the innermost heart of Asia; it established direct connections with India; rumors reached the companions of Alexander of an enormous island of Taprobane in the Southern Ocean, an island which we now recognize to be Ceylon. With the voyage of Nearchus came a better understanding of the Indian seas; and subsequently under Seleucus I (Nicator), Megasthenes, who was sent as ambassador to the court of an Indian potentate on the Ganges, gave a detailed description of the tribes and products of Hindustan, more extensive notes on Taprobane, and—unfortunately—a repetition of the fabulous legends of Ctesias. Patroclus, in command of the easternmost provinces of the kingdom of Antiochus I, provided some valuable statistical and geographical facts about the peoples of the Caspian region, although he was quoted as an authority for the belief that the Caspian communicates with the outer ocean and that it is an easy matter to sail thence to India.

Geography at Alexandria

In addition to the reports of travelers and eyewitnesses, the establishment of Greek control over Egypt and the greater part of southwestern Asia led to a scientific awakening that centered in Alexandria. One of the greatest triumphs of Hellenistic science was the geographical and astronomical school that flourished at Alexandria under the Ptolemies. Eratosthenes and Hipparchus were undoubtedly the most famous representatives of this school, and in them we see the culmination of Greek scientific geography; for their work, all things considered, surpassed that of Claudius Ptolemy, and the work of no other man approached it. Though Eratosthenes' researches were significant mainly in the field of mathematical geography, he made use of much of the regional knowledge which was available in the library at Alexandria and which he could gain from enterprising Greek traders, administrators, and soldiers who had actually visited the countries with which he deals in his treatises.

One striking result of this broadening of regional knowledge was the lesson it taught in regard to the countries south of the Tropic of Cancer. The progress of exploration in Upper Egypt and in India showed that these countries were not only habitable but thickly settled. Adherents of what we have called the Cratesian theory were obliged to acknowledge that the tropic could not be taken as the beginning of the burning zone. Eratosthenes pushed the limit of the *oikoumene* as far south as latitude $11\frac{1}{2}°$ N.[169]

Hellenistic Regional Knowledge

While Greek military enterprise had been opening up the Orient and exploratory enterprise penetrating the tropics, an important advance was made in the direction of the northwestern seas and the British Isles. The voyage of Pytheas of Marseilles, about 330 B. C., had brought within the scope of ancient knowledge Britain, Scandinavia, Thule, and the frozen ocean beyond. Thus, in the Hellenistic period the frontiers of knowledge included the Orkneys, Shetlands, Faroes—or whatever of the northern isles was meant by Thule—the Canaries, tropical Africa, and Ceylon. No further notable extension of these borders seems to have been made until the first century after Christ, except that vague rumors of a people called "Seres" and of the use of silk had crept into the Roman world in Virgil's time. This may have indicated acquaintance with China, although Horace took the Seres to be a tribe of Central Asia.[170] The Scythian invasions which overwhelmed the Greek kingdom of Bactria and the conquest by the newly risen power of Parthia of the provinces of the Seleucids east of the Euphrates tended to cut all communication with the interior and farther parts of the Asiatic continent; but the Mithridatic wars, as described by Theophanes, familiarized the public with the local geography of Armenia, Pontus, and the Caucasus. Similarly Caesar's campaigns in Gaul, Germany, and Britain opened Western Europe to the Roman world.

Regional Knowledge of Mela and Pliny

The most complete and accurate summing up of the regional geography of the ancients was the *Geography* of Strabo, written in Greek probably shortly before 17 A. D. But, as we have seen, this work was unknown to our period of the Middle Ages, when men had to rely on Latin writers like Pomponius Mela and Pliny, whose writings were of distinctly inferior quality and included a great deal of fabulous and worthless material. Devoid of that critical judgment which characterized Eratosthenes and Strabo, Mela and Pliny were content to bring together huge quantities of miscellaneous information, much of which was derived from antiquated Greek sources. Mela, for example, closely follows Herodotus' description of the marvels of Asia, and Pliny retails many of the fanciful legends of Ctesias and Megasthenes. Pliny's contributions to geography were somewhat more satisfactory than those of Mela; for he added some details about Asia that had not been mentioned before, especially in his description of Serica and of India and in his account of the monsoons. On the other hand Mela was the first writer to mention the Baltic Sea, or "Sinus Codanus," which he described as a great gulf full of islands.

The "Periplus of the Erythraean Sea"

Nearly contemporaneously with Pliny there came an advance in the knowledge of the Indian Ocean in the anonymous Greek *Periplus of the Erythraean Sea*, a manual for sailors and merchants. This is of interest because it gave indications of the existence of coasts and islands beyond India, the islands of Chryse, the land of the Seres, and, at the end of the earth to the east, a region of "Thin"—the first mention of the word "China" in the West unless we take into account the "Sinim" of Isaiah xlix, 12, which may or may not have referred to the great nation of the Far East.

At about the same time, as we have already seen, the upper reaches of the Nile, possibly as far as the great marshes of the White Nile in about latitude 9° N., were explored by the expedition described by Seneca and Pliny which Nero sent out to solve the age-long mystery of the sources of the river of Egypt.[171] Pliny accordingly placed the southern border of the *oikoumene* some $7\frac{1}{2}°$ south of the position to which Eratosthenes had assigned it, or at about latitude 4° N.[172]

Limits of Ancient Regional Knowledge on the South and East

Before the days of Marinus of Tyre and Ptolemy the limits of geographical knowledge were again much extended both southward and eastward. The Ptolemaic map depicts a wealth of detail in the interior of Africa, although we are unable to say with assurance what most of this detail represents in reality.[173] Ptolemy certainly had some knowledge of the great lakes and mountains of east-central Africa. The snow-covered mountains which he placed at the sources of the Nile may be associated with reports derived from the east coast of Africa, of Kenya, Kilimanjaro, or possibly the Ruwenzori range.[174] Farther to the west he describes a river, the Nigir, flowing from a region south of the country of the Garamantes (probably modern Fezzan) to the westward into a lake near the Atlantic. It seems altogether likely that by this river he meant the Niger. Ptolemy mentions two expeditions that had been made at an unknown period to the south from the land of the Garamantes, one under Septimius Flaccus, who arrived at the country of the Ethiopians after three months' journey, and the other under Julius Maternus and the king of the Garamantes, a four months' journey to a country called Agisymba, abounding in rhinoceroses. Ptolemy's regional knowledge certainly extended as far south as the equator, and he was well aware of the fact that the equatorial zone is inhabited.

In the east, also, the Ptolemaic map reveals an advance in knowledge over its predecessors. Chryse appears as a peninsula, and other islands and coasts are shown that certainly indicate familiarity with the Malay Peninsula and China, possibly also with Borneo and Java. We shall find, however, that these valuable extensions of knowledge eastward and southward were universally lost sight of in the West in the Middle Ages and that cosmographers were united in placing India or Paradise as the farthest end of the world in the one direction and either the shores of the Ethiopian Ocean immediately beyond the Garamantes or the edge of the uninhabitable zone at the tropic or not far beyond it, as the extreme limit in the other.[175]

CHAPTER II

THE CONTRIBUTION OF WESTERN CHRISTENDOM BEFORE 1100 A. D.

INTRODUCTION

The geographical lore of antiquity was carried over to the Western Europe of the Crusading age by the Christians of the first eleven centuries of our era and by the Moslems. In this chapter we shall study the manner in which it was transmitted, transformed, and augmented by Christian agencies.

Scriptural Influence on Early Medieval Geography

Our primary problem is to examine the effects of Christianity on geographical knowledge and belief, effects which sprang in large measure from men's varying attitudes toward the Bible. Some believed that Scripture contains the absolute and only truth, but others were willing to grant a partial authority to pagan teachings. The evolution of science was profoundly modified by the conflicts between these divergent tendencies of thought and by the efforts made to reconcile one with the other. The general result spelled disaster to clear thinking in geography. Moreover, many of the facts which the scholars of antiquity had gathered together were wholly lost sight of in the confusion that accompanied the disintegration of Roman civilization. The horizon of the known world was narrowed from the wide bounds it had reached in the time of Ptolemy.[1] New information acquired by exploration and travel was ignored; and a host of legends, fancies, and false theories took the place of the reasonably accurate body of information which the Greeks and Romans had possessed.

Ignorance of the Best Work of Antiquity

During these long years Constantinople was the only great metropolis of Christendom, the only center where the arts and sciences of civilization were cultivated without interruption. We might expect, therefore, that the Byzantine influence upon Western geography would be as marked as it was upon Western art and architecture. But this was not the case. However much the scholars of Constantinople may have been interested in the historians of antiquity, they neglected the geographers; and the scientific geography of the Greek Empire was at best a work of lifeless compilation and commentary. Furthermore, knowledge of Greek was at no time widespread in the West until the Renaissance, and the great majority of Western scholars were profoundly ignorant of Byzantine literature.[2] For their geography the men of the Occident turned rather to the Bible and to the mediocre and worse than mediocre works of an age of intellectual degeneracy. Solinus, Martianus Capella, Macrobius, Aethicus of Istria, and Orosius became authorities from which later writers derived their facts.

Scientific Stagnation During the Early Middle Ages

The earlier Fathers of the Church, whatever may have been their merits as theologians and dialecticians, were not distinguished by an ability to understand the truths of natural science or to combat error in that field. With the establishment of the barbarian kingdoms between the sixth and eighth centuries came an epoch of mental stagnation in nearly all realms of science and scholarship. Learning in general and geography in particular suffered almost universal eclipse. Yet dark and ignorant as the times may have been, the torch of civilization was kept burning, if feebly, by a few Irish and English monks[3] and by contacts with the Levant that were maintained through Greek, Asiatic, and Egyptian traders in the principal cities of Europe.[4] If not much authentic geographical information was contributed to Western society by these agents of enlightenment, they served to disseminate certain geographical legends and traditions destined to seize a strong hold on the Western imagination.

In the days of Charlemagne came the new awakening sometimes known as the "Carolingian Renaissance;" and, although tenth-century Europe relapsed temporarily into a torpor, a current of theological interest and, with it, interest in the natural sciences had by then once more set in—a current which was to reach full flood at the time of the Crusades.

SOURCES

What works widely read during these centuries served as sources of geographical information for the scholar of the era of the Crusades?

THE BIBLE

First and foremost we must place the Bible. Certainly in the pagan world no one book had ever held the paramount position in the minds of thoughtful men that Scripture held during the Middle Ages. As we saw in the Introduction, the two great fountainheads of medieval geography were the works of Greek philosophers and historians and the Bible. The geographic material in Scripture is neither very extensive nor very explicit in comparison with the contributions of such writers as Strabo and Ptolemy to the geographic education of mankind, and yet so tremendous was its authority that it tended at one time completely to supersede classical teachings. Slight and confusing as may have been its geographical references, the man of the Middle Ages attached to all of them paramount importance. Simply compare a map of the world reconstructed from Ptolemy's data [4a] with one of the crude Beatus sketches reflecting Biblical beliefs, [4b] and some of the changes which the reading of Scripture had wrought become strikingly apparent.

Genesis was the most important book of the Bible from the geographical point of view. Here we find, in the history of the Creation, texts which were the starting point of many speculations about the origin of the world and the elucidation of which was attempted in many a long commentary on the Works of the Six Days.[5] Furthermore, in Genesis we find the description of Paradise and its four rivers, which figured largely on most medieval maps, and the account of the division of the earth among the descendants of Noah, which lay at the bottom of the crude ethnography of the Middle Ages. By some writers the description of the tabernacle of the Lord and its furnishings [6] was regarded as an allegorical account of the heavens and earth. Gog and Magog, described in Genesis, Ezekiel, and Revelation, were prominent among the supposed medieval tribes of Asia.[7] And in the apocryphal Acts of the Apostles, which, though technically not a part of Scripture, were often given the authority of Scriptural truth, we find accounts of the preaching of the Gospel in far lands, India, Ethiopia, Babylonia.[8]

Writings of the Church Fathers

These and many other incidental references gave rise to those relatively restricted portions of the vast mass of patristic literature which deal with geography, but which nevertheless inevitably marked out the channels that certain elements of geographic thought and tradition were destined to follow until the beginnings of the Renaissance. How these passages were interpreted was, then, of great importance.[9]

Interpretation of the Bible

According to the Church Fathers there were four methods of interpretation; but for our purposes we need consider only two of these, the literal and the allegorical.[10] Both led to pitfalls: the literal interpretation tended to narrow the thought and make it correspond to the exact words of a text; the allegorical, unjustifiably to expand the meaning of simple statements.[11] To these dangers were added the difficulties and contradictions due to the manifold authorship of Scripture and to the misunderstanding of passages woefully faulty from the textual point of view.

Yet the writers of the early Christian age were in most cases unaware of these pitfalls and did not even know when they had fallen into them. Faith in the truth of the Holy Word was usually sufficient to render men supremely oblivious to conflicting and inconsistent assertions that would otherwise have been revolting to reason. Tertullian said: "When we believe, we desire nothing besides belief. For we believe this in the beginning: that there is nought which we need to believe beyond it."[12]

Classical Influences

This faith in the truth of the written Word persisted throughout the Middle Ages and down to our own day. During the earliest Christian centuries the Bible was sometimes regarded as the only source of truth, and the teachings of pagan writers were often looked upon with abhorrence. Lactantius Firmianus (early fourth century), with an inconsistency characteristic of many of the Church Fathers, made use in his *Institutiones divinae* of the classical authors themselves to prove the supposed fallacies and evils of pagan science.[13] About the fourth century men began to try to amplify and expound the fundamental Biblical truths by appeal to the legacy of classical learning. To effect a reconciliation and combination of Christian teachings with the classics—especially the works of Plato and his followers—became one of the main preoccupations of theologians. Platonic and Neoplatonic influences made themselves felt in the thought of churchmen and scholars, and among the most popular works of the entire period was Chalcidius' translation of the *Timaeus* of Plato. Neoplatonism was interwoven into the theological system of Augustine.[14] In the ninth century it appears in the writings of the great Irish scholar, John Scot Erigena.[15] In the tenth and eleventh centuries the Platonic commentary by Macrobius on Cicero's *Somnium Scipionis* enjoyed an immense vogue;[16] it was read by the mathematician and astronomer Pope Sylvester II (Gerbert) at the end of the tenth century and on the threshold of our period aroused the protests of the more old-fashioned churchmen like Manegold, who objected to the seeds of heresy which it contained.[17]

Encyclopedic Compilations

For more strictly geographical, rather than "cosmogonic" or cosmological material, we must turn to the encyclopedias rather than to the thoughtful and speculative theological books of such men as Augustine. Like the mighty volumes of Aristotle or the *Natural History* of Pliny these encyclopedias were attempts to encompass and to put in convenient form the entire range of human knowledge. The most significant was the *Etymologiae sive originum libri XX* of Isidore of Seville (died 636 A. D.). This large compilation of miscellaneous information served as a model of style and composition as well as a mine out of which later writers dug their "facts." For the geographical portions of the *Etymologiae*, Isidore used the Bible and classical authorities alike; he derived much from Orosius and Solinus; and, though it is doubtful whether he was acquainted with Pliny at first hand,[18] he incorporated in his book not a little Plinian material taken from Solinus. Isidore's method was followed, and much of his work copied, by the Irish and English monastic encyclopedists of the eighth and ninth centuries. We find a great deal from Isidore in the Venerable Bede's (died 735 A. D.) *De natura rerum*, in Raban Maur's (776–856 A. D.) *De universo*, in Dicuil's *De mensura orbis terrae* (825 A. D.), as well as in the *De imagine mundi* of our period. John Scot Erigena, the great Platonist of the eighth century, stands out among his contemporaries as one of the most original and critical scholars of the Middle Ages. The range of his interests was very broad, and it seems probable that he understood Greek. In his *De divisione naturae*, beside the Latin sources which Isidore, Bede, and other encyclopedists had copied, he made use of the *De nuptiis Philologiae et Mercurii* of Martianus Capella and also of various Greek works, including the *Geography* of Ptolemy.[19] Martianus Capella was held in high favor during this epoch, and his works were commented upon by such men as Remy (Remigius) of Auxerre, the master of Gerbert, and by Adam of Bremen.[20]

Miscellaneous Geographical Writings

Closely akin to the geography of the encyclopedias, and not infrequently borrowed from by the encyclopedists, are a number of miscellaneous writings, which, though intrinsically of slight value, nevertheless profoundly affected the development of geographical ideas. The most important of these was the brief description of the countries of the world forming the second chapter of the first book of Orosius' *Historiae adversus paganos* (fifth century). Enjoying great popularity, as is testified by the existence of over two hundred manuscripts, this was much plagiarized by later scholars: parts of it became incorporated into Isidore's *Etymologiae;* it was translated into Anglo-Saxon by King Alfred the Great;[21] and during our period it was extensively quoted and copied by nearly all who attempted to write on geographical subjects. Another of this miscellaneous group is a seventh-century cosmography in barbarous Latin, a pretended translation of a fictitious work originally written in Greek by Aethicus of Istria.[22] We find set forth here for the first time many of those marvels of Scythia and the northern regions employed by later writers to add interest to their pages. Priscian's sixth-century translation of the geographical poem[23] of Dionysius Periegetes was also extensively quoted. In the middle of the seventh century an anonymous cleric of Ravenna wrote a description of the world in five books. Though entirely the result of compilation, this cosmography is in many respects the most elaborate and interesting geographical book dating from the early medieval West. The sources quoted and utilized are extremely varied, including the Bible, "Jordanis" (Jornandes), Ptolemy, Orosius, Isidore, and possibly the Tabula Peutingeriana, in addition to a number of Greek, Roman, and Gothic writings otherwise unknown.[24] The main importance of the work of the Ravenna geographer in relation to the geography of the Crusading age lies in the fact that a large portion of it was included in a compilation made by a certain Guido in 1119.[25]

Legends

During the twelfth and thirteenth centuries many legends were current in the West, some of which contained geographical elements. Though we shall have occasion to discuss this subject in greater detail later on, the fact should be brought out here that the origin of most of these legends may be traced far back into the centuries before the beginning of the Crusading age.

Perhaps the most significant was the cycle of stories of the exploits and adventures of Alexander the Great which originated in a Greek history purporting to be the work of Callisthenes, a companion of the Macedonian conqueror, and is hence known as the *Pseudo-Callisthenes.* Written in Alexandria about the beginning of the third century after Christ, this work subsequently became widely dispersed through the East, where translations were made into Syriac, Arabic, Ethiopic, and other Oriental tongues. Put into Latin by Julius Valerius about the middle of the fourth century, again translated in the tenth century,[26] given further Latin vernacular renderings with many additions at later dates, the Romance of Alexander had come, by the time of the Crusades, to form the nucleus of a mass of stories and fables whose scenes were laid in distant Asiatic countries. With it had been associated those mysterious tales and prophecies of Gog and Magog whose origins were ultimately connected with the Biblical revelations of the end of the world.[27] Alexander the Great and Gog and Magog appear in the *Pseudo-Methodius*, a book of prophecy which foretold the dread events of the Last Day. Rendered into Latin at an early period from a Greco-Syrian original, the *Pseudo-Methodius* made a deep impression on the medieval mind, especially at the time of the Mongol invasions in the early thirteenth century.

Writers of our period like Gervase of Tilbury and Giraldus Cambrensis also drew on the legends found in Geoffrey of Monmouth's mythological history of Britain, many of which had entered into the composition of the Romance of King Arthur. Some of the latter were of slight geographical interest.

Finally, the mythology and folklore of Ireland, with infusions from classical and even Arabic literature, gave rise to the story of the wanderings of St. Brandan [28] among mysterious islands in the Western Ocean, an account of which we have in a manuscript dating back perhaps to as early a period as the ninth century.[29]

Books of Travel and Description

The most important books describing actual travels and explorations written between the conversion of Constantine and the Crusades were for the most part in languages unknown to the men of the West—Greek and Arabic. Zemarchus' account of the tribes and trade of Central Asia [30] and the *Meadows of Gold* of Al-Masʿūdī, wherein were described things personally seen by the travelers between Spain and Burma and south as far as Madagascar, were treasures of geographical lore unknown to Occidental readers of this age.

In Adam of Bremen's *Gesta Hammenburgensis ecclesiae pontificum*, written in the latter half of the eleventh century, we find a description of the countries of the North. This was based on knowledge acquired from the voyagings of the Northmen between the eighth and eleventh centuries and, together with the Sagas, will be discussed in a later chapter.

From the varied narratives of Christian pilgrims the Western student might have gleaned some arid details about routes eastward and about the topography of the Holy Land.

THE HISTORY OF THE UNIVERSE

We saw in the first chapter that Plato, Aristotle, Seneca, and most of the other Greek philosophers had believed that the universe is eternal, though subject to ever-recurring destructions by fire or water, followed by "rebirths" (*palingeneses*).[31] Aristotle had attributed to the stars control over all occurrences in the sphere below the moon; not only over physical and material happenings, but over the mind and will. He had believed that this was by virtue of the fact that the celestial bodies are formed of a divine substance different from the four corruptible elements which constitute the sublunar world. On this theory of the stars had been built the "science" of astrology.

Christianity Opposed to Belief in an Eternal Universe

What could be more antagonistic to such ideas than the teachings of the Bible? The antagonism, however, was not felt by all the Fathers of the Church. The fascination of Platonism led many to seek for analogies between Greek and Biblical cosmology. Clement of Alexandria, for instance, thought that the destruction of the world by fire prophesied in Deuteronomy (xxxii, 22) was one of those general burnings which would occur when the stars find themselves in conjunction in Cancer.[32] Indeed, it was a common belief, and one shared by Augustine, that the Greeks themselves had actually derived the best of their theological concepts from the Bible.[33] But the glaring contradictions between Scriptural and classical cosmology could not be overlooked even by the Augustinians, and classical theories of the periodicity of the universe in general were vigorously combated. Christian monotheism could never be reconciled with a fatalistic doctrine that attributed to the stars in their control over the destinies of the world a quality that approached the divine; and through Christian teachings the astrology built on this doctrine was largely discredited and the stars stripped of their divinity.[34] This alone was enough to strike a deathblow at the idea of the unvarying periodicity of the universe under celestial controls; but other arguments equally potent were leveled against it. Augustine refused to believe that Christ had been incarnated an infinite number of times in the past or was destined to suffer the Passion an infinite number of times in the future.[35] Origen declared that another Adam, another Moses, another Judas were unthinkable and asked how the belief in the stellar control of man's actions and volition could be reconciled with the Christian doctrine of the freedom of the will.[36]

Perhaps the most fatal argument lay in the express contradiction, by the Old Testament account of the Creation, of the Hellenic idea of an eternally recurrent universe.[37] Neoplatonist and Peripatetic alike had denied that there ever had been a first day or a first Great Year.[38] Yet the words of Scripture are very definite and very explicit: "In the beginning God created heaven and earth." Neither Christian nor Jew could question the meaning of these words nor think otherwise than that all things were created at a certain fixed and calculable point in time or else, following Augustine, that the universe and time were created simultaneously.

In spite of these fatal objections, neither the Great Year theory nor astrology perished completely in the Middle Ages. Lingering on underground, they gave an heretical and pagan tinge to the thought of many a philosopher and theologian during our twelfth and thirteenth centuries and thereafter.[39]

The Creation

Even the Scriptural history of the Creation did not wholly satisfy the inquiring curiosity of theologians or philosophers.

One of the primary problems dealt with by scholars was the problem of the first chapters of Genesis. This inquiry led into the domain of metaphysics and theology: through it men hoped to arrive at an understanding of the nature of God and of his relation to the universe, to time, and to man. It also led to innumerable speculations about the actual manner in which the will of God operated in fashioning the world and to discussions of this question from very diverse points of view—literal, allegorical, transcendental. Indeed, there were even a few writers, notably the Venerable Bede, who went so far as to try to reconcile a physical conception of the processes of creation with the account given in the Bible [40] and who thus prepared the way for more rationalistic studies of the Works of the Six Days in the centuries which were to follow.

SHAPE AND SIZE OF THE EARTH

Early Christian Belief in a Flat Earth

Prevalent among most peoples in an early stage of their intellectual development is the natural and obvious theory that the earth is a flat disk covered by a dome-shaped heaven. This view was held by the Assyrians, Chaldeans, Egyptians,[41] and, as we saw in the first chapter, by the early Greeks; it was long believed by the Jews [42] and is found in the Koran;[43] it was undoubtedly reflected in the words of Scripture, although what is said there on the subject is by no means definite and occurs in connections wholly incidental to other subjects. We read in Isaiah (xl, 22):[44] "It is he that sitteth upon the circle of the earth, and the inhabitants thereof are as grasshoppers; that stretcheth out the heavens as a curtain and spreadeth them out as a tent to dwell in."

This can hardly be called an exhaustive dissertation on the shape of the universe, yet on it and on other scraps even less detailed were erected the medieval arguments in favor of the flatness of the earth, a firm belief in which was probably held by the majority of the earlier Church Fathers, especially those of the East.[45] Not only were the ancient proofs of sphericity overlooked; but such ideas were regarded as heretical, and elaborate new systems were raised on the weak foundations of little-understood Scriptural texts. The most remarkable theories of the universe, however, were devised by the Greek fathers Patricius, Cosmas Indicopleustes, and Severian of Gabala.[46] They remained unknown to the men of the Western world and consequently do not concern us. The Latin father Lactantius contented himself with endeavoring to prove by pseudo-scientific means that the earth is not a sphere; a spherical heaven, he argued, does not necessitate a spherical earth; and the idea of the possibility of antipodes was to him thoroughly absurd.[47]

Early Christian Belief in a Spherical Earth

On the other hand, the theory that the earth is a globe never, perhaps, suffered complete eclipse.[48] Augustine was non-committal in this regard, evidently troubled and puzzled by contradictory statements in the Bible and in the writings of classical astronomers.[49] Isidore quotes writers of antiquity who favored a spherical earth, though if we interpret correctly texts in the *De natura rerum*[50] and *Etymologiae*[51] we are impelled to think that he himself conceived of a flat earth surrounded by a spherical heaven. The Venerable Bede, on the contrary, did not mince matters; he stoutly maintained that the earth is a sphere and cited as proof the fact that stars visible in one latitude are invisible in another.[52] After the so-called Carolingian Renaissance the world of thinkers seems gradually to have outgrown the primitive notion of a flat earth. To the *De nuptiis Philologiae et Mercurii* of the Neoplatonist Martianus Capella may be ascribed much of the credit for keeping alive the doctrine of sphericity during these centuries. This immensely popular work, with its condensed argument in favor of a globe-shaped earth, doubtless contributed to the formation of the opinions of men like John Scot Erigena, Gerbert, Hermann of Reichenau, and Adam of Bremen, adherents to the only theory compatible with any observation better than the most superficial and any reasoning better than the most trivial.[53]

Size of the Earth

With the reëstablishment of the belief in a spherical earth we find men again making conjectures about its size, though there is no evidence that attempts were made in Christendom (as in the Moslem world) actually to measure the circumference. In the ninth century John Scot Erigena gave, from Martianus Capella, a full explanation of the famous Eratosthenic measurements.[54] An unknown author of the ninth or tenth century of a work on geometry often attributed to Gerbert also explained, from Capella, Eratosthenes' method of measuring a degree;[55] and the eleventh-century mathematician Hermann of Reichenau[56] had learned (possibly from Macrobius) how the length of a degree could be ascertained from observations of the pole star. His result, 700 stades, was the same as that of Eratosthenes, a fact which alone indicates that he did not himself undertake any measurement. Thus we see that as a result of the Platonic movement between the ninth and eleventh centuries knowledge of one of the most magnificent achievements of classical geographical investigation had been revived.

ZONES AND THE ANTIPODES

Zones

Most Greek thinkers had agreed in dividing the earth's surface into five zones, though they differed as to whether or not the equatorial zone was habitable. By Ptolemy's time the discovery of countries in the heart of the tropical regions and possibly beyond had exploded the old idea of an equatorial ocean and fiery belt around the middle of the globe. Unfortunately the broader regional knowledge which had been at Ptolemy's disposal was lost in the Middle Ages, and older views reappeared. The maps of the period show us the encircling ocean in which Homer had believed, and nearly all writers of the patristic age thought that Africa has a very limited extension toward the south.[57] Beyond Africa, they said, lies an equatorial ocean and an equatorial zone uninhabitable on account of heat.

The Antipodes

Whether or not there were other regions of the world on the other side of this equatorial zone or beyond the waters of the western ocean, and whether or not such regions were inhabited, were questions which piqued the curiosity of the Church Fathers. The possibility of antipodal regions—perhaps continents—must, in the logic of things, have been admitted by those who were ready to believe that the earth is a sphere; and even those who were not believers in the sphericity of the earth were prone to discuss the possibility of a fourth, or austral, continent, usually called by analogy the region of the antipodes, lying immediately south of the equatorial zone.[58] Bede adopted Crates' theory of two oceans encircling the earth, east and west, and north and south, dividing its surface into four temperate habitable areas; and after the interest in Macrobius had become widespread in the ninth century this theory undoubtedly must have been generally familiar if not generally accepted.

Whether or not the antipodes were actually inhabited was another matter. Lactantius, who thought that the world is flat, was a determined opponent of the possibility of inhabited antipodes for physical reasons. His arguments were obvious but seem puerile to us: "Is there any one so stupid," he asked, "as to believe that there are men whose feet are higher than their heads?"[59] It puzzled him to explain how trees could grow upside down or rain fall upward. More serious were the religious objections to the possibility of inhabited regions in other parts of the earth, for this was as antagonistic to the words of the Bible as the Great Year theory and antagonistic in much the same way. The theory of the antipodes, as generally presented in association with the theory of a fiery equatorial zone, presupposed the existence of other races of men absolutely cut off from our race. How, then, inquired Augustine,[60] could such races be descended from Adam, who, the Bible tells us, was the forefather of all men? How could Christ have died for antipodeans? How could the Gospel have been preached in "the four corners of the earth" if half the earth is cut off from our quarter by tropical fires? How could the text of Romans x, 18, be true which says: "Yes, verily, their sound went forth over all the earth, and their words unto the ends of the whole world"? Isidore [61] and Bede [62] categorically denied the possibility of inhabitants of antipodal regions. Their authority, together with the strength of their arguments and the arguments of Augustine, were sufficient to arouse suspicions of the man who ventured to believe in this doctrine. Such a man must certainly be a heretic. A tenth-century interpreter of Boëthius wrote: "God forbid that anybody think we accept the stories of antipodes, which are in every way contradictory to Christian faith."[63] In the middle of the eighth century the question reached a head in a controversy between St. Boniface and a certain Virgil, bishop of Salzburg.[64] The latter, who doubtless thought that there were antipodal regions if not antipodeans, was accused by Pope Zachary, to whom St. Boniface had complained, of holding "perverse and iniquitous doctrines regarding another world." Unfortunately we do not possess Virgil's own account of the incident and are unable to tell exactly what these doctrines were.[65] At all events, belief in antipodes contained the seeds of bitter religious quarrels and was one of the charges brought against Cecco d'Ascoli, who, after our period, was burnt to death for holding this and other damning convictions.[66]

PHYSICAL GEOGRAPHY

In the field of physical geography slight was the contribution of the early medieval writers.

Meteorology

Classical ideas about the atmosphere were repeated and garbled,[67] little progress was made in the development of earlier theories, and little new was added but superstition. Isidore, followed closely by Bede and Raban Maur, was the primary authority in matters of meteorology.[68] The ancient view persisted, that the polar regions were uninhabitable on account of cold and the equatorial zone on account of heat. The sort of popular meteorology that prevailed is illustrated in an early ninth-century treatise written by Agobard, archbishop of Lyons, and entitled *Against the Absurd Opinion of the Vulgar Touching Hail and Thunder.*[69] This was an attack on charlatans who claimed that they could control the weather, produce storms and hail at will, and who asserted that there is a region, called Magonia, "whence ships come in the clouds" (Poole's translation).[70] Natural enough as it is for the uneducated in any age to believe such things,[71] the significant fact here is that Agobard did not attempt to invoke scientific arguments to confute the claims of the impostors. Poole says: "He disdained to allege scientific reasons to overthrow what was in its nature unreasonable. He could only fall back on . . . broad religious principles. He argued that God's relation to nature is immediate and least of all conditioned by the artifices of men."[72]

The Waters Above the Firmament

One distinctly new idea, however, was introduced by the Bible into the circle of what we may, with a slight stretch of the imagination, consider the medieval physical geography of the water element. This new conception tended to revolutionize theories based on classical physics and to cause much confusion and doubt in the minds of the Fathers of the Church. The orthodox classical physicists had held that the elements normally form four concentric spheres surrounding the center of the universe, in order, from the heaviest to the lightest, earth, water, air, fire. Genesis (i, 6–7) states that "God said: Let there be a firmament made amidst the waters; and let it divide the waters from the waters. And God made a firmament, and divided the waters that were under the firmament from those that were above the firmament." Though belief in waters above the firmament is found in the cosmologies of the ancient Egyptians and Persians and is there closely associated with belief in a disk-shaped earth covered by a dome-shaped heaven, water in such a position was very far removed from its proper place in the scheme of nature of Aristotle and his followers. The Church Fathers, nevertheless, were unwilling to doubt the actual existence of these waters, and in general they accepted the text literally.[73] Gregory of Nyssa even went to the extent of imagining mountains on the back side of the firmament and that the waters were contained in the hollows and valleys between them.[74] Others thought the waters were in the form of clouds or fine drops. Jerome, Josephus, Ambrose, and Bede all held that the waters were crystal.[75] Augustine was non-committal, though he gathered together the statements of many who had expressed concrete views on the subject.[76] Ambrose argued from analogy that if the earth can hang in the center of the universe without support so also can the waters hang unsupported above the firmament.[77]

The purpose which the waters were to serve was also a thorny problem. Ambrose said they were intended to cool the axis of the universe, overheated by its perpetual rotation;[78] others thought that they were meant to screen the earth from the fiery heat generated by stars and sun;[79] others that they were stored up as a reservoir to supply hydraulic resources at the time of the Great Flood.[80]

The Congregation of the Waters

According to the description of the Creation in the book of Genesis "God also said: Let the waters that are under the heaven be gathered together into one place; and let the dry land appear. And it was so done." The difficulty in explaining this text was to account for what became of these waters. Great as are the seas, they were not considered large enough to absorb all the primordial waters, and consequently arguments were elaborated in favor of the existence of vast reservoirs within the earth. Bede, for example, was of the opinion that the waters under the firmament at first took the form of clouds and that when they became condensed and fell as rain the water was sequestered in caverns of the earth's interior.[81]

Of even greater significance was the assertion that God had gathered the waters below the firmament into "one" place. This could mean nothing else than that all the waters of the earth, whether in subterranean reservoirs, oceans, lakes, rivers, or in the atmosphere, must be connected and must constitute a unit. Probably with this idea in mind Isidore wrote: "The abyss is the deep water which cannot be penetrated, whether caverns of unknown waters from which springs and rivers flow, or the waters which pass secretly beneath, whence it is called abyss. *For all waters or torrents return by secret channels to the abyss which is their source*" (Brehaut's translation).[82] Certainly most medieval theorizing about the origin of springs and rivers[83] was dependent on the doctrine of a "congregation of waters." In further elaboration of this doctrine it was often said that the water of the sea found its way by underground channels to the Garden of Eden and returned again to the sea, flowing first through a subterranean passage and thence through the four rivers of Paradise. Augustine maintained that the words of Genesis (ii, 6), "But a spring rose out of the earth, watering all the surface of the earth," mean that all the waters of the earth come from a single source.[84] Rainfall as a source of springs and well water, however, was also recognized,[85] and Gregory of Nyssa accepted and elaborated the classical theory of the transmutation of earth into water.[86]

The Nile Flood

The strange phenomenon of the flood of the Nile brought forth no new theories during the Middle Ages, and Isidore, whose words were most often copied, reverted to the explanation of Thales that the flood was caused by the building of sand bars at the mouth of the river during the summer when the etesian winds blow.[87]

The Earth Upon the Waters

Another Biblical phrase that provoked discussion of the problems of hydrography was in the one hundred and thirty-fifth Psalm (Vulgate): "Praise ye the Lord of lords, . . . Who established the earth above the waters" (*qui firmavit terram super aquas*). Many writers took this literally and thought of the earth as actually floating upon water, held up by the arbitrary force of God's will. A few, despite the explicit words of Scripture, were inclined to doubt; they either explained the phrase by urging that the word "above" (*super*) should be taken to mean "beside" or argued that all that was meant here was that the land rises to a higher level than the sea.[88] The difficulty was also avoided, as was frequently the case with puzzling Scriptural passages, by saying that the passage was allegorical and should not be taken literally.

The Sea

There is not much to record about the development of knowledge or theory concerning the physical geography of the sea. The ancients themselves had known little enough about the sea to pass on to an age when maritime ventures were almost unknown—to learned men at least—and certainly we cannot find a great deal of marine lore in the Bible. Occasional glimmerings of intelligence, however, break the darkness of the times in this respect. Dicuil, for instance, in his *De mensura orbis terrae*, questions Fabianus' statement that the sea is at most fifteen stades deep. "Has Fabianus measured its depth?" he asks; "if not, how can we believe what he says?"[89] Bede understood the difference in density between fresh and salt water; and in accord with Isidore and others he explained why the seas do not overflow their banks by pointing out that water is constantly being removed into the air and into the land.[90]

Though the Church Fathers stood out valiantly against those teachings of astrology which tended to exaggerate the powers of the heavenly bodies, they were none the less ready to admit that the moon may exert a physical attraction on the ocean and in that way may produce the tides. Basil even explained that there is a corresponding lunar control over the atmosphere.[91] Augustine and Ambrose believed that the moon causes tides;[92] and a certain Augustine, writing in the seventh century, described the spring and neap tides and tried to show how they follow not only the moon's phases but also the equinoxes and solstices. He made a serious mistake by placing spring tides at the time of the solstices.[93] Bede corrected this in his *De natura rerum*, apparently from personal observation—a rare thing at this time—and noted a number of tidal peculiarities which had not been commented on before.[94]

Not all writers attributed the action of the tides to the moon. Most significant among the opponents of the lunar theory was Paul the Deacon (720–780 A. D.). In his *Historia gentis Langobardorum* he described[95] the maelstrom on the coast of Norway. He asserted that this gigantic whirlpool and another one, which he placed off the coast of Ireland, made the tides by sucking in and spewing out vast quantities of water twice a day. With the fashion of reading Macrobius a theory became popular that the flood and ebb result from the impact of opposing ocean currents; and in the twelfth century, as we shall see later,[96] William of Conches and Giraldus Cambrensis made curious combinations of the theories of Paul the Deacon with those of Macrobius.

The Lands

There was no science of geomorphology in the Middle Ages. The medieval mind interested itself for the most part only in those natural phenomena that force themselves upon the attention or seem out of the ordinary. Commonplace and static elements of the earth's surface such as hills, valleys, and plains were taken more or less for granted by those who sought to explain the secrets of Nature. In the geographical writings of the period, on the other hand, not a little space was devoted to volcanoes and earthquakes. Their violent and spectacular qualities have made these the object of interest throughout all time. And yet in the early Middle Ages there seems to have been no originality in observing them or in speculating about their causes. Men were content uncritically to accept what classical writers had said.[97] Isidore, for example, following Aristotle and Pliny, wrote that volcanoes were burning mountains rather than vents for deep-seated terrestrial fires and that the whole of Sicily was filled with seams of sulphur and bitumen, readily kindled by the winds into flame. The eruption of Etna, more especially, was caused by winds driven down into the interior of the earth by the waves of the Strait of Messina.[98] This theory of vulcanism was reiterated by Bede, Dicuil, and the multitude who copied from Isidore's work. Other writers explained volcanoes as the outlets of profound subterranean fires,[99] a view fostered by Plato and one that gained authority in the minds of many of the Church Fathers as well as of laymen through the widespread belief, derived from classical mythology[100] as well as from the Bible, that the heart of the earth is the seat of Hell.[101]

THE MEDIEVAL ATTITUDE TOWARDS LANDSCAPE AND SCENERY BEFORE 1100 A. D.

Man has been accustomed to look upon the geographical elements of the earth's surface from widely different points of view. So far we have been concerned with the record of his scientific or pseudo-scientific investigations of these elements. Let us now turn for a moment to his emotional attitude toward them. The impression made upon the heart and imagination by the aspects of countryside, mountain, and sea has constantly changed with changing religious and philosophical beliefs and with shifting social régimes. We may estimate the character of these changes in a multitude of descriptions of landscape and scenery scattered throughout the whole realm of literature.

Esthetic Appreciation of Nature in Antiquity

It is probably safe to assert that there prevailed in antiquity a genuinely esthetic appreciation of nature. If the Greeks seldom made conscious efforts to paint word pictures of the form and colors of their land, their poetry and drama none the less show in many a turn of phrase that they were alive to its beauty. The Romans rejoiced in the tranquil serenity of mild and cultivated landscapes as an escape from the welter of city life.[102] Perhaps the Roman attitude toward nature was tinged with pessimism, with regret that beauty is transient, that man's span of life is short, and that all too soon we must cease to find solace in the loveliness of the world.[103] With the crystallization of Latin literary forms there appeared a stereotyped conception of the ideal landscape in which the essential elements were always the same: a rich meadow shaded by laurels, myrtles, and elms and watered by a murmuring stream, clear and cool; a placid spot where eternal spring prevails and where rain and storm, frost and heat are alike unknown.[104] This formula was used by the Latin poets in describing the blessed Isles of the Hesperides and the Elysian Fields; ultimately it was employed by the Christians in picturing the terrestrial Paradise.[105]

Early Christian Attitude Towards Nature

A new and different spirit pervaded the early Christian's attitude towards nature. His thoughts were turned to the world to come and to the glory of the Kingdom of God.

The more austere and ascetic of the Church Fathers believed that, as it is sinful to take pleasure in things of this world, so also sin must lurk in the breast of him who derives personal and esthetic satisfaction from scenes of natural beauty. This is one of the reasons why hermits retired to deserts and rugged mountains, where they might no longer be tempted either by things of the flesh or by the charm of green and level meadows or of rolling, cultivated hillsides. Among some of the hermits there arose an actual love for the grandeur of the very wildernesses to which they betook themselves. Jerome regarded the desert as a place of beauty: in deep valleys, rough mountains, and steep rocks he saw not only negative excellence, in so far as these were free from the pollutions of "civilization," but also a congenial background for his work and thought.[106] The eremitic movement was primarily characteristic of the Eastern branch of Christendom, but it extended to the West, where its influence was powerful during the early centuries of our era.[107] Nevertheless an ascetic disdain for the haunts of man and glorification of the wilderness was, at best, alien to Western modes of thought. The normal habit of the Occidental Christian was, rather, to take joy in the immensity of earth and heaven and in the marvelous detail of the created world because these stand as manifestations of the unity and glory of the Deity, symbols of the omnipotence of God.

Revival of Esthetic Feeling in the Middle Ages

On the other hand, pleasure in a landscape by reason of the merely personal satisfaction it affords the beholder was exceptional before the time of the Renaissance. But, though exceptional, an esthetic as distinguished from a religious or transcendental love of nature was by no means wholly lacking. Certainly from the eleventh century onward we find many poems and letters that testify to the existence of a truly pagan enjoyment of scenery. Whether this can be said of the earlier periods is more doubtful. Ganzenmüller, whose important study of the feeling for nature in the Middle Ages we are following in this connection, maintains that the term "Carolingian Renaissance" is more or less of a misnomer because under Charlemagne the classical spirit was lacking, even though classical forms of expression were revived; that the classical influence on descriptions of landscape was but rarely felt; and that we find at that time nothing of the subjective and pessimistic attitude of the Roman poets. In short Ganzenmüller concludes that the feeling for nature was altogether Christian.[108]

However this may be, there is no question that throughout a century or more before the age of the Crusades individuals not only among the laity but even in the monasteries were openly writing poems of earthly love and openly lauding the beauty of natural scenery in more or less the vein of the Romans.[109] This was but one aspect of the worldly tendency in Church and society which brought about the Cluniac and later movements of reform.

MATHEMATICAL GEOGRAPHY AND CARTOGRAPHY

Mathematical Geography

We may pass over the mathematical geography of the Christian period before 1100; no discoveries were made, nor were there any attempts to apply the results of older discoveries. Gerbert, indeed, in his *Liber de astrolabio*, gives a few details of the division of the earth's surface into seven climates, details which he had probably derived entirely from Latin authors like Pliny and Martianus Capella.[110] Though Gerbert owed much to Arabic writers, he did not draw from them the semi-geographical portions of his writings. Certainly in the strict application of mathematical geography to the determination of positions—latitudes and longitudes—nothing was done in the West. Ptolemy was forgotten, and the labors of the Arabs in this field were as yet unknown.

Maps

Though very few maps dating from these centuries are actually in existence, maps were then made in no inconsiderable numbers.[111] Three circumstances convince us of the truth of this statement. In the first place, we find frequent references to lost maps in contemporary literature. Then again, many of the cosmographies and encyclopedic works, such as those of Orosius, Isidore, and the Ravenna geographer, show undeniable indications that they were either compiled from maps or else were accompanied by maps as illustrations. And, finally, most of the examples of twelfth- and early thirteenth-century cartography can only have been derived from older models, some of which in the final analysis may well have been inspired by the cartography of the period of the Roman Empire.[112]

With a few exceptions[113] the existing specimens of the cartography of Western Europe dating from before 1100 may be classified as regards form in four more or less well-defined groups, representatives of each of which are also found from the Crusading age and even later. The character of the maps was largely determined by the purposes intended to be served.[114]

Macrobian Maps

The first group consists of outline diagrams illustrating Macrobius' division of the earth's surface into zones and is to be found in manuscripts from as early as the ninth century. This group cannot properly be said to include true maps.[115]

T-O Maps

The second group is made up of simple representations of the three continents, often called T-O maps (Figs. 1a–1b). On these the known world is shown as a circle within which a T is drawn dividing it into three parts. East is at the top. The upper compartment, that above the crossbar of the T, represents Asia; the two lower compartments, Europe and Africa. The surface is usually unadorned with vignettes or conventional symbols of any sort, and the legends are reduced to a minimum. It seems likely that Augustine had before him such a diagram when he wrote a passage in *De civitate dei* which describes to perfection the division of the known world as the T-O maps show it, and it may well be that the map which Orosius must have used when

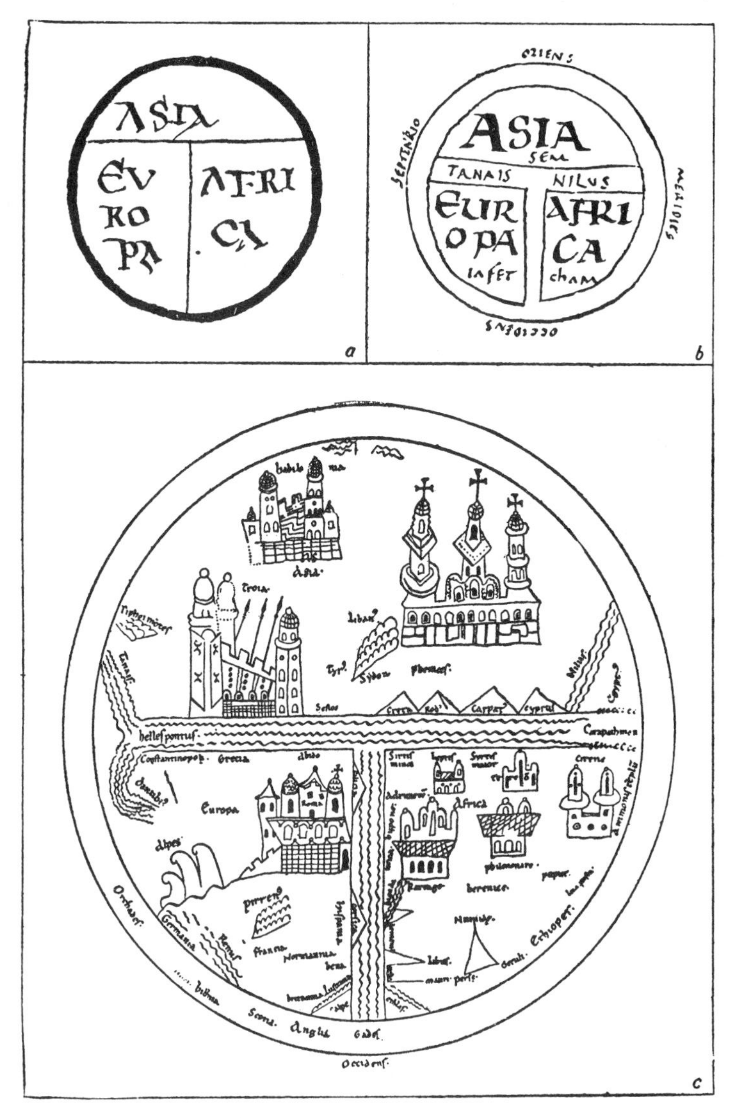

FIG. 1—Types of T-O and Sallust maps. (Figs. 1a and 1b from Santarem, *Essai*, 1849–1852, atlas, vol. i, pl. 5, figs. 5 and 1; Fig. 1c from Miller, *Mappaemundi*, vol. iii, 1895, fig. 43.)

he wrote the geographical chapter of his history was a modified example of the same type. An extremely large number of T-O maps are to be found in codices dating from the eighth century onward, illustrating the writings of Isidore, Bede, Raban Maur, and others.[116]

Sallust Maps

Closely akin to the T-O maps, but somewhat more elaborate, are the sketches of the third group (Fig. 1c). These accompany manuscripts of Sallust's works and may have been drawn to illustrate a passage in Sallust's *De bello Jugurthino* describing briefly the countries of the known world. The T-O form is carefully followed, but legends and pictures add a touch of life. The oldest example (tenth century) is strictly classical and fails to show Jerusalem, a stock feature in most medieval maps. Later specimens reveal the influence of the Christian tradition, and upon them Jerusalem figures as an immense church or castle.[117]

Beatus Maps

The fourth group is by far the most interesting. In the latter part of the eighth century a priest, Beatus, of the Benedictine abbey of Valcavado in northern Spain wrote a commentary on the Apocalypse, destined to become very popular in later times. To demonstrate graphically the division of the world among the twelve apostles, which is spoken of in a passage included in this commentary, either Beatus or one of his contemporaries drew a map. Though the original of this is not now extant, no less than ten subsequent maps for which it served as a model are preserved in manuscripts of the tenth century and later. The researches of Miller[118] have shown that three of these ten were probably derived from a fairly full and faithful copy of the original, but that the others represent merely a generalized outline. The best example, the so-called St. Sever map, dating from about 1050 and now in the Bibliothèque Nationale at Paris, displays an immense wealth of detail, legends, vignettes, and pictures of all sorts (Fig. 2).

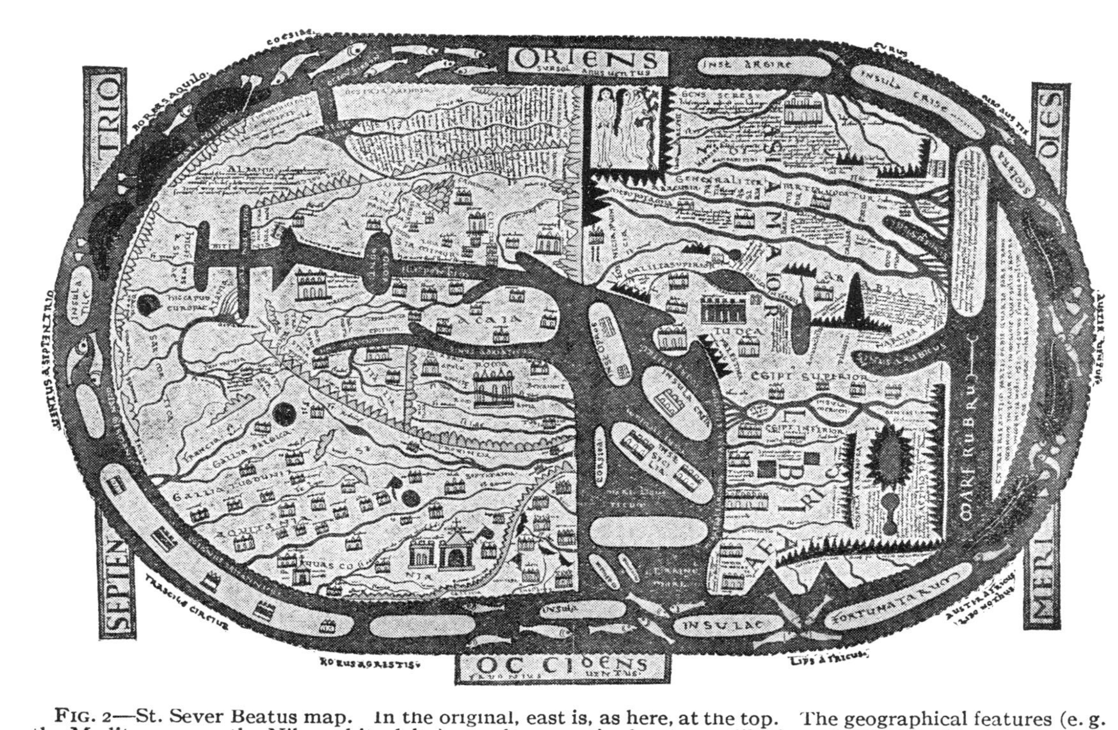

FIG. 2—St. Sever Beatus map. In the original, east is, as here, at the top. The geographical features (e. g. the Mediterranean, the Nile and its delta) may be recognized more readily, however, by viewing the map with north at the top. (From Miller, *Mappaemundi*, vol. i, 1895, colored reproduction in pocket.)

REGIONAL GEOGRAPHY

Limited Geographical Horizon in the Early Middle Ages

In the first chapter, under the heading "The Expansion of Regional Knowledge," was discussed the expansion of actual knowledge of the earth's surface, and a careful distinction was made between that section dealing with actual knowledge and the preceding sections of the chapter which had been concerned with theories. We cannot make this distinction in speaking of the regional geographical ideas of the early Christian centuries, for fact and fancy were irrevocably blended. In the Greek and Roman age knowledge of the earth's surface was widened by exploration, trade, wars, and conquests; but in the early Middle Ages the limits of the accurately known world contracted, and the ocean, Asia, Africa, even Western Europe itself, became domains of legend and fable.

This does not mean that exploration, trade, and conquest did not progress. Commerce in silk flourished in the sixth century between Byzantium and the nations of Central Asia, and much knowledge of those distant countries was thereby acquired in the Greek world.[119] Between the eighth and the beginning of the twelfth centuries the Northmen had penetrated in their open ships to the innermost recesses of the White Sea[120] and westward as far as Iceland, Greenland, and the shores of America. Throughout the Middle Ages there was an intermittent flow of pilgrims to and from the Holy Land. At a very early date the Italian cities began to lay the foundations of their great Levantine trade. Why, then, was geographic knowledge not enriched by all this activity? There were many reasons. The spirit of the age turned the scholar's mind almost exclusively to religious and theological matters. He felt no particular interest in voyages unless they had some religious significance. He cared nothing about the exploits of piratical Norse rovers in subarctic seas or about things that Byzantine traders and diplomats might have seen in the heart of Asia. Even if he could have read the languages in which the stories of these discoveries were written, he probably would not have troubled to investigate them. The pilgrim, forcing his way through hardships and privations to the Holy Land, was certainly stirred by no interest in the geography of the lands and seas through which he passed beyond that of finding the best and quickest practicable route. Once arrived in Palestine, he may have felt some slight enthusiasm about studying out the topography of the sacred places. On the whole, however, pilgrim narratives added as little to Western geographical knowledge of the East as American soldiers' letters during the World War added to our geographical knowledge of France.

Medieval Conception of the Known World

The usual medieval conception of the known world was of a circular or oval area, divided into three continents. Asia occupied the eastern portion and was cut off from Europe by the Tanaïs (Don) and from Africa by the Nile. The Mediterranean, piercing the center of the western section, separated Europe from Africa. The relative size of the continents was variously represented; Asia was usually thought to be much larger than either Europe or Africa. The two latter were believed to be of about the same size.

Paradise

One of the principal Biblical contributions to medieval geography was Paradise with its four rivers.[121] In the maps of the period, the garden is drawn at the easternmost limits of the world in accordance with the words of Genesis (ii, 8), "And the Lord God planted a garden eastward in Eden."[122] Martianus Capella, however, by following a Greek tradition which placed the Hyperboreans in a favored and delightful country of the far north, caused certain of the Church Fathers to look northward for Paradise.[123] Modeling their account of Paradise on the Biblical description and on the ideal landscape of the Roman poets,[124] the men of the Middle Ages conceived of the garden as a deliciously cool and shady meadow, made beautiful with flowers of many sorts, watered by murmuring streams, and redolent with sweet odors.[125] Many theories were elaborated concerning the surroundings of the forbidden garden.[126] In order that men be kept out, an impassable barrier must have encircled it. Some believed that this was an immense wall; others, a ring of flames; others, mountains and deserts. Some placed Paradise on an island in the ocean; Cosmas removed it beyond the ocean to the shores of unknown lands in the east; Augustine, Origen, and Philo regarded it as allegorical and not real at all.

Rivers of Paradise

"And a river went out of Eden to water the garden; and from thence it was parted, and became into four heads" (Gen. ii, 10).[127] These four heads were the sources of the four rivers of Paradise: the Pison, later thought to be either the Indus, the Ganges,[128] or, sometimes, the Danube; the Gihon, or Nile; the Hiddekel, or Tigris; and, finally, the Euphrates. It was a little difficult for some persons at first sight to understand how all these rivers, whose upper reaches were known in reality to be very far apart, could actually spring from one source.[129] Many cosmographers were even tempted to place Paradise in Armenia, near the known sources of the Euphrates and Tigris. In general an appeal to the simple theory of the existence of subterranean watercourses sufficed to solve the problem and to explain the otherwise absurd belief that the Nile had its headwaters in the far east beyond the Red Sea.

Asia

Gog and Magog

Asia was frequently made the scene of Paradise and of the creation of man. Here, too, medieval tradition placed Gog and Magog,[130] whose advent at the Last Day should bring destruction to the world. There are three different Biblical accounts of Gog and Magog. On the basis of Genesis (x, 2), which makes Magog a son of Japhet, a Jewish tradition conceived of this shadowy and fearful personage as the progenitor of the Scythian tribes. In the book of Ezekiel (xxxviii, xxxix) we read the prophecy of the ravages and destructions of "Gog, the land of Magog, the chief prince of Meshech and Tubal," who should issue with his terrible hordes from the north and bring death and devastation to the lands of Israel. Finally, in Revelation (xx, 7) we are warned that "when the thousand years shall be finished, Satan shall be loosed out of his prison, and shall go forth and seduce the nations which are over the four quarters of the earth, Gog and Magog, and shall gather them together to battle, whose number is as the sand of the sea." Here "Gog and Magog" are not the names either of men or of a country, but rather of savage tribes. Most medieval writers, following the Jewish tradition, thought of these tribes as Scythian barbarians of the north—so Josephus, Jerome, and Isidore, though Eusebius believed that they were Kelts, and Jerome referred to a certain history which identified them with the Goths; one chronicle even made the Aquitanians their descendants.[131]

The apocalyptic story of Gog and Magog spread widely in the Orient as well as through the Christian world. In the East, curiously enough, it was made a part of the Romance of Alexander. We read in the Koran [132] that the "two-horned Alexander" built a great wall of bronze and pitch and brimstone, behind which he enclosed the wild peoples of Yajūj and Mājūj (Gog and Magog) until they should break forth on the day of the Last Judgment. This story was probably told for the first time in connection with Alexander the Great by Procopius in his *De bello Persico*.[133] It formed one of the most important parts of the immensely popular work, the *Pseudo-Methodius*, which foretold with considerable detail the events of the Last Day.[134] It entered into later versions of the Romance of Alexander itself, although it formed no part of the versions of the *Pseudo-Callisthenes* or of the translation of Julius Valerius.[135]

Romance of Alexander the Great

The Romance of Alexander, one of the most widely known of the various cycles of medieval legend, deserves some comment here because the scene of most of Alexander's exploits was laid in Asia. The Romance contains some fantastic geographical details concerning the East in general and India in particular. The classical stories of the monsters and marvels of these mysterious lands are here preserved in attractive form. We meet with Amazons and mermaids, griffons, and men who live on the smell of spices. We have a text of correspondence between Alexander and the Brahmin king, Dindimus, in which the latter explains to the Macedonian conqueror his religion and the simple habits of the Brahmins.[136]

St. Thomas in India

India was also supposed in the Middle Ages to have been visited by St. Thomas, the Apostle,[137] who was said to have built therein a great castle for King Gundophorus. Though little geography is to be gleaned from the apocryphal legends of St. Thomas and St. Bartholomew in India and of St. Matthew in Ethiopia, they served to carry the reader's mind to distant corners of the earth and are of passing interest to us because certain elements of the story of St. Thomas became part of the fabric of the great twelfth-century legend of Prester John. If we are to believe the *Anglo-Saxon Chronicle*,[138] an Englishman visited India in the ninth century, for we are told that King Alfred sent a certain Sighelm to the shrines of Saints Thomas and Bartholomew in A. D. 883.

Africa

Africa was utterly neglected. Unlike Asia, it did not become the habitat of legend and fable. Supposedly of small extent and made up mostly of desert, it failed to arouse much interest until long after our period. The universal testimony of cosmographer and cartographer during the entire age under consideration was to the effect that the African continent stops well to the north of the equator at the borders of the sea.

Europe

Europe was of course less a land of romance than Asia, but geographical ideas concerning it were crude enough, as a glance at any contemporary map or at the brief and dry catalogue of facts given in the encyclopedic works will show. Isidore, Orosius, and Bede added little to what classical writers had already said. Local mythology tended to creep into the geographical conceptions of the best-known countries and to blur what had been in classical times fairly distinct and clean-cut conceptions.

Explorations to the North

In one quarter, however, to the north, the horizon of geographical knowledge was immensely widened. The inner shores of the Baltic, of which the Romans and early Christians had known next to nothing, became from the eighth century familiar ground to the Northmen. Furthermore, the widespread rovings of these adventurous seamen carried them not only westward and southward to harry Britain, France, and Spain and to penetrate into the Mediterranean but also northward along the long stretch of Norwegian coast. Alfred the Great appended to his translation of Orosius an account of the journey in 890 of Othere of Halogaland around the North Cape and into the White Sea even as far as the shores of Biarma Land (near modern Archangel; the word "Biarma" is said to be related to the Russian "Perm"). In later years Norse expeditions visited the remote coasts of Finnmark and Biarma, seeking trade and carrying war and destruction.[139]

The Atlantic

The maritime wanderings of the early Irish and their successors, the Northmen, gave rise to a circle of legends regarding fabulous islands in the Atlantic and fabulous voyages among them. The poetic imagination of both Kelt and Viking contributed marvelously to the growth of these tales. Great and often misguided ingenuity has been shown in modern times in attempts to find the seeds of truth from which these stories may or may not have sprung.[140] The most famous legend and the one destined to exert the strongest influence on the imagination of the future told of St. Brandan's journeyings among enchanted isles and fantastic seas to the west and northwest of Ireland. Actual discovery in these quarters is recorded in the pages of the ninth-century Dicuil, who narrates the finding of Thule by Irish priests some thirty years before his time (825 A. D.) and describes the cold of those regions and the long twilights at the time of the summer solstice, when one day merges into the next.[141]

The Northmen reached Iceland in 860 and settled there a few years later; Greenland was discovered by them in 877, though it was not colonized until the close of the following century.

America Reached by the Norsemen

Icelandic rovers also reached America in the latter years of the tenth century.[142] The *Landnámabók*, compiled from an original version written about 1200, tells how, about the year 983, Ari Marsson "was driven out of his course at sea to White-men's-land (*Hvitramanna-land*), which is called by some persons Ireland the Great (*Irland-it-mikla*); it lies westward in the sea near Wineland the Good; it is said to be a sail of six *doegr* west of Ireland" (Reeves's translation).[143] Though we may not be certain whether this brief passage is rightly to be interpreted as referring to America, it is undeniable that soon after Ari Marsson's discovery the northeastern shores of our continent were visited by Biarni, the son of Heriulf, and by Leif, the son of Eric the Red, and that the latter were followed by Thorfinn Karlsefni and others.[144] Sailing southwestward, these adventurers came to the shores of a barren country of flat stones which they called Helluland; thence they coasted southward past the forested Markland and past long beaches and sand reefs, until they reached Wineland, with grapevines, a mild climate, and savage inhabitants (or Skraellings). From some of the latter, captured by Karlsefni in Markland, the Icelanders learned that "kings governed the Skraellings" and that "there was a land on the other side over against their country which was inhabited by people who wore white garments and yelled loudly and carried poles before them to which rags were attached" (Reeves's translation). This land they identified with White-men's-land, or Ireland the Great.

CHAPTER III

THE CONTRIBUTION OF THE MOSLEMS

There is no necessity here of giving a general review of the very broad field of Arabic geography. The works of the foremost Mohammedan geographers, Al-Mas'ūdī, Ibn Ḥauqal, Al-Iṣṭakhrī, were unknown in Europe during the Middle Ages, and formal Arabic geography certainly contributed next to nothing to the knowledge of the earth possessed by the Occidentals of the Crusading age.

SOURCES

Other branches of Arabic science, however, profoundly influenced the development of European thought at this time. As transmitters of classical learning to the West, the Saracens reintroduced fragments of the geographical lore of the Greeks. The two classical authors in whom they had taken the deepest interest were Aristotle and Ptolemy. Their most important contribution to Western geographical knowledge was to make known to the West geographical speculations in the works of these men and in the various treatises which the Moslem writers themselves had composed under Peripatetic and Ptolemaic influences.

Influence of Aristotle

Aristotle held a position of preëminent authority among the Moslems in all matters scientific. Arabic scholars had received his writings both through Syriac translations and direct from Greek texts. Vast commentaries on his works were made by Avicenna (Ibn Sīnā, 980–1037 A. D.) in the Eastern Caliphate and by Averroës (Ibn Rushd, 1126–1198 A. D.) in Spain. Aristotelian astronomy, as distinguished from Ptolemaic, was reproduced with modifications in the work *On the Sphere* of Al-Biṭrūjī of Cordova, known to the Christians as Alpetragius.[1] By the end of the twelfth century, owing to the rising interest in

Aristotelianism in Europe (the "flood of Aristotelianism," as Duhem calls it), translations had been done from the Arabic into Latin of a large number of Aristotelian works on astronomy, physics, meteorology, and many other subjects.[2] It was in these works that most of Aristotle's thought and observation in geography had found expression. Aristotelian physical geography, transmitted through these channels, was destined to dominate the geographical speculations of many Christian writers of the thirteenth century.

Influence of Ptolemy's "Almagest"

The Moslems of the Eastern Caliphate also had become familiar with Ptolemy's *Almagest* and *Geography* through Syriac translations and through versions of the original Greek text.[3] A manuscript of the *Kitāb al-Majisṭī*, or *Almagest*, was translated into Arabic in the days of Hārūn ar-Rashīd by that caliph's vizier, Yaḥyā, and other translations appeared during the middle part of the ninth century. Study of the *Almagest* stimulated Arabic scholars and incited them to write such original treatises of their own as Al-Farghānī's (Alfraganus') *On the Elements of Astronomy*, Al-Battānī's *On the Movements of the Stars*, or *Astronomy*,[4] and Ibn Yūnūs' *Hakīmī Tables.*

Influence of Ptolemy's "Geography"

Furthermore, Ptolemy's *Geography* was certainly known to the Moslems in Syriac translations and probably also in copies of the original Greek text.[5] With the *Geography* as a model a number of Arabic treatises, usually entitled *Kitāb ṣūrat al-arḍ*, or *Book of the Description of the Earth*, were composed at an early period of Islam and served as bases on which later geographical writers built more complex systems. One of the most significant was the *Kitāb ṣūrat al-arḍ* of Al-Khwārizmī, composed about the time of Al-Ma'mūn (813–833 A. D.), the full text of which was discovered forty-four years ago by Spitta.[6] From another book of the same sort and title Al-Battānī derived the geographical details included in his *Astronomy.*[7] The latter was translated into Latin during the twelfth century; and Al-Khwārizmī's work was known in Europe at second hand.[8]

Az-Zarqalī and the "Toledo Tables"

Ptolemy was studied in the western as well as in the eastern centers of Islam. Toledo, notwithstanding its conquest by the kings of Castile in 1085, long remained a scientific center, where the Arabic spirit of investigation lingered on among Jew, Christian, and Moor. It was largely through Spanish channels that the Latin West found its Oriental inspiration in astronomy and astrology.[8a] About 1080 Az-Zarqalī, of Toledo,[9] who had devised a new type of astrolabe, wrote various works on astronomical subjects, including a commentary on a series of astronomical tables that had been constructed by a group of Jewish and Moslem scholars before his time.[10] These so-called *Toledo Tables*, with Az-Zarqalī's *Canons* explaining them, contained some incidental geographical information derived in part from Ptolemy's *Geography* and from Al-Khwārizmī.[11] They were rendered into Latin in the twelfth century by the famous Gerard of Cremona, who probably found in Spain most of the manuscripts from which he made his many Latin translations.[12]

Geography in Sicily

Ptolemy's *Geography* was also studied in Sicily under the Moslem emirs and their successors, the Norman kings. From the eleventh century date several Arabic descriptions of Sicily now known only in fragments but bearing eloquent witness to a true enthusiasm for geography prevalent among the Moslem aristocracy of the island.[13] The Normans, who became masters of Sicily between 1060 and 1071, preserved much that was best of Arabic traditions and culture, and Moslem scholars played a brilliant part in the intellectual life of the court. Roger II himself was a devotee of geography, occupying much of his spare time in collecting Arabic geographical treatises and in questioning travelers about distant parts of the earth. "He gave himself up to this work tirelessly for fifteen years, never ceasing to examine personally into all geographical questions, to search for their solution and to verify facts, in order that he might obtain in complete form all the information that he desired" (from Jaubert's translation of Edrisi).[14]

Edrisi

At Roger's instigation and with his aid Al-Idrīsī, or Edrisi (as the name is more usually written), who had come to the Sicilian court from Spain, undertook a great series of geographical labors. Little is known of the life of Edrisi besides a few details to be gleaned from later biographers[15] and what he himself tells us in the preface to his *Geography*, as it is usually known, or, to cite its Arabic title, *The Recreation for Him Who Wishes to Travel Through the Countries*, which was completed in 1154 or later.[16] We know that he constructed for Roger a celestial sphere and a disk-shaped map of the world, both of silver. Furthermore, we are told that Roger provided him with special facilities for the construction of maps and for the compilation of his great treatise. It appears that the king and Edrisi together selected "certain intelligent men, who were despatched on travels and were accompanied by draftsmen. Just as soon as these men returned Edrisi inserted in his treatise the information which was thus communicated to him." On the basis of observations made in the field, data derived from Ptolemy and earlier Arabic geographers were correlated and brought up to date. The book and the maps which were drawn to elucidate the book are for this reason unquestionably among the most interesting monuments of Arabic geography; furthermore, the book is the most voluminous and detailed geographical work written in twelfth-century Europe. After a very brief description of the earth as a globe, the hemispheres, climates, seas, and gulfs, Edrisi launches into a long and minute account of the regions of the earth's surface. He takes up the seven climates in order, dividing each climate into ten sections, an arrangement that is artificial to excess. None the less, Edrisi's works are of exceptional quality when considered in comparison with other geographical writings of their period, partly by reason of their richness of detail but mainly because of the scientific method used, the coöperative employment of many observers, and the critical correlation of their observations—a procedure which was indeed unlike that adopted by Latin scholars of the time.

INFLUENCE OF SICILO-MOSLEM GEOGRAPHY

The question of the full extent to which the fruits of this Sicilian geographical school became known in the Latin Europe of the late twelfth and early thirteenth centuries is a matter that awaits further investigation.

Certainly the influence of Edrisi's *Geography* could not have been great in the world of letters or else traces of it would more easily be detected in Western literature. Unlike a multitude of Arabic writings of far less intrinsic value, the *Rogerian Description* (as the *Geography* of Edrisi is often called) found no Gerard of Cremona to put it into Latin, and the authoritative geographical knowledge of the Western world was destined to develop unenriched by the treasures which Roger and Edrisi together had amassed.

On the other hand, there is no question but that the Sicilo-Norman enthusiasm for geography exerted an indirect influence on the evolution of geographical knowledge, an influence that was to make itself felt more especially after the close of our period. This enthusiasm for geography was the product of a mingling of Arabic scientific and scholarly traditions with Norman maritime enterprise in an island which occupied a central position in relation to the world of its day. It was an enthusiasm that arose partly from pure love of knowledge but also in very large degree from the practical necessities of a sea-faring people, and it was early applied to the solution of the problems of navigation. In the words of De La Roncière, "The use of coast charts was destined to become general in Sicily; a rational method of navigation to be substituted for the routine of pilotage, and thus the way was prepared for the progressive conquest of the world."[17] As De La Roncière goes on to point out, the Genoese learned the arts of navigation from the Sicilians in the early thirteenth century and transmitted them subsequently to the Spaniards, Portuguese, French, and English; and a new science of the sea was developed upon the foundations originally laid by Sicilian Moslems and Normans.[18]

Oriental Ideas Transmitted to the West

Besides the classical heritage, the Moslems also transmitted some peculiarly Oriental ideas to the West. Al-Khwārizmī was the author of a treatise with astronomical tables, the translation of which by Adelard of Bath usually goes under the name of *Khorazmian Tables*.[19] The original work was a redaction of a book drawn ultimately from Hindu sources and known as the *Little Sindhind*.[20] Thus it was from Hindu sources, as is shown by this work, that the Mohammedans got their idea of the world center of Arin. Hindu religion, furthermore, contributed something toward the molding of Greek and Moslem doctrines of the periodicity of the universe and of the Great Year—doctrines which became widely known in the West through Hermann the Dalmatian's Latin translation of the Persian Abū Ma'shar's book, *The Great Book of the Introduction*, entitled in the Latin, *Liber introductorius in astrologiam*.[21] Hindu influences were also felt in an anonymous but widely read Arabic treatise falsely attributed to Aristotle in the Middle Ages and called *Liber de proprietatibus elementorum*.[22]

ASTRONOMICAL GEOGRAPHY; THEORIES OF THE TIDES

Turning now from the sources to the material substance of the contribution of the Moslems, we find that, except in so far as it brought a knowledge of Aristotle to Europe, it added little to Western notions either of physical or of regional geography. Though the Moslems entirely failed to share with the Western World their wide practical acquaintance with lands and seas, the Arabic writers did nevertheless introduce some new ideas in the fields of astronomical—or, better, astrological—geography and in the closely allied study of tidal phenomena.

The Great Years

The theory of the Great Years was very popular among the Orientals, possibly because it appealed to their fatalistic spirit.

Arabic astronomers adopted Ptolemy's calculation of the length of the Great Year at 36,000 terrestrial years[23] and seem to have believed that after every complete revolution of the sphere of the fixed stars, the planets, as well as the fixed stars, will find themselves in the same relative positions that they held at the beginning of the revolution.[24] The Arabic work on this subject most read in the Latin West was Hermann the Dalmatian's translation of Abū Ma'shar's book, in which it was explained that astral influences—especially the perpetual circulation of the fixed stars—are the cause of everything which is born and dies and of everything which occurs between birth and death on this earth.

Cosmic Cycles and Geographical Changes

In much the same way that the Chaldeans, Hindus, and Greeks had done, the Moslems worked out a theory of the supposed influence of these cosmic cycles on geography.[25] The most striking elaboration of the theory was made by the "Brothers of Piety and Sincerity," who formed a philosophical school in the tenth century after Christ. In the great encyclopedic work[26] produced by this school (which, incidentally, contains many other interesting speculations on the subject of physical geography) gradual alterations in the relative position of land and sea are ascribed to almost imperceptible changes in the longitude of the fixed stars resulting from the precession of the equinoxes. Not only do lands and seas change places, but various types of terrain; in the course of time "cultivated land becomes desert, desert becomes cultivated land, steppes become seas, and seas become steppes or mountains."[27]

Whereas this curious theory was accepted by the Aristotelian Al-Biṭrūjī, the author of the pseudo-Aristotelian *Liber de proprietatibus elementorum* vigorously opposed to it the following argument.[28] If the fixed stars revolve around the earth in 36,000 years, the land ought to revolve around the 34,000 miles which he believed make the circumference of the earth in the same time, or, as we may infer, at a rate of slightly less than a mile per year. We should therefore expect to find certain cities much nearer the coast and other cities farther from the coast than they used to be. The anonymous author says that if the theory were valid one ought to be able to observe great changes in the position of such places as Arin, Ceylon, Byzantium, and Rome in relation to the sea. But since, as a matter of fact, no such changes are apparent, the whole theory of the transposition of land and sea falls to the ground.

Obvious as it may seem to us, this reasoning is remarkable at a time when actual observation as a foundation for, or check on, theorizing was rare indeed; and hence it is gratifying to note that the *Liber de proprietatibus elementorum* with its argument against the Great Year, rather than the encyclopedia of the "Brothers of Piety and Sincerity" with its argument for it, was the work on this subject that was read by Occidental scholars.

Theories of the Tides

The Moslems did not add much to the classical theories of the tides which they transmitted to Christendom. Their fundamental work concerning tides was that treatise of Abū Ma'shar which we have already mentioned, a work from which, as Duhem says, all the Middle Ages learned the laws of the ebb and flood.[29] Here, in the chapters on the moon,[30] a full description is given of the various characteristics of the tides together with copious speculations regarding their causes. The actual observations of fact were exact and careful. Abū Ma'shar explains with not a little accuracy the relation of the tides to the moon's rising and setting, to her phases, and to the position of the sun; he understood that winds might cause exceptionally high water; he recognized the influences of local topographic features, that some seas display different tidal phenomena from others and that the flood waters may be retained by reefs, or valleys, or deep bays. On the other hand, Abū Ma'shar's treatment of the causes of the tides was less successful. Though he believed firmly that the moon produces the ebb and flood, he failed to account for the presence of the high tide at the time of the moon's opposition. His explanation of the moon's attraction of the waters was in keeping with astrological methods of reasoning. Our satellite was supposed by astrologers to be of peculiarly aqueous nature and for that reason exceptionally capable of governing the movements of the liquid element of the earth.

Other theories of the tides entered the West from Arabic sources. Al-Biṭrūjī's *On the Sphere* ascribed their origin not to the moon but to the general circulation of the heavens.[31] Averroës, in a commentary on the *Meteorology* of Aristotle, devoted a confused chapter [32] to an attempt at showing that ebb and flood are the results partly of currents produced by differences in level between the ocean and certain seas and partly of the moon's attraction of the waters. The possibility of differences in level between seas and ocean had probably become known to the Spanish scholar through some garbled rendering of Eratosthenes' observations on the currents and levels of the Mediterranean.[33]

Measurement of a Terrestrial Degree

That the Saracens also were interested in the more strictly mathematical aspects of astronomical geography is emphatically proved by the fact that they undertook actually to measure the length of a terrestrial degree [34] and thereby to determine the circumference of the earth. Some knowledge of this great work came to the Western world in our period through translations of the *Astronomy* of Al-Farghānī.[35]

Geographical Positions

The Arabic investigations, however, which most profoundly interested the men of the West were those concerned with the determination of the location of places on the earth's surface rather than those whose aim was to find the size of the globe. Stimulated by their interest in Ptolemy, the Moslems felt a special need for the accurate knowledge of positions, for upon such knowledge depended the construction of mosques, which, according to religious law, must face in the direction of Mecca. Astrology also necessitated this type of investigation. In order to cast a horoscope one must know what stars are overhead at a particular moment; and, to ascertain this, one must know latitude and longitude. In the Arabic astronomic works there occur rules for determining positions and tables of the latitudes and longitudes of places throughout the world.[36]

One of the most practical results of Arabic investigations in this field was a reduction of Ptolemy's exaggerated estimate of the length of the Mediterranean Sea. The Greek geographer gave the length as 62° or about half again too long. Al-Khwārizmī cut this figure down to about 52°, and, if we are right in our interpretation of the available data, Az-Zarqalī still further reduced it to approximately the correct figure, 42°. As we shall see in a later chapter, the results of these corrections became known in the medieval West.[37]

The Moslems, as a general rule, measured longitudes from the prime meridian which Ptolemy had used, that of the Fortunate Islands (now the Canaries), situated in the Western Ocean at the westernmost limit of the habitable earth; but individual writers came to make use of another meridian farther west, a meridian destined to become known to the Christian world as that of the True West as distinguished from the supposed border of the habitable West.[38] Abū Ma'shar, on the other hand, referred his prime meridian to a fabulous castle of Kang-Diz, far to the east in the China Sea.[39]

Arin

The western prime meridian was commonly supposed to be 90° from a mythical city called Arin (or Arim) situated on the equator, halfway between the farthest east and the farthest west. This city was said to have neither latitude nor longitude, and its meridian came arbitrarily to be placed at 10° east of that of Baghdad. The idea of Arin probably originated among the Hindus,[40] who believed that the city of Langka in Ceylon (or perhaps Sumatra)—the abode of devils—lies on the equator. They traced their prime meridian from Langka through Odjein, a place in India, to Mount Meru at the north pole—the abode of angels. Odjein was transliterated into Arabic as "Arin" or "Arim" and was shifted by the Moslems to the equator. It was made known to the Christian world through such works as Adelard of Bath's translation of the *Khorazmian Tables* (which, as we have already seen, was an Arabic redaction of a Hindu work) and Plato of Tivoli's translation of Al-Battānī's *Astronomy*. In the latter, Arin was represented as a cupola or tower; and on Christian maps and diagrams of the Middle Ages it was not infrequently so depicted.

ARABIC EXPLORATION AND TRAVEL

This sums up briefly a few of the more significant original ideas that the Moslems added to twelfth-century geographical knowledge in the West. By way of contrast, it is not out of place briefly to recall what they had actually accomplished in the field of geographical investigation.[41] Moslem trade between the seventh and ninth centuries reached China by sea and by land; southward it tapped the more distant coasts of Africa, including Zanzibar; northward it penetrated Russia;[42] westward Mohammedan navigators saw the unknown and dreaded waters of the Atlantic. Al-Mas'ūdī speaks of the presence of Moslem traders in the heart of Europe, in a country to which he gave the name Ad-Dir (probably Bohemia).[43] Arabic literature abounds with descriptions of the lands within these wide borders; of their products and kingdoms and marvels, true and fanciful. But all this was destined to remain a sealed book to the man of the Latin Occident,[44] who as a rule felt little genuine interest in the world beyond his immediate ken. He looked to Arabic books for practical aid in making calendars and star tables and horoscopes; he looked to Arabic translations and commentaries on Aristotle for help toward a better understanding of the dark and hidden meaning in the words of Scripture. The geographical knowledge which he acquired from the Moslems during our period was merely incidental to other interests, a sort of flotsam borne in on the great wave of astrologic and Aristotelian lore sweeping into Europe at this time.

CHAPTER IV

THE SOURCES FOR THE PERIOD 1100–1250 A. D.

INTRODUCTION

To gain anything approaching complete understanding of the status of the geographical lore in Western Europe during the Crusading period, one would be obliged to undertake the colossal task of ransacking practically all the available literature of this age. From an examination of selected specimens of various types of document, however, we may arrive at a fairly correct conception of the kind of geographical thought and information that was current. Certainly our view of the subject would not be materially modified by the further accumulation of illustrative examples. We must, none the less, look to a large variety of sources: to the writings of theologians, philosophers, historians, chroniclers, and topographers; to maps, poetry, romances, and even to works of art. These show us what the sedentary man of the Middle Ages could learn of geography through reading and study. Pilgrim narratives, letters, commercial and diplomatic treaties, and many other miscellaneous documents throw light upon the actual extent of travel during this century and a half.

Writers of the Middle Ages did not specialize as we do at the present day. They treated subjects of the most diverse nature within the pages of the same book. We shall group their productions into a few broad categories: philosophical and theological writings that were read for the most part by the scholar and churchman; translations from Arabic scientific treatises and other works written under Arabic influence; encyclopedic compilations or attempts to encompass the whole range of human learning, also for the scholar, and popularizations of these in prose and verse for the intelligent layman; histories and chronicles; pilgrim narratives and other records of travel; topographical works; and, finally, maps.

Other more instructive classifications might well be made.

One in which the works were grouped according to the type of thought of which each is the expression might bring out the conflicting intellectual crosscurrents of the age. In such a classification the great differentiation could be emphasized between writers bound by respect for authority and writers of originality and independence; between those who interpreted the words of Scripture literally, those who interpreted them allegorically, and those who went so far as to neglect or to doubt them. The classification which follows, based upon the purposes which the various groups of writings were intended to serve, is merely one of convenience.

THEOLOGICAL AND PHILOSOPHICAL WORKS

The distinction between theology, philosophy, and the physical and natural sciences was not sharply drawn during the earlier Middle Ages. Only after the ninth century did the tendency to mark off theology and philosophy as separate spheres of thought become gradually evident,[1] and it remained for a much later age to set off the physical and natural sciences from philosophy.

Theological Works

Though not much geography is found in the strictly theological writings of our period, those portions of them which deal with the Creation embody cosmogonic and cosmographic speculations which have a geographic character for reasons that have already been explained.[2] Many of the philosophical writings, on the other hand, are rich in passages of geographical interest; for the physical geography, like the natural history, of the Middle Ages was the province of the philosopher.

Peter Abelard

Among the outstanding theologians of the twelfth century was Peter Abelard (1079–1142), whose tragic history is well remembered. In his *Expositio in hexaemeron*, *Sermones*, and more famous *Sic et non* we find a few scattered observations of a geographical character. Though Abelard's fame rests upon the keenness of his reasoning and the destructive brilliance of his dialectic, his position when dealing with the Works of the Six Days was that of mystic.[3] We shall have occasion to see how the geographical passages from his works reveal a love of elaborate allegory.

Hugh of St. Victor

The monastic school of St. Victor in Paris was preëminently a center of twelfth-century mysticism.[4] A leading figure here was Hugh of St. Victor, who held the direction of studies after about the year 1125 and who enjoyed during his lifetime (he died in 1141) a great reputation for learning in things divine.[5] Among Hugh's writings we find *Adnotationes elucidatoriae in Pentateuchon*, containing speculations on the Creation, and the curious treatises *De arca Noë mystica, De arca Noë morali*, and *De vanitate mundi*,[6] which display a love of symbolism and include the exposition of a strange theory of the westward course of the tide of civilization.[7]

Hildegard of Bingen

Hildegard (1098–1179 or 1180), abbess of a Benedictine convent near Bingen on the Rhine, was another lover of the symbolic. Her mystic exaltation took the form of visions in which were revealed to her the secrets of the universe. With the knowledge thereby attained she served her fellow man as a prophetess and healer of disease. Besides a series of letters, she wrote three works recording her visions: *Scivias sive visionum ac revelationum libri tres* (1141–1150), *Liber vitae meritorum* (1158–1162), and *Liber divinorum operum simplicis hominis* (1163–1170). She was also probably the author of two treatises, *Subtilitates diversarum naturarum creaturarum* and *Causae et curae*, which, though not avowedly the record of visions, could hardly have been written except as the result of some form of religious experience.[8] Her "cosmology and physiology," as Thorndike points out, were none the less in essential conformity with "the then prevalent theories of natural science" although she "displays no little originality in giving a new turn to the familiar concepts." She does not, however, "evolve any really new principles of nature."[9]

Peter Lombard and Peter Comestor

To turn from the imaginative and visionary writings of Hugh and Hildegard to the more coldly intellectual theology and philosophy of the age, we find in the *Sic et non* of Abelard the first example of a new method of handling philosophical and theological questions. This so-called didactic method was destined to find its culminating expression in the mighty volumes of Thomas Aquinas. Its essence was to incite discussion by placing in juxtaposition divergent and contradictory Scriptural and patristic texts on the same subject. Abelard did this in the *Sic et non* without giving interpretations of his own. Peter Lombard (died 1164), who in his *Sententiae* followed Abelard's method, usually gave in addition his own views on a subject, though not infrequently the reader was left faced by two or more conflicting theories. It might almost be said that the *Sententiae* served to standardize the orthodox doctrine of the age. Shortly after Peter Lombard's death Peter Comestor (the "eater"), at one time dean of the cathedral church in Troyes and lecturer in Paris, produced an extensive treatise entitled *Historia scholastica.* This compilation of commentaries on Scripture enjoyed an immense popularity at a later period, especially towards the close of the thirteenth century.[10] Comestor, like Peter Lombard, represented the more orthodox point of view.

THE SCHOOL OF CHARTRES: ITS INTELLECTUAL INDEPENDENCE

Unusual intellectual independence was displayed during the twelfth century by the philosophical writers of the school of Chartres[11] and by those who came under their influence. Well known early in the eleventh century, this cathedral school had acquired, in the first half of the twelfth, a European reputation, founded on the boldness and originality of its masters and on the widespread influence which they exerted through their pupils and associates.

Bernard and Theodoric of Chartres

Two brothers stand out preëminently among them, Bernard and Theodoric (or Thierry). Very little in detail is known about the life of either. Bernard was probably born late in the eleventh century and was chancellor between 1124 and 1126.[12] He enjoyed an immense reputation and was called by John of Salisbury the most perfect Platonist of his century.[13] It seems likely that he died before 1130 and was not the same man as Bernard Sylvester of Tours, with whom he has often been confused.[14]

We know even less of Theodoric, who enjoyed a contemporary fame as great as, if not even greater than, that of his brother. Theodoric was mentioned by a disciple as the foremost philosopher of the whole of Europe.[15] Master of the school (*magister scholae*) in Chartres in 1121, the successor to Gilbert de la Porrée as chancellor in 1141, he produced a large work on the seven liberal arts (the *Heptateuchon*) and a treatise describing the Creation.[16] The latter, entitled *De sex dierum operibus*, was in many respects unique, representing a remarkably rationalistic discussion of a subject in the treatment of which any display of reason or independence almost inevitably was deemed heresy.[17]

Adelard of Bath; Hermann the Dalmatian; Robert of Retines

Bernard and Theodoric maintained scholarly connections throughout Western Europe and counted many famous men among their disciples. The Englishman Adelard of Bath[18] belongs to their broader circle, for it is likely that he was acquainted with the Chartres scholars, at least by reputation, and his important work, *Quaestiones naturales*[19] (dating from between 1107 and 1142), shows that he held many ideas in common with the most famous of Bernard's pupils, William of Conches. In his wide travels[20] and in his translations from the Arabic[21] Adelard exemplifies another phase of the awakening intellectual life of the age, a turning to Moslem literature for new sources of information and inspiration beyond the standard and easily available collections of classical, Scriptural, and patristic authorities.

Among the disciples of Theodoric may also be counted the travelers and translators from the Arabic, Hermann the Dalmatian (or Hermann the Carinthian) and Robert of Retines, to whose translations we shall later have occasion to refer.[22]

Bernard Sylvester

Very closely akin in spirit with the scholars of Chartres was Bernard Sylvester, who taught at Tours in the fifth decade of the twelfth century.[23] It has long been a moot point whether or not Bernard Sylvester was the same as Bernard of Chartres. There are very potent arguments in favor of identifying them, among the most convincing being the remarkable manner in which the philosophy of the *De mundi universitate* (or *Cosmographia turonense*),[24] written by Bernard Sylvester between 1145 and 1148, gives expression to theories which John of Salisbury ascribes to Bernard of Chartres. Yet, despite these extraordinary similarities, the weight of evidence seems opposed to the theory that the two names refer to the same man.[25] In any case, if Bernard Sylvester was not the brother of Theodoric of Chartres, he was acquainted with Theodoric and with the latter's work, for it was to Theodoric that he dedicated the *De mundi universitate.*

William of Conches

Another member of the Chartres group, William of Conches, was a disciple of Bernard of Chartres in his youth. He taught at Chartres probably as early as 1126. Between 1140 and 1150 he acted as tutor to the young Henry and Geoffrey Plantagenet.[26] Hauréau says that William believed that "la philosophie tient subordonnées à ses principes généraux, comme deux sciences subalternes, la théologie et la physique."[27] His most significant book, the *De philosophia mundi*,[28] throughout exemplifies this attitude and reveals to us a mind deeply interested in physics and natural science for their own sakes and a desire to explain the phenomena of the universe according to natural and observable laws. The rationalism of his philosophy brought him into conflict with the ecclesiastical authorities and necessitated his retracting various opinions late in life.[29] He died either in 1150 or 1154.

Alexander Neckam

The scholars of the Chartres group formed the intellectual élite of their age. More in keeping with the normal habit of the period than their mode of thought was the manner in which the Englishman Alexander Neckam dealt with matters of natural science. Born in 1157, Neckam had become a professor at the University of Paris by 1180; later in life he returned to England, became abbot of Cirencester in 1213, and died in 1217.[80] His principal works were *De naturis rerum*, in prose, and a verse paraphrase and enlargement of it entitled *Laus sapiencie divine*, or *De laudibus divinae sapientiae*.[81] In these works we see that Neckam, though inspired by a lively curiosity and even by some degree of understanding of experimental and observational science, was on the whole less original and less courageous intellectually than either Theodoric of Chartres or William of Conches. Instead of trying to explain rationally the phenomena of nature as these earlier writers had done, he was nearly always content merely to describe these phenomena as facts and to draw lengthy moral lessons from them.

These are merely a few characteristic representatives of the host of theologians and philosophers of the twelfth and early thirteenth centuries. Their works serve to illustrate widely diverse tendencies of thought: the heretical independence of the scholars of Chartres as contrasted with the mysticism of Hugh of St. Victor, the orthodoxy of Peter Lombard and Peter Comestor, and the cautious inquisitiveness of Alexander Neckam. Though these men differed in mental caliber, their learning was based almost exclusively on the Latin writings of classical and earlier Christian authors, and most of their geographical knowledge was borrowed from the sources we have discussed in Chapters I and II. But our period was also memorable by reason of the influx of a new body of learning destined to bring about profound modifications in the methods of European scholarship and to add materially to the sum total of European knowledge. This new body of learning was made available through translations from the Arabic.

TRANSLATIONS FROM THE ARABIC; WORKS WRITTEN UNDER ARABIC INFLUENCE; ARISTOTELIANISM AND ITS OPPONENTS

The enthusiasm for the work of translation which prevailed during our period foreshadowed a far broader enthusiasm of the same sort that marked the great age of the Renaissance. Only a relatively few scholars, however, were familiar with Greek; and the number of direct translations from the Greek was limited.[32] The men of the Crusading age received the results of Greek scientific investigation primarily through the medium of the Moslems.

We saw in Chapter III how the Moslems had translated certain works of Aristotle, of Ptolemy, and of the Hindus and had themselves composed sundry treatises under Peripatetic, Ptolemaic, and Hindu influences. Many of these Arabic translations, in turn, were converted into Latin by Occidental scholars of our period.[32a]

Western interest in Moslem science centered at first on the translation of astronomical and mathematical treatises and somewhat later on Arabic versions of Aristotle. Indirectly through both of these channels important geographical conceptions gained currency in Europe.

Adelard of Bath; Peter Alphonsi

Among the early translators of astronomical and mathematical treatises was Adelard of Bath, whose connections with the school of Chartres we have already mentioned. Through Adelard's Latin version of the so-called *Khorazmian Tables*[33] of Al-Khwārizmī, made in the year 1126,[34] knowledge of the Hindu conception of a world center, Arin, was introduced into Europe. The *Khorazmian Tables* had found their way to Spain by the beginning of the eleventh century and were there adapted from the era of Yezdegerd to that of the Hejira by a certain Maslama al-Majrīṭi of Madrid.[35] In addition to Adelard's version of Maslama's work, there is reason to believe that the *Khorazmian Tables* were also put into Latin by Hermann the Dalmatian.[36]

A contemporary of Adelard of Bath was the Jew, Peter Alphonsi[37] (or Petrus Anfusi), who was baptized in 1106 at the age of forty-five and subsequently became an ardent devotee of Christianity. His *Dialogus cum Judeo* contains references to Arin and a few significant observations on astronomical geography.

John of Seville; Plato of Tivoli

In 1135 John of Seville (also known as Johannes Hispanensis, or John of Luna) translated Al-Farghānī's *On the Elements of Astronomy*,[38] a work from which John of Holywood borrowed much of the materials that he incorporated into his *De sphaera* and which thereby was fated to produce a profound effect on the future development of astronomical geography during the later Middle Ages. Gerard of Cremona also translated the same work.[39]

From about 1140 dates Plato of Tivoli's version of the *Astronomy* of Al-Battānī,[40] a close rendering into Latin of Al-Battānī's chapters on the theory of astronomy but not of the astronomical and geographical tables that followed in the original Arabic. Our interest in the chapters lies in the fact that they contain (Chapter 6) a brief general description of the inhabited earth widely differing from those found in contemporary Latin geographical works.

"Marseilles Tables" and "Toledo Tables"

Preserved in a twelfth-century manuscript of the Bibliothèque Nationale is a set of astronomical tables for Marseilles dating from 1140, the work of a certain Raymond of Marseilles.[41] The *Canons*, or introductory explanation, of these tables are drawn largely from the astronomical *Canons* of Az-Zarqalī;[42] the tables are an adaptation for the meridian of Marseilles of the *Toledo Tables*. Both Az-Zarqalī's *Canons* and the *Toledo Tables*, with their modifications like the Marseilles set, contained not a little incidental material of importance from the point of view of astronomical geography, including a list of cities with their latitudes and longitudes derived ultimately from Al-Khwārizmī.[43] That this material enjoyed wide popularity during our period and later is proved by the existence of a large number of manuscripts.[44] One of the translations of Az-Zarqalī's *Canons* was done by the hand of the famous Gerard of Cremona, as we have already seen in Chapter III.[45]

Robert of Retines; Hermann the Dalmatian; Daniel of Morley

It is almost certain that before 1143 the *Astronomy* of Al-Battānī was again put into Latin, this time by Robert of Retines[46] (or Robert of Chester). We do not, as in the case of Plato of Tivoli's version, possess the text of this translation, though we have what was probably Robert's adaptation to the meridian of London of Al-Battānī's and Az-Zarqalī's astronomical tables. This adaptation, for 1149–1150, forms a continuation of tables for the meridian of Toledo in 1149.[47] Furthermore, Al-Battānī is cited, and some of the geographical ideas expressed in his *Astronomy* are reflected, in the as yet unpublished *Liber de essentiis* of Hermann the Dalmatian, who was a close associate of Robert and a student of Theodoric of Chartres. The *Liber de essentiis* was written at Béziers in 1143.[48] Robert also adapted Adelard's *Khorazmian Tables* to the meridian of London.[49] Another Englishman, Roger of Hereford, was probably the maker of tables for the meridian of Toledo and certainly of a series for Hereford dating from 1178, based on tables for Toledo and Marseilles.[50] Towards the end of the century, still another Englishman, Daniel of Morley, journeyed to Spain in search of Arabic astronomical lore. Here, at Toledo, he came in contact with Gerard of Cremona. On his return to England he took with him "a precious multitude of books" and, "to explain the teaching of Toledo to Bishop John of Norwich" (1175–1200),[51] wrote a work called *De philosophia*, or *Liber de naturis inferiorum et superiorum*, the astronomy of which, as in the case of John of Holywood's *De sphaera*, was mainly based on the writings of Al-Farghānī.

Gerard of Cremona; John of Holywood (Sacrobosco)

At about the same time, Gerard of Cremona produced a short independent treatise, the *Theorica planetarum*,[52] which became a stock text from which later writers borrowed extensively. This is merely a summary of the *Almagest*, produced apparently before Gerard made his famous translation of that great work in 1175,[52a] and is of interest to us because it contains an account of methods of transposing astronomical tables to different longitudes. It had certainly been read by the author of the London tables of 1232,[53] a set which, in addition to being of astronomical value, contains a few incidental notes of geographic importance.

The *De sphaera* [54] of John of Holywood (also known as John of Halifax, or John Sacrobosco), dating from the very end of our period, includes citations from Al-Farghānī's *Astronomy* as well as from classical authors and was the most influential work in the field of astronomical geography of its century, though the intrinsic value of its contents was not great.

Aristotelianism Introduced Through Arabic Works

The translators of Arabic mathematical and astronomical works during the twelfth century prepared the way for an event of the first magnitude in the intellectual history of the Middle Ages—the reintroduction of Aristotelian learning into the West.[55] It would lead us far beyond the bounds of this study to try to discuss the immense influence of Aristotelianism on the development of European philosophy and theology in and after the thirteenth century. Something of the geographical content of Aristotle's writings on physics and natural science, however, was indicated in Chapter I, and it was during the closing years of the twelfth and the beginning of the thirteenth centuries that these works began to gain a hold on European thought. Their influence at this time was for the most part exerted through roundabout channels: probably in some cases through Latin translations of Arabic translations from the original Greek; unquestionably in others through Latin translations of Arabic translations of Syriac translations from the original Greek; and in still others through Latin translations of Arabic commentaries on Aristotle or of works inspired by his writings. The desire or ability to tap the sources of Aristotelian lore by direct recourse to

Greek texts themselves was exceptional before the middle of the thirteenth century.

The precise date when the Occident became acquainted with the *Physics* and *De caelo* is a matter of some doubt. It is likely that Avicenna's version of these two books had been converted into Latin at Toledo before the middle of the twelfth century by Dominicus Gondisalvi,[56] who worked there under the patronage of Archbishop Raymond, but the extent to which these early translations influenced European science is a subject of controversy. It has been suggested by Duhem that Latin translations of Aristotle were known to the scholars of the Chartres school, Theodoric, Gilbert de la Porrée, and William of Conches, passages in whose works certainly reveal some familiarity with Peripatetic theories.[57] On the other hand, there are no actual citations of Aristotle which would enable us to prove that the passages in question show first-hand knowledge of the books of the Stagirite.[58] The fact that much Peripatetic thought had been brought to the West through the writers of the late Roman and earlier Christian periods often makes it difficult, in the absence of actual citations, to distinguish between what had been learned from these earlier sources and what was contemporaneously derived from the Moslems.

Gerard of Cremona

We are on much firmer ground when we turn to the work of Gerard of Cremona,[59] for we know as a fact that before his death in 1187 this indefatigable translator had put into Latin, of the works of Aristotle of geographical interest, the first three books of the *Meteorology*,[60] the *Physics*, the *De caelo et mundo*,[61] and the *De generatione et corruptione*.[62]

Michael Scot

Michael Scot, who died in 1236 [63] and was remembered by later ages as a great magician, was another student of Aristotelian science. After studying in Spain this Scotsman became court astrologer of the Emperor Frederick II in Sicily. He learned Arabic and composed treatises on astronomy, astrology (*Liber introductorius* and *Liber particularis*), and physiognomy under the influence of Moslem learning. He also undertook the translation of sundry works on alchemy and astronomy, among them the treatise of Al-Biṭrūjī, based on Aristotelian astronomy, and Aristotle's *De caelo* with Averroës' commentary. Associated with the *Liber particularis* we have the text of a questionnaire [64] which Frederick II presented to Michael and which reveals something of that versatile Emperor's burning interest in cosmology and physical geography. The philosopher's "brief statements" in reply "concerning hell, purgatory, heaven, and the terrestrial paradise are followed by an account of the marvels of nature—strange lakes and rivers of the East, wondrous metals, stones, plants, drugs, and animals, with their respective virtues" (Haskins).[65] Michael in this connection also gives expression to familiar, traditional opinions on the earth as a sphere, though he includes some original observations on volcanoes and hot springs.[66]

Aristotelianism in the Thirteenth Century

By the time of Michael Scot Aristotelian theories of physics and of physical geography as introduced through Moslem channels were finding fairly general currency in the West. Arnold the Saxon, for instance, in his encyclopedic treatise written perhaps about 1225, gave citations from the *De caelo et mundo*, the *Meteorology*, and the *Physics*, as well as from Averroës and other Arabic admirers of Aristotle.[67] Aristotelian cosmology, astronomy, and metaphysics, however, were not accepted by Western scholars until after a strenuous intellectual battle had been waged over them. Serious efforts were made to place these teachings forever under the ban of the church. In 1210 and 1215 strict prohibitions against the study of the Averroïstic versions of the *Physics* and *Metaphysics* were issued by the authorities of the University of Paris.[68] This shows that by that time not only had the commentaries of Averroës been translated but that they must have become popular.[69] Indeed, the popularity of Aristotle and Averroës was destined to increase despite all prohibitions, and by the middle of the thirteenth century they became prescribed studies in the curriculum of the University of Paris. Aristotelianism dominated the scientific thought of the late thirteenth and fourteenth centuries; and the physical geography of the great encyclopedist, Albertus Magnus, was largely based upon it. Albert, indeed, was sometimes unjustly called Aristotle's ape.

Opponents of Aristotelianism

On the other hand, there were many individuals who, though accepting the teachings of Aristotle and his Arabic commentators in regard to specific facts and theories, were none the less sternly opposed to blind and uncritical adoption of them.

William of Auvergne

William of Auvergne, bishop of Paris from 1228 to his death in 1249, was leader of the ecclesiastical party that stood out against the study of Aristotelian philosophy and theology in that city. It was nevertheless true, as Duhem tells us, that William's erudition "had received in abundance additions from sources which had not enriched the erudition of earlier centuries: that is from the works of Aristotle and Arabic authors." [70] The *De universo* of William contains much material on cosmology and natural history.

Robert Grosseteste

The great English churchman, Robert Grosseteste, bishop of Lincoln from 1235 until his death in 1253, presents an even more striking example of the scholar, well read in Aristotelian and Arabic learning, who was prone to question many of the Peripatetic doctrines. Grosseteste deserves a high place in the history of medieval science by reason of the depth of his scholarship and the originality of his ideas. His style, however, is often difficult and obscure. From the geographical point of view several of his treatises are of unusual interest. The *De sphaera* is devoted to problems of astronomical geography. In the *De impressionibus aëris seu de prognosticatione* rules are laid down for the preparation of weather forecasts based upon astrological considerations. The *De luce seu de inchoatione formarum* explains Robert's theory of the Creation. The *De natura locorum*, in which the influences of celestial rays upon the earth's surface are discussed, gives expression to many views that were elaborated in fuller detail by Robert's more famous pupil and intellectual successor, Roger Bacon.[71]

ENCYCLOPEDIC WORKS

Our period was marked by the production of encyclopedic works the object of which was to bring together as much human knowledge as possible in convenient, readable, and, frequently, in popular form. These encyclopedias carried on the traditions of Pliny, Solinus, Isidore, Bede, and other earlier writers and for the most part were lacking in originality. Made up of paraphrases and word-for-word excerpts from older books, they exemplify better than any other type of literary production the respect which the man of the Middle Ages felt towards the authority of the written word and his lack of critical acumen. Their immense popularity shows that they satisfied a distinct want: the lore contained in them, however worthless and puerile it often may seem to us, formed an important part of the intellectual cargo of the medieval mind. It is imperative, therefore, that representatives of this type of work should be consulted by anyone who wishes to arrive at a just estimate of the status of medieval knowledge.[72]

Most of the geography of the encyclopedias was a geography handed down from classical times, a geography but distantly related to contemporary facts and one in which fabulous elements tended to persist and multiply at the expense of sound and accurate information. Yet it was the geography of the majority of the lettered men, and the man who did not himself actually travel found here practically the only convenient means of learning about the countries of the world. He might pick up occasional details of routes to Rome and Palestine from pilgrims, traders, or soldiers; but only in the pages of the encyclopedias could he find anything approaching a systematic treatment of the earth and its various parts.

"De Imagine Mundi"

The most widely read book of this nature was the *De imagine mundi*, which dates from about 1100. Though this has often been attributed in recent years to Honorius of Autun (it has also been ascribed to St. Anselm and with far greater probability to an unknown Honorius Inclusus), the evidence at hand is insufficient to warrant us in coming to any definite conclusions on the vexed question of its authorship.[73] The general character of the compilation is illustrated by a remark at the close of the dedicatory letter: "I place nothing in this work except that which is approved by the best authorities."[74] The main source of the geographical chapters was the *Etymologiae* of Isidore, though the author also drew directly from Orosius.[75] It seems likely, indeed, that the geographical chapter of Orosius served as a basis for the entire compilation and provided an outline which was embellished by copious excerpts of detail from the more elaborate writings of Isidore, Augustine, and Bede. Furthermore, it is even probable that the unknown author had a map before him.[76] He appears to have borrowed directly from the *Collectanea rerum memorabilium* of Solinus his account of the marvels of India, though elsewhere he taps Solinus at second hand through the medium of Isidore.[77]

Lambert's "Liber Floridus;" Guido's Encyclopedia

Dating from approximately the same period is a similar work, the *Liber floridus* of Lambert. Practically all we know of the author is that he was a canon of St. Omer early in the twelfth century.[78] His book, a hodgepodge of notices, geographical and otherwise, from Isidore, Bede, Martianus Capella, Raban Maur, and others, though it did not enjoy popularity comparable to that of the *De imagine mundi*, nevertheless by no means lapsed into obscurity during the centuries that followed. There are at least eight manuscripts of it preserved in the libraries of Europe, and it was referred to with high praise by writers of the thirteenth century.[79] The manuscripts are illustrated by crude maps, among the few remaining relics of twelfth-century cartography.

Of much the same nature is an encyclopedic compilation made by a certain Guido, probably an Italian, in 1119.[80] It contains excerpts from a variety of sources, including Isidore, the Romance of Alexander, Paul the Deacon, and, more especially, the anonymous Ravenna geographer.

"Lucidarius"

The *De imagine mundi* became an important source for later writings. It was a standard authority during the closing years of the Middle Ages for those who deliberately undertook to give a geographical description of the earth. The *Lucidarius* (or *Aurea gemma*) was a popular encyclopedia written in German towards the end of the twelfth century at the order of Henry the Lion. Though embodying the peculiar and fabulous features of the *De imagine mundi,* it omitted the drier but more correct geographical and topographical details.[81] The principal source of much of the natural science in the *Lucidarius* was William of Conches' *De philosophia mundi.* The *Lucidarius* was translated at a later date into Danish, Dutch, and Bohemian,[82] and from it were derived the geographical portions of the famous *Hortus deliciarum* of the abbess Herrad of Landsperg.[83]

Gervase of Tilbury

Another widely read book that came under the influence of the *De imagine mundi* was the *Otia imperialia* of Gervase of Tilbury,[84] a protégé of Otto IV and by him appointed marshal of the kingdom of Arles. The *Otia,* composed to entertain the emperor during the leisure moments of his struggle with Frederick II, is in large measure a compilation of facts, fables, and theories borrowed from earlier works. The cosmological chapters are drawn from Peter Comestor's *Historia scholastica,* the geographical ones from Orosius, Isidore, and, more particularly, the *De imagine mundi,* which furnished a framework into which the statements of the other writers were made to fit.[85] The large number of manuscripts of the *Otia* bears witness to its great popularity.

JACQUES DE VITRY

Jacques de Vitry, bishop of St. John of Acre until 1220, in his *Historia hierosolymitana* [86] also borrowed from the *De imagine mundi*, especially in describing Palestine and Asia. His interest in the remarkable caused him to include, as had been done by the authors of the German *Lucidarius*, most of the fabulous elements of the earlier book as well as to add fabulous stories from other sources. It was these stories, derived in part from the *Historia hierosolymitana* and in part directly from the *De imagine mundi*, that accounted for the great popularity of a poem to which we must now turn.

"L'IMAGE DU MONDE"

This poem, the *Image du Monde*,[87] destined to be read for over three centuries, was decidedly the most important of the many works that felt the influence of the *De imagine mundi*. Like its Latin predecessor, it is an attempt at the popularization of universal knowledge. The work of popularization, however, was here carried to the stage of translation into a popular tongue, which rendered the book available to a much broader circle of readers. The style was vivid and not lacking in originality, and the subject matter contained sufficient of the grotesque and unexpected to assure the poem a long-lived success. Though the question of authorship and exact date is a somewhat perplexing one, it seems likely that the *Image du Monde* was partially composed in Metz in 1245 or 1247 by a certain Gossouin and within the following two or three years was added to either by Gossouin himself or by a certain Walter of Metz, to whom the entire work has occasionally been attributed.[88] Prior, however, to the composition of the second verse redaction by Gossouin or Walter, the poem had been put into a prose form,[89] from which translations were subsequently made into Hebrew, Judeo-German, and English (the last by Caxton in 1480).

"KONUNGS-SKUGGSJÁ"

From the very end of our period there dates an Icelandic dialogue of more or less encyclopedic scope, a work which might well be called a northern counterpart of the *De imagine mundi.* This *Konungs-Skuggsjá*, or *King's Mirror*,[90] written about the year 1250 or perhaps as late as 1260, contains chapters that reveal to us something of the status of Scandinavian knowledge of the geography and natural phenomena of Iceland, Greenland, and the Arctic seas. But, like the Sagas, so far as we know, it was not translated into Latin or into the vernacular tongues, and the type of knowledge contained in it remained until the great age of discovery virtually the exclusive property of the peoples of Iceland and of the far north of Europe.[91]

Great Encyclopedias of the Thirteenth Century

We cannot well leave the subject of encyclopedic compilations without mentioning such gigantic thirteenth-century productions as the *Specula* of Vincent of Beauvais,[92] the various writings of Albertus Magnus,[93] and the relatively less ambitious popularizations of Bartholomew Anglicus,[94] Brunetto Latino,[95] and others.[96] The *Opus majus* of Roger Bacon is also encyclopedic in scope. These great works contain a wealth of reference the systematic study of which would unquestionably shed much additional light on the substance of medieval geographical knowledge. The innumerable pages of Albertus Magnus, indeed, show not a little originality; and Roger Bacon stands somewhat apart from his contemporaries as a fearless exponent of scientific method.[97] On the whole, however, there is no very essential difference between the geography of these men and that of their less well-informed and perhaps less diligent predecessors. This is one reason why we have felt justified in failing to treat them in detail. Another reason is that adequate treatment of the geography of the thirteenth-century encyclopedists would fill another volume at least the size of the present one.

Dante

A figure, however, whom we cannot refrain from mentioning in this connection, though he lived after 1250 and though his genius far transcended that of any encyclopedist of any age, is Dante. Much of the information amassed by the laborious compilers of encyclopedic works (especially Brunetto Latino) was fused by the poet into the *Divine Comedy* and molded into his various prose writings. The universality of Dante's knowledge embraced the geography and cosmography of his age. Though we shall not attempt to deal with Dante's geographical lore [98] in the pages which follow, it would be a serious mistake to omit all reference to one who flourished so soon after the end of our period and who, besides being a poet of all time, was an outstanding figure in medieval scholarship and, incidentally, in the history of medieval geography.

The reader who wishes to investigate the geography of Dante and of the encyclopedists of the thirteenth century will find brief summaries and references in Notes 92–98 to the present chapter.

HISTORIES, CHRONICLES, SAGAS, EPIC POEMS

The writings of the historians and chroniclers of the Middle Ages, though they do not as a rule include systematic expositions of geography, nevertheless often contain incidental geographical matter of no slight interest. The present section is devoted to a very few selected specimens of historical narrative of the Crusading age, whether prose or verse, that are of particular significance from the geographical point of view.

Otto of Freising

Among the outstanding medieval historians was Otto of Freising.[99] A man of intelligence and breadth, steeped in the academic literature of his age, Otto, though never going out of his way to write of geographical subjects, always maintained an attitude of open and receptive interest toward all branches of science. The range of his literary and scholarly learning is a key to the intellectual attainments of the average man of the world of his period. Born about 1114 or 1115 of a noble or even royal family—his maternal grandfather was the Emperor Henry IV—Otto studied in Paris probably early in the second quarter of the century. After his return to Germany in 1132 or 1133, he became a Cistercian and was subsequently made bishop of

Freising. His principal works were a *Chronicon*, running from the beginning of the world to the year 1146, and the *Gesta Friderici*, recording the deeds of Frederick Barbarossa down to the year 1156 and continued after that date by Ragewin (or Rahewin).[100] Among other classical authorities Otto may have used Seneca's *Quaestiones naturales:* most of his geographical ideas, however, were derived from Isidore and Orosius and from certain unknown "topographers" whom he cites as giving details on the rivers of Europe.[101]

Gunther of Pairis

On the *Gesta Friderici* was based an historical poem composed about 1186 by Gunther of Pairis (in Alsace), of whom we know next to nothing.[102] This work, the *Ligurinus*, adds little of material nature to the sources from which it was taken, although the poet converts the simple, straightforward narrative of Otto and Ragewin into a poem vividly expressed. It has been shown that the *Ligurinus*, even though the work of a German author, is a typical product of the poetical school of France of the late twelfth and early thirteenth centuries.[103] Where the writer expands and converts into verse Otto's and Ragewin's words describing natural features of the earth's surface and geographical regions, he displays a sense of color and a feeling for nature that are striking,[104] even though the actual epithets employed are hackneyed and drawn from well-known classical models. Furthermore, in the description of Germany he departs so widely from his literary sources that it seems more than likely that he actually based his lines on personal acquaintance with the country.[105]

Walter of Châtillon; William the Breton

Two other historical poems of the same school and of analogous character to the *Ligurinus* are the *Alexandreis*[106] of Walter of Châtillon (also known as Walter of Lille), written about 1180, and the *Philippis* of William the Breton, published about 1225.[107] These are Latin hexameter epics modeled on Virgil and Lucan; full of allusions to Latin literature and mythology, they also show originality and a power of accurate description of scenes and country.[108] The *Alexandreis* sings the deeds of Alexander the Great; the *Philippis* the exploits of Philip Augustus of France.

Historians and Histories of the Crusades

Our period was the age of the reopening of the Levant and the regions of the Black Sea to Western knowledge through the Crusades and through the expansion of commerce that came in their train. The historians of the Crusades, consequently, furnish us with geographical notices of a kind differing from the stereotyped and secondhand geography of the encyclopedias. The items in the Crusaders' records are often the results of actual experience. They give us an impression of freshness lacking in the pages of dry compilations like the *De imagine mundi*. But the Crusaders were not geographers and were without any true geographical instinct. They rarely felt an interest in anything besides the immediate events they were undertaking to describe or in matters not purely practical or utilitarian.[109]

The most important work, from this point of view, is the *Historia rerum in partibus transmarinis gestarum* of William of Tyre (born 1130).[110] This covers events in Palestine and in the Crusaders' states during the years between 1095 and 1185 and abounds in observations on the products and appearance of the country, on the habits of the Arabs—whose language William had probably learned[111]—and on other peoples of the East.

The *Gesta regis Ricardi*, which has sometimes been erroneously ascribed to Benedict of Peterborough,[112] records the voyage of Richard Coeur-de-Lion to the Holy Land in 1190. In the description of the routes to and from Palestine[113] we find a wealth of detail about the countries, isles, and seas traversed. The distinctly nautical style and content in places make it seem not at all improbable that a part of the book at least was derived from some sailing manual. Roger of Hoveden in his *Chronica*[114] (to the year 1201) made use of the same sources as those on which the author of the *Gesta regis Ricardi* drew, though Roger's account is fuller and more detailed, especially regarding Spain. Another source for the Crusade of Richard Coeur-de-Lion is the *Estoire de la guerre sainte* by Ambroise,[115] a professional writer, who took part on the expedition and who described the Holy Land with less understanding than William of Tyre almost exclusively from the point of view of the sufferings and hardships experienced by the Crusaders.

The *Prise de Constantinople* [116] of Robert de Clari, a history of the Fourth Crusade by a participant, is the work of a man of relatively humble estate but of a man who felt more or less genuine interest in strange peoples and their customs. This interest is manifested particularly by the data that he gives on the Komans of the Russian plains, some of whom he undoubtedly had seen on the streets of Constantinople.

A letter from the patriarch of Jerusalem to Innocent III, entitled *La devision de la terre de oultremer et des choses qui i sont*,[117] was composed about 1200 in reply to a request from the Pope for information concerning the Saracen countries. In this anonymous work a geographical sketch of Egypt and Palestine shows that its author had no limited acquaintance with the Moslem faith and the Mohammedan peoples.

Scandinavian Historical Works

The geographical knowledge acquired by the Crusaders became the common property of all Western Europe. That which was acquired by the Vikings, on the other hand, was disseminated practically not at all among the peoples of the Latin West. Brief mention, therefore, must suffice for the Scandinavian sources, even though of all European folk the Vikings were the most adventurous voyagers and their geographical horizon the widest.

The introduction of Christianity marked the end of the heroic age of Norwegian and Icelandic history. It also ushered in an extraordinary period of literary productivity, the age of the Sagas [118] and Eddas.[119] The composition of the Sagas began in the twelfth and lasted on into the fourteenth century, but the events which they relate occurred far back in pagan days. For the most part bald but telling narratives of adventure, war, and litigation, they devote little space to comment or description; and the numerous place names mentioned are referred to as if the reader were already familiar with them.

The records of the farthest voyages of the Vikings to the shores of Wineland the Good were not given the final written form in which we now know them until after the close of the thirteenth century.[120] On the other hand, the history of Iceland was told by Ari Frodhi (1067–1148) in his *Íslendingabók*;[121] and the chronicles of the settlement of the coasts of this isle and of the discovery of Greenland are recorded in the *Landnámabók*,[122] or *Book of Settlements*, the original of which probably dates from the twelfth century. The famous *Heimskringla* of Snorri Sturluson, the greatest of early Scandinavian historians, records the history of the kings of Norway. Its title means "the Round World," and the prelude consists of a brief geographical description of the principal countries of the world. The text includes no less than sixteen Sagas, among them that of Sigurd the Crusader chronicling an adventurous voyage (1109) of a king of southern Norway to the Holy Land by way of the Strait of Gibraltar and homeward overland. Scattered geographical references are found in other Sagas and in the *Icelandic*[123] and *Greenland Annals*[124] which, though written after our period, throw light on events that took place before the mid-thirteenth century.

Latin Histories of the North

Besides the Sagas, three historical works written in Latin by Northern writers of our age deserve particular mention inasmuch as they all contain geographical descriptions of the Scandinavian world. The first of these is the history of Adam of Bremen. On strictly chronological grounds Adam, who died about 1076, belongs before the opening of the Crusading age. We shall discuss him, however, among the historians of the twelfth and early thirteenth centuries, to whose works his writings are more akin in spirit than to those of the earlier Middle Ages. Adam was canon of Bremen and master of the cathedral school of that city in the time of the great Archbishop Adalbert, who had "made Bremen an Arctic Rome and his court the greatest center of Northern learning" (Beazley).[125] The archiepiscopal province of Bremen was the largest in the entire medieval church, including all of Scandinavia, Iceland, Greenland, the Orkneys, the Faroes, and the Hebrides. Adam was thus placed in a most favorable position to gather together materials on the geography and history of these northern lands. His great work (called sometimes *Gesta Hammenburgensis ecclesiae pontificum,* sometimes *Historia ecclesiastica,* and sometimes *Bremensium praesulum historia*) is in four books, the last of which deals with the geography of the North. Much of this was based on information derived from contemporaries; but Adam was also well read in Latin literature and often quotes and copies from the works of Macrobius, Martianus Capella, Solinus, and Orosius.

From somewhat more than a century later we have another Latin history of the Scandinavian North—if Saxo Grammaticus' curiously heterogeneous combination of mythology, folklore, poetry, and accurate observation deserves the name of history. The first book of this work, known as the *Gesta Danorum*, contains a formal geographical sketch of Denmark, the Baltic, the Scandinavian Peninsula, and remoter countries and isles beyond the Atlantic, wherein fact is blended with romance. There are also occasional observations of geographical interest scattered through the later books.

Finally, in an anonymous *Historia Norwegiae* dating from the early thirteenth century we find an introductory passage on the geography of the regions with which this history deals: a concise description of Norway is followed by briefer comments on the tributary islands, Iceland, Greenland, the Orkneys, and the Faroes. Especially interesting are the author's observations upon the volcanoes of Iceland. The contents show that, like Adam of Bremen and Saxo Grammaticus, the writer must have been familiar with the standard geographical books of the Middle Ages, with Bede and Solinus, and perhaps with Isidore and Pliny. The *Historia Norwegiae,* however, can never have enjoyed great popularity, or else more than one manuscript would be known at the present day.[126]

LEGENDS

Many of the legends of our period contain material of geographical significance, and a few of these may claim our particular attention.

ROMANCE OF ALEXANDER

The stories of Alexander the Great served to direct men's attention eastward, for, besides narrating the adventures of the Macedonian conqueror, they gave, as we have already seen,[127] details of a sort about the geography of Asia, particularly of India.[128] Not only were the earlier Latin versions derived from the *Pseudo-Callisthenes* paraphrased and copied by historians,[129] but new elements were added to the cycle—notably the *Iter ad Paradisum*,[130] an account of Alexander's journey to Paradise. Walter of Châtillon (or of Lille), about 1180, composed in the style of Lucan a great Latin hexameter poem entitled *Alexandreis*, based in part on the legendary stories of the Macedonian and in part on the more authentic histories of Justin and Quintus Curtius.[131] The widest currency, however, was given to the Romance through its translation into the vernacular tongues. The oldest French version, which covers the earlier portion of the Romance only, was written by Alberic of Besançon (early twelfth century?) in octosyllabic verse of the dialect of the Dauphiny.[132] This was translated into German by one Lamprecht and was rendered into the *langue d'oïl* in decasyllabic form.[133] The Romance reached its highest vernacular development in a version in alexandrines,[134] the joint composition of Lambert li Tors of Châteaudun, Alexander of Bernai (or of Paris), and Peter of St. Cloud. The existence of more than twenty manuscripts testifies to the popularity of this great poem, which is a sort of mosaic from various sources.[135] Much of it came from the *Pseudo-Callisthenes* through the medium of Valerius, the *Epitoma* of Valerius, Alberic of Besançon, and the decasyllabic poem; but some elements can be traced back to Orosius, Justin, Quintus Curtius, Eustatius, and Josephus, and the texts show many later interpolations of unknown origin. The Romance in alexandrines was drawn upon in its turn by later compilers. From the mid-thirteenth century there dates a poem, probably by one Eustace of Kent, which incorporates much material from this and other sources.[136] It includes miscellaneous geographical elements; and certain of the manuscripts are adorned with a wealth of magnificent miniatures, representing, among other things, the marvels of India and all the fantastic creatures encountered by Alexander throughout the East.

Prester John

During our period the belief was spread abroad in the existence of a numerous Christian population in Asia. We find an account of Christians in India in an anonymous report of the visit of a certain Patriarch John of India to Rome in 1122, the authenticity of which is apparently confirmed in a letter of Odo, abbot of St. Remi in Rheims, to a certain Count Thomas.[137] Of far greater importance was the fabulous story of Prester John. Belief in this mighty Christian potentate and his immense kingdom may be traced in large measure to the widely read *Letter of Prester John*, dating in its earliest form from before 1177,[138] addressed in some manuscripts to the Byzantine Emperor[139] and elsewhere to other Western monarchs. The popularity of this is attested by the fact that Zarncke, its editor, knew of no less than eighty manuscripts. The question of the sources of the *Letter* in its original form is obscure, though the origins of the numerous interpolations can nearly all be explained. Much, certainly, was borrowed from the Alexander stories, and much from the legend of St. Thomas in India; other parts are indubitably connected with the great Oriental reservoir of fabulous and miraculous lore. The account of the visit of Patriarch John to Rome and the *Letter of Prester John* constituted the principal sources of an anonymous and highly fanciful description of India and of Prester John's country found in a twelfth-century manuscript in the Heiligenkreutzerstift, near Vienna, and commonly called the *Elysaeus* account.[140] The *Letter of Prester John* was not only extensively read in its various Latin versions but was translated into French, Italian, German, and English.[141]

St. Brandan

Another legend which enjoyed perhaps an even greater popularity was that dealing with the wanderings of St. Brandan (or Brendan) in the Western Ocean. The story occurs in several distinct forms.[142] The Latin version had already taken shape before our period opened and perhaps dates back to the ninth century or earlier. From it was derived in part an Anglo-Norman version composed in 1121, which ultimately found its way into the *Image du monde.* The legend furthermore gained currency among the Teutonic peoples in a somewhat different version developed probably from a twelfth-century French original.

PILGRIM NARRATIVES; MISCELLANEOUS RECORDS OF TRAVEL

The travels of pilgrims and traders during the Middle Ages have been the subject of more careful research in recent years than many other aspects of our study.[143] Consequently, it will suffice merely to give a very brief statement of the more significant pilgrim records dating from the Crusading age.

Christian Pilgrim Narratives

The first pilgrim after the conquest of Jerusalem in 1099 who has left a fairly complete account of the Holy Land was the Anglo-Saxon, Saewulf,[144] a traveler who visited Palestine in 1102 and 1103, combining trading enterprise with religious zeal. From the middle of the century the journeys of John of Würzburg,[145] of his follower Theoderic,[146] as well as of the Icelandic abbot, Nikulás Bergsson [147] of Thverá, deserve mention because in these records we find a personal touch that distinguishes them from the majority of similar narratives. The latter as a rule show that the pilgrims, like the medieval men of learning, suffered from that tendency, so characteristic of their age, to copy slavishly what others had said rather than to rely on their own powers of observation. This is particularly well illustrated by the majority of pilgrim records dating from after the early years of the twelfth century, when, as Beazley puts it, a decline had set in, "hastened by the compilation of standard guidebooks, which may be faintly described as legendary and inaccurate, and from which the later pilgrim narratives blindly copy, to the ever growing exclusion of anything independent or scholarly. Two of these handbooks, known as the *Old* and the *New Compendium*, are the source of most of the tracts on the Holy Road which have been left us, under various names, from the time of the Second Crusade to the close of the Middle Ages."[148] To this dry, guidebook type belong the narrative ascribed to Fetellus, archdeacon of Antioch,[149] and a series of anonymous accounts of pilgrimages dating from the twelfth and early thirteenth centuries. Though several of these contain more or less original matter, the desiccating influence of the *Old Compendium* is nearly everywhere apparent.[150]

Besides the pilgrims other travelers were on the road, and the records of their travels have in some cases come down to us. The journeys of Giraldus Cambrensis through Wales and Ireland will be discussed in the next section, on topographical works. Narratives of travel are also occasionally to be found in historical works and chronicles, poems, and letters.

Letters of Travel

The letter was an honored form of literary expression throughout antiquity and the Middle Ages. Carefully composed epistles of the ecclesiastic and educated man of the world were looked upon as more than mere media for the conveying of information. Not infrequently they were highly polished specimens of stylistic art, worthy of finding a permanent place in literature. From our point of view, they are of interest for the personal accounts of journeys which they sometimes contain.[151] Guy of Bazoches, for instance, who was precentor of the church of St. Stephen at Châlons, gave a brilliant description of his experiences and of what he saw on the Crusade of 1190 in a series of letters to his nephew and to others.[152] Conrad of Querfurt, bishop of more than one see in Germany during the last years of the twelfth century, wrote enthusiastically of his wanderings through Italy in a letter preserved for us in Arnold of Lübeck's *Chronica Slavorum*.[153] A thorough study of the epistolography of the Crusading age would surely reveal a wealth of geographical lore.

Jewish Travelers

The Jews of the Middle Ages often journeyed farther afield than their Christian contemporaries. Their travels, for the most part in the interests of commerce, though in some instances in the nature of pilgrimages to Jerusalem, a city holy to Jew and Christian alike,[154] were facilitated by the presence of Hebrew communities in nearly all the cities of Europe and Western Asia. Strongly imbued with the racial consciousness of a vigorous and often oppressed people, the members of these communities did all in their power to receive the travelers and speed them on their way. The books composed by such Jewish wanderers as Benjamin of Tudela and Petachia of Ratisbon have been preserved and are invaluable as geographical records. It should be remembered, however, that they were written by men of a despised race and in a tongue unknown to the Christians of the West and that the geographical lore which may have been widespread among the more intelligent Hebrews never became an integral part of the geographical knowledge of Christendom. Hence in the pages which follow and which deal primarily with the geographical knowledge of Western Christendom but relatively little space can be devoted to Jewish geography.

A few words, nevertheless, must be said of Benjamin and of Petachia.

Benjamin of Tudela

Rabbi Benjamin came from the small Spanish city of Tudela on the Ebro. It was probably about the year 1159 that this observant wanderer journeyed eastward from his native town, moving leisurely through southern France, Italy, Greece, Constantinople, and thence by sea to Syria. After a thorough examination of the cities of Syria and Palestine he made his way overland to Baghdad. It is unlikely that he penetrated beyond Mesopotamia, though on his homeward journey he visited Egypt sometime before 1171 and returned to his home in Castile in 1173. He appears to have kept a record as he went along, and from a critical examination of his book it is possible in a general way to reconstruct his route. He describes in detail the cities he passed through and the distances in days' journeys, though not the directions, from one to another. He notes particularly the names of the leading Jews of each place and gives estimates of the numbers of the Jewish population. Indeed, probably one of his main purposes was to get in touch with Jews of as many countries as possible in order to determine where they were treated well. One result of the Crusades was an outburst of persecution of Hebrews throughout Christendom, and Benjamin, besides traveling for the sake of trade, was undoubtedly seeking for places "where his expatriated brethren might find an asylum" (Adler).[155] But, as well as revealing an interest in the Jewish inhabitants of the regions he traversed, his book gives us many significant data in regard to commerce and politics, monuments and natural features. For the regions actually visited by Benjamin this information is accurate and precise, but for the farther parts of Asia it becomes confused and often legendary.[156]

Petachia of Ratisbon

The second of the great Hebrew travelers of the twelfth century was Rabbi Petachia of Ratisbon in Bavaria. In the ninth decade of the century Petachia traveled eastward from Prague through Poland, Russia, Transcaucasia, and Kurdestan to Baghdad, whence he returned homeward by way of Palestine. The outward journey was a most unusual exploit for this time, traversing the steppes of Russia then infested with wild Tatar tribes. Unfortunately, much that was most important and significant in Petachia's book appears to have been removed by Rabbi Yahudi the Pious, "who acted as Petachia's literary mouthpiece" (Beazley).[157]

TOPOGRAPHICAL WORKS

We must now examine a few works on the geography and topography of local regions.

Godfrey of Viterbo

In a manuscript of the mid-twelfth-century writings of Godfrey of Viterbo, and in all probability to be ascribed to Godfrey, there is a poem entitled *Denumeratio regnorum imperio subjectorum.*[158] The writer explains his purpose in the following terms: "Not the wars of kingdoms are here set forth, but their fortune (pride?), their rivers, the extent and kind of regions which constitute them, the types of customs, the manner of harvesting and of trade."[159] In the course of the poem he treats of Rome, of Apulia and other Italian districts subject to Rome, of the kingdom of the Lombards, of Venetia, of "true France"—by which he means the lands of the Franks along the lower Rhine—of Basel, of Alsace, of Strasburg, of Worms; but, though much of the detail constitutes a poetic geography of peoples and cities, little attention is paid to physical features.

Gervase of Canterbury

Among the lesser writings of the English chronicler, Gervase of Canterbury, we find a *mappamundi* dating from about the year 1200.[160] This is a brief account of England, its dimensions[161] and languages, followed by a table in three columns showing, for each county, (1) the most important ecclesiastical officers, archbishops, bishops, abbots, and priors; (2) the names of the churches; and (3) the religious orders and mother churches to which the various ecclesiastics appertained. After this there follows a list of hospitals, castles, islands, fresh- and salt-water springs, and other curiosities.

Giraldus Cambrensis

By all means the most important topographical works of our period, however, came from the pen of Giraldus Cambrensis, or Gerald of Barry (*c.* 1146–*c.* 1222).[162] This active and intelligent Norman-Welsh ecclesiastic, who at the time had already made one visit to Ireland, was appointed chaplain to Henry II in 1184 and in the following year was sent as counselor to the young Prince John on the latter's expedition to Ireland. During the expedition he collected materials for two treatises, the first of which, the *Topographia Hiberniae*, was completed in 1188.

Though Giraldus' knowledge of Ireland in reality was limited, barely extending beyond the areas occupied by the English, though his impression of the Irish people was prejudiced and hostile, and though he overburdens us with the recitation of marvels, his books show, none the less, that their author possessed a keen interest in natural history and geography and that his powers of observation were far from mediocre. The second treatise, the *Expugnatio Hiberniae*, or history of the English conquest of the island, contains much less geographical material than the *Topographia*.

In 1188, when Henry II was about to start out on the Crusade, he sent Archbishop Baldwin of Canterbury into Wales to preach there and urge the people to take the cross. Giraldus accompanied the archbishop on this tour and subsequently wrote an account of it in his *Itinerarium Kambriae*. Together with the *Descriptio Kambriae* that followed a few years later, this contains many accurate and important remarks and notes on the physical and human geography of Giraldus' native land.

These treatises on Ireland and Wales hold a unique position in the literature not only of our period but of the entire Middle Ages. Brewer, in his introduction to the collected works of Giraldus, says that the *Topographia Hiberniae* is a "monument of a bold and original genius" and that Giraldus "must take rank with the first who descried the value and, in some respects, the proper limits of descriptive geography."[163] Though this may be a little too strong, we readily agree with Dimock's estimate of the treatises on Wales: "His account of the land and the people of Wales will bear very honourable comparison with any topographical attempt that had appeared up to his time and with any that appeared for many ages afterwards."[164] Giraldus was in a very real sense the forerunner of the modern writer of the better sort of book of travel. His works reveal to us a mind keenly interested in the results of its own observation and not merely in collecting what others had said. Giraldus was certainly enthusiastic, and we are almost tempted to say that he was endowed with an "outdoor" and even "Rooseveltian" interest in the world about him.

Before leaving the topographical works, mention should be made of a little anonymous guide to the monuments and antiquities of Rome, the *Mirabilia urbis Romae*,[165] dating from the late twelfth century and widely read during the years that followed.

MAPS

From the age of the Crusades date several of the most characteristic medieval maps. These highly important sources, which serve so admirably to illustrate the geographical conceptions of the time, have been made the object of such thorough and careful research by Konrad Miller,[166] the results of whose investigations are well summarized in Beazley's *Dawn of Modern Geography*,[167] that it hardly seems necessary here to devote a great deal of space to them. Let us merely indicate what the more important maps were, and show in a general way their relation to the literature of the age, leaving for Chapter XI a brief discussion of them as typifying medieval geographical thought.

We saw in Chapter II that the maps of the world drawn before 1100 and now extant could nearly all be classified in four groups.

Zone Maps

1. Of the first, zone maps, or diagrams illustrating the division of the earth's surface into zones, examples occur in twelfth- and thirteenth-century manuscripts of Macrobius, of the *De imagine mundi*, of Lambert's *Liber floridus* (Fig. 3), of William of Conches' *De philosophia mundi*, of Herrad of Landsperg's *Hortus deliciarum*, and of John of Holywood's *De sphaera*.[168] The Paris manuscript of Peter Alphonsi's *Dialogus* also contains two related diagrams, one showing the eccentricity of the sun's orbit and the other the division of the northern hemisphere into climates. Arabic influence upon Peter Alphonsi is revealed by the fact that south is at the top of his diagrams, instead of east, according to the almost universal custom of medieval Christian cartography.[169]

T-O Maps and Sallust Maps

2. The diagrammatic T-O group are also represented. By all means the most interesting of these is a map preserved in a manu-

script in St. John's College, Oxford, and dating from 1110. Somewhat more elaborate than others of the same type, this one assigns Greek names to the cardinal points of the compass, a circumstance which has given rise to a plausible conjecture that it may have been a copy of an original found in the Levant at the time of the First Crusade.[170]

FIG. 3—Zone map in an early twelfth-century manuscript of Lambert of St. Omer's *Liber floridus*, viz. Ghent Codex 2, fol. 24 vo. East is at the top. (From Miller, *Mappaemundi*, vol. iii, 1895, fig. 59.)

3. There also date from our period several examples of the ornamented T-O maps drawn to illustrate Sallust's works.[171]

Beatus Maps

4. We saw that the existing specimens of that series of maps of the world drawn to elucidate a passage in Beatus' commentary

on the Apocalypse appear to have come from two sources: (*a*) maps which were modeled closely on the original map of Beatus or a contemporary copy and (*b*) those which were merely generalized outlines of it.[173]

a. A map dating from 1203 and preserved at Osma in Old Castile comes nearest to the original in design and form, if not in

FIG. 4—Osma Beatus map dating from 1203 showing the division of the world among the twelve apostles. East is at the top. (From Miller, *Mappaemundi*, vol. i, 1895, p. 35.)

the richness of detail (Fig. 4). Alone of all the Beatus type this shows the heads of the twelve apostles scattered over the earth's surface. Another map, probably derived from the same source, is to be found in the Bibliothèque Nationale in Paris; though it is rich in detail, little attempt was made to show localities in their proper relative positions, and consequently the geography represented is chaotic to an extreme.

b. There are also three or four maps dating from our period from the second source. Their main interest lies in the remarkable naïveté of workmanship.

MAPS OF LAMBERT, GUIDO, HENRY OF MAYENCE, AND OTHERS

In addition to the above, for which we have prototypes from the period before 1100, there are a number of maps of the world of the twelfth and early thirteenth centuries, the prototypes of which either have been lost or never existed. Among the most notable of these is one found in certain manuscripts of Lambert's *Liber floridus*.[173] It was compiled from the usual medieval authorities, Isidore, Orosius, Julius Honorius, Martianus Capella, Pomponius Mela, Solinus, the *Pseudo-Callisthenes*, and the Bible, though there also appear upon it a few names that could have been taken only from contemporary sources. The influence of Macrobius is most strikingly revealed, for, unlike most other medieval maps which indicate the known world (Asia, Europe, and Africa) as occupying the entire area or by far the greater part of the world disk (as in the Beatus group), Lambert's map divides the disk along its diameter by a zone representing the course of the sun and places in the southern hemisphere an austral continent of magnitude equal to that of the *oikoumene*.[174]

Guido's compilation of geographical works, made in 1119, contains in two manuscripts not only a T-O map but also a map of the world accompanying a selection from the book of the anonymous Ravenna geographer and a detailed map of Italy and the surrounding lands. The map of the world is peculiar because of the enormous area which the Mediterranean occupies. Miller believes it to be a reduced sketch of a large map of the world and holds that the detailed map of Italy is a copy of a small portion of this same original.[175]

A compilation of the *De imagine mundi*, put together by one Henry, canon of the Church of St. Mary in Mayence, in 1110 and preserved in a late twelfth-century copy in Cambridge, England, contains a world map (see below, p. 245, Fig. 6, inset). Though indirectly made from the sources that the writers of the *De imagine mundi* and other medieval cosmographies utilized, it was probably not compiled directly from the *De imagine mundi* but rather from a large wall map. Its affinities to the immense late thirteenth-century world disk in Hereford Cathedral make it seem possible that both had a common source. In addition to the older nomenclature, about a dozen more modern place names are to be found upon it.[176]

A map of the world which somewhat resembles that of Henry of Mayence is also to be found in two manuscripts of the *Chronica maiora* (or *Historia maiora*) of Matthew Paris. Though there are many names that have come down to modern times, the geography is meager and poor, in striking contrast to the detail of Matthew's map of Britain,[177] to which reference is made below.

To complete the discussion of *mappaemundi*, mention must be made of a very small but very neat little map in a late thirteenth-century Psalter in the British Museum. If this was not actually drawn during our period, it undoubtedly had predecessors much like it, and it shows marked resemblances to the map of Henry of Mayence as well as to the Hereford and Ebstorf maps.[178]

Regional Maps

Several of the regional maps, or maps of limited areas, dating from our period may be merely fragments or copies of small portions of maps of the world. This is certainly true of the map of Europe in the Ghent manuscript of Lambert's *Liber floridus*, which depicts that continent crammed into slightly more than a quarter of a circle with no attempt to show the articulations of the coast. The Guido map of Italy, as we have already seen, probably represents a portion of a larger map, and the same can possibly be said of the maps of the East and of Palestine which follow a treatise by Jerome, entitled *De situ et nominibus locorum Hebraicorum*, or *De Palestinae locis*, in a manuscript now in the British Museum. Though these two maps were actually drawn in the twelfth century, they represent the cartography of a very much earlier age and perhaps may be attributed to Jerome himself.[179] They were drawn to illustrate the Biblical geography of Palestine and the Orient, and they show a great wealth of Scriptural legends. Other legends were taken from profane sources, such as the writings of Isidore, Orosius, Julius Honorius, Dionysius, and the Romance of Alexander; and affinities to the Peutinger Table show that the draftsman was under the influence of the cartography of the Roman imperial epoch.

Among the regional maps that had no connection with *mappaemundi* are plans of Jerusalem ("Situs Ierusalem") accompanying twelfth- and thirteenth-century manuscripts of an anonymous work written about 1109 and entitled *Gesta Francorum Ierusalem expugnantium* (Fig. 7, p. 250, below). Though these plans reveal many names from the early Crusading age, their outlines as a whole—the fact, for instance, that Jerusalem is shown to be circular instead of rectangular—make it seem probable that they represent a schematic diagram of the Holy City going back to as early as the sixth century and brought up to date by the anonymous compiler of the Crusading epoch.[180]

Matthew Paris' Maps of Britain

In addition to the map of the world of which we have spoken already, the works of Matthew Paris contain no less than five regional maps.[181] Two of these, the "Situs Britanniae" and the "Schema Britanniae," are simple diagrams of Britain and are of no particular importance. The other three are far more significant. The first, a pictorial itinerary of the route from London to southern Italy, with legends in Old French and Latin, delineates vividly towns and principal topographic features. The second is a map of Palestine which superficially resembles that of Jerome; the names, however, are in French, and the legends refer to places familiar to the contemporary pilgrim and Crusader. Finally come the three manuscript variants of Matthew's map of Britain, which, as Beazley observes, "among all designs of purely medieval origin . . . show the best evidence of critical study, the most systematic attempt at the exact delineation of a particular country"[182] (for one variant, see below, p. 343, Fig. 9). There is a profusion of detail and accuracy in the representation of the relative position of places refreshing when we contemplate the confusion and credulity manifested in the earlier works. This map is also the first example of late medieval cartography in which north instead of east is shown at the top of the sheet.

CHAPTER V

THE PLACE OF GEOGRAPHY IN THE MEDIEVAL CLASSIFICATION OF KNOWLEDGE

Geography in the Middle Ages did not form a distinct and separate science. The student who learned anything of geography learned it incidentally to the study of other subjects and never thought of it as sufficiently dignified to enjoy a place by itself in the scholastic curriculum. Even the word "geography" was scarcely ever used.[1] The term *cosmographia*, sometimes employed to distinguish certain aspects of our subject from geometry, included practically all branches of natural history, the sciences of animals, rocks, monstrosities, and meteorological phenomena. On the other hand, cosmography did not comprise many of the topics with which we are concerned, particularly those lying on the border line between geography, astronomy, and geology. The question of the origin of the earth was in the province of the theologian of the Middle Ages.

Geography Included Under Geometry

The well-known seven liberal arts formed the foundation of the work in the medieval schools. From them the student might advance to higher researches in philosophy and theology, but the seven arts were the base of all learning.[2] Martianus Capella's *De nuptiis Philologiae et Mercurii* was an attractive and somewhat imaginative exposition of the arts and had become one of the most popular of medieval textbooks long before the twelfth century.[3] Here each art is personified as a gorgeously clad woman, and the seven together compose the escort of "Philosophy."

In practical teaching, the arts were divided into two groups: the trivium, comprising grammar, rhetoric, and dialectic (or logic); and the quadrivium, arithmetic, geometry, astronomy (astrology), and music. Geoffrey of St. Victor, in his *Fons philosophiae*, gives[3a] an allegorical description of the arts as a spring which divides into two main streams, the trivium and quadrivium, that in turn separate into three and four lesser streams respectively. The teaching of practically all the natural science of the Middle Ages was included in the quadrivium. Geometry was generally expanded to include geography and quite naturally so in view of prevalent opinions regarding its origin. Adelard of Bath, in his *De eodem et diverso*, repeats an old story to the effect that in the early days men began to set up stones as boundaries.[4] Disputes about claims inevitably arose, in Libya because of sand, and in Egypt because the Nile often obliterated or destroyed the stones. This necessitated the invention of the science of geometry, or surveying, by the application of which the bounds might be replaced so that it would be "possible for all the centuries to have an everlasting rule for the measurement of land."[5] Out of the invention of geometry, Adelard adds, arose subsequently the custom of subdividing territory into areas of various sizes.[6] Thus it happened that geometry had become closely allied in the classical and medieval mind with matters of geographical or topographical interest. Capella includes his long geographical discourse among chapters devoted to geometry and makes his symbolical figure of the latter science carry in one hand a compass and in the other a sphere to represent the terrestrial globe.[7] Alan of Lille, in the *Anticlaudianus*, describes Geometry as carrying a scale with which she measured the earth: "The maid carries a rod by which she encircles the entire earth."[8] In the sculptured figures of the cathedrals Geometry is often depicted compass in hand.[9]

Geography Included Under Astrology

Geography was not always placed in a subordinate position to geometry in the quadrivium. In the *De divisione philosophiae* of Dominicus Gondisalvi, which follows the Aristotelian rather than the Platonic division of knowledge, we find our science grouped under astrology. Of the latter art, Dominicus says,[10] there are three parts: the first is concerned with the number and shape of the heavenly bodies; the second with their movements; and the third with the earth, those regions that are inhabited and those that are not, the climates, and the varying influences exerted by the location of places and the revolutions of the universe over happenings on the earth's surface.[11]

Geography and the Aristotelian Division of Learning

Both geometry and astrology belonged in the quadrivium. Where did the higher study of the arts of the quadrivium fall in the general classification of knowledge?

The medieval mind tended to seek for a logical and symmetrical subdivision of the sum of all knowledge. The desire for systematization found its supreme expression in the great philosophic structures of the thirteenth century, the systems founded on Aristotle and devised by such men as Albertus Magnus. Prior to the thirteenth century confusion had reigned. According to the Platonists, who divided philosophy into logic, ethics, and physics, the study of the mathematical and natural sciences—and, therefore, of geography—fell under the heading of physics. Aristotle, more logically perhaps, had divided the subject matter of all human learning into two great categories, theoretical knowledge and practical knowledge. Theoretical knowledge included physics, mathematics, and metaphysics (or theology). The studies of the quadrivium were thrown by the Aristotelians under the heading of mathematics: geography, then, became to those who followed the Aristotelian classification—Gondisalvi, Hugh of St. Victor,[12] Roger Bacon—a sub-department of mathematics.

But on the whole we need not linger over this topic, because the question of exactly where geography belonged in the artificial systems devised by the medieval mind was largely a matter of academic interest even in the Middle Ages and was without influence on the actual condition of the geographical lore of that time.

PART II

THE SUBSTANCE AND CHARACTER OF THE GEOGRAPHICAL LORE OF THE TIME OF THE CRUSADES

CHAPTER VI

COSMOGONY, COSMOLOGY, AND COSMOGRAPHY

In the preceding chapters the attempt has been made to show the origins of a large part of the geographical lore of the Crusading epoch, the sources from which we may learn about it, and where it stood in the classification of learning. Now we may turn to our central theme: an estimate of its actual substance and character.

This geographical lore was in no sense a unified body of knowledge and belief. It was no more a unit than the religious thought of the age, or the philosophy, astronomy, or morals. No one in the Middle Ages was acquainted with all the facts and theories with which we shall have to deal. Mental caliber, credulity, critical spirit, curiosity, opportunities for research and for travel—these all varied widely with the individual and determined his geographical concepts. Nevertheless, though there was no unity of knowledge or belief in regard to specific facts and no unity of point of view, the reader will not fail to perceive, in the multitude of illustrative details which are presented, that certain habits of thought and modes of expression were typical of the epoch as a whole.

We must first discuss what was known and believed about the earth in its larger relations, both in time and space, to the remainder of the universe: opinions about the Creation, about the size and shape of our terrestrial globe, about the influences exerted by the heavenly bodies in determining or affecting geographical conditions upon its surface.

In the Introduction we explained why it is justifiable when dealing with ancient and medieval geography to wander into the fields of cosmogony and cosmography far beyond what are now regarded as the rightful limits of geography. The present chapter, it is hoped, will make clear how closely medieval conceptions of the present condition of the earth may be connected with the medieval idea of the origins and nature of the universe.

GENERAL CHARACTER OF THE COSMOLOGY AND NATURAL SCIENCE OF THE PERIOD

These difficult questions of cosmogony, cosmology, and cosmography excited keen and vivid thinking because they lie on the border between philosophy and theology. Men were more interested in attempting to solve the insoluble mysteries of God and the universe than they were in the world of nature immediately surrounding them. Immense and weighty volumes were written in commentary on the Works of the Six Days, wherein complicated arguments were elaborated with the finesse of scholastic logic. In an age of faith, the religious enthusiasm of the architect and artisan was transmuted into lofty cathedrals; that of the theologian turned to the elucidation of the words of Scripture. To analyze these words, to comment upon their minutest detail, to reveal the meaning that presumably lay behind them was not only a work of piety and devotion but an absorbing intellectual pastime for keen-witted thinkers. In more concrete realms of natural science, the epoch was characterized by little enough observation and creative thought. The teachings of Plato, of Aristotle, and of the other available classical, Arabic, and early Christian authorities were accepted and adopted uncritically. Very different was the case with matters of cosmogony and cosmography. Here was highly controversial ground where classical opinions were either enthusiastically defended as casting light on Scripture or else bitterly attacked as subversive of all truth.

The Chartres Group: Bernard Sylvester and Theodoric

We have seen in Chapter IV that the scholars of the Chartres group and their pupils during the early twelfth century were endowed with peculiar freedom of thought.[1] We note in the works of Bernard, Theodoric, Adelard of Bath, William of Conches, and Bernard Sylvester a wide departure from authoritative, orthodox theology. Theodoric, William, and the two Bernards were readers of Chalcidius' translation of the *Timaeus*, of Macrobius, and perhaps of the writings of the great ninth-century Platonist, John Scot Erigena, and all four felt the powerful and seductive attraction of Platonism. Bernard Sylvester was almost an out-and-out pagan, so much so, indeed, that his writings can hardly be considered to lie within the pale of Christian theology.[2] Theodoric and William tried harder to reconcile Platonism with the teachings of the church, yet they did so in a rationalistic spirit almost as abhorrent to strict orthodoxy as the paganism of Bernard Sylvester. Theodoric expressly stated in his *De sex dierum operibus* that he was going to explain the different Works of the Six Days "according to physical principles," and, following the letter of the text,[3] he proposed to avoid all allegorical and moral interpretations of Scripture. He believed that the best way to attain a genuine knowledge of God was through an accurate understanding of what God had created; and his explanation of the Creation, as we shall soon see, was independent to a degree that amazes us in a writer of his time. The following phrase is particularly significant where Theodoric extols Moses' treatment of the Creation in Genesis, saying: "He shows in a rational manner the causes out of which this world has come into existence and the order of time in which this same world was founded and adorned." [4] Hauréau writes of the first book of Theodoric's commentary: "Quant au premier livre, essai d'accord entre la Genèse et le *Timée*, où l'on voit la religion et la philosophie conspirant à résoudre le plus grave et le plus obscur des problèmes, le problème de l'être, et se déclarant satisfaites de l'avoir résolu, ce premier livre est . . . de plus grand intéret." [5]

Adelard of Bath and William of Conches

In the *Quaestiones naturales* Adelard of Bath gives vent to his scorn for the mentality that blindly accepts beliefs merely because they have the weight of authority behind them. In an extraordinary passage he expresses these ideas thus (as translated and paraphrased by Professor Haskins[5a]): "'It is hard to discuss with you,' Adelard tells his nephew [in the dialogue form of the *Quaestiones naturales*], 'for I have learned one thing from the Arabs under the guidance of reason; you follow another halter, caught by the appearance of authority, for what is authority but a halter?' . . . 'If reason is not to be the universal judge, it is given to each to no purpose.'[5b] . . . While plants spring from the earth by God's will, this does not act without a reason.[5c] Human science must first be listened to . . . and 'only when it fails utterly should there be recourse to God' as an explanation."[5d]

William of Conches shows the same spirit where he insists that God acts reasonably and not capriciously. He writes: "I am aware that some people assert, 'Though we do not know how this happens to be so, we know that God can make it so.' Wretched ones! What is more craven than to talk in that way! Because God can do something is no sign that he actually does it, nor any reason why he should do it, nor any reason why it is useful that it should be done. For God does not do whatever he can do. To employ a rustic expression: 'God can make a calf out of a tree trunk,' but does he ever do so?"[6] William apparently, unlike Theodoric, thought that we are justified in avoiding irrational deductions from Scripture by an appeal either to an allegorical interpretation or—what is even more surprising at a time when the word of authority was usually regarded as all-sufficient—to one's own intellect: "We may begin our reasoning from the authority of a master, but it should be perfected by our own intellect."[7]

Concept of Natural Laws

Thus we see in the writings of Adelard, Theodoric, and William that the approach was tentatively made toward the acceptance of the doctrine that the universe is governed by natural laws. This doctrine, upon which the edifice of modern science has been built, was also given partial expression by other thinkers of the twelfth century. John of Salisbury stated in effect that a sequence of causes gives rise to all things that we may perceive with our senses, that we call these causes nature, that nothing happens that is not the result of natural causation even though the operation of this causation may be concealed from us; finally, that the first cause of all is the will of God.[8] Alan of Lille clothed a similar theory in allegory by personifying Nature in poetic form as the representative of God and making her say: "Hear how in this universe, as in a great city, order is established by the control of a majestic government" (Moffat's translation).[9] Much the same opinion was expressed by an anonymous Scandinavian historian of the early thirteenth century in his Latin *Historia Norwegiae*. After describing a terrible volcanic upheaval from the bottom of the sea,[10] this writer adds that many people regard such occurrences as prodigies, believing that the world itself thereby gives warning of its own destruction.[11] Citing Solinus, he goes on to set forth a purely physical explanation of earthquakes and volcanic eruptions and adds that, though it may not be possible to attain to clear-sighted understanding of these phenomena and of the major marvels of the world, they should not be looked upon as prodigies nor considered as portents of universal cataclysm. On the contrary they are, as it were, the servants of the all-knowing and immutable founder of the universe to whose nature through some marvelous process they have been placed in bondage.[12]

The Orthodox Tendency

This sort of reasoning, however, was exceptional. In the mid-twelfth century the appearance of Peter Lombard's *Sententiae* tended to divert the theologian's mind from Platonic and rationalistic studies and to restore Church Fathers and Scripture to paramount authority.[13] We look in vain for traces of the liberal attitude of the Chartres scholars in the orthodox works of such prolific writers but perhaps less clear thinkers as Peter Comestor, Giraldus Cambrensis, Gervase of Tilbury or even Alexander Neckam. Giraldus' *Symbolum electorum* [14] contains a cosmography in verse which explains the Scriptural view of the Works of the Six Days, and though we feel in this poem the influence of the Peripatetic physics—which by this time were becoming universally known—no attempt was made to expound the work of the Creation according to physical laws. In the *Topographia Hiberniae*[15] Giraldus illustrates his own attitude and the dominant attitude of his age by the moral he draws from the story of eagles which occasionally fly so high that they scorch their wings in the sun. This he compared to the hopeless vanity of the man who tries to solve by reason or by knowledge God's riddles of the Creation and of the universe. Neckam also despairs of explaining the mysteries of nature and asks, "Who may comprehend the causes of things?" He describes thunder and lightning briefly but adds, "The herald of the thunder fills the mind with terror and shows how great is the creator thereof."[16] Even Michael Scot, who enjoyed the patronage of the enlightened, scientifically minded Emperor Frederick II, attributed the fact that the waters of the spherical earth are held in place to "a secret virtue . . . beyond human ken and merit" (Haskins).[17] Gervase of Tilbury reproduces uncritically in his *Otia imperialia*[18] the ideas compiled by Peter Comestor regarding the Creation. These were strictly correct opinions on which no suspicion of heterodoxy could be thrown. Comestor went out of his way to express opposition and antagonism to Platonic teachings.

Effects of Influx of Arabic Science

The conventional orthodox position, however, did not remain unchallenged. The influx of Moslem Aristotelian lore at the end of the twelfth century was held to be as menacing to the integrity of the ecclesiastical tradition as any of the Platonic doctrines. But, though stern prohibitions were leveled against the study of Aristotle and his Arabic interpreters, the seductions of Aristotelianism could not be resisted, and those elements of Peripatetic science which did not seem utterly outrageous to Christian theology became the accepted and authoritative science of the West in the mid-thirteenth century. William of Auvergne, bishop of Paris, stood out valiantly against what he regarded as teachings subversive of Christianity and of morals and in his vigorous opposition to Aristotelianism even went so far as to adopt many of the Platonic doctrines that had been popular among the scholars of Chartres during the preceding century.[19] But translators like Gerard of Cremona had done their work too well, and the enormous tomes of Albertus Magnus were based to a large extent on the learning of the Stagirite.

THE CREATION

The usual medieval treatise on the Works of the Six Days as described in the Book of Genesis deals with many problems. Some of these are abstruse and metaphysical: questions of the nature of God and the nature of time and space. With these we are not concerned. Others are more concrete: questions of the materials out of which God made the universe and of the actual manner in which he worked.

Problems

For the sake of clearness let us state some of these questions as follows. (1) The question of whether matter existed prior to God's creation of the world. That is to say, Did God fashion the universe out of a pre-existing substance or did he make it out of nothing? (2) The question of the manner in which the universe was fashioned after it was once "created." (3) The question of what furnished the light during the first three days before the creation of the sun. (4) The problem of whether the Six Days were actual divisions of time or merely hypothetical divisions of the process of creation. (5) The question of the nature of the waters above the firmament. (6) Various problems arising in regard to the nature and location of Paradise and of the four rivers flowing from Paradise. The first four problems are discussed briefly in the present chapter. That of the waters above the firmament is left for Chapter VIII (on waters), and that of Paradise for Chapter XII (on regional geography).

The Preëxistence of Matter

(1) Did matter exist prior to God's creation of the universe as we now know it?

Consistently with his Platonism, Bernard Sylvester thought that God formed the universe out of what he termed *materia primordialis*—a chaotic mingling of the elements that had coëxisted with God before he converted the universe into its present shape.[20]

The Orthodox View

Theodoric of Chartres, on the other hand, explicitly denied the coëxistence of the *materia primordialis* with God before the Creation. In this respect he showed himself far less divergent than Bernard from the Christian point of view. The work of the first day, he said, was the creation from nothing of the *materia* of the universe, out of which earth and heaven, fire and water and life were to be evolved.[21] This *materia* was the *hyle*, or chaos, of the ancient philosophers, he explained, and was designated by Moses in the book of Genesis under various names.[22] For example, when Moses wrote, "In the beginning God created the heaven and the earth" (Gen. i, 1) the words "heaven" and "earth" referred to chaos; when Moses wrote, "And the earth was without form and void" (Gen. i, 2) the word "earth" referred to the primordial mixture of land and water, a mingling of land that was not solid and of water that was not liquid. Air and fire at that time were of about the density of water.

Theodoric's interpretation of the initial process of the Creation was entirely in keeping with the views of more orthodox writers. Peter Lombard, for instance, wrote as follows: "In the beginning God created the 'heaven,' that is to say the angels, and the 'earth,' by which is meant the material which composed the four elements. The latter were as yet in the confused and formless condition to which the Greeks gave the name of chaos, and this was before any day."[23]

Peter Comestor also set forth an orthodox view of the Creation. In his commentary on Genesis he revealed a love of the number three and classified everything possible into groups of three.[24] He pointed out how Moses had avoided three errors. "First, that of Plato, who had conceived of three coëxistent things, God, *ile* (*hyle*, or chaos), and time, and that the world was made out of *ile;* second, that of Aristotle, who had conceived of two coëxistent things, the world and the fashioner thereof (*mundus et opifex*)*;* and third, that of Epicurus, who had also conceived of two, space (*inane*) and matter in the form of atoms, and that in the beginning natural processes had brought together certain atoms to form water, others to form earth, and others to form fire. Moses, however, had said that God alone was eternal and that the world was created out of nothing, for there was no matter in existence prior to the 'Creation.'"[25] "In the beginning" meant in the beginning of time as well as of matter, for time and matter were coëternal.[26]

A Rational View

William of Conches refused, on rational, physical grounds, to believe in the possibility of a chaos preëxisting the Creation.[27] Having accepted the classical doctrine whereby the four elements were arranged in concentric spheres in order from heaviest to lightest,[28] he was unable to conceive of a time when they could have been so intermingled that they contradicted this law, though there may have been a time, he conceded, when the earth was completely enveloped in a thick mantle of water reaching very high and when air and fire themselves were denser than they now are. Such a condition, William thought, was that described in Genesis i, 2.[29]

Processes of the Creation

Theodoric of Chartres' Theory

(2) How was the universe converted into its present form after God had once created it?

Most commentators answered this either by saying or tacitly implying that it was through the immediate operation of God's will alone. Theodoric of Chartres' theory, therefore, is peculiarly interesting, becaue Theodoric maintained that the formation of the universe resulted from what we should now style a series of purely mechanical and chemical reactions which began, once the composition of the *materia* was completed, on the first day. For its time this was an extremely hazardous view, akin in some respects to the modern belief in the sufficiency of physical and chemical action to produce practically all observable phenomena.

Let us examine Theodoric's theory in a little greater detail. In Genesis i, 2, we read the words, "And the spirit of God moved upon the face of the waters." Theodoric explained that by the "waters" was meant the whole of matter:[30] the "spirit of God" was that which was destined to give order and form to the chaos, that is to say the "force which fashioned" or "operated" (*virtus artifex* or *virtus operatrix*). Plato had called this force the World Soul, the Christians called it the Holy Ghost,[31] and through its agency the evolution of the universe out of chaos by physical processes was rendered possible.

Coincidently with the creation of the original *materia* the universe had assumed a rotary motion,[32] each complete rotation marking a day. In the further unrolling of the universe, fire was the active element (*artifex et efficiens causa*), earth the passive element, and air and water stood as intermediaries between fire and earth. During the first rotation, or first day, the fire heated and illumined the inferior elements in such a manner as to cause the air to be released from them (*aer ex inferioribus elementis spissatus*), and thus the atmosphere came into existence.[33] On the second day the fire, by illuminating the air, transmitted heat to the third element, water, which rose in the form of clouds. Some of this vaporized water ascended so high that it passed into the second heavenly sphere, where it became the "waters above the firmament," the firmament itself, according to Theodoric, being the atmosphere.[34] So much water in this manner was absorbed out of the original *materia* that inevitably on the third day the earth appeared like islands in the midst of the waters remaining behind. Theodoric compared these to islands that are formed when water dries after it has been spilled upon a table. Immediately the heat of the atmosphere was mingled with the humors of the earth, and the latter thereby received the power of producing vegetable life, herbs and trees. On the fourth day the stars were formed out of the waters which had been drawn above the firmament. On the fifth day the heat of the universe brooded over (*incubuit*) the waters of the earth's surface and gave birth to fish and birds. Finally, on the sixth day, the life-giving heat reached the earth; and from it the animals were created, including, of course, man.[35]

William of Conches' Theory

William of Conches' theory of the Creation did not differ a great deal from that of Theodoric, except that the *materia primordialis* was not, in his opinion, a chaotic mingling of the elements; for within it, he thought, as we have already seen,[36] that the elements were arranged in their proper order according to accepted classical laws of physics. The lands were uncovered by the removal of the waters, though this took place later in the process according to William than it did according to Theodoric. William attributed the drying off of the waters partly to the warmth of the stars (which were not formed until the fourth day) and partly to the creation of the water and land animals on the fifth and sixth days respectively.[37] In different portions of this primordial land, when it was just in the act of emerging from the waters, fiery, watery, earthy elements were present in varying quantities. This condition gave birth to divers varieties of animals. Where the fiery element was in excess, choleric animals, like the lion, came into being; where the water element prevailed, phlegmatic animals, like the pig; and the earthy element produced melancholic creatures like the ass and cow. At the one and only place where the combination was absolutely equal, man appeared. Woman, on the other hand, was made from a combination almost like that of man but one in which the colder elements were very slightly in excess, because the warmest of women by nature is colder than the coldest of men! This last, an extremely free and heretical and from our point of view unchivalrous theory, William retracted in his old age.[38]

Function of Light in the Creation

(3) What was the nature of the light which God made when he said, "Let there be light"? Although Augustine had interpreted this passage allegorically or mystically as referring to the creation of the world of the angels,[39] he had also suggested that God might have created an actual body of light corresponding to the sun. Bede [40] developed the latter suggestion and maintained that there must have been a luminary revolving around the earth as does the sun. In the twelfth century Hugh of St. Victor and Peter Comestor, both of whom interpreted Scripture more or less literally in this respect, followed Bede. Hugh maintained that this original light was like a luminous cloud which rose in the east and set in the west,[41] and Comestor spoke of it in much the same terms.[42] Other theologians, however, refused to believe that such a light could have actually existed and reverted to Augustine's first explanation that by the light was meant the world of angels as distinct from the world of evil spirits below.[43] Peter Lombard re-

ferred to both interpretations, though he appears to have been inclined to favor the more literal and materialistic theory of Bede.[44]

With Robert Grosseteste light is made to play the leading part in the entire process. In his unpublished *Hexaemeron*[45] and in the *De luce*[46] he sets forth a theory of cosmogony which was derived in part from the Moslems but in essentials was original.[47] We trust that the following brief statement of the theory does not do violence to the thought of Grosseteste as expressed in the *De luce*. He conceived of light as the first corporeal form and also as giving form to the *materia prima* of the universe. By radiating through the unformed *materia prima* the light converted it into a sphere. Thereupon the light made its way from the outer edge of the sphere towards the center. As it passed through the various realms of the universe it diffused, rarified, and purified the *materia* of each, but with each stage of its advance its powers were diminished and correspondingly the potentiality of each successive realm of being purified was diminished. Thus thirteen concentric spheres were produced, nine celestial spheres and four spheres of the elements, and each of these was more complex, dense, and impure than its neighbor above.

The Nature of the Six Days

(4) Were the Six Days described in the book of Genesis actual divisions of time? The words of the Bible seemed to be contradictory on this point. From the words of Genesis alone one would gather that the completion of the universe was accomplished in six days. On the other hand, we read in Ecclesiasticus (xviii, 1), "He that liveth forever created all things together" (Qui vivit in aeternum, creavit omnia simul). According to Theodoric of Chartres[48] these two statements referred to different events. The passage in Ecclesiasticus applied only to the creation of the *materia primordialis* on the first day. The works of the succeeding days were the result of the automatic development of natural processes by which the universe became as we now know it. Belief in the reality of the duration of the Six Days was shared with Theodoric by most commentators, such as William of Conches, Hugh of St. Victor,[49] Peter Lombard, and Peter Comestor. Au-

gustine, however, had argued in a more abstruse vein that the "days" were not actual units of time but that they represented merely so many distinct operations in the work of creation.[50] And in our period Arnold of Chartres urged that the Creation was carried out in one day and all at once (*uno die et semel*).[51]

Eternity of the Universe

Though they differed in the details of interpretation, these theories were all based on the fundamental acceptance of the axiom, deduced from Scripture, that God created the universe out of nothing. In Chapter II was explained the antagonism between this view and the Aristotelian doctrine of an eternal, periodically reformed universe. Certainly, among Christians of our period, no one believed either in the eternity or in the periodicity of the universe, although the existence and nature of these concepts were well known. Both theories were set forth in Seneca's *Quaestiones naturales*,[52] in translations of Plato's *Timaeus*[53] and of Aristotle's *Meteorology*[54] and *De generatione et corruptione*,[55] and in translations from the Arabic such as the *Liber introductorius in astrologiam* of Abū Ma'shar[56] and the pseudo-Aristotelian *Liber de proprietatibus elementorum*.[57] When William of Conches specifically denied the possibility of more than one deluge he may have had in mind the pagan association of Noah's flood with the Great Winter.[58] Certainly one of the primary objections of the orthodox Christians to the acceptance of Aristotelian science during the early years of the thirteenth century lay in the fact that Averroës, the great interpreter of Aristotle, was firmly convinced that the universe is eternal.[59] William of Auvergne also vigorously attacked the Aristotelian theory as it found expression in Avicenna's commentary on the *Metaphysics*[60] and Robert Grosseteste leveled destructive criticism against it in his *Summa super libros octo Physicorum*, a commentary on the *Physics* of Aristotle, and in other works.[61]

Bernard Sylvester's Account of the Creation

Before leaving this aspect of the subject, a few words should be said about two other accounts of the Creation that found literary expression in Western Europe during our period. Very dissimilar, these two accounts are akin only in the circumstance that they were both based upon the mythology of an older age and that, though written by Christians, neither referred in any way to the Scriptural story. One was the remarkable allegory in Bernard Sylvester's *De mundi universitate*, the other the Icelandic myth of the Creation as recorded in the *Edda* of Snorri Sturluson.

In the *Megacosmus*, or first part of the *De mundi universitate*, Bernard tells us of the confusion of matter in the eternal ages that preceded the "Creation."[62] Nature, personified, laments to "Nous," or Providence, about this confusion and demands that the universe be put into an orderly condition: "Nous," moved by the appeal, carries out the task, separating the elements, arranging the nine hierarchies of angels, placing the stars in the firmament and regulating their orbits, ordering the four winds, and, finally, fashioning the earth in the midst of the universe. The last process gave Bernard occasion to digress and to tell of the riches and beauties of this earth.

The *Microcosmus*, or second part of the book, goes on to relate the story of the creation of man. "Nous" sees the barren desolation of an inanimate world and orders Nature to undertake the work of peopling it. With the aid of Urania, goddess of the stars, Nature seeks for Physis, goddess of life, whom she finds in the terrestrial paradise after Urania has conducted her on a long journey through the heavenly spheres. Here she tells Physis her mission; and Physis carries out the fashioning of a human body, in which the soul is then established. Thus was man created.

No comment is needed to bring out the pagan character of this account, wherein the Six Days are not even mentioned! It would probably be wrong, however, to assume that this work of literary imagination, any more than Snorri's graphic record of the beliefs of his forefathers, represents a formulated and accepted doctrine of its author.

The Icelandic Account

The Icelanders were converted to Christianity in the mid-eleventh century, and the mythology of their pagan days still remained fresh in their minds and hearts during the period we are studying. The old gods were looked upon with affection, and the old story of the Creation was remembered with sympathetic understanding. The Icelandic myth of the Creation is one of great beauty and vigor. In it is revealed the impression made upon the minds of a northern people by struggles against the cold and stormy darkness of the subarctic winter. The outline of the story, which is worked out in much detail in the *Eddas*, is about as follows.[63]

In the beginning a great abyss lay between the icy rivers and the drizzling rains and blasts of wind of the north and the blazing heat of the south. This was before heaven and earth and sea were made. "And Fimbultyr said: Let the melted drops of vapor quicken into life, and the giant Ymer was born in the midst of Ginungagap[64] [the abyss]. He was not a god but the father of all the race of evil giants. This was Chaos.

"And Fimbultyr said: Let Ymer be slain and let order be established. And straightway Odin and his brothers . . . gave Ymer a mortal wound, and from his body they made the universe; from his flesh, the earth; from his blood, the sea; from his bones, the rocks; from his hair, the trees; from his skull, the vaulted heavens; from his eyebrows, the bulwark called Midgard. And the gods formed man and woman in their own image of two trees, and breathed into them the breath of life. Ask and Embla became living souls, and they received a garden in Midgard as a dwelling place for themselves and their children until the end of time. This was Cosmos" (Anderson).[65]

MACROCOSM AND MICROCOSM

All medieval accounts of the Creation culminate in the creation of man, as modern outlines of evolution conclude with man's evolution from lower forms of life. Christian theology taught that the universe itself was made for man, a view that persists even to this day. Grosseteste asserted that when man "no longer requires the processes of generation and corruption which the movements of the heavens cause, the heaven itself will cease to move and time will be no longer."[66] Rupert of Deutz explained that mountains were placed upon the earth to protect human beings against the winds.[67] But if the universe and all its parts were made for man, medieval thinkers held, with the Stoics of antiquity,[68] that man himself was a lesser universe (*minor mundus*), or microcosm, comprising all the elements both physical and spiritual which constitute the greater universe, or macrocosm.

The doctrine of man as the microcosm had its roots far back in antiquity. Medieval writers from the time of Isidore elaborated upon it with detail and ingenuity. In the literature of our period it occurs in many a passing comparison of the phenomena of nature with the human body, such as that of the *De imagine mundi* where rivers are compared with blood vessels.[69] It forms an important element in the cosmology of Bernard Sylvester's *De mundi universitate* [70] and of Herrad of Landsperg's *Hortus deliciarum.*[71] Hildegard of Bingen's writings are full of similes and medical recommendations based upon it (Fig. 5).[72] In her *Subtilitates* the abbess says: "In the creation of man from the earth other earth was taken, and all the elements served man because they perceived that he lived; both the elements and man worked together to each others' advantage in all relationships."[73] The thought is expressed more clearly in the *Causae et curae:* "Oh, man! Look at man, for man has in himself heaven and earth and all other things that are created, and his form is one and in him all things lie hidden."[74] To illustrate the detail in which Hildegard worked out this theory we may do no better than to quote from Thorndike's summary. "She compares the firmament to man's

---

EXPLANATION OF FIG. 5—The human figure here represents the microcosm in the midst of the universe. The heads of the animals give rise to the winds, which Hildegard believed controlled the movements of the celestial bodies (see p. 171). The blast originating in the human head at the right and moving in a counter-clockwise direction runs opposite to the movement of the firmament. "This blast did not give forth his breath earthward as did the other winds, but instead thereof it governed the course of the planets" (*Liber div. op.*, in: Migne, *Pat. lat.*, vol. cxcvii, col. 791, as cited by Singer, *op. cit.* p. 28).

In another miniature from the same manuscript (fol. 9 ro) shown in Singer, *op. cit.*, pl. VII, the universe is revealed in much the same manner with the human figure as the microcosm. There is also represented the macrocosm, as a larger figure standing behind and holding the sphere of the cosmos; only its head, feet, and hands appear.

head, sun, moon, and stars to the eyes, air to hearing, the winds to smelling, dew to taste, and 'the sides of the world' to the arms and sense of touch. The earth is like the heart, and other creatures in

FIG. 5—The macrocosm, the microcosm, and the winds, from a miniature in an illustrated codex of Hildegard of Bingen's *Liber divinorum operum* in the Municipal Library at Lucca, fol. 27 vo. (Redrawn, by permission, from Singer, *Scientific Views and Visions of Saint Hildegard*, 1917, pl. VIII.) For explanation, see bottom of opposite page.

the world are like the belly. In the *Liber divinorum operum* she goes into further detail. . . . From the top of the cerebral cavity to the 'last extremity of the forehead' there are seven distinct and equal spaces, by which are signified the seven planets which are equidistant from one another in the firmament. An even more surprising assumption as to astronomical distances is involved in the comparison that as the three intervals between the top of the human head and the end of the throat and the navel and the groin are all equal, so are the spaces intervening between the highest firmament and lowest clouds and the earth's surface and center. . . . As the heart is stirred by emotion, whether of joy or of sorrow, humors are excited in the lungs and breast which rise to the brain and are emitted through the eyes in the form of tears. And in like manner, when the moon begins to wax or wane, the firmament is disturbed by winds which raise fogs from the sea and other waters."[75] The preface to the *Subtilitates* contains another discussion of the microcosm in the course of which the stones of the earth are likened to bones and it is pointed out that the earth has sweat, humors, and other by-products of the body.[76] Much of the argument of the *Causae et curae* is based upon the assumption that the very diseases of man have their counterparts in the facts of the macrocosm.

SHAPE, MOVEMENTS, AND SIZE OF THE EARTH

When once created, what form did this universe take, and the earth within it?

SPHERICITY OF THE UNIVERSE

Nearly all the authors of our period appear to have shared in the belief that the universe is a sphere and that the earth is situated in its center. Lambert of St. Omer says in his *Liber floridus:* "We say the earth is the center, that is, the point in the middle of the sphere." "For the earth is located as a central point in the midst of the celestial circle through which the sun passes."[77] Robert Grosseteste stated that the sphericity of the universe was necessitated by the nature of the substances composing the heavenly bodies and that it could be proved by simple astronomical observations.[78] There is, perhaps, an echo of Pythagorean mathematical doctrines in the exposition which we find in the *Image du monde*, that the world is round since God desired it to be so, because roundness is the most perfect of all forms.[79] Al-Farghānī, whose work was translated more than once during our period and formed the basis of much that is found in John of Holywood's *De sphaera*,[80] had said that there was no difference of opinion among learned men that the universe was a sphere. That the earth is in the center of the heaven, he asserted, was shown by the fact that half the heaven is always visible from all parts of its surface.[81] The author of the *De imagine mundi* had also thought the same way:[82] he compared the universe to a ball, or to an egg of which the shell corresponds to the upper heavens, the white, to the upper air, the yolk, to the lower air, and the *pinguedinis gutta*, or drop of grease in the center, to the earth.[83] Gervase of Tilbury,[84] who borrowed the idea from Comestor,[85] and the author of the *Image du monde*[86] make similar comparisons, although Peter Abelard,[87] William of Conches,[88] and Daniel of Morley conceived of the four parts of the egg as corresponding exactly to the four elements.[89] Michael Scot compared the earth, surrounded by water, to the yolk of an egg and the spheres of the universe to the layers of an onion.[90]

In her *Causae et curae*, on the one hand, and in her *Scivias* and *Liber divinorum operum*, on the other, Hildegard of Bingen makes contradictory statements in regard to the position of the earth in relation to the heavenly spheres. Scientific consistency was not, perhaps, the ascetic abbess's strongest quality, and too much emphasis should not be laid upon contradictions found in the writings of one who believed herself to be favored by special divine revelations. The passage in the *Causae et curae*, however, diverges so widely from current medieval opinion that it is worth translating. "The earth," writes Hildegard, "is of moderate size and is near the base of the firmament, because if it were in the center of the firmament, then it would have to be larger; and even so it would easily fall and be shattered to pieces, had it the same expanse of air beneath that there is above."[91] On the contrary, in her *Liber divinorum operum* she tells how she saw in a vision the universe as a wheel[92] and that "in the midst of the air the earth was placed in such a way that the air measured an equal distance above the earth, below the earth, and on either side of the earth." [93]

Shape of the Earth

Most writers of the Crusading age thought the earth also was a sphere, though there was less unanimity in this belief. The *De imagine mundi* calls it a sphere, whence comes the term *orbis.*[94] William of Conches [95] furnishes us with the Aristotelian proofs of sphericity. If the earth is flat, he says, it would be day at the same time in the farthest east as in the farthest west. Certain stars are visible in one latitude that cannot be seen in another, and this would not be the case if there were no curvature from north to south.[96] John of Holywood, following Al-Farghānī, gave two proofs that the earth is round and two that the water is round.[97] That there exists a swelling or curvature of the earth (*tumor terrae*), he says, is shown by the difference in the time of eclipses between places in the east and west as well as by differences in the visibility of stars.[98] The curvature of water surfaces is demonstrated by the fact that a person standing at the foot of a mast is frequently unable to see objects visible to somebody at the masthead. Furthermore, since water is a homogeneous body, all parts of it must partake of the nature of the whole. Therefore it follows that because a drop is round, the mass of the waters of the earth must also be spherical.[99]

Gervase of Tilbury has been accused of believing that the earth is square, though the evidence in the text of the *Otia imperialia* on which this accusation is based is very slender; and other texts would seem to support the opposite contention, that he accepted the theory of sphericity.[100]

Two passages in the *Causae et curae* of Hildegard can apparently be explained only on the supposition of a flat earth.[101] Hildegard seems also to have been haunted by the old belief that bulked so large in the imagination of Cosmas Indicopleustes,[102] the belief that the earth rises into an immense mountain in the north.[103] She asserted that this mountain prevented the light of the east from penetrating the darkness of the north and the darkness of the north from obscuring the light of the east. On the other hand, in her visions the abbess more than once saw the earth as a globe.[104]

In the writings of the mystic Hugh of St. Victor we have a typical medieval allegorical interpretation of the words of Scripture regarding the earth's form, with instructions as to how a map of the world ought to be made.[105] Hugh compares the *orbis terrae* to an "oblong circle," or oval, drawn around the ark, touching each corner. An oval shape was necessitated by the rectangular ground plan of the ark. Within this oval the *mappa mundi*, or map of the world, is to be drawn, with the front of the ark facing the east, and its rear, the west. In the segment formed to the east, between the ark and the circle, is Paradise; in that to the west the resurrection will take place; the chosen will go to the right, and the damned to the left into Hell, which forms the segment toward the north. Beyond this "oblong circle" another circle is to be drawn to show the zones, and the space between the two is the atmosphere.

One hesitates to draw conclusions from this as to what shape Hugh imagined the earth to be; probably he himself had no very definite theory. The picture which his description seems to invoke in our minds is that of a flat oval earth covered by an ovoid heaven, and certainly it is in every respect inconsistent with belief in a spherical earth.

Immobility of the Earth

However men may have thought about the shape of the earth, there was no questioning the fact that it stands immobile and firm. Doctrines like that of the Pythagorean Philolaus had no place in medieval thought.[106] The ignorant, nevertheless, were often puzzled by the problem of what supports the earth. The author of the *De imagine mundi* was content uncritically to explain that no fulcrum or support is necessary for this purpose but that the "divine power" is all-sufficient.[107] He quoted the one hundred and third Psalm: "Who hast founded the earth upon its own bases: it shall not be moved for ever and ever."

Theodoric of Chartres, Adelard of Bath, and John of Holywood, on the other hand, adduced proofs of the immobility of the earth which had been derived indirectly from Aristotle. Theodoric asserted[108] that the earth does not gain its compactness either from its inherent nature, because earth is actually observed on occasions to become mingled with air; or from the weight of the overlying atmosphere and sphere of fire, because these have no weight. What, then, keeps it from flying to pieces? Here Theodoric appealed to the Peripatetic reasoning that the circular motion of the heavens necessitates the existence of a solid and immovable body in the center.[109] All heavy bodies acquire their *substantia*, or solidity, from the motion of light bodies; and conversely light bodies derive their motion from heavy bodies.

The *Quaestiones naturales* of Adelard of Bath is in the form of a dialogue between Adelard and a nephew who asks questions. The nephew was much puzzled by the fact that, whereas heavy objects like rocks need a piece of wood or other support to hold them up in the air, the earth as a whole, much the heaviest of all, requires no such support.[110] Adelard replies first that the earth does not fall because there would be no utility in its doing so; then he proceeds to show by a rational argument (*rationabiliter*) why the earth does not need a support. The principal quality of earth he says, is heaviness; heavy bodies naturally seek the lowest position (*infimum*); the lowest position of a spherical body like the universe is its center—though why this latter proposition is so, Adelard fails to make clear. At all events, the earth tends to seek the center of the universe, just as a stone thrown into an imaginary hole piercing the center of the earth would come to a halt there.[111] Since the center of the universe is one point, not several, the earth forms a single unit, not several; and for these reasons, moreover, the earth is stable and immobile.

John of Holywood explained[112] the same thing more briefly than Adelard by simply stating that the immobility of the earth is due to its weight, since it is the nature of all heavy things to seek the center of the universe and since the earth is the heaviest of all elements. Both Adelard's and John of Holywood's arguments suggest the Aristotelian doctrine of an equilibrium of forces around the center of the globe, though this doctrine is not cited in so many words. Like most medieval writers, Adelard and John seem only partially to have understood the obscure texts from which they derived their proofs and to have left out many links in their chains of reasoning.

Size of the Earth

Though the geocentric hypothesis prevailed in the Middle Ages, there is plenty of evidence to show that the smallness of the earth in relation to the heavenly bodies was understood.[113] William of Conches had thought that the sun was eight times as big as the earth.[114] In the *Image du monde* this theme is elaborated:[115] we are told that it would take more than a hundred years for a rock to fall from the heavens; that the earth is like a tiny star in comparison with the immensity of the cosmos and is one hundred and sixty-six and three-twentieths times smaller than the sun.[116] John of Holywood quoted Alfraganus (Al-Farghānī) to the effect that the smallest fixed star is larger than the earth[117] but that the dimensions of such a star are as but a point in the firmament. He argued that the extreme smallness of the earth is proved by the fact that it is possible to see the middle of the firmament (*medietas firmamenti*) not only from the center of the earth but also from the earth's surface.[118] His argument, which certainly proves nothing as it stands, is evidently a confused reflection of Ptolemy's reasoning in the *Almagest*.[119]

As to the actual size of our planet various figures were occasionally quoted. The *De imagine mundi*[120] gives Posidonius' estimate of the circumference as 180,000 stades, or 12,052 miles (*duodecies mille millaria et quinquaginta duo*). The *Image du monde*,[121] however, gives 20,428 miles. Eratosthenes' 252,000 stades appears in Lambert of St. Omer's *Liber floridus*[122] and John of Holywood's *De sphaera*.[123] In the latter work it is cited on the authority of Ambrose, Macrobius, "et Eristenis philosophorum," along with a brief account of the great Alexandrian geographer's method of measurement.

ZONES, THE ANTIPODES, AND "CLIMATA"

The surface of the terrestrial sphere, surrounded as it is by the heavens, is naturally subjected directly to the influence of the heavenly bodies. We must now examine those general phenomena of the globe as a whole which were conceived to be consequences of the earth's shape and position in relation to the remainder of the universe, postponing for a later chapter the study of the more local features of the *oikoumene* (or habited quarter), which also result from the same circumstances.

Zones

The most primitive observation reveals the fact that the heavenly bodies in their course through the sky revolve around two points and mark out certain circles. Very elaborate and often admirable discussions of the celestial poles, Arctic and Antarctic circles, equator, tropics, and ecliptic, are to be found in the numerous astrological and astronomical works of our period.[124] The study of these matters was already a highly developed science, but except in its geographical bearing it does not fall within our province.

We saw in Chapter I that ancient astronomers had drawn imaginary circles around the terrestrial sphere corresponding to the circles of the heavens and had designated these lines as the boundaries of zones on the earth's surface.[125] The classical theory of five zones, divided from each other by parallels of latitude, was accepted by the geographical writers of the twelfth and early thirteenth centuries, although, as in classical times, opinions diverged widely regarding the characteristics of each zone. All, however, believed that the two polar caps were cold and that the equatorial regions were hot. For example Bernard Sylvester says in his *De mundi universitate:*[126] Nous, or Providence, "encompassed the earth with five parallels; on the one hand the extremes are frozen, on the other the central portions are hot. Also she made temperate two zones by placing on both sides of them the coldness of the extremities and the course of the sun over the midst of the earth."

Uninhabitability of Polar Caps and Equatorial Zone

Furthermore, a widely prevalent but not universal theory made the polar caps and equatorial zones not only cold and hot but also uninhabitable. The author of the *De imagine mundi* [127] and Gervase of Tilbury [128] plagiarized what Isidore had written on this subject.[129] They called the five circles separating the zones and the zones themselves from north to south, respectively, *septentrionalis* (our Arctic Circle and North Polar zone), *solstitialis* (our Tropic of Cancer and North Temperate zone), *equinoctialis* (our Equator and Torrid zone), *brumalis*—or *hyemalis* according to Gervase—(our Tropic of Capricorn and South Temperate zone), and finally *australis* (our Antarctic Circle and South Polar zone). Of these they thought that only *solstitialis* was habitable. William of Conches likewise believed[129a] in uninhabitable torrid and frigid zones, though he rejected the theory that in the heavens above the sphere of the moon there are qualities of heat and cold corresponding to those of the terrestrial zones.

Austral Continent and Antipodal Regions

Speculation was rife as to what lay beyond the equatorial zone and in those mysterious parts of the earth of which man had no knowledge. Rumors and conjectures of an austral continent and of antipodal regions figure widely in the geographical literature of the age. A fourth continent beyond the equatorial ocean (or Mare Rubrum) is shown on all the Beatus maps. It is represented as a strip of land along the southernmost edge of the earth (see Figs. 2 and 4, pp. 69 and 123, above). A legend, taken from Isidore, informs us on the St. Sever map that "In addition to the three parts of the world, there is a fourth part beyond the ocean in the midst of the south and unknown to us on account of the heat of the sun. Within its confines the antipodeans are fabulously said to dwell."[130] The Osma Beatus map locates the *skiapodes*, or sunshade-footed men, here (see Fig. 4). Confusion between true antipodal regions on the opposite side of the world and an austral continent lying south of the equator was not uncommon in antiquity and during the Middle Ages.[131] Belief in the latter did not necessarily involve belief in a spherical earth, and it has been argued that the Roman cartographers (whose maps may have inspired Beatus) showed such a fourth continent south of the equator, even though they did not deem the question of the sphericity of the world worthy of serious consideration. The Beatus maps themselves may easily be reconciled with an implicit belief in a flat world disk.

While this may be true of the Beatus maps, it cannot be said of the *mappamundi* of Lambert of St. Omer or of references to the antipodes elsewhere in the literature of our period where it is impossible to question the conviction in the cartographers' or writers' minds that the earth is a sphere.

On Lambert's map the austral continent occupies half of the circle of the earth. A long legend explains,[132] in terms similar to those of the St. Sever Beatus map, that this region is unknown to mankind because of the sun's heat; that philosophers say the antipodeans dwell here; and that winter prevails during our summer. In addition to the austral continent, Lambert indicates without a shadow of doubt his faith in the existence of other antipodal regions. A large island on the western margin of his map is labeled, "Here dwell the antipodeans, but they have a different night and opposite days."[133] We know from other parts of the *Liber floridus* that Lambert was strongly influenced by Macrobius. A Macrobian sketch of a spherical world showing the five zones is inserted in the Ghent and other manuscripts. This reference to the antipodes can only apply to the unknown regions on the opposite side of the globe, beyond the meridional ocean which, as we have seen in Chapter I, had been described by Crates of Mallos and popularized in Macrobius' *In somnium Scipionis commentarius* and in Martianus Capella's *De nuptiis Philologiae et Mercurii*. Belief in a spherical world is essential to belief in these theories.

The Cratesian Theory

Crates of Mallos' conception of the arrangement of the world, introduced to Western knowledge through the works of Macrobius and Capella, was well known in our period. William of Conches, Adelard of Bath, and Bernard Sylvester all show the influence of the Crates-Macrobian system in their belief in a great equatorial ocean.[134] Giraldus Cambrensis and the author of the *De imagine mundi*, by their explanation of the causes of the tides, make it plain that they accepted the same opinion. Geoffrey of St. Victor gives a clear exposition of it in his *Microcosmus*.[135] Robert Grosseteste adopts it in his *De sphaera*, explaining carefully the two seas that encircle the earth and calling the equatorial sea "Occeanus" and that which includes the poles "Amphitrites." He believed that only one of the areas of land separated by these seas is inhabited.[136] The same idea is reflected in words of the *Image du monde* [137] to the effect that only a quarter of the earth's surface is inhabited and in the recommendation to the reader in his imagination to cut the globe into four quarters like an apple and to think of the habitable part as occupying the surface of one of the quarters. Godfrey of Viterbo points out the significance of the golden ball of empire which formed part of the regal insignia of the Holy Roman Emperors upon which, he said, the fourfold division of the lands of the earth's surface was shown.[138] Among the imperial treasures (*Reichskleinodien*) in Vienna the golden apple dating from the twelfth century is of this form. Two bands encircling the regal ball at right angles represent the Cratesian idea of oceans girdling the earth.[139]

In one version of the legend of St. Brandan there is a curious passage where not only the possibility of antipodal regions is indicated but the pious necessity of belief in such regions.[140] St. Brandan is here reported to have read in an old book that beneath this earth there is another world, where day prevails when it is night with us. Unable to accept such a story, Brandan burned the book in a fit of exasperation; and as a punishment for his incredulity God made him voyage nine years upon the seas. What the book was we are not informed, but perhaps we do not err in assuming that the poet had in mind a copy of the *In somnium Scipionis commentarius* or possibly the *De nuptiis Philologiae et Mercurii.*

Persistence of Belief That Antipodal Regions Were Inhabited

An essential feature of the theory as it had been expounded by Macrobius and Capella, however, was the insistence that the other three temperate areas are inhabited by races of men like our own. As belief in the existence of inhabitants in the antipodal regions rested in our period on the authority of Capella and Macrobius and was subjected to lively discussion and controversy, it is not out of place for us to observe what these two writers had actually said.

Capella, after briefly stating that three out of the five zones are uninhabitable on account of cold and heat, declared that the other two are tempered by a wind which encourages life.[141] The inhabitants of the quarter south of us, beyond the equator, he called *antoikoi;* those of the quarter also in the southern hemisphere but beyond the north-south ocean, who have winter when we have summer, *antichthones.* Those in our own temperate zone beyond the ocean, who have the same summer and winter as ours but who have night when we have day, he called *antipodes.*[142] No commerce or communication is possible between us and these other groups of human beings, nor between one group and any of the others. Macrobius set forth this theory in similar terms,[143] expressly emphasizing the point that reason teaches us that the southern zone must be inhabited because its climate is temperate like ours. However, he added, it is not peopled by men like ourselves—Greeks, Romans, barbarians—nor shall we ever be able to learn what sort of men the inhabitants actually are.

Though, as we have seen, out-and-out belief in antipodeans was heretical during the epoch we are studying, there is plenty of evidence to show that the possibility of such a thing was an attractive subject of speculation. The legends on the Lambert maps to which reference has been made above would alone be sufficient to convince us of this. William of Conches spoke very guardedly on the matter;[144] his avowed theory was that the other temperate regions were habitable but not actually inhabited. But are we not justified in thinking that in denying the existence of antipodeans he was merely making a verbal concession to theological prejudice, especially when he went on to explain that, if there were people dwelling in other quarters, they would be called *antoikoi*, *antipodes*, and *antichthones*, and that some would have summer when we have winter, others night when we have day?

Gervase of Tilbury relates a fanciful story which might be interpreted to show that he too liked to dally with the pleasing fancy that there may be antipodeans, even though elsewhere he rejects such a possibility. He tells of a cave in a mountain belonging to the domain of the castle of Bech in Great Britain.[145] From this there nearly always blew a violent wind; but once, when the wind did not happen to be blowing, a swineherd entered the cave to look for a breeding sow which had wandered in. Here he found an open plain with cultivated lands and harvesters bringing in their crops, and from the harvesters he recovered his sow. To this Gervase adds, "It was an extraordinary circumstance that wintry coldness coming from these subterranean harvest fields seemed to penetrate into our hemisphere, which phenomenon I think ought to be attributed to the sun's absence and presence elsewhere."[146]

Manegold's Arguments Against This Doctrine

The most convincing proof of the persistence in the early twelfth century of a tendency to believe in antipodeans is furnished by the fact that Manegold in Alsace,[147] sometime after 1103, saw fit to write a vigorous pamphlet attacking a certain Wolfelm of Cologne, whom he accused of harboring an heretical opinion. Manegold's *Contra Wolfelmum opusculum* illustrates admirably the orthodox, or even obscurantist, point of view. He accused Wolfelm of adhering to Macrobius' teachings about the four inhabited quarters of the earth. Granting that there are four such quarters, he demanded, how can the teachings of the Holy and Apostolic Church, buttressed by all the authority of the Fathers, the patriarchs, and the prophets from the earliest times, be true? And how can we believe the prophecies that the Savior will come to bring salvation to the entire human race, if these branches of the human race are cut off from the rest, as Macrobius would have it, by the zones and temperatures of the earth's surface? How could the prophecy have been true, "All the ends of the earth will bow down before our God (*salutare Dei nostri*), if certain ends of the earth are inhabited by men to whom the voice of the prophets and the apostles could not reach through impassable tracts of water, of cold, and of heat?"[148]

Habitability of the Equatorial Region

Macrobius' theory was also contradicted from a position opposite to that of the orthodox churchmen. The study of Moslem astronomy brought to Europe the opinion that the equatorial zone itself was not only habitable but actually inhabited. In the preamble to the *Marseilles Tables*[149] of Raymond of Marseilles, which reproduces ideas expressed by the Spanish-Moslem astronomer Az-Zarqalī, we have an explanation of the current theory among "philosophers" of the uninhabitability of the polar and equatorial regions. The latter the author of the treatise refuses to believe because the city of Arin and the temple of "Jupiter Arenosus" are both known to lie within the equatorial zone. He proceeds then to explain why it is physically possible for the regions beyond the equator to be inhabited.

Peter Alphonsi,[150] also influenced by Arabic reasoning, argued that the existence of Arin on the equator was sufficient evidence of the habitability of the equatorial regions and gave a glowing account of the temperate climate and attractions of those parts of the world. Man can live throughout the entire area covered by the seven climates, he maintained, and, as his interpretation of ancient authorities led him to suppose that the first climate began at the equator, he was convinced that the equator also would support human life. On the other hand, he did not agree with the preamble to the *Marseilles Tables,* for he maintained that the parts of the earth in the southern hemisphere beyond Arin were not habitable. This was because the sun, on account of the eccentricity of its orbit, approaches much nearer the earth in those climes than it does in more northern latitudes. In this way he accounted for the excessive cold of the Arctic and polar regions and a (supposed) excessive heat of the trans-equatorial zones.

Plato of Tivoli's translation of Al-Battānī's work brought to Western knowledge another Arabic discussion of the probable characteristics of the areas of the earth's surface unknown to man.[151] As to the equator, Al-Battānī said, it was uncertain whether men had actually been there or not. The climate, however, could not be excessively hot, because the sun in crossing the zenith, as it does twice a year between the tropics, does not remain directly overhead very long. Al-Battānī saw no reason why winters and summers should not be temperate in countries along the equator and believed that these latitudes must have, in fact, a climate not greatly unlike that of Aden and Yemen, which, however hot it may seem to the European, apparently did not impress the Arabs by its torridity. The unknown districts of the world, Al-Battānī went on to explain, comprise eleven-twelfths of the whole. Though no man had ever reached them, he thought it not irrational to suppose that they were like the known parts, for the sun and stars must pass across them and produce in the same way winter and summer, the tides of the sea, and animal and vegetable life.

Grosseteste on the Habitable Parts of the Earth

When we come to the close of our period, we find that Robert Grosseteste, bishop of Lincoln, and after him his more famous pupil Roger Bacon, like Peter Alphonsi, took over from the Moslems much geographical and astronomical lore which they interpreted and freely criticized.

In a book entitled *De lineis angulis et figuris* Grosseteste elaborated some general principles relating to the incidence and reflection of rays from celestial bodies. The *De natura locorum* is an attempt to show how far these principles may be used to account for various phenomena of the earth's surface. Grosseteste conceived of celestial rays and influences as emanating in an infinite number of cones, or "pyramids," as he called them, the apexes of which were the celestial bodies; the longer and more oblique these pyramids, the weaker the effect of the rays upon the earth's surface and vice versa.[152]

Let us see how Robert applied the principle of the pyramids to explain conditions in the equatorial zone, in the southern hemisphere, and in the polar regions.

The Equatorial Zone

Logically the equatorial zone should be scorched and burnt by the sun because the pyramids are there the shortest and the angles at which the rays reach the earth approach nearest to a right angle. As a matter of fact, Robert had it on the authority of Ptolemy and Avicenna that, whereas the subtropical regions are intensely hot, the subequatorial zone is not only temperate but extremely temperate (*temperatissimus*); indeed, he said, theologians place Paradise under the equator in the Orient. A modification of the principle of the pyramids was therefore necessary. In his readiness to admit such modifications of rules that he had laid down, Robert showed an open-minded and a scientific spirit. In order to allow for the circumstance of a supposedly temperate equatorial region, he stated that the heat received during the daytime must be neutralized by the coolness of the nights, since day and night between the tropics are always approximately the same length, as they are in the latitudes of Europe during spring and autumn only.[153]

The Southern Hemisphere

The southern hemisphere, on the other hand, Robert thought to be uninhabitable on account of the intense heat of summer and bitter cold of winter. The excessive heat he ascribed to the fact that the eccentricity of the solar orbit around the earth brings the sun no less than five degrees nearer the earth during the southern summer than it approaches during the northern summer.[154] The pyramids, or lines of heat radiation, are therefore shorter and the heat is more intense.[155] Conversely the southern winter must be colder than that of the north because the sun at that season is farthest from the earth.

Granting a geocentric universe, this reasoning was sound though its consequences were exaggerated. It is quite true that the earth is nearer the sun in the summer of the southern than in the summer of the northern hemisphere, yet no extreme results flow from this circumstance, and there is no great difference in the amount of heat received by each hemisphere.[156]

An exaggerated idea of the differences in temperatures north and south of the equator led Robert,[157] and after him Roger Bacon,[158] to doubt the validity of the theory of the precession of the equinoxes. This phenomenon would inevitably produce a gradual shifting of the climatic conditions of the southern hemisphere to the northern, and, as a result, the latter would presumably in the course of time become uninhabitable. Since this seemed incredible to Grosseteste and Bacon, they were impelled to deny the possibility of its cause.

The Polar Regions

In discussing the climate and habitability of the polar regions,[159] Robert cites a work, *De vegetabilibus* (erroneously ascribed to Aristotle in the Middle Ages) and a commentary upon it. Here the extraordinary view was expressed that no plants or animals could survive in the polar zone because the heat of the sun would burn them up! This view originated in the known fact that the sun shines continuously for half the year at the pole and at no time sinks very far below the horizon. The commentator pointed out that the sun never retires more than 23° out of sight and that it is capable of illuminating and heating the atmosphere at 18° below the horizon. The theory, however, failed to take into account the very important fact that the sun's rays reach the polar regions at a sharply oblique angle and that consequently their powers of generating heat are limited. This circumstance together with the "observations and reasoning of Aristotle, Ptolemy, and other authorities" led the Bishop of Lincoln conclusively to reject the singular theory of the *De vegetabilibus* and to attribute to the polar zones a climate that, in so far as it was dependent upon the disposition of the heavens, rendered these regions uninhabitable on account of the cold. Nevertheless, he recognized that there might be accidental local conditions, such as the presence of mountains of peculiar shape, capable in the polar regions of producing areas of intense heat or of delightfully temperate climate. But to this subject we shall revert in a later section devoted to the influence of mountains on climate.[160]

CHAPTER VII

THE ATMOSPHERE

At the present time we divide the study of the atmosphere into the sciences of meteorology, devoted to the investigation of individual and local atmospheric phenomena, and climatology, devoted to the investigation of the geographical distribution of weather conditions throughout the world as observed during long periods of time. We may make the same arbitrary division in dealing with the theories current in the twelfth and thirteenth centuries. Meteorology and climatology, however, merge into each other. Some understanding of one is absolutely essential to an understanding of the other, and hence we must take certain meteorological theories into consideration before attempting to deal with the more truly geographic subject of climatology.

METEOROLOGY

Probably the most complete and satisfactory extant treatment of meteorology from our period is to be found in the writings of William of Conches, whose interest in physics and in the natural sciences led him to study carefully the views of Seneca and also to express at great length opinions of his own about the atmosphere.[1]

Composition of the Atmosphere

In the first place, William had very definite ideas concerning the composition of the air. The aerial and aqueous spheres, he said, act as intermediaries between the spheres of fire and earth.[2] The qualities of the two latter are opposite; but the atmosphere partakes more or less of the qualities of each, for neither sphere is made up exclusively of one element. William was an atomist: he thought that matter is composed of minute atoms and that each atom is the smallest conceivable particle of one of the four elements.[3] He explained that the atmosphere, which extends up as far as the moon's orbit, contains in addition to the aerial atoms a certain number of aqueous particles in its lower levels and of fiery atoms higher up. Hence its density and humidity decrease progressively from the earth's surface upward; the higher air is clear and lucid, the abode of good demons or angels, messengers of God to man, whereas the lower air is full of clouds and constitutes the abode of evil spirits.[4]

These parts of the atmosphere formed two out of five concentric regions into which William divided the entire universe.[5]

Temperature

With much acuteness of observation, William recognized the fact that the sun's influence on the denser air of low altitudes is far more potent than it is on the rarer strata above.[6] Though heat comes from the sun, he said, it is not apparent until it becomes mingled with humidity. In valleys the air, lying stagnant and damp, is easily heated, whereas the dry upper levels remain cold even though the sun's warmth passes through them. The presence of this coldness explains why snow is found on the summits of the highest mountains, for the belief that mountain snow is due to cold north winds William branded as false, observing that snow often occurs on the south as well as on the north sides of the peaks. Robert Grosseteste also held that the air at high altitudes is much colder than it is near the surface.[7] This, he said, was because the heating effect of the sun's rays is inoperative on account of the transparency of the medium. At the surface heating takes place as a result of reflection and condensation of the solar rays.[8] The cold air at high levels explains the origin of perpetual snow on mountain tops. Hail is generated in these strata, rain at lower levels. Robert cited as proof of this the fact that birds of prey fly high in summer to cool off and that cranes and many other birds descend into the valleys to escape the icy chill but fly up the mountain sides to avoid the heat.[9]

Upper Levels of the Atmosphere

In contrast with these opinions of William of Conches and Robert Grosseteste, which were based apparently on more or less direct observation, we find echoes in our period of a doctrine that had its roots in classical mythology—the doctrine that above a certain height on mountain peaks the air is undisturbed by wind and unsullied by clouds.[10] Hermann the Dalmatian hints at this in his *Liber de essentiis.* In the course of a discussion of the dimensions of the habitable area of the earth's surface that had probably been suggested by the reading of Arabic works he explains that the living offspring of the earth require for the maintenance of life a certain heavy, "greasy" terrestrial vapor which, "as Aristotle determined from the height of Olympus, does not rise more than sixteen stades above the earth's surface. Here consequently would seem to be the upper limit of our habitable zone. Possibly this might be measured by means of the rainbow, which, according to the description of Hipparchus, reaches from the clouds themselves down to the surface of the earth. But since Hipparchus' description is not accurate nor is the figure of the rainbow a semicircle, we leave the matter for whosoever may wish to prove it."[11] Peter Alphonsi, who was also influenced by Moslem thought, placed the upper limit of the clouds at sixteen miles,[12] a figure which may have been derived from the same origin as Hermann's sixteen stades. Peter Comestor inserted in his *Historia scholastica* some observations in regard to the tranquillity of the summit of Mount Olympus and the physiological effects of the rarity of the atmosphere.[13] So quiet and untroubled by winds is this peak that letters written there in the dust remain legible for a year. The air is too thin even to support the life of birds, and several philosophers who climbed the mountain would have been unable to remain on top if they had not held to their faces sponges soaked with water and in this way made it possible to breathe by attracting denser air to their nostrils.[14]

Clouds

In this connection a puzzling question seems to have occurred to William of Conches. If the general rule holds that the atmosphere is rarer higher up than on the earth's surface, how then does it happen that the upper air so often becomes dense in the form of clouds? To this William gave the correct answer,[15] that clouds are not composed of air of greater density than the surrounding parts of the atmosphere, but that water vapor arising from below is turned into clouds by the cold. True as it may be, this idea does not fit in very well with William's theory of the coldness of the higher altitudes. First he maintains that one of the main reasons why the upper air is cold is because it lacks dampness; then he goes on to explain that dampness rising to a great elevation is converted by the cold into clouds. Though there is no direct contradiction of two statements here, one cannot but sense inconsistency and looseness of thought of a sort that pervades all medieval natural science, though William of Conches on the whole was rather less illogical and less inconsistent than most of his contemporaries.

Much the same explanation of the effects of cold on the condensation of water vapor is found in the *Dialogus* of Peter Alphonsi,[16] where it is shown that the sun draws a damp vapor from the sea and a dry humor from the land. Out of a combination of these, clouds are formed which rise until they reach a height of about sixteen miles. Here, coming in contact with strata of cold air, they are prevented from ascending any higher, and the damp vapor may be precipitated in the form of rain.

Precipitation

William of Conches also endeavored to explain rainfall.[17] This phenomenon may result, he said, from various causes: either from the conversion into drops of water of dense vapors arising from the earth, from the actual transformation of air into water through the influence of cold, from the tumbling back to earth of some of the water which the sun raises to itself for its own nourishment,[18] or, finally, from water swept up by the winds off the surface of streams, lakes, and swamps. That the last was possible he believed to be demonstrated by the fact that frogs sometimes fall with raindrops![19]

Theodoric of Chartres gives a clear statement[20] of the theory of evaporation, condensation, and precipitation in terms that sound almost modern. Heat, he says, causes water to ascend into the atmosphere in minute drops which form clouds. If the heat increases, these droplets turn to pure air; if it diminishes, they coalesce into rain. The most minute drops are constricted by a cold wind into snow; when the drops are large they are converted into hail by the same agency.[21]

Topographic influences on precipitation were partially understood by Giraldus Cambrensis, who believed that the influence of land—particularly hilly land—frequently tends to change the vapors of the air into mists and clouds, or rain and snow.[22] In the seas off Ireland, for instance, water is attracted into the atmosphere in immense quantities; the temperature being equable, the water is neither consumed by an excess of heat nor turned to snow by an excess of cold but is altered into rain, a process greatly facilitated by the presence of many mountains in Ireland.

Floods; The Deluge

An excess of rainfall results in floods. William of Conches believed that under normal conditions the warmth of summer counteracts the excessive dampness of winter but that a long series of cool, damp summers will end in floods and, conversely, a series of hot, dry summers will end in droughts. But, however many local floods there may be, only one *diluvium*, or deluge, is possible.[23]

Whence came the waters of the Deluge? This was a question which puzzled some of the commentators on Scripture during the Middle Ages. Adelard, though he did not believe it himself, cited a theory that the purpose of the waters above the firmament was to furnish these waters.[24] Peter Comestor,[25] followed by Gervase of Tilbury,[26] said that they came partly from the bowels of the earth and partly from the air above and that they rose higher than the tops of the mountains of today,[27] to the level to which the vapors of burnt offerings ascend. Gervase also spoke of a curious theory that there may have been no rain in Paradise nor anywhere on the earth until the time of the Deluge.[28] The vegetation in the Garden was watered in these early days by the heavenly dew. The argument that no rain fell until the Deluge was based, he said, on the words of God to Noah: "I will no more curse the earth for the sake of men; . . . seed-time and harvest, cold and heat, summer and winter, night and day shall not cease" (Gen. viii, 21–22). Gervase adds: "Perhaps the four seasons were not yet fully distinguished one from the other, since not until the time of the Deluge were the waters gathered into clouds." [29] According to the *Liber divinorum operum* of Hildegard the temperature was far hotter before the Deluge than it has been since, and "the men of that time possessed great bodily strength in order that they might endure this heat. The Deluge reduced the temperature, and men since have been weaker" (Thorndike).[30]

Winds

The winds interested the men of the twelfth and thirteenth centuries even more than rainfall. Popular notions of winds, rain, and storms as manifestations of magical powers or evil spirits,[31] though universally believed among the unlearned, were not given serious consideration by the majority of scholars. Isidore, Bede, Raban Maur, and those who copied from them during our period—the author of the *De imagine mundi* [32] and Gervase of Tilbury in his *Otia imperialia*—defined wind as air in a disturbed and agitated condition,[33] Adelard of Bath said it was dense air moving in a particular direction,[34] and William of Conches used Seneca's definition, "Wind is air flowing one way." [35]

Hildegard of Bingen made the winds play a supremely important part in the dynamics and physics of the universe. To the winds she ascribed the movement of the firmament from east to west and of the planets from west to east.[36] Were it not for the winds, she said, the fires of the south, the waters of the west, the shadows of the north would burst forth over the earth. The four winds are the wings of God's power; were they to move forward at once all the elements would be confounded and split asunder, and they would shake the sea and dry up its waters.[37] As the body of man is held together by the soul, so the whole firmament is kept intact by the winds lest it be corrupted; and the winds are invisible like the soul, which comes from the mystery of God [38] (see Fig. 5, p. 149).

What causes the wind? William of Conches made one of the most elaborate attempts in many centuries to answer this,[39] for, though borrowing largely from Seneca, he added some significant observations of his own. In the first place he argued that local winds are produced by various local causes, as, for instance, when air enters a cavern, on account of its *labilitas*, or fluidity, it tends to force out the air already there and thus to make a commotion which generates wind. We may be allowed to suppose here that William has in mind a cavern with two entrances, for it is difficult to understand how such an effect could be produced in a cavern with only one. Similarly, William thought that waters entering the hollows of the earth tend to force out the vapors therein contained and thus to produce blasts and even earthquakes. A damp vapor in rising might cause a wind to blow on account of the removal of its weight (*ex ponderatione sua*). William borrowed the idea that winds may result from the destruction and flattening out of clouds directly from the ἐκνέφτα, or "cloud breezes," of Aristotle and Seneca. Adelard of Bath also attributed the origin of certain winds to local exhalations of vapors off the surface of land and water. "Marshes and valleys give up a great deal of dense air, which in the natural course of things rises upward; further, when they are loosened, they give back to its natural position much moisture of water which they had previously held imprisoned; add to this that I do not exclude from my statement the actual air which is the content of earth" (Gollancz's translation).[40]

Atmospheric Circulation

The most original theory of the winds was not any of those which attempted to account for purely local breezes but an explanation propounded by William of Conches of the circulation of the atmosphere as a whole. Unlike our modern conceptions of atmospheric circulation based on the observation of facts, William's ingenious theory seems to have been the product of his own vivid imagination. It was founded on a persistent idea, dating back to classical times, that disturbances in the water can produce currents of air. Gervase of Tilbury, for example, states in so many words that "mountains and water cause winds" and that the swift-flowing Rhone makes the *mistral* that blows over Provence and Dauphiny.[41] William of Conches [42] believed that there are two ocean currents trending east and west out of the equatorial ocean. Each of these was supposed to divide in two at the extremities of our *oikoumene*, making four currents which collide at the North and South Poles in the ocean perpendicular to the equatorial ring (Amphitrites). The cardinal winds are generated at four points, at the two junctions of the oceans where the currents divide and at the poles where they collide. The western division gives rise to Zephyr, the eastern to Eurus, the collision at the North Pole to Boreas, and the one at the South Pole to Auster. It may happen, however, that one of the currents will on occasion flow more strongly than its opponent and will push the point of collision beyond the pole. This displacement of the point of collision explains the blowing of the collateral winds. Absurd as it may be in itself, this theory is of interest to us mainly because it shows that William understood that a broad system of atmospheric circulation is possible and assigned to it, as well as to local breezes, a purely physical cause. Curiously enough, it is the exact reverse of our modern conception of the usual relation existing between atmospheric and ocean currents, for now we understand that the winds are more effective as the cause of the ocean currents than vice versa.

William also maintained, as we shall see later,[43] that the tides are produced by the impact of ocean currents. Why then, it was asked, if the tides are of daily, periodic occurrence, do not the winds, which he tells us result from the same cause, show a similar periodicity? To this William replied [44] that the winds in fact do show such regularity but that it is not apparent to us for two reasons: in the first place, wind produced by these causes does not always reach the part of the earth where we happen to be; and, secondly, the resulting wind may blow at such a high altitude as not to be noticed by men on the ground—an observation now well known to be true.

Names of the Winds

Classical names for the winds were almost universally employed. The distinction between cardinal and collateral which was made by William of Conches goes back to the Greeks,[45] who had conceived of four cardinal and four, six, seven, or eight collateral winds. Seneca's[46] rose of twelve winds, the idea of which in its essentials had been derived from Posidonius, Timosthenes, and, ultimately, from Aristotle, was adopted by Isidore, who passed it on to the Middle Ages, though terrible confusion (which, happily, it is not necessary for us to unravel) reigned at all times regarding the names employed to designate its elements.[47] In addition to the classical terms, our modern names were already familiar. In the Ghent manuscript of Lambert of St. Omer's *Liber floridus*[48] there is a diagram in which the winds are called "ost-ost," "sud-ost," "sud-sud," "sud-west," "west-west," "nord-west," "nord-nord," and "nord-ost." This terminology was used in the time of Charlemagne[49] and is probably of Anglo-Saxon origin,[50] although it has been suggested that the terms are corruptions of Latin words—"ost" from "Augustus;" "ovest," or "west," from "ob est;" "nord" from "novus arctus," etc.[51]

Qualities of the Winds

To the various winds classical and medieval writers liked to attribute qualities—or, at any rate, descriptive adjectives, "cold" or "hot," "dry" or "damp," "stormy" or "calm," and the like—but there was little enough uniformity in making these distinctions. Some writers of our period seem to have been content merely to repeat what had been said in classical times; others, like William of Conches or Giraldus Cambrensis, showed more independence. Boreas was probably universally regarded as cold and Auster as hot, but beyond this we cannot generalize.[52] William of Conches[53] conceived of the winds as partaking of the qualities of the regions over which they blow: Auster, coming from the South Pole and hence originally frigid like Boreas, in its passage across the torrid, equatorial zone becomes hot and dry—an observation which may perhaps be founded on some knowledge of the *sirocco* of the Mediterranean. On the other hand, Giraldus Cambrensis, undoubtedly from personal acquaintance with the water-laden south and southwest gales of the British Isles, calls Auster damp and rainy in winter. Similarly Giraldus breaks with classical tradition when he speaks of the east wind, or Eurus, as pure and clear, a bringer of fair summer weather, strikingly different from Zephyr, wet and cloudy from the sea.[54]

Local Winds

We find occasional descriptions—some of them from personal observation, no doubt—of winds peculiar to particular parts of the world. Gervase of Tilbury, as we have seen, tells of very violent blasts in the Rhone valley,[55] supposedly generated by the current of the river in a region now famed for the furious *mistral* that sweeps across Dauphiny and Provence from the north. In another connection[56] he tells of a valley in the Kingdom of Arles, once so shut in by precipitous mountains that no winds at all entered it and that it consequently was sterile and useless. In the time of Charlemagne, however, Caesarius, the archbishop of Arles, filled his glove with sea breezes and let them forth in the valley; thus originated a wind known as *pontianum*, which wrought an immediate change in the character of the place and caused it henceforth to become fertile and healthy. This wind was doubtless the breeze now called *pontias* that blows at Nyons in the Department of the Drôme; but as to its miraculous origin Gervase is merely repeating one of many popular medieval stories.[57]

William of Tyre[58] describes in vivid terms the *simoom* of the Arabian desert and how men have to lie flat on the ground at the time of its passing: equal to a storm at sea, it sweeps down upon the traveler waves of sand as huge as those of the sea and causes grave danger to persons who would cross the desert.

CLIMATOLOGY

The most important factor in determining the atmospheric climate of any given region is the amount of sunlight and heat received. This, in turn, depends largely on geographical latitude. As we have already discussed the broad climatic divisions of the earth's surface in zones, it remains here for us to deal merely with what was known of climatic conditions within the *oikoumene*.

Hot and Cold Climates

Climatic differences between northerly and southerly latitudes were well understood. Classical writers had told of the coldness of the regions beyond Thule, and in the *De imagine mundi* [59] we read that in those parts the sea is frozen and perpetual cold prevails. An interpolation into Solinus' *Collectanea rerum memorabilium* dating perhaps from our period contains a vivid and possibly exaggerated description of the cold of Iceland: "These people also are good Christians, but in winter they dare not leave their underground holes on account of the terrible cold. For if they go out they are smitten by such terrible cold that they lose their color like lepers and swell up. If by chance they blow their nose, it comes off and they throw it away" (Nansen's translation).[60] Giraldus Cambrensis praises the temperate climate of Ireland, placed between the torrid warmth of Spain and the rigors of Iceland;[61] and the chroniclers and historians of the Crusades give evidence of first-hand knowledge of the terrific summer heats in the Holy Land.[62] Ambroise says, for example:

> "Ca c'est entur la seint Johan
> Que la chalur tote rien seche
> En la terre, tele est sa teche." [63]

Benjamin of Tudela's extensive travels made him familiar with countries of widely different climate. The peculiarities of some of these he notes briefly. Writing of Russia, for example, he remarks that "no one issues forth from his house in winter time on account of the cold. People are to be found there who have lost the tips of their noses by reason of the frost" (Adler's translation).[64] Similarly it was his belief that in Khulam (or Quilon) in southern India no one left his home all through the summer on account of the sun.[65] A hint of the intensity of the Mesopotamian summer is given in a description of a hospital in Baghdad, which Benjamin had perhaps seen, "where they keep charge of the demented persons who have become insane through the great heat. . . . and they chain each of them with iron chains until their reason becomes restored to them in the winter time" (Adler's translation).[66]

Distribution of Climates

William of Conches, in his usual manner, tried to generalize on climates. He said that our habitable portion of the earth's surface is not of an even temperature throughout. The parts nearest the torrid zone, Ethiopia and Libya, are hot and dry; the northern parts near the frigid zone are cold and damp. Furthermore, though for us it is less easy to see exactly why, the West is cold and dry, and the East warm and damp. The symmetry of the system is perfect: climates vary in a direct ratio with distance, or, as William puts it, "Aequaliter vero distans, aequaliter est temperata." [67]

Climatic Differences Between East and West

Men were not so well agreed in the Middle Ages regarding differences of climate between East and West as regarding those between North and South. Bartholomew Anglicus [68] believed the West to be cold and damp and the East hot and dry, an opinion unlike that of William of Conches in that it may well have been based on actual observation rather than on theory. Giraldus Cambrensis in the *Topographia Hiberniae* gives a long discourse [69] on climatic and other differences between the Orient and Occident, in which his main contention is that, though the air is clearer, finer, and more "subtle" in the East, the stormy and damp climates of the West are better for the health. The true climate of the Orient—that is of the Levant—had been made known to the Occidental world through the Crusaders, who often dwelt with insistence on its disagreeable and injurious qualities, especially the heat, dust, and thirst of the Syrian summer, which dried cisterns and carried disease and death in its train. In the East, Giraldus says, everything threatens the traveler, and he writes a word of warning against doing many of those very things which the modern wanderer in the Levant knows to be imprudent: such as going uncovered, sitting on rocks, or overeating.[70]

Topographic Influences Upon Climate

The Sea

During our period we find several descriptions of local climatic conditions and of variations due to topographic features like sea and mountains. A vivid impression of the wild marine weather of the North Atlantic off the coast of Ireland is given us in the narrative of St. Brandan's wanderings. The saint and his companions were forced to remain three months on an island because of storms with furious gales, rain, and hail.[71] Giraldus Cambrensis[72] pictures the turbulent climate of Ireland, an isle surrounded by vast seas, unprotected and exposed to all the blasts. He was especially struck by the thick and rainy westerly gales, Zephyr and Corus, which bend over the trees in the seaward parts of the island. However violent the winds, Giraldus maintained that Ireland is the most temperate of all lands:[73] snow there is infrequent and when it comes lasts but a short while. Though cold weather accompanies all the winds, it never becomes too cold, and green grass grows in the pastures at all times of year. Yet so constant is the dampness, so prevalent the rain and clouds, that a clear day is rare indeed.

Mountains

William of Conches speaks in general terms of the influence of mountains on climate. We have seen how he recognized the fact that the tops of mountains are colder than the valleys below.[74] In another connection[75] he explained that places cut off from the north winds by mountains have dry, warm conditions and are good for winter residence, though less desirable in summer. The opposite is true of places on the north sides. Similarly, places exposed to the east are warm and damp with a pleasant autumn but bad spring weather, and the converse is true of places with a western exposure. This systematic arrangement is deduced from William's fundamental and oversymmetrical conception of the various climatic characteristics of the cardinal points of the compass.

Gunther of Pairis, in his *Ligurinus*,[76] embellishes a description of the mountain ranges of Italy with an imaginative discourse on how they influence the climate: the Apennines temper the moist, summer heat of the south wind, and the crags of the Alps cut off the cold northerly gales of Boreas and Arctos. Giraldus Cambrensis says[77] that Ireland, like all other mountainous districts, produces an abundance of rain. In the *Itinerarium Kambriae*[78] he explains that the lake of Brecknock (Llangorse) in Wales is encircled north, west, and south by high mountains. The great range of Cader Arthur to the south, by cutting off the rays of the sun, renders the climate in the vicinity of the lake both pleasant and healthy. The valley of Ewyas, completely surrounded by mountains (now the Black Mountains), is constantly the resting place of clouds, strong gales, and rain, which make it, in Giraldus' opinion, an extremely healthful locality.[79]

We cannot leave this subject without alluding again to the theoretical discussion of the influence of mountains on the climate of the polar regions that is found in that most interesting treatise of Robert Grosseteste, the *De natura locorum.* The bishop of Lincoln recognized the fact that insolation is greatly reduced in high latitudes owing to the obliquity of the sun's rays and that the climate normally should be too cold to sustain life. He believed, however, that the presence of very high mountains, Rhipaean, Hyperborean, and others to which the authorities referred, might totally neutralize the effects of position in relation to the sun's rays. "Some of these mountains," he wrote,[80] "are smooth of surface, like the salt or rock hills that are found in many places, and others are in the nature of crystal, as divers authors and explorers testify, so that the reflection from them is good. As a result of this they are able to cause the rays all to converge and to produce a powerful effect. From these two accidental causes, that is from the smoothness of the mountains and from their concave shape, there is an intense heating of the air in certain regions around the pole. The great height of some of these mountains also cuts off the cold of the north, and thus certain localities may well be intensely hot." On the other hand, Grosseteste had learned from Capella, Pliny, Solinus, and "many others who describe the regions of the world that in the Hyperborean Mountains next to the pole there are men who are called Hyperboreans from these mountains. And they enjoy the most temperate and healthy of climates and as a result live to such an age that they grow tired of life and without other cause throw themselves off of high rocks into the sea and die. The cause of this may be assigned to the form of the mountains beneath which they dwell, inasmuch as these mountains are smooth and of even surface, nor are they concave but are elongated (*oblongam*) and convex or of some other shape which does not concentrate the heat in those regions but on the contrary renders the climate temperate." [81]

Influence of Climate on Man

In the literature of our period we find several observations about the influence of climate on man. Gervase of Tilbury [82] maintained that the character of the different European peoples varies with varying climatic conditions. "According to the diversities of the air the Romans are grave, the Greeks fickle and unreliable, the Africans sly and crafty, the Gauls fierce, and the English and Teutons powerful and robust."

In another connection [83] he explains that the violent *mistral* of the Rhone valley generates in this region men who are windy, empty-headed, inconsistent, and most unreliable in their promises. The supposedly mollifying influence of a warmer climate on the Lombards is hinted at by Otto of Freising.[84] Otto believed that these tribes gave up their ferocity on settling in Italy, where they adopted Italian customs, partly because they married Italian women but partly also because of the nature of the country and climate (*ex terris aerisve*). We have already seen how Giraldus Cambrensis stressed the healthy qualities of damp and humid Ireland in contrast with the disease-breeding Orient. Even the most delicate persons thrive in Ireland, he said, and though the Eastern air may endow men with keener wits and intelligence, the West gives them stronger bodies and a more martial spirit.[85]

Climate of Rome

If we may believe Otto of Freising [86] and Gunther of Pairis,[87] the climate of Rome was even more noxious and dangerous in the twelfth than in the nineteenth century. Otto tells us that Frederick Barbarossa's army arrived in Rome in midsummer when the Dog Star was on high. It was a time when the ponds, caverns, and ruinous places around the city were exhaling poisonous vapors, and the air in the entire vicinity had become densely laden with pestilence and death. Gunther enlarges on this, giving a circumstantial, though probably fanciful, account of the effects of the terrible Roman summer on the German army, especially of the disease and malaria engendered by the climate and foul condition of the city.[88]

CHAPTER VIII

THE WATERS

THE WATERS ABOVE THE FIRMAMENT

Rationalistic Beliefs

"And God made the firmament and divided the waters which were under the firmament from the waters which were above the firmament" (Gen. i, 7).

We saw in Chapter II that this text had induced many of the earlier Church Fathers to devise strange theories about the waters above the firmament. The idea of Jerome, Josephus, Ambrose, Isidore, and Bede that these waters were in crystalline, or frozen, form met with opposition from those who were influenced by classical science and especially by the writings of Aristotle. Abelard in his *Expositio in hexaemeron*[1] discussed in considerable detail various opinions about the existence of solidified water above the firmament, though personally he was inclined to think that the air sustains the water in the form of very fine drops. That much heavier objects may sometimes be supported by air or water he proved by citing examples of cases where this is actually known to happen, as where a needle may be made to float on water. Theodoric of Chartres and William of Conches approached the problem from an even more rationalistic standpoint. Theodoric[2] held that water, when subjected to sufficient heat, turns into "pure air." On the second day of the Creation the fire element heated the water element in such a way that large portions of the latter rose as high as the moon and were there suspended in vaporous form "above the top of the sky" (*super summam coeli*). As a result the atmosphere became intercalated between the liquid water of the earth's surface and this water vapor above the firmament. The firmament itself, Theodoric contended, was merely the air and was so called either because it "firmly" supported that which was above it and enclosed that which was below it or else because it "firmly" gripped the earth on all sides. William of Conches also argued against the possibility of frozen water above the firmament.[3] This, he declared, is quite contrary to reason: frozen water is solid and heavy, and the place for solid and heavy substances in the constitution of the universe is either on or beneath the earth's surface. Then again, water in or near the celestial sphere—which is the abode of fire—would either extinguish the fire or else itself be consumed. William objected to juggling with the Aristotelian laws of physics. He explained the Biblical text by asserting that the firmament is the atmosphere and that the waters "above" it are in reality nothing more than the clouds within it.[4] On the whole, he concluded that the text should be interpreted allegorically rather than literally.

Literal Beliefs

In decided contrast with these more or less rationalistic theories was Michael Scot's bold assertion that beyond the realm of fire and above the eighth heavenly sphere comes a "multitude of waters,"[5] or Gervase of Tilbury's extraordinary account of a sea either in or above the atmosphere. To prove the existence of such a sea Gervase told[6] how "in his time some people coming out of a church in England found an anchor let down by a rope out of the heavens, how there came voices from sailors above trying to loose the anchor, and, finally, how a sailor came down the rope, who, on reaching the earth, died as if drowned in water" (White).[7] William of Auvergne, Platonist of the early thirteenth century and staunch opponent of Aristotelianism, also found no difficulties in the way of literal belief in the waters above the firmament. Ignoring the arguments of Peripatetic physics, he wrote:[8] "Nobody in the world is either amazed or horrified at the presence of fire beneath the waters and more especially beneath the earth. This is proved to the eye by the fiery outbreaks from three mountains (that is Vulcano, Etna, and Chimaera). Why then should one wonder so much that water is found above the heavens?"

Hildegard of Bingen gave expression to some views, probably original with her, regarding the waters above the firmament.

In the *Causae et curae* she speaks of "the waters of the great sea which surrounds the world and forms as it were a flank to those waters which are above the firmament, because the height (*summitas*) of those which are above and the extreme edge (*extremitas*) of those which are below the firmament are mutually joined together."[9] In the *Solutiones* she characterized the celestial waters, asserting that they neither increase nor decrease (implying perhaps that they are disturbed by no tides) but that they have remained just as they are now since God created them. They are unlike the waters of the earth inasmuch as they are far more fine in texture and entirely invisible to human eyes.[10]

Purpose of the Waters

What purpose is served by the waters above the firmament? Gervase of Tilbury declared that they supply the earth with dew.[11] Abelard said that there were two opinions on this subject.[12] The first was that the waters were originally placed in the heavens in order to be used in the Deluge. To this he was opposed, because the Psalms show that the waters were still in existence in David's time, long after the Flood. If there had not been waters above the firmament in David's time, how could the latter have sung: "Praise ye the Lord . . . ye heavens of heavens and let all the waters that are above the heavens praise the name of the Lord"?[13] Abelard was more inclined to favor the second theory, that the waters were intended to temper the heat of the upper celestial fires. He felt, however, with more or less reason, that this entire problem presents great, if not insoluble, difficulties.

THE CONGREGATION OF WATERS

There is an abundance of evidence that the authority of the Bible was invoked to support a theory that the waters beneath the firmament must constitute one unit, or "congregation of waters." This view, as we saw in Chapter II, was based on the assertion in Genesis that God "gathered together the waters in one place." Peter Abelard,[14] Peter Comestor,[15] and Hugh of

St. Victor[16] all maintained that there are great subterranean reservoirs connected with the seas and rivers of the surface in such a way that the whole hydrographic system of the earth forms a single unit. Prior to the action of God in gathering them together these waters in the primordial chaos were supposed to have been disseminated in the form of vapor, which took up vastly more room than the liquid into which God's power later concentrated them.

Connection Between Seas and Rivers

That many writers believed in the connection between the seas and the rivers and in the consequent unity of the waters is shown by numerous passages. Medieval thinkers, as we have seen, were constantly preoccupied by the doctrine of the microcosm, the theory that the human body includes all the elements which constitute the universe and is indeed in itself a miniature replica of the universe. This appears in a statement in the *De imagine mundi* that the whole interior of the earth is filled with channels like the blood vessels that permeate the body.[17] Whenever and wherever a man digs into the ground he is sure to find water. A constant circulation is maintained between the ocean and the waters of the surface of the land through these passages and through the air.[18]

William of Conches held that the great ocean in the equatorial zone is the source of all dampness in the earth (*fons humoris*) and that the land is seamed with canals full of water derived from that source.[19] Peter Alphonsi describes the circulation of the waters from the sea into the atmosphere by evaporation, thence in the form of rain to the rivers, and so back to the sea.[20] Peter Comestor, however, held that the river which springs from Paradise and divides in four is the source of all the water of the earth;[21] and Gervase of Tilbury, who follows Comestor in this respect, mentions in another connection that springs have their sources in the sea.[22] Perhaps if he had analyzed the question he would have said that the waters of the sea must find their way at some time through the rivers of Paradise and thence to the springs.

The Earth Established on the Waters

The phrase in the Psalms, that God established the earth above or on (*super*) the waters,[23] also proved puzzling to the thinkers of our period. The easy explanation that such a phenomenon might be due to the arbitrary working of God's will was not always readily accepted. Some commentators on the Psalms observed dubiously that it surpassed their understanding.[24] Alexander Neckam stated that it might possibly refer to waters beneath the earth, since "Alfraganus [Al-Farghānī] says that the sphere of the waters and of the earth are one." Saints who had expounded the phrase, he added, tried to explain away the difficulty by referring to the colloquial manner of saying that Paris is founded "on the Seine." "The truth of the matter, however, is that the terrestrial paradise is above the waters, since it is above the sphere of the moon."[25] An allegorical interpretation was also resorted to, and the reader was told to conceive of "earth" as being the Church and "the waters" as the many peoples upon which the Church is founded.

Peter Abelard, in an interesting passage in the *Expositio in hexaemeron*,[26] gave an interpretation of this phrase as well as of the text about the "congregation of the waters" which seems to foreshadow a theory later to be elaborated by Brunetto Latino and destined to gain a firm grip on the hydrographical conceptions of many individuals until as late as the eighteenth century. Abelard wrote: "When the waters receded into one part of the earth, the other parts were uncovered, as was written: 'God, who established the earth on the waters.' As any globe may be immersed in water in such a way that one part of it rises above the water, even so the globe of the earth rests in the waters so that one side of it is contiguous with the sea and causes the sea to permeate through its veins, whence springs and rivers take their rise. The waters of this sea, in truth, are congregated into one place and are consequently deeper than if they were diffused, unless, perchance, the fact that they may be drawn off through the veins of the earth makes them less deep." We have seen that Abelard and William of Conches compared the universe to an egg in which the four parts correspond to the four elements, fire, air, water, and earth.[27] This was the theoretical arrangement of the elements according to the logical application of Aristotle's physical laws. As a matter of fact, the aqueous sphere does not completely envelop the earth, as it should if this theoretical arrangement were carried out in nature. How, then, could it be explained that a portion of the earth's surface is not covered by water? Robert Grosseteste, without attempting a physical explanation, answered this question from the teleological point of view, echoing the words of Genesis. "Truly it is a fact," he wrote, "that, in order that the animals of this earth might have a habitation and refuge, the water receded into the concave parts of the earth and the surface of the land appeared dry and distinct. And so the land with the waters contained upon it is like a sphere of earth." [28] Later writers were not willing to accept such a simple declaration and looked for physical and mechanical explanations. For instance, Brunetto Latino assigned to the spheres of earth and of water each a different center, placed in such positions in relation to one another that the aqueous sphere covers the sphere of earth to a great depth on one side (the southern hemisphere) but on the opposite side leaves dry the portion inhabited by man.[29] Certainly the passage we have quoted above shows that Abelard may well have had something of this sort in mind.

THE OCEANS AND SEAS

Relative Areas of Land and Sea

We saw in Chapter I that two theories prevailed in ancient times as to the distribution of land and water: the oceanic theory, that the *oikoumene* is surrounded by water; and the continental theory, that the oceans of the earth occupy relatively small and enclosed basins. Though the writers of our period held to the oceanic hypothesis, they had various and conflicting notions in regard to the size of the ocean or oceans which surround the known world. The great popularity of Martianus Capella and Macrobius, who both held the doctrine that there are three areas of land corresponding to our *oikoumene* in the three quarters of the earth's surface, must have rendered impossible any widespread acceptance of a theory like the one hinted at by Abelard, that all of the earth's surface except the *oikoumene* is covered by water; and the definition of the ocean as a zone or hem surrounding the inhabited world, not infrequently given in our period, certainly does not imply the existence of water areas of immense size in comparison with the land areas.[30] Furthermore, the Second Book of Esdras, which, though apocryphal, enjoyed high authority in the Middle Ages,[31] gave the reader an opposite impression. Here it was stated: "Upon the third day thou didst command that the waters should be gathered in the seventh part of the earth: six parts hast thou dried up, and kept them, to the intent that of these some being planted of God and tilled might serve thee." "Upon the fifth day thou saidst unto the seventh part, where the waters gathered, that it should bring forth living creatures, fowls and fishes: and so it came to pass." Roger Bacon uses this text from Esdras to reinforce his argument that, relatively speaking, the water surface of the world is very restricted in comparison with the land surface.[32]

Explanation of Uniform Level of Sea Surface

Into the sea there pours at all times a vast volume of water from the rivers. Neckam moralized mournfully on this [33] and compared the flow of fresh water into the salt depths with the way in which greater powers absorb lesser and the way in which the voluptuousness of this world—a sham sweetness—is turned to bitterness and salt; but he did not attempt to explain the puzzling physical problem of why the surface of the sea fails to rise and overflow the lands.[34] Most writers who dealt with the latter problem appealed to the theory of the *congregatio aquae:* since all the waters of the earth form one unit, they must inevitably make their way back from the sea through various routes to the sources of streams.[35] Other explanations, however, were sometimes brought forward. Adelard of Bath believed that the stars and sun absorb a certain amount of water.[36] The author of the *De imagine mundi* was convinced that the fresh water entering the sea is partially consumed by the salt of the deeps and partially evaporated by the winds and taken up into the sun.[37]

Salinity of the Sea

The two characteristics of the oceans that distinguish them from bodies of fresh water and have always aroused men's curiosity are their saltness and their tides. The *De imagine mundi* gives a popular etymology of the word *mare* from *amarum*, meaning bitter or salty.[38] Though there is no attempt in this book to show reasons for the salinity of the sea, the author followed Isidore and Bede in the opinion that the water at great depths is more bitter and salt than near the surface and that evaporation draws off the fresh water only and leaves the bitter and dense elements behind; similarly, that part of the sea water makes its way back to the sources of the springs, deposits its salt in the land, and bursts forth fresh and purified from its passage through the earth. In the *Image du monde*, on the other hand, there is a naïve explanation of why the sea is salt.[39] Great saline mountains in the deeps are said to be constantly dissolving away and thereby imparting a peculiar character to the water. Adelard of Bath, Gervase of Tilbury, and William of Conches treated the subject a shade more rationally, perhaps, in attributing the saltness to the influence of heat. Adelard says,[40] "I consider the cause of the saltness of the sea to be the heat of the sun and planets. For, since the true ocean passes through the heart of the torrid zone and since the course of the planets runs through the same zone, though obliquely, the ocean must of necessity be heated by such a great heat of the heavenly bodies that it is thereby rendered salt." This explanation, he adds, is even subject to proof: for along coasts nearest the ocean, sea water "when dried in the sun on the rocks" may readily be converted into salt without any artificial aid; in more distant seas the water must be boiled and reboiled before this effect is produced. Furthermore, in summer all sea water is salter than in winter.

William of Conches[41] and Alexander Neckam[42] also followed Aristotle in believing that water in its purest form has an insipid taste but that it is thickened and rendered salt by the sun's heat in the torrid ocean, whence it is distributed to the other seas by currents. Gervase of Tilbury tends to exaggerate this theory:

we read in the *Otia imperialia* [42] of a lake in the County of Aix, near Arles, the waters of which are congealed into ice by the cold of winter and into salt by the heat of August. This led Gervase to conclude that it would be impossible to sail around the earth, because the all-encircling ocean would be frozen stiff in the north and thickened into solid salt in the south.

Tides

If we discard fanciful ideas like that of Richard, prior of St. Victor in Paris (died 1173), to the effect that the tides are produced by the breathing of some great submarine monster or spirit,[44] we find two distinct groups of tidal theories prevalent in the twelfth century: as Duhem defines them, the physical and the astrological. The astrological theories, which explained the tides by the influence of the moon, had been expounded before the period we are studying by Posidonius, Pliny, Bede, and the Moslem Abū Ma'shar. The physical theories had been set forth by Macrobius, who had believed that the tides were due to the impact of ocean currents, and Paul the Deacon, who had attributed them to the action of great whirlpools. Although twelfth-century students added little to these earlier opinions, they made some remarkable combinations of them, and their observations were distinguished by a few close records of actual tidal phenomena.[44a]

Lunar Causation

Bernard Sylvester explained the tides by lunar causation alone[45] and attributed to the moon the power of attracting and repelling not only the waters but also terrestrial substances,[46] inasmuch as the moon is the nearest planet to the earth, the largest, and consequently the most powerful.[47]

In the following century we find that Robert Grosseteste saw in the effects of lunar rays upon the bottom of the sea sufficient cause for the ebb and flood. If in their broad outlines the ideas of the bishop of Lincoln are plain enough, the individual steps of his argument are neither clear nor coherent. They are of sufficient interest, nevertheless, to justify an attempt at interpreting them.[48] We have already alluded to Robert's theory of rays emanating from the celestial bodies in the shape of cones or "pyramids" and to his principle that the power of these rays is inverse to the obliquity of the angle at which they meet the earth's surface and to the length of the pyramids.[49] When the moon is rising, Grosseteste explains in the *De natura locorum*,[50] the rays are very oblique and the pyramids long: hence the power of the rays is much too weak to disperse vapors that have accumulated on the sea floor or to draw these vapors up into the air. The result is that the vapors tend to displace the waters in the depths, to rise in bubbles to the surface, and thus to produce flood tides. As the moon approaches the meridian the rays become less oblique, the pyramids shorter, and the lunar power consequently greater. The moon now disperses and consumes the vapors and draws them up into the air from the depths of the sea. By the time our satellite reaches the meridian, the vapors are entirely consumed, "and, since the cause ceases, the effect also ceases; and the waters of the sea naturally flow back into their proper place in order not to create a vacuum." Hence the ebb begins.

Grossesteste does not make clear what generates the vapors, though he probably meant us to assume that they were produced by the heat due to the reflection of the moon's rays upon the sea floor. In another treatise, the *De impressionibus elementorum*,[51] he explains how reflected rays, though not necessarily the rays of the moon, in passing through a transparent body of water may create heat at the bottom.

The problem of the flood tide when the moon is in the opposite hemisphere of the heavens still remained. Grosseteste's obscure explanation of this runs about as follows: "Many try to give a reason for this difficult circumstance on the grounds that opposite quarters of the universe are of the same composition (*commixtionis*) and consequently produce the same effects. But this explanation falls short, since it is false to assert that there are any actual replicas of the stars of one quarter of the heavens in another quarter, inasmuch as the earth interposes its bulk between a planet in one quarter and the quarter opposite. Moreover, even were this explanation true, an explanation of the original cause would be required. That is to say, it would be necessary to ask why the opposite quarters are of the same composition and consequently exert the same effect. The fact is that the reflection of rays solves this problem, since the rays of the moon are multiplied on the stellar heaven. Because the stellar heaven is an opaque body, we are consequently not able to see it, though it nevertheless is very luminous according to Alpetragius and Messalahe [*sic*]. Other reflected rays fall on the opposite quarter at right angles."[52]

Terrestrial Causation

Most writers found that the astrological, or lunar, theory alone was insufficient to explain all the peculiarities of the tides and made appeal, as well, to physical theories—in particular to that of Macrobius. This is given in varying terms by Adelard of Bath, Lambert of St. Omer, William of Conches, and Giraldus Cambrensis. Macrobius, as we have already observed, had conceived of four ocean currents issuing out of the great equatorial ocean and flowing north and south in the girdling ocean which includes the poles.[53] These currents run together somewhere in the polar regions; the waters rebound on themselves (*ex repercussione ingurgitur retro mare*) and in this way cause the ebb and flow. Lambert of St. Omer in his *Liber floridus* seems to have accepted the Macrobian theory much as it stands,[54] but Adelard harbored doubts as to the sufficiency of the impact of the waters against each other to produce a tidal rebound and thought that some mountain or other mass of land must interpose to produce such an effect.[55]

William of Conches cites two theories of tidal controls:[56] the first is that of Macrobius; the second, confusingly stated, suggests Adelard's hypothesis of an interposing mass of land. William says, in effect, that the tides are due in part to the existence of mountains submerged beneath the sea, against which the waters are attracted forward and then repelled, producing an oscillating motion. As to this, we may well be led to inquire how Macrobius, Adelard, and William explained this oscillating motion, for certainly two steadily flowing currents meeting each other or running against submerged reefs would not create any such motion. Unfortunately in this we are left unsatisfied by our medieval writers, who characteristically here, as often elsewhere, were content, when stating that one phenomenon causes another, to leave entirely to the imagination the explanation of the manner in which such causation is actually effected.

William did not rule out all lunar control over the ebb and flood but explained the spring and neap tides by variations in the moon's power of heating and drying the atmosphere. This power, he thought, is at a minimum both when the moon is full and when it is new. Consequently we have high spring tides at these times, and vice versa. William's theory is the reverse of Abū Ma'shar's:[57] that the tides are caused by the active attraction by the moon of the humid elements on the earth's surface. William fails to show us why the tides should be in flood when the moon is rising toward the meridian and why spring tides should occur when there is a full moon. Abū Ma'shar, on the other hand, fails to explain why there is a flood tide when the moon is on the other side of the earth, in the opposite celestial hemisphere.

Alexander Neckam gives what is, to say the least, an unsatisfactory treatment of the tides.[58] After quoting the scientific opinions of others, he remarks that to explain the ebb and flow of the waters is a problem that cannot be solved. Then, in his customary vein, he adds the moral observation that the tides are like the persecutions of the Christians and that they should not fill one with too much despair, for after they have risen they always subside again in the due course of time.[59]

William the Breton wondered at the tides but, like Neckam, refrained from trying to explain their cause and said that God alone understands this and no man can comprehend it either now or ever.[60] He was amazed that such a wide, deep, and powerful stream as the Seine at Rouen could be forced back upon itself by the waters of the sea and made to flow in the opposite direction through a space of land across which its normal current could scarcely pass in three days. Was this due to the fact that fresh water is less powerful than salt? Or does the fresh water find the salt water odious and reçoil before it? Or does the stream do reverence, as it were, to its mother, the sea, falling back before her and then when the tide turns following behind her respectfully? None of these explanations was William ready to accept as true. "For us who live our human lot here below, it is sufficient to know the fact; it is not allowed to us to know the cause."[61]

Giraldus Cambrensis' Tidal Studies

The most elaborate tidal studies of our period are in the pages of Giraldus Cambrensis' *Topographia Hiberniae*, where we find a combination of the astrological theory of Abū Ma'shar, the whirlpool theory of Paul the Deacon, and the ocean-current theory of Macrobius. Giraldus said that when the moon passes the meridian the waters begin to recede from the coasts of Britain and to retire into hidden submarine reservoirs.[62] The moon, being the heavenly body that controls all things humid on the earth, when full causes the tides to rise to unusual heights. A little further on in his discussion, Giraldus explains that at the four opposite parts of the ocean there is a force that violently attracts the sea water, producing a sort of periodic swelling and sinking; this is connected in some manner with a belief in Giraldus' mind that greater quantities of fresh water enter the sea at the extremities of the earth and in the vicinity of the poles than elsewhere, though on what he based this supposition and how it produced the results which he ascribes to it, he does not explain. Giraldus' theory also owes much to Macrobius' hypothesis of the effects of the collision of ocean currents on the tides, as well as to Paul the Deacon's whirlpool theory, for he explains elsewhere[63] that philosophers mention the existence of four whirlpools at the opposite ends of the earth and that some people attribute to these the causation of tides and storms of wind. Each of the whirlpools resembles a great vortex in the northern seas towards which the waters of the sea rush together, to be absorbed in secret caverns as if in an abyss; ships approaching too near are sucked in and destroyed.

The most interesting feature of Giraldus' tidal studies, however, are not these general speculations regarding causes but some very neat observations made on the British and Irish coasts. In the first place, he remarks on the choppy water of the Irish Sea, which presumably he connects with tide rips.[64] He then goes on to discuss the difference in the hour of high water at various Irish ports, at Milford Haven in Wales, and at Bristol in England. When the tide is at the half-ebb in Dublin, at Milford Haven it is at the half-flood, and near Bristol just beginning the rise. Let us see what the facts of the case are at the present day.[65] On February 1, 1919, half-ebb occurred at Dublin at about 2:30 P. M., half-flood at Milford Haven only about an hour and a half later, and low water had occurred at Bristol half an hour earlier. In other words Giraldus' observations on the relative times of the tides at these three points were unusually accurate. Furthermore, he explains that at Wicklow, on the Irish coast opposite Wales, the water falls at the same time that it rises throughout the sea in general. When Giraldus here speaks of the "sea in general" he perhaps had in mind tidal observations made at other points on the coast not far to the south. Modern tide tables show that near Arklow, only about fourteen miles away, it is low water some two hours and a half earlier than at Wicklow. The water, consequently, is rising at Arklow for two hours and a half while it is still falling at Wicklow. That Giraldus was familiar with Arklow is shown by the fact that he mentions a river entering the sea there and describes a curious rock in the harbor.[66]

Finally, Giraldus states[67] that when the moon has passed the meridian the waters first recede from the coasts of Britain but that on the Irish coasts in the vicinity of Dublin full flood corresponds to this recession of the waters. In the vicinity of Wexford, however, flood waters do not correspond with the flood at Dublin but rather with the flood waters on the British coast at Milford Haven. Giraldus was mistaken, if we are right in interpreting his words to mean that he thought that the tidal undulation which produces high water at Dublin is a different wave from that of Wexford or Milford Haven. No tidal undulation enters the Irish Sea from the north, and consequently the ebb and flood at all of these places is caused by the same wave. On the other hand, this wave reaches Dublin nearly five hours later than it reaches Wexford and Milford on the opposite shore, and the accuracy of Giraldus' data on the time of these tides is further confirmed by modern tide tables, which show that flood water at the Welsh port may occur only twenty-four minutes earlier than at Rosslare Point, the entrance to Wexford Harbor.

It would be interesting if we could know how Giraldus gathered these data. Probably they were pieced together from incidental observations of sailors or fishermen, for certainly no systematic investigation of tidal phenomena could well have been undertaken at Giraldus' time.[67a] It is typical of an immense amount of close and accurate knowledge that has always existed along with ignorance and superstition among the more humble workers of this world, knowledge that until recent years has but rarely found literary expression.

Other Marine Phenomena Noted by Giraldus

Giraldus certainly was not always so fortunate in his discussion of marine phenomena. He taxes our credulity a little when he tells of a rock in Arklow harbor on one side of which the water rises while it is falling on the other,[68] though this may perhaps have resulted from some local play of currents and eddies. It is less easy to find an explanation of a story which he relates of a recession of the sea at "Crebonensus" (Proconnesus?) near Constantinople.[69] Here, during eight days at the time of the festival of St. Clement, the waters fell back in order to allow pilgrims to go to the saint's shrine. This kind of miracle, to be sure, had the support of Biblical authority in the story of the parting of the waters of the Red Sea to permit the passing of the children of Israel; and we find a similar tale in the *Otia imperialia*,[70] where Gervase asserts that the Sea of Pamphylia was divided for Alexander the Great, because God wished to destroy the Persian kingdom by means of the Macedonian. The lake (or river) which in the legend surrounded the church of St. Thomas in India was also said to go dry at regular intervals to permit pilgrims to approach.[71]

In his description of South Wales, Giraldus Cambrensis gives an account of marine encroachments on the land and perhaps of coastal subsidence. A great storm on this sandy coast laid bare a forest hitherto covered by the waters. Trunks of trees appeared with marks of the ax upon them, fresh as if cut only the day before. Giraldus was convinced that the marks dated from inconceivable antiquity, perhaps even from the time of the Flood.[72] The wood was overwhelmed, he said, by the constant and ever increasingly violent advance of the sea; and certainly it is well known in modern days that the waves long have been eating into the coast of Pembrokeshire and that the uncovering by storms of buried forests and stumps is a commonplace occurrence there. Perhaps we are justified in interpreting Giraldus' remarks by assuming that the forest had not, as he states, previously been covered by water but more probably by marine sands or muds, which subsequently were removed from the stumps by storm waves.

St. Brandan and the Spirit of the Sea

Less scientific—or perhaps we had better say less prosaic—than the writings we have just been discussing but fully as replete with understanding of the ocean and its various moods, is the legend of the wanderings of St. Brandan. The style and spirit of this entire story shows that it must have been composed by men filled with a sense of the immensity and mystery of the Atlantic.[73] Probably the tale had its roots in the reports of actual voyagings of Irishmen blown far out to sea. Although there is much of the marvelous and supernatural borrowed from older tradition, the tone of the legend as a whole rings true to nature. Certainly it was not written by a landsman. At one time St. Brandan and his companions sailed north for three days, and the sea became "as it were coagulated through an excess of calmness."[74] It has been suggested that this refers to the semi-solid "Liver Sea" of Germanic legend, itself perhaps an echo of the reports of Pytheas and other classical writers about clotted sea waters north of Thule and in the Western Ocean.[75] On another occasion the travelers came in sight of a high column of clearest crystal apparently not far away, though it took three days to reach it.[76] So great was its height that they could scarce discern the summit, and as they drew near they saw that it was covered by a silvery canopy of marvelously fine texture. They passed through a hole in the canopy and entered a sea whose waters were so clear that the base of the column could be seen resting on the earth at the bottom of the sea. For an entire day they sailed along one side of the column. If we discard from all this what is obviously fabulous or borrowed from the vision of Ezekiel [77] or from the description of the New Jerusalem in Revelation,[78] may we not be justified in supposing that the sight of a great iceberg flashing in the sun gave rise to the story of the crystalline column and that the canopy represented curtains of fog hanging about its flanks?

St. Brandan and his crew also had other glimpses of the bottom of the sea [79] through waters of such remarkable transparency that they thought they could almost touch the beasts of various kinds lying there. When mass was said on board, these beasts rose and circled about the ship but did not molest the saint and his party. After seven days' voyage with sails set they had scarcely crossed this stretch of translucent water.

Bottom of the Sea

We find other accounts of the bottom of the sea and even of visits made to it, in the legendary writings of our period. Gervase of Tilbury [80] tells of an individual named Nicholas Pappas, a dweller on the shores of the Strait of Messina, who was forced by King Roger II of Sicily to dive into the waters. Being well known to the submarine monsters, he escaped all danger from molestation by them and afterwards used to tell about a grove beneath the "Strait of Pharo," how the tides wash first one way and then the other through the branches of the trees, and how he had seen submarine mountains, valleys, fields and woods, and trees with acorns on them. Gervase adds that our faith in the truth of this story may be increased by noting the fact that acorns are often washed ashore along the neighboring coasts. Nicholas also used to occupy himself by warning ships of the approach of storms and showing sailors how to calm the waters with oil. At a later period the legend became current [81] of a man named "Piscis" or "The Fish" (possibly this should be substituted for the "Pappas" of Gervase) who was accustomed to swim under the Strait of Messina, having been sent there in the first place to rescue a chalice cast into the sea by King Roger.

Alexander the Great, according to one version of the Romance of his adventures, also made a visit to the sea floor.[82] After he had crossed a desert infested with ferocious beasts, he called his companions together and complained that, in view of the fact that he had conquered the greater part of the world, he knew enough about the inhabitants of the land and now wanted to learn something of the inhabitants of the sea. He then proceeded to descend in a glass cask to the bottom of the deeps; there, among other things, he noted that the large fish eat the small ones, an observation whose novelty hardly seems to have justified the effort expended to make it.

THE WATERS OF THE LANDS

Let us turn now to the waters of the lands—ground water, sources (wells, springs, fountains), rivers, and finally lakes.

Ground Water

In our period the existence of water in various forms underneath the surface of the land was well understood. Bernard Sylvester says:[83] "A watery humor is diffused all through the lap of the land and makes streams and rivers, swamps and lakes." William of Conches attributed [84] the origin of the water in springs and wells to (1) underground streams, or, as he called them, "cataracts," which pass through wells en route from one part of the earth to another, and (2) the sweat of the earth (*sudor terrae*), or minute particles of water percolating through small holes in the earth much as human sweat percolates through the pores of the body. William maintained that the existence of underground watercourses as a source of well water was proved by the fact that wells near rivers are constantly full and that whatever happens to the water of a well in a given district is likely to happen to the water of all the other wells in the vicinity, showing that there must be some intercommunication between them. That springs and wells were constantly replenished in dry times was proof to William—as to modern geographers—of the existence of the sweat of the earth, or what we now call "ground water," which permeates the interstices in rocks, gravel, and sand alike. It is possible, however, that William believed that the *sudor terrae* was actually generated by the earth. This was undoubtedly the opinion of Adelard of Bath, who discusses the subject in terms very similar to those of William.[85]

The Sea As the Source of the Waters of the Land

Most of this subterranean water, as we have already seen, was supposed during the Middle Ages to come from the sea, whence it made its way inland either through the atmosphere in the form of rain or directly through the land. We need cite but two texts to show how firmly this idea was rooted in the medieval mind. One is from a sermon of Bernard of Clairvaux, the other from a questionnaire prepared by the Emperor Frederick II. It would perhaps be hard to find two men who stood at more diametrically opposite intellectual poles, and yet both, in this case, shared the same conviction.

Bernard, characteristically, treated the matter symbolically. "The sea," he said, "is the source of fountains and rivers; the Lord Jesus Christ is the source of every kind of virtue and knowledge. . . . What? Are not pure purposes, just judgments, holy aspirations, one and all streams from that same source? If all waters seek incessantly to return to the sea, making their way thither sometimes by hidden and subterranean channels, so that they may go forth from it again in continual and untiring circuit, becoming visible once more to man and available for his service, why are not those spiritual streams rendered back constantly and without reserve to their legitimate source, that they may not cease to water the fields of our hearts? Let the rivers of divers graces return from whence they came, that they may flow forth anew. Let the heavenly shower rise again to its heavenly source that it may be poured anew and still more plentifully upon the earth" (Eales's translation).[86]

Frederick II propounded to Michael Scot a list of questions on matters of cosmology and physical geography. Regarding most of these matters the Emperor was in doubt and perplexity, but concerning the waters of land and sea he was sure. "For we greatly wonder at these things," he said, "knowing already that all waters come from the sea and passing through divers lands and cavities return to the sea, which is the bed and receptacle of all running waters" (Haskins' translation). [87]

A most elaborate discussion of the qualities of the waters of the lands is found in the *Causae et curae* of Hildegard of Bingen.[88] Hildegard likewise assumed that the water of wells, springs, and rivers is derived from the ocean which surrounds the earth.[89] She also believed that the nature of the water varies widely in different parts of the ocean and consequently that the quality of the water of the land depends on the part of the ocean from which it comes. Furthermore, she maintained that some of the waters of the sea do not lose their salinity in passing through the land but that other waters are rendered fresh before they appear upon the earth's surface. Upon the basis of these assumptions Hildegard proceeded to analyze the qualities, sanitary, medicinal, and gastronomic, of waters both fresh and salt according to their derivation from the four cardinal points and from the northeast and northwest. Her analysis was meant as a practical guide for those who wished to use water for drinking and bathing with a minimum risk of disease, though she fails to explain how one is to determine the ultimate source of a specific spring, well, or river. Without undertaking a detailed examination of Hildegard's argument, we may note that, unlike Giraldus Cambrensis, who regarded the East as the fountain of poisons, she believed that the waters of the Orient were the purest and most healthful of all. On the other hand, she held that the putrid and corrupt elements of the earth were concentrated in the Western Sea and that waters coming from that quarter were very dangerous unless boiled.[90] The Southern Sea harbored an immense quantity of venomous worms and small animals, and consequently waters from it were not good for cooking or drinking. As we shall see in the next chapter,[91] Giraldus Cambrensis' discussion of the different qualities of the East and West was probably based in some measure on observation. The same can hardly be said of Hildegard's theories. We cannot but feel that they were the offspring of an unusually ingenious imagination, though the prophetic abbess undoubtedly attributed them to divine inspiration.

Hildegard went on to assert that swamp waters are dangerous from whatever part of the earth they come, since they contain vile and noxious damp elements of the ground and the poisonous spume of worms. Such waters should not be used unboiled except for washing. Well and spring waters which flow from swamps are equally bad, though as a general rule all waters arising from an unsanitary source become purer the farther they flow. Water from deep wells is usually better and smoother (*suavior*) for cooking, drinking, and other uses of man than the water of flowing springs; the latter, in turn, is better than river water, which should be avoided because of the impurities it receives from the air. The water of small, clear, pure rills is excellent for both men and cattle.

Effect of Land on Waters Which Spring From It

The land itself might produce varying effects on the water within it, and thus on the wells and fountains which spring from it. In summer, William of Conches tells us,[92] the pores of the earth are open, and the warm vapor (*fumus*) contained therein can escape. Consequently the heat of the earth is loosed, and the springs and wells are cooler than in winter, when the cold constricts the earth's pores and keeps the heat in. It is very easy to understand what gave rise to such a theory when we consider the fact that water always preserves a more uniform temperature than the surrounding air. Hot and putrid springs, the *De imagine mundi* tells us,[93] are caused by the ground water coming into contact with subterranean caves full of sulphur that is sometimes ignited by the winds. In some places serpents, by poisoning the earth and the ground water which passes through it, indirectly cause the water sources of a region to become noxious.[94] Michael Scot, in a somewhat repetitious and not wholly clear passage, explained in effect that the hot and boiling springs of Italy and Sicily are produced by waters arising out of subterranean cavities where the native heat of the interior of the earth in combination with the winds produces a violent combustion of sulphur and "white-hot rocks" (*petre calidissime*).[95]

Miraculous Wells and Springs; Geysers

Wells and springs, like lakes, seem to have appealed to the imagination of men at all times, and the description of their peculiarities occupied disproportionate space in medieval books of marvels. Giraldus Cambrensis mentions wells with petrifying properties in Ulster, Norway, Britain, and Cappadocia;[96] and Saxo Grammaticus expresses great wonder at a spring in Iceland the exhalation or foam of which is capable of turning the softest substances almost instantaneously into the hardest stone.[97] Gervase of Tilbury describes a salt well in the diocese of Worcester.[98] Though these are reasonable enough, it is a little more difficult to explain Giraldus' belief in wells which ebb and flow like the tides,[99] especially when he insists that some of them are situated far from the sea.

Giraldus describes an absolutely miraculous spring in the province of Munster in Ireland.[100] When touched or even looked at by a man, this spring will proceed to inundate the entire province with rain. The rain does not stop until a priest, virgin from birth and especially deputed for the purpose, celebrates mass in a chapel not far away and, having blessed the waters, conciliates the spring by sprinkling into it the milk of a one-colored cow. Giraldus remarked parenthetically that this was a barbaric ceremony and quite lacking in reason. Gervase of Tilbury tells of a lake in Great Britain which would produce a storm when certain words were chanted over it and of a fountain in the Kingdom of Arles which would cause rain if a stick or stone were thrown into it.[101] These tales, indeed, are but examples of a widespread belief among primitive and ignorant folk that man can attain the secret of the magical control of the elements. Sir James G. Frazer cites them with similar examples from other peoples and ages as illustrations of the doctrine that a "way of constraining the rain-god is to disturb him in his haunts. This seems to be the reason why rain is supposed to follow the troubling of a sacred spring." [102]

In treating the water element in his *De naturis rerum*, Alexander Neckam rushes over the problems of the four rivers of Paradise and of why the sea is salt to come to a discussion of springs,[103] about which he relates many marvels, appending to each a little moral lesson. For example, he tells of two founts in Italy, one of which turns the feathers of white birds black, and the other the feathers of black birds white. He suggests the analogy of the former to contemporary worldly knowledge that darkens minds glowing in the brightness of innocence; and of the latter to true wisdom that renders serene minds obscured by the shades of vice.[104] Then he goes on to discourse about springs that rise when some one throws a red cloth into them; a spring that boils up with much noise, as if in annoyance, when men talk near it; a spring that gives flame to an unburnt torch and puts out a lighted one; and a spring whose water, when thrown upon a certain rock in its neighborhood, causes a storm of wind, rain, and hail to arise. These are but a few of many remarkable sources that Neckam describes and places in various parts of the world, drawing on Solinus, Isidore, and the mass of medieval pseudo-science that flourished in all countries.

More convincing is Saxo Grammaticus' circumstantial account of certain water holes in Iceland. In these the water sometimes wells up in abundance and is thrown high into the air in a shower of drops. At other times the flow is quiescent, and the water seems to be sucked into the holes deep in the earth where it scarce may be seen. This description is obviously based on reports Saxo had received from eyewitnesses of the geysers of Iceland.[105]

The Fountain of Youth

The most remarkable and most sought-for of sources has always been the Fountain of Youth. In the first letter of Prester John we find the description [106] of a grove at the foot of Mount Olympus, not far from Paradise, in Central Asia. In this grove there is a spring that wafts forth odors of all kinds, varying from hour to hour, by day and by night. Its waters give eternal youth to any one who bathes therein, restoring him to the bodily strength and vigor that he possessed at the age of thirty-two. Closely parallel to this account, though probably not derived from it, is a description in the Romance of Alexander[107] of a fountain that receives its waters from the Euphrates, one of the four rivers of Paradise, and which four times daily has the power of rejuvenation. Two old men who jumped in emerged looking exactly as if they were thirty years old. Akin to the Fountain of Youth, but less powerful in its action, is a spring described by Gervase[108] in Staffordshire, England, to which he attributed the ability of restoring energy to men when weary. But this is true of any fresh mountain pool.

Rivers

As to the source of rivers, we need add nothing to what has already been said about the "congregation of waters" (*congregatio aquae*) and about springs and fountains. It was commonly thought in medieval and classical times that two or more rivers may rise from one source and flow off in diverse directions. The most striking example of this was furnished by the Scriptural four rivers of Paradise, which, though rising from one stream, were believed to find their way to at least three different seas. In commenting on the rivers of Paradise, Gervase of Tilbury expressly asserts[109] that not only is it possible for more than one stream to rise from the same headwaters but that the same rivers may again mingle and again separate their waters. Giraldus Cambrensis describes[110] how the Shannon of Ireland rises in a lake between Connaught and Munster and thence divides into two branches flowing in opposite ways, one southward to the "Sea of Brandan," the other northward into the Northern Ocean. It is true that in regions of imperfect drainage development, like Ireland, northern North America, and parts of the Amazon Valley, two small streams occasionally do spring from a single source. On the other hand, it is entirely contrary to the laws of hydrography that two or more full-grown rivers should either leave a lake and depart across country in different directions or, except in the case of deltas, owe their origin to the separation of the waters of a single large stream. Classical and medieval geographers, however, were not acquainted with this law, and the words of the Bible justified the writers of geographical books, even down to as late a date as the eighteenth century, in making broad rivers divide into separate branches and wander at random over the country.

Giraldus Cambrensis noted several other peculiarities of rivers.[111] For example, he remarked that the stream at Wicklow which flows across the harbor (we may presume in a channel through mud flats) is brackish at ebb tide; a similar river at Arklow is fresh.[112] Tide water, he said, does not mingle with the River Conway in North Wales.[113] Elsewhere he observed that the term *aber* in Welsh is applied to all those places where one stream flows into another.[114] The River Dee is not affected by rains, but the winds make it rise.[115] It changes its bed every year, and, as its course forms the boundary between England and Wales, these changes are interpreted as omens foretelling whether the English or the Welsh are going to be the more successful in their combats with each other during the succeeding year.[116]

The Nile Flood

In his consideration of the problem of the flood of the Nile, Abelard gives a curious example of the symbolic interpretation of scriptural and geographic matters which was also characteristic of the writings of Bernard of Clairvaux.[117] Isidore had followed earlier classical authorities in describing the flood as due to the building up, by the etesian winds, of sand bars at the mouth of the river during the winter.[118] Abelard, from Bede's rendering of Isidore's text,[119] adopted the same theory in his discussion of the Nile in the *Expositio in hexaemeron*.[120] He also discussed the Nile flood in a sermon on the text, "And the Lord, the God of hosts, is He who toucheth the earth, and it shall melt: and all that dwell therein shall mourn: and it shall rise up as a river and shall run down as the river of Egypt" (Amos ix, 5). In the sermon [121] he compared the rising of the Lord at the resurrection to the Nile: as the river fructifies the land, so the Lord strengthened the despairing hearts of his disciples. Abelard then quoted the passage from Bede just mentioned, and proceeded to interpret it as follows: The Nile coming down from Paradise is like unto the wisdom of God descending from above to give us to drink as from a fountain. Egypt is like unto the carnal darkness of this world. Its river enters the sea through seven mouths, which are obstructed when the wind blows and causes the backing up of the waters that can find no outlet. Thus, after the resurrection of the Lord but before the sevenfold grace of his spirit could find its way out into the broad sea of the nations, it was impeded as were the waters of the Nile. In other words, the apostles, through fear of the Jews, were held in Judea blinded, as it were, and for some time were not permitted to go forth as if from Egypt and through their preaching to bring about a rebirth of mankind. What does the wind represent, Abelard asks, if not the temptation of the devil? And what the sand, if not those men who at the turning of the ages wavered this way and that, held fast by earthly desires and temptations? [122]

It is hardly necessary to point out the contrast between this sort of geographical speculation and that of William of Conches. Better perhaps than any other text with which the writer is familiar, these ideas of Abelard illustrate that absorption, so often characteristic of medieval thought, of scientific and geographical interests into those of theology.

Lakes

Abundance of lakes is characteristic of glaciated countries like New England, Switzerland, Scotland, Sweden, Wales, and Ireland. Giraldus Cambrensis was impressed by the number of lakes in Ireland, where, he says,[123] they are more numerous than in any other part of the world. Giraldus and Gervase of Tilbury describe many lacustrine marvels.

In tracing the history of Ireland, Giraldus says [124] that about three hundred years after the Deluge four ponds suddenly broke forth from the bowels of the earth and that this was repeated at the time of the third colonization of Ireland under Neimhith.[125] Two ponds in Wales [126] were said to have burst their bounds and overflowed the neighborhood on the night of the death of Henry I. Before a great war, during which a province of central Wales was ravaged, a certain lake turned green, and old men described a similar portent just before the devastation of Wales by "Hoel, son of Moreduc" (Howel, son of Meredith).[127] The Lake of Brecknock in Wales appears sometimes a greenish color and sometimes ruddy as if penetrated by veins of blood.[128] Perhaps Giraldus was reminded of this by the mud-streaked appearance of mountain tarns after a rain, but it is less easy to explain the buildings, pastures, gardens, and orchards which he declares were occasionally visible beneath the surface. On the other hand, all who are familiar with inland waters in cold latitudes know the booming sounds they emit when frozen, which Giraldus compares to the moaning of a large herd of animals. These noises, he said, were caused by the sudden outrush of air imprisoned beneath the ice. At the top of Mount Snowdon, according to Giraldus, there are two lakes, one containing a floating island blown by the winds.[129] The most interesting lake with which Giraldus deals, however, is Lough Neagh in Ireland. This, he said,[130] lies in Ulster and is of remarkable size, thirty miles by fifteen. Though the relative proportions are right, the actual size is exaggerated, the dimensions being fifteen English miles long by from five to eight broad. The origin of the lake he attributed to an inundation that came as a punishment for the unnatural crimes of the natives of the region. This led him to a comparison of the story of Lough Neagh with the Biblical history of the destruction of the Pentapolis and the origins of the Dead Sea.

The Dead Sea has always exerted a potent fascination over the minds of men. The uncanny natural features of its basin, and the terrible story associated with them, have been objects of curiosity from the very earliest times. Gervase of Tilbury goes into some detail on the subject.[131] The five cities, he says, were submerged, on account of the sins of their inhabitants, in a salt and sterile lake called the Dead Sea, where neither bird nor fish can live. The sea is open to no ship; nay, it even rises over everything not impregnated with bitumen, probably because of the living men within it. If any one by any means immerses a living creature in it, the living being immediately leaps out.[132] A burning torch will float on the lake, an extinct one will sink. There was certainly an infernal quality about the Dead Sea, and it was even supposed that beneath its waters there was an entrance into Hell.

Gervase tells of the discovery of another mouth of Hell near Pozzuoli in southern Italy.[133] A bishop John of Pozzuoli was said to have discovered a pond whose waters were opaque but would become clear and translucent when oil was thrown upon them. Exploring about its shores one day, the bishop heard the sounds of lamentation coming from beneath the waters and, casting oil upon them, was horrified to behold, far down in the depths, the gateway to the infernal regions! Elsewhere[134] Gervase tells of a lake on the summit of Mount Cavagum (Canigou) in Catalonia, inhabited by devils, who raise a storm when stones are thrown in to disturb them.

CHAPTER IX

THE LANDS

The inquiring curiosity of men as well as of children is not first stimulated by those things which seem most usual and commonplace. The latter are taken for granted. Science originates rather in the wonder aroused by the extraordinary or by the impressive. Only after a long process of development does it turn to the study of the homely and the obvious.

The truth of this is illustrated in the medieval geography of the lands. Geomorphology, or the science of land forms, was very much in its infancy during our period and for many centuries thereafter. Only rarely did the man of the Middle Ages seek for an explanation of the origin of the familiar features of the earth's surface which he saw around him day by day. If he described a landscape in terms that often reveal love of its beauty or, at least, appreciation of its productive capacity, he was almost totally blind to the possibilities of profounder analysis of its nature. A plain was a plain, a valley a valley because God had made it so.

The present chapter will deal mainly with the character of these external, unscientific descriptions of land forms. The attempt will be made, however, to point out a few notable exceptions to the general rule, a few cases where men sought for a deeper meaning in the aspects of nature than the meaning written upon the surface.

CLASSIFICATION OF LAND AREAS

Quantitative and Qualitative Subdivisions

There are two ways of subdividing and classifying areas of land, the quantitative and the qualitative.

Adelard of Bath gives us an example of a quantitative subdivision where he tells in his *De eodem et diverso* [1] that the inventor of geometry split the known world into parts (or, perhaps, continents), the parts into provinces, the provinces into regions, the regions into localities, the localities into territories, the territories into fields, the fields into centuries, and the centuries into *jugera* (acres).

The author of the *De imagine mundi*, borrowing from Isidore,[2] makes a qualitative subdivision.[3] Land, he says, may be grouped under six different heads, *terra* being the name applied to the entire element of earth. The six kinds of *terra* are: (1) *tellus*, fertile; (2) *humus*, infertile, because of an excess of moisture; (3) *arida*, waterless, like Libya, dried up by the sun; (4) *sicca*, rather less dry than *arida*, but where, nevertheless, all precipitation quickly disappears, as in Judea; (5) *solum*, so called from its solidity, as mountainous land (*a soliditate ut sunt montana*); and, finally (6) *ops*, or wealthy land, like that of India, where gold and gems abound.[4]

In addition to such variations in the character of the lands, it was a common view that certain localities are by nature either peculiarly noxious or else peculiarly free from poisons. Gervase of Tilbury notes [5] an area near Pozzuoli which resembled a dried-up swamp but proved fatal to all animals venturing upon it. Elsewhere [6] he repeats, in connection with the tree of life spoken of by Alexander in his supposed letter to Aristotle, a widespread tradition of a land where no man could die even though he were decrepit with old age and might wish for relief from the cares of this world.[7] The *Image du monde* [8] attributes a similar quality to an island in the northern seas. When the inhabitants wished to die they had themselves taken to Tylle (Thule), where they might expire in peace. Giraldus Cambrensis describes [9] such an island in a lake in Ireland, as well as an island where no females could live.

Giraldus Cambrensis' Comparison of East and West

Probably, however, the most striking study of the varying qualities of different regions is Giraldus Cambrensis' elaborate comparison of Orient and Occident.[10] In Chapter VII we discussed this writer's belief that the atmosphere of the West is far healthier than that of the East. But not only is the air better, he asserted, but also the land itself, and of all the lands Ireland is the most healthy. No venomous reptiles can exist in the Emerald Isle. Giraldus attributed this phenomenon not to the beneficent work of St. Patrick in driving out the snakes [11] (this story, he said, was merely a pleasant fiction) but rather to some natural deficiency in Irish soil that had existed long before St. Patrick's time. He explained further that no poisonous reptiles could survive in Ireland even when they were brought there;[12] toads, when carried over on ships, burst open as soon as they are thrown ashore; and the dust of Ireland, when sprinkled on poisonous creatures of any sort, kills them instantly.[13] The East, on the other hand, Giraldus called [14] a fountain of poisons (*fons venenorum*), and he waxed most eloquent on its terrors:[15] poisonous animals abound, the waters are always polluted, and death lurks on every hand; but the farther away from this Oriental source of poison one travels, the less its effect, until in the extreme West it exerts no influence at all, just as the sun's rays are weaker the farther one goes from beneath the zodiac.

This distinction between Eastern and Western climate and conditions of terrain may to a limited extent have been based on actual observation. Undoubtedly the pilgrim and Crusader suffered more from disease and hardship when traveling in the Orient than they did at home, because they were not acclimatized to Levantine conditions of life and did not understand what was necessary for the preservation of health; and this may well have produced the unfavorable impression of the East which found its way in exaggerated form into the pages of the *Topographia Hiberniae.*

MOUNTAINS

Mountains are the most imposing natural features of the lands.[16] Though there did not exist in the Middle Ages anything comparable to that love of mountains for their own sake which developed later and of which we see an early manifestation in the ascent of Mont Ventoux by Petrarch in April, 1336, the very bulk of the hills, nevertheless, impressed men's imaginations, and medieval literature is full of notices concerning mountains.

Origin of Mountains

In regard to their origin, Peter Comestor asserts that the mountains may not have been as high at the time of the Flood as they now are,[17] and Gervase of Tilbury cites the opinion of some that there were no mountains at all on the face of the earth before the Deluge.[18] Bartholomew Anglicus[19] conjectured that in the very beginning the earth was a plain covered with waters, the movements of which produced the valleys, while the heights were the ridges that remained separating the valleys; many mountains also were the result of great telluric convulsions and were full of caverns that give forth immense volumes of water and form the sources of rivers.

In a translation by Alfred of Sareshel of an Arabic work,[20] perhaps that of Avicenna, we have a strikingly modern description of the geological processes resulting in the production of mountains by the forces of erosion and by the accumulation of soil and earth. "Mountains may arise from two causes, either from uplifting of the ground, such as takes place in earthquakes or from the effects of running water and wind in hollowing out valleys in soft rocks and leaving the hard rocks prominent, which has been the effective process in the case of most hills. Such changes must have taken long periods of time, and possibly the mountains are now diminishing in size. What proves that water has been the main agent in bringing about these transformations of the surface is the occurrence in many rocks of the impressions of aquatic and other animals. The yellow earth that clothes the surface of the mountains is not of the same origin as the framework of the ground underneath it but arises from the decay of organic remains, mingled with earthy materials transported by the water. Perhaps these materials were originally in the sea which once overspread all the land" (Geikie's translation).[21]

If, in reading the above passage, we feel that we are dealing with ideas that could well stand in the light of modern science and that in this passage at least geomorphology has emerged from its infancy, we are brought back to the Middle Ages when we turn to Rupert of Deutz's teleological explanation of the reasons why God created deep valleys and high mountains on the land. According to this mystic, these features were made to serve as a protection to the human wanderer upon the surface of the earth from the violence of the winds which would otherwise have unlimited power over all things, as they do on the Libyan desert or on the ocean.[22]

Their Size and Height

The fact that, great as mountains may appear to men, they are in reality but insignificant in comparison with the size of the entire earth, was partially appreciated by the author of the *De imagine mundi*, when he remarked[23] that, if we could look down on the earth from the air above, the entire height of the mountains and depth of the valleys would seem less than the width of the fingers of one who holds a very large ball in his hand.

We find occasional speculations regarding altitudes. Peter Comestor, followed by Gervase of Tilbury, asserted[24] that Olympus reaches up into a region of calm, windless air; and William of Conches held[25] that the presence of snow on mountains is due to the rarity of the air at high altitudes. Gervase stated,[26] on the authority of Posthumianus in the *Dialogue* of Sulpicius Severus[27] (a historian of the fourth century of our era), that Sinai is so lofty that its peak is very near the heavens and that consequently it is impossible to go there.[27a]

Miraculous Mountains

Mountains and hills might have miraculous qualities. Giraldus Cambrensis told[28] of heights in Mona and in the northern part of Britain, beyond the Humber, over the crests of which no shouts could be heard; and Gervase of Tilbury described[29] Mount Cavagum (Canigou) in Catalonia, with a miraculous lake, the dwelling place of devils, on its summit; on one peak there lies perpetual snow and ice in a spot where the sun never shines, and a river of golden sand flows from its base. In the Romance of Alexander, the conqueror was said to have passed near a mountain which made brave men cowards and cowards brave.[30] On another occasion,[31] Alexander and his army became lost in a perilous valley among wild peaks; they could not find their way out unless one man sacrificed himself for the others by remaining in the valley. Alexander himself volunteered to remain, and the army escaped in the midst of fearful tempests; but subsequently Alexander was conducted out by a devil whom he found in the place and to whom he did a good turn.

Accurate Observation of Orographic Phenomena

On the other hand, during our period there was not a little reasonably accurate observation of the phenomena of mountains. Bernard Sylvester, for example, pointed out that mountains are bad plowland largely because of the thinness of the soil on their steep slopes.[32] Gervase of Tilbury noted that many of the high hills of Wales, though they might have firm and rocky bases, were characterized by watery and boggy summits.[33] Giraldus Cambrensis pictures the characteristics of the Welsh hills and brings out their combination of crag and pasture land. In one passage he tells of Mount Ereri—called by the English "Snowdon," or mount of snows—which has such an extent of pasture lands upon it that it could supply the flocks of the whole of Wales.[34] The land of Meiryonidd (Merioneth) he spoke of as a wild, rough region, with mountains so broken and irregular that it frequently took all day for the shepherds to gather together in one spot,[35] even though they might have been within earshot of one another in the morning.

Appreciation of the Beauty of Mountains

It is not hard to believe that during our period some men had the beginnings of a genuinely esthetic appreciation of the beauty of mountains. Bernard Sylvester tells of the orographic systems of the world in terms not lacking in color and poetic appreciation.[36] He writes that the world is strung with mountains like nerves in a body and goes on to enumerate and describe them: "Clear Olympus, which looks down on the clouds; Parnassus, with double yoke; Lebanon, in its woods;" Sinai, Athos, Eryx, Pindus, Othrys, Pelion, Caucasus. Though he merely repeats classical names and classical designations, the whole long passage could hardly have been written by a man wholly blind to the grandeur of his subject. Giraldus Cambrensis tells about the Church of St. David, now known as Llanthoni Abbey, in the midst of the hills of southern Wales. "Here the monks, when they sit down in their cloister to rest and take the air, see in all directions over the high gables of their roofs the peaks of the mountains bounding their horizon and, as it were, touching the sky. They see the wild deer pasturing on their summits, and at about the hour of the prime or shortly before in clear weather they see the sun appearing over the mountain crests."[37] This certainly shows that the writer found delight in the restful qualities of a highland landscape.

If Walter of Châtillon had not at some time in his life felt the elation of a view at dawn from a mountain summit, he could hardly have written the brilliant description in the *Alexandreis* where he tells how Alexander, at the moment when the sun began to gleam upon the surface of the sea, rushed forth from his camp and climbed upon a steep peak whence his vision embraced the bounds of Asia. Looking out over fields green with crops, over many a forested mountain and meadow lavish in its rank grass, over many a city with its encircling walls and many a vineyard and elm tree entwined with vines, the conqueror exclaimed: "Enough! my friends: this land alone satisfies me. To you I leave Europe and your native country."[38]

Religious Attitude Towards Mountains

Ganzenmüller in his book on the feeling for nature in the Middle Ages cites several important texts which illustrate the religious attitudes towards mountains that must have prevailed throughout our period. We shall see a little later that Bernard of Clairvaux in one of his letters spoke of mountains as symbolizing the aspirations of the haughty and worldly.[39] But others believed that there is a godly quality about the heights. The biographer of bishop Altmann of Passau, writing in the twelfth century, tells us that one day the bishop, accompanied by an immense crowd of people, climbed a mountain near Mautern in Lower Austria firmly believing that those who serve God here below will climb to the corners and bounds of heaven.[40] Eadmer records of Anselm of Canterbury that on one occasion, when the latter happened to find himself on a high summit, he was so refreshed by the clear air and solitude that he remarked: "Here is my resting place: here will I dwell."[41] St. Francis of Assisi must have felt the same mystic love of mountains that he felt for birds and animals and that he expressed so beautifully in his hymn to Brother Sun, for did he not in 1224 go into retreat at La Verna, a remote, forest-covered peak in the Casentino,[41a] and did he not, as he left, turn back and bless the mountain as he had blessed the birds? At the present time the lower slopes of La Verna are bare and sun-baked. The summit, buttressed by massive ledges, is covered with a beautiful wood, and from it the eye wanders over Tuscany, across the ranges of the Apennines, and to the eastward catches a glimpse of the Adriatic. That St. Francis should deliberately have chosen this place of exceptional charm for a retreat; that he should have made a long, hard journey to reach it; and, above all, that here he received the supreme glory of his life reveal to us something far deeper than mere esthetic satisfaction in the beauty of nature. To St. Francis the quiet summit of the mountain was a symbol of the peace and tranquillity of heaven and of eternity.

Normal Medieval Feeling About Mountains

But for the most part mountainous regions were regarded as places of grimness and horror. The many journeys over the Alps made in the Middle Ages by pilgrim, soldier, and trader brought forth few comments on aught else than the hardships of the way. Otto of Freising tells[42] how in September, 1155, Frederick Barbarossa's army passed through a narrow gorge in the Alps above Verona where robbers impeded its passage. Otto's description is very brief and simple; the road, he says, runs between high cliffs on one side and the unfordable river on the other. Gunther in the *Ligurinus*[43] elaborates on this by the copious addition of words emphasizing the terrors of the route: the narrow track wide enough for only one person at a time to proceed; on one side the "cloud-swept crags of the jagged

Alps," on the other a chaotic, whirling stream; these combined to fill the passer-by with fear.

Perhaps the most striking narrative of a mountain passage dating from our period tells of the crossing of the Great St. Bernard Pass by the abbot of St. Trond and the archdeacon of Liége in 1128.[44] Having celebrated Christmas at Piacenza, the travelers arrived at the beginning of winter in the village of Restopolis (Étrouble) in the valley leading to the pass, Mons Jovis; here they were snowbound until after New Year's Day. Finally the native guides were able to conduct them on to St. Rhémy farther up the valley close to the final ascent. "Frozen as it were in the jaws of death" they remained here a day and a night, constantly menaced by the gravest danger. The small village was full of travelers, many of whom had been overwhelmed by the avalanches which kept falling from the high cliffs on either side. Some of these unfortunates had been suffocated, and others so badly hurt that they were disabled.[45] The ecclesiastics were obliged to spend several miserable days in this "accursed spot," but at last they were able to prevail on their guides to lead them onward. A procession was organized, the guides in the lead, clad in thick felt hats, gloves, and with spikes in their boots to enable them to cross the ice; then came other storm-bound travelers; the horses and the clergy, who were physically the weakest, brought up the rear. Just before leaving, the party stopped for mass in a chapel. While the service was going on, ten of the guides who had gone ahead were engulfed by an avalanche and killed. This so alarmed the prelates that they retreated to Restopolis; but at last good weather came, and on January 6 they managed to get across the pass with no great difficulty.

In 1188 John of Bremble, a monk of Christ Church, Canterbury, visited the Great St. Bernard Pass. He wrote about it as follows to his sub-prior, Geoffrey, and gave expression to what Gribble correctly calls the "normal medieval view of mountains:"[46] "I have been on the Mount of Jove; on the one hand looking up to the heaven of mountains, on the other shuddering at the hell of the valleys, feeling myself so much nearer heaven that I was sure that my prayer would be heard. 'Lord,' I said, 'restore me to my brethren, that I may tell them that they come not to this place of torment.' Place of torment, indeed, where the marble pavement of the stony ground is ice alone, and you cannot set your foot safely; where, strange to say, although it is so slippery that you cannot stand, the death into which there is every facility for a fall is certain death" (Gribble's translation).

Glaciers

As a general rule the medieval traveler took no interest in glaciers. Journeys across the Alps were such hazardous undertakings that even the traveler of scientific tastes could have had little opportunity or inclination to investigate the phenomena of the ice. A passage in the *Gesta Danorum* of Saxo Grammaticus, therefore, is doubly remarkable because it gives us some specific details regarding the glaciers of Iceland. After speaking of the ice floes breaking on the shore, Saxo writes: "There is also there another type of ice which runs between the rocks and passes of the mountains. This undergoes certain changes: it is subject to a process of transposition in which the upper parts sink down to the bottom and the lower parts arise to the surface. It is reliably asserted that persons who happened to be passing over the flat surface of the ice have fallen into crevasses and gaping fissures and that, soon after, their dead bodies have been recovered without a trace of ice above them. This circumstance has led many people to believe that whomsoever the icy caldron takes into its lowest depths, it will deliver again shortly after upside down."[47] Though this passage shows that Saxo did not have a clear conception of what he was trying to describe, it was certainly based upon some knowledge, though slight, of glacial phenomena. It is a well-known fact that on its arrival at the lower portion of a glacier, ice that at higher elevations was at the bottom often comes to the surface and brings with it materials scraped from the glacial bed or objects that may have fallen into the crevasses. This passage of Saxo has been cited as the earliest occasion in literature in which the motion of glacial ice was recognized.[48]

VOLCANOES AND EARTHQUAKES

Visits to Volcanoes

Volcanoes are a type of mountain that attracted particular attention, and, though the men of medieval and ancient times were certainly not mountain climbers,[49] there are a few records of their having deliberately visited volcanoes out of curiosity or scientific interest. It is well known that Pliny the Elder perished in an attempt to investigate the eruption of Vesuvius in 79 A. D., and during the twelfth century the Sicilian scholar and administrator, Henricus Aristippus, is said to have made a careful study of the volcanic phenomena of Etna, not without danger.[50] In the legend of St. Brandan's voyage we find an account of the manner in which a companion of the saint lost his life in an attempt to scale a fiery peak on an island in the northern seas.[51]

The writer of the second verse redaction of the *Image du monde* also tells us that he himself had made the ascent of Mongibel (Etna), and his observations are so detailed and realistic that we cannot but believe that he is telling the truth.[52] His object was to see what comes out of the smoking mouth of the mountain. He noticed that the fire which issues forth soon turns to vapor and smoke; that the rocks of the mountain resemble "foam of iron" (*escume de fer*—pumice or some other volcanic ejecta); that the land about the mountain is broken (*esparse*) and appears to be blasted and burned (*bruslée et arse*). The volcanic heat touched (*ting*) his bare hand, and a gentle sweat broke out over his body; but near the summit he was able to slake his thirst from frozen snow. On the way down he had the curious experience of hearing thunder in the clouds below him. When he finally got back to the city, the people thought he was a fool (*musard*) for venturing into a place with such a bad reputation. He adds that some people say that Mongibel is the highest mountain in the world. That it is much higher than appears from below, he himself had demonstrated. It can be seen from no less than two hundred leagues away at sea.

Volcanic Region of Southern Italy and Sicily

The two volcanic regions known to the medieval world were Southern Italy and Sicily on the one hand and Iceland on the other. Gervase of Tilbury describes Vesuvius and the volcanic features about Naples;[53] he says that in the vicinity of Pozzuoli there are hills with sands near the summit so hot that they hinder persons from ascending across them. On the very outskirts of Naples he speaks of a high mountain, called Mons Virginum, overlooking the sea and the surrounding country. In the month of May it belches forth a terrifying smoke with firebrands that turn to the color of carbon when burnt out. This would seem to indicate the presence of a vent connecting the mountain with the infernal regions. ("Unde illic quoddam inferni terreni spiraculum asserunt ebulline.") The south wind blows a hot dust from the volcano which ruins the crops and fruits of the neighborhood and tends to render the land barren and sterile. To this fairly clear description of a volcano Gervase adds a fantastic tale about the preventive measures which Virgil [54] took to avert the disaster caused by the hot winds; the poet erected a statue holding a horn which automatically tooted whenever the south wind began to blow, and for some reason repulsed the blast.[55] Recently, however, the statue had either gone to pieces with age or else had been destroyed by malice, for the damage done by the volcanic blasts was once more repeated as in bygone days.

The traveler Conrad of Querfurt looked with interest upon the volcanic features of the Phlegraean Fields to the northwest of Naples and drew attention to the confused labyrinth of passages in the interior of Monte Barbaro and to the hot springs, subterranean channels of boiling water, and other wonders of the region.[56]

Guy of Bazoches, who passed through Sicily on the way to the Holy Land, included in a letter to his nephews a striking word picture of Etna. "Sicily," he wrote, "fears not to pierce the clouds with its immense mountain summits. Etna towers above all of these with its flaming crests upon which the opposing elements strive with each other tirelessly and indomitably in an immense conflict. For though Etna incessantly sends forth scorching heat, its summit, none the less, is white with snow, and with a wintry garment it covers its burning shoulders." [57] Guy mentioned also the "Isles of Vulcan" in the Sicilian Sea, "the interior of which were said to glow with eternal fires. Eolus once dwelt in these isles and was in the habit of dispensing their smokes, which were stirred up by the winds, and hence he came to be called the king of the winds." [58] The *Image du monde* refers to a volcano two leagues distant at sea from Sicily; this may have been Vulcano or possibly Stromboli, though in any case the distance was underestimated.[59]

Michael Scot on the Eolian Isles and Etna

Michael Scot brought together information about the volcanoes of the Eolian (Lipari) Islands and of Sicily which he included in a discourse on natural phenomena that he prepared for his patron Frederick II.[60] He speaks of "Strongulus" (Stromboli), "a mountain which is in the midst of the sea," of "Strongulinus" (Strombolicchio), "Vulcanus" (Vulcano), "Vulcaninus" (Vulcanello?), "Moncibellus" (Etna), and the isle of Lipari, "on which there are all manner of fine trees and grains." From the summit of Stromboli and "Strongulinus," a lesser mountain than Stromboli, great fiery flames are continuously emitted. The other four, he declares, emit flames only when the south wind (*Auster*) blows; and, when the flames cease, a mighty smoke issues from them. The eruptions are often accompanied by showers of scorched rock and sometimes with roots of trees (? *sticiones lignorum*) and cinders; the ground is covered and the air obscured as stream waters are clouded with sand. Glowing bombs are hurled aloft like sparks from a furnace; when these fall to the ground they burst into fragments, great and small, and in these fragments is found the pumice which writers use. This pumice floats on the sea and is carried ashore, where the people collect it for building walls and for uses similar to those to which we put bricks. Liquid sulphur is also gathered by sailors from the surface of the sea thereabouts in baskets and bowls. The nearer this may be obtained to the mountains whence it boils forth, the better its quality.

Volcanoes of Iceland

In the *Topographia Hiberniae* of Giraldus Cambrensis we find a description of the volcanic eruptions of Iceland.[61] After remarking that thunder and lightning are rare in the northern isle, he goes on to explain that there is another and even worse affliction than these; every year or two fire bursts out of a certain part of the island like a whirlwind with a violent gale and melts everything in its path; he adds that the cause of this phenomenon and whether it originated above or below ground are unknown. Into two manuscripts of Solinus, the oldest of which dates from the twelfth century, there was inserted some additional information about the northern isles. We are told that the marine ice on the coasts of Iceland "ignites itself on collision, and when it is ignited it burns like wood" (Nansen's translation).[62] Adam of Bremen had also spoken of ice that appeared to be black and dry on account of its age and burned when kindled.[63] Though it has been suggested that this impression may have been derived from mists arising from the ice, the story was perhaps, as Nansen observes, "due to statements about volcanoes and boiling springs which have been confused with it. The black color and dryness of the ice may have been due to confusion with lava or with floating pumice stone in the sea."[64]

More definite information concerning the volcanic activity of Iceland reached Saxo Grammaticus about a century after the time of Adam of Bremen. Saxo refers to a mountain there which perpetually glows like a star with its burning flame, and it seemed to him no less marvelous that the eruption could occur in a region of such extreme cold.[65] In the *Historia Norwegiae* the fiery outbreaks of Mons Casule (Hekla) are likened to those of Etna, and an immense submarine eruption is described; over a space three miles wide the sea had boiled and bubbled as in a caldron; the earth was upheaved and out of the submarine depths there arose fiery fumes, and a mighty mountain sprang from the sea.[66] This perhaps refers to a submarine eruption that took place off Cape Reykyanes in 1211.[67]

In the *King's Mirror* the volcanic activity of Iceland is compared with that of Sicily, and the curious statement is made that, unlike the subterranean fires of the Mediterranean isle, those of Iceland will burn neither wood nor earth. On the other hand, they will burn the hardest stones and pieces of rock just as easily as oil.[68]

St. Brandan's Visits to Volcanic Isles

St. Brandan in the course of his wanderings came across two fiery islands.[69] The first was eight days' sail to the north of the mysterious crystal column we have already mentioned. It was a rough, treeless, and rocky isle covered with the forges of smiths. Though the saint wished to keep clear of this dangerous spot, a wind sprang up which drove his vessel towards it. One of the smiths threw a gigantic mass of molten slag at the voyagers; but luckily he missed the ship, and the slag fell into the sea, sending up huge clouds of steam. This was a signal for all the smiths to start heaving lumps of molten ore at the vessel, running back and forth from their forges to heat them. Soon the entire island was burning and blazing like a furnace, and the sea around boiling like a kettle. The saint and his party miraculously escaped from this peril, but throughout the entire day they could hear an immense din and shouting from the isle; and even when they had drifted out of sight the tumult came to their ears, and their nostrils were afflicted by a terrible stench. Soon the wanderers approached the second fiery isle; their first sight of it revealed a mighty mountain on the northern horizon, with its peak enveloped in what appeared to be a thin cloud but in reality was smoke. They landed on the shores of the island, and one of Brandan's companions who endeavored to climb the steep, high crags and investigate the summit was burned to death by the fires. Happily for the others, a wind arose which drove the ship southward, whence they saw the island now clear of smoke and spouting flames into the air, so that the whole mountain appeared to be aglow.

It has been suggested that these stories were derived from classical and Celtic mythology. The first island brings to mind pagan tales mingled with Christian traditions of devils and the infernal regions; perhaps it owes something to the Homeric account of the isle of the Cyclops. But why, we may ask, did Irish writers place such fiery phenomena in the cold and rainy seas surrounding their home? Is it not possible that early Irish poets had heard vaguely of the volcanoes of Iceland and that nebulous reports of them, modified by the influence of classical and Christian traditions, took the form which we find in the legend of St. Brandan's voyagings? May it not be significant that the fiery islands of St. Brandan were reached only after northerly wanderings?

Volcanoes As Gates of Hell

Volcanoes were often popularly supposed to be the entrances into Hell or else little independent scenes of punishment and dwelling places of devils. Michael Scot would not decide "whether the gate to the lower regions is" in the volcanoes of the Lipari Islands and Sicily "or in the northern isle seen by St. Brandan. . . . " But, he said, "whatever the way in, Hell is in the bowels of the earth, and there is no way out" (Haskins).[70] St. Brandan, seven days' journey to the south of the second island just described, found Judas sitting alone on a rock in the midst of the sea.[71] In the course of their conversation, Judas explained that he was imprisoned every day excepting Sundays and Christmas in the mountain which they had seen erupting. On these days, through the infinite mercy of Jesus Christ, he was permitted to come out and cool off. The bishop of Pozzuoli, Gervase of Tilbury tells us,[72] on several occasions heard the wailings and lamentations of the damned during his walks in the volcanic country near his city and had actually seen the gates of Hell in a lake near by. Icelandic mythology conceived of a gigantic hell under and inside of Mount Hekla.[73] The *King's Mirror* placed in the volcanic fires of Iceland a scene of punishment for souls.[74] In addition it speaks of a cold hell, belief in which seems natural to Northern peoples and is also expressed in Saxo Grammaticus' description of the moanings and wailings to be heard in the clashing of ice floes on the cliffs and crags of the Icelandic coast.[75]

Causes of Vulcanism

Medieval writers did not add much to what the Greeks and Romans had said in regard to the causes of vulcanism. In general they accepted the theories of Isidore and Pliny. Sicily, a typical volcanic region, was supposed to be cavernous and full of sulphur and bitumen strata which, when ignited and kept burning by the air, throw off smoke, vapor, and flames and, when a strong wind blows upon them, vomit forth masses of sand and rocks.[76] Gervase of Tilbury elaborates confusedly on this theme,[77] saying that there are many fires and earthquakes in Sicily because beneath that land there is a mighty abyss, the bottom of which is unknown to man. Near at hand are immense caverns and broad caves, wherein winds are conceived from the whirling of the waters, for mountains and waters create winds—mountains by offering an obstacle to the air. Though he does not say so specifically, we may conclude that Gervase believed that earthquakes and other volcanic phenomena were caused by these winds trying to escape from the interior of the earth. This was certainly the opinion of Michael Scot, who pointed out that masses of sulphur and other white-hot rocks (*petre calidissime*) are made to burn by the native heat of the earth's interior and by the winds which enter the earth's crust in remote regions (*in extremis partibus*) and force their way downward through passages, tubes, and caverns. These winds are volatilized and given explosive force by contact with the sulphur and hot rocks. When they burst forth again into the atmosphere they have all the attributes of fire and flame—sparks, ashes, cinders—and are supposed by many people to be genuine fire, though as a matter of fact they are by nature quite different because the waters ever present in the subterranean cavities fail to extinguish them. So intense is the heat produced by the sulphur and other combustible materials that the world would be entirely consumed by the winds that would blow over them if they were on the earth's surface. Hence it is a great mercy of God that he has hidden them away in the depths of the ground and has thus made impossible the destruction of the world by this cause and that he has permitted men to dwell and cultivate their fields on the mountains beneath which such evil forces are buried.[78]

Alexander Neckam defined a volcano as a subterranean fire

which, though bound to the earth with one foot, seeks to spring aloft with the other. He believed that volcanic rocks contain gases within them which when kindled produce eruptions.[79]

Though these passages reveal to us belief during the Crusading age in the presence of heat and fire in the inside of the earth, the teachings of Plato and many of the Church Fathers that the sources of volcanic fires spring from immense subterranean reservoirs of fire do not appear to have been given much credence. Though the earth's crust and even its innermost heart might be interpenetrated with cavities into which air, water, and fire enter, confidence in the essential solidity and massiveness of the earth prevailed, and theories which would admit of the presence of bodies of water or of fire of any great extent within the heaviest and most solid of the elements were not regarded as worthy of serious consideration. Hell, however, was almost universally placed at the very center of the earth by medieval theologians and geographers alike.[80]

Earthquakes

The majority of medieval writers believed that earthquakes are caused by the same physical forces as those which produce volcanic eruptions, the violent stirring of winds,[81] vapors, or exhalations within the earth's crust.[82] In the *Quaestiones naturales* of Adelard of Bath, which takes the form of a dialogue between uncle and nephew, the nephew finds it difficult to reconcile the stability and immobility of the earth, which his uncle had just demonstrated, with the well-known fact that the earth sometimes quakes and trembles. To this Adelard replies that, while it is true that the earth may occasionally move in particular localities, it does not move as a whole[83] and that earthquakes are caused by the air contained within the earth and have nothing whatever to do with the intrinsically stable qualities of the earth as a globe. He then proceeds to give the Aristotelian explanation of the causes of earthquakes.[84] The *De imagine mundi*, followed by the *Image du monde* and by Bartholomew Anglicus,[85] also assigns the same causes; and William of Conches explains[86] that earthquakes are the result of waters descending into underground hollows where they encounter vapors, condensed into cloudlike form by the coldness of the earth's interior; these vapors, in turn, produce telluric movements by forcing their way to the surface. Neckam repeats much the same explanation but adds the usual allegorical lesson:[87] the land symbolizes the Church, which, although on the whole serene and firm, may well be shaken now and then by purely local troubles and disturbances.

The medieval chronicler took delight in mentioning prodigies of nature that came to his attention, and of these prodigies earthquakes were among the most striking. The *Gesta regis Henrici Secundi*, under the year 1178, records a terrific earthquake at Oxenhale in England: [88] some land owned by Hugh, bishop of Durham, rose up like a tower, so that its highest point was on a level with the summits of the hills and higher than the highest pinnacle of the churches (*templorum*); after remaining like this from nine o'clock until nightfall, it collapsed at sunset with a terrific noise that frightened all the onlookers. The earth then absorbed the tower of land and in its place there remained until the time of writing a well of immense depth as a perpetual testimony to the occurrence of this phenomenon. In the same chronicle, under the date of April 15, 1185,[89] we find a more typical and less fantastic description of an earthquake felt throughout almost the entire length of England; rocks were shattered, stone houses fell in ruins, and the metropolitan church of Lincoln was broken asunder from top to bottom.

DESERTS

The deserts of the Orient impressed the medieval writer in much the same way as mountains, by the obstacles and difficulties which they presented to the traveler. William of Tyre dilates [90] on the terrors of drought in the desert and explains how the Saracens carry in great sacks on camels water sufficient to serve man and beast for many days at a time; he pictures impressively the horrors of the sand storms that may spring up at any time. In the Egyptian desert, he says, the land is so dry and barren that no manner of tree can grow there. The features of the desert are also described in the *Letter of Prester John.*[91] This fabulous Christian potentate of the East tells us that in the great Sandy Sea which lies in his country the sands are disturbed by the wind and form endlessly moving waves like the waves of the real sea. But the analogy with the sea is carried a trifle too far when he goes on to assert that fish are found in the Sandy Sea. He adds that from certain mountains, three days' journey away, a river of stones flows down and, running three days a week, sweeps both rocks and logs into the Sandy Sea, but they disappear in the sands and are never seen again. If we remove the halo of fable surrounding all this, we discern here an account of a desert of dunes, with dry watercourses entering it, a feature common enough in southwestern Asia and northern Africa. On the whole, however, little was known of deserts in Western Europe in the Middle Ages, and, though the waste places of Asia and India are constantly mentioned in the Romance of Alexander, the descriptions of them are wholly fanciful.

ISLANDS

Origins

The men of the West at this time were familiar with many islands. Giraldus Cambrensis takes up the problem of the origin of the islands of the earth and in particular the question of whether they were formed at the time of the Deluge or long before or long after.[92] His opinion seems to have been that some time after the Flood the lands became replete with animal life and that it was then that the islands came into existence, not violently and suddenly but little by little out of alluvial deposits.[93] In his emphasis on the gradual and non-catastrophic manner of their formation, Giraldus by hazard enunciates a sound geological doctrine which contrasts favorably with the theories he elsewhere expresses about the violent and sudden appearance of lakes.

Miraculous Islands

Like mountains and lakes, islands were convenient topographic units to which the medieval mind was wont to attribute fabulous and supernatural qualities. Gervase of Tilbury, for example, describes a certain isle in the sea off the coast of the Kingdom of Arles—Lirniensis, perhaps the Isle de Lérins—where no worms ever are found.[94] He was unable to decide whether this was due to the extreme holiness of a colony of monks which once dwelt on the island or to some natural peculiarity of the soil. At all events, this reminds us of the tradition about the inability of poisonous reptiles or noxious animals of any kind to exist in Ireland.

Giraldus Cambrensis speaks of a floating island in a lake on the summit of Mount Snowdon.[95] This was said to be blown about by the winds, and shepherds were much startled now and then to see their cattle transported on it from one side of the lake to the other. Giraldus explains this reasonably enough as follows: a portion of the shore had become bound together and made firm and solid as if by ropes formed from the roots of the willow and other plants. After being gradually increased in size by the addition of alluvium it finally broke off. The violent winds prevalent in the vicinity then drove it back and forth over the surface of the lake. This story undoubtedly had a basis of truth, for it is well known that sod floats about on the surface of one of the lakes near Snowdon, but that it could carry cattle upon it is a decided exaggeration.

Islands of St. Brandan

The most marvelous of the islands mentioned in medieval legend were those which St. Brandan visited.[96] The first one he came to, a high and rocky crag rising abruptly out of the sea, was doubtless suggested to the mind of the poet by one of the forbidding islets in the seas off the western coast of Ireland. Thence the saint and his crew voyaged in turn to an island entirely covered with sheep, to one that proved to be the back of a gigantic fish called Jasconius, to one full of miraculous birds that could speak, to one that put them in mind of Paradise, to a rocky isle full of forges and smiths, to an isle where there dwelt a certain hermit, Paul, who had lived there forty years without food but for thirty years had been fed by a certain beast; [97] and finally the saint himself attained the island which was the goal of all his wanderings, the Saints' Land of Promise (Terra repromissionis sanctorum), or Paradise—a reminiscence perhaps of the Hesperides, or Happy Islands, of Greek mythology.

Giraldus describes an isle off the Irish coast which would seem to be akin to Brandan's Jasconius.[98] Doubts were raised as to whether this peculiar island was a whale or some other monster or whether it was really land; for some youths had tried to disembark upon it, but, just as they were about to set foot ashore, it disappeared beneath the waves. The next day it reappeared and the same thing was repeated. Finally, on the third day, one of the young men shot a red-hot arrow into it; this seems to have stabilized it, for the island did not disappear again and ultimately proved to be habitable. From this Giraldus argued that as fire is the most noble of the elements no phantasm can withstand its power.

INFLUENCES OF GEOGRAPHICAL ENVIRONMENT

On Plant and Animal Life

In the writings of the Crusading age we find a few scattered remarks on the relationship between geographical features and environment and the life of man and animals, or on those branches of our science now called biogeography and anthropogeography. The writings of Bernard Sylvester furnish us with some striking examples. The Platonic and realist conception of the unity of all matter, which was exemplified in the theory of a World Soul and expounded in vivid terms by Theodoric of Chartres, led Bernard in his *De mundi universitate* to emphasize the close interrelations of all natural phenomena and the influences of the various elements and parts of the universe upon each other. He stressed, for example, the importance of astrological influences, by attributing to the moon control over the tides and other terrestrial phenomena.[99] In geography he emphasized the influences of terrain on plant and animal life. Thus he says "fruitful land gives birth to wolves, desert to lions, arid land to serpents, woods to bees."[100] Elsewhere he explains how the plane tree grows in flat country, the alder in valleys, the box among rocks, the willow on the banks of streams, the fragrant cypress in the mountains, the sacred vine on the slopes, and the olive in well-worked loam.[101] Neckam also recognized that the growth of plants was governed by the qualities of the earth.[102] Only about the center of the globe is there really true earth; the surface which we cultivate is not true earth because it is intermingled with particles of air, fire, and other substances. Consequently it follows that in the same territory there may grow herbs by nature both warm and cold and that in certain places oats thrive well and in others barley.

There is a very striking passage in Hildegard's *Subtilitates* explaining in much detail the influence of various kinds of soil upon agriculture.[103] Hildegard asserts that there are divers types of soil (*terra*)—black, white, and red. White soil is pallid and sandy and contains much humidity in the form of large raindrops: because of this quality white soil produces great vines and apple orchards but is rather less well adapted for the raising of grains. The latter may better be cultivated upon soil characterized by humidity of finer texture and minuter drops. Black soil contains too much cold and dampness to produce more than a moderate yield; red soil, on the other hand, has the right balance of dampness and dryness and hence produces a quantity of fruits, which, however, through their very abundance fail to attain perfection. And so Hildegard proceeds with a discussion that would have been of a highly utilitarian character, had it only been based more directly upon the observation of the facts of nature.

On Man

The influence of geographical environment on man is also noted by some of the writers of our period. Otto of Freising explains [104] that the Lombards on entering Italy gave up their wild customs and adopted Italian ways, partly because they married native women but partly as a result of the nature of country and climate. Giraldus tells how the plains of southern Wales are far more pleasant to live in than those of the north.[105] The latter region, on the other hand, has not only better natural defenses but a richer soil and is more fertile in producing men of strength and power. Gunther in the *Ligurinus* [106] enlarged on Ragewin's simple description (in his continuation of Otto of Freising's *Gesta Friderici*) of the wild ferocity of the natives of Poland by saying that their fierceness and savagery is due partly to the nature of the soil and partly to the influence of their neighbors.

Topography As a Natural Defense

In the same connection these authors try to show that topography may often serve as a natural defense against hostile invaders. Giraldus speaks of Wales [107] as a country easily defensible because of the depth of its valleys and the immensity of its woods, waters, and swamps. The remnants of the ancient Britons who were driven here were able to hold out and preserve their independence against both Angles and Normans. On the other hand, those who were driven into the southern promontory (Cornwall), where the land was not by nature so easy to defend, yielded to the conqueror. In another connection [108] Giraldus speaks of the difficulties any one would encounter in trying to conquer such a rough country as Wales and one so well fortified by nature. Gervase of Tilbury also testifies to the strong natural defenses of Wales,[109] specifying how the Welsh, when enemies appear, take to the bog lands on the mountains, which they can easily cross through an agility resulting from long familiarity. Here they either escape from their enemies or lie in wait to inflict grave harm on them. Giraldus [110] tells that the islands in the lakes of Ireland were used for refuges as well as for dwelling places by the lords of the surrounding districts; and Ragewin [111] speaks of the natural defenses of Genoa, hemmed in on one side by mountains and on the other by the sea.

Theory of the Westward Flow of Civilization

We may close this account of the relations of man with his geographical environment with a few words about a strangely fatalistic theory which prevailed among certain thinkers and in particular among the mystics. It was a theory that civilization flows from the East to the West and that when it reaches the uttermost limits of the West the human race will meet its doom and extinction. Severian of Gabala had said in the fourth century: [112] "God looked into the future and set the first man in that place [Paradise, in the East] in order to cause him to understand that, just as the light of heaven moves toward the west, so the human race hastens towards death; but that it is just as reasonable to expect a future resurrection from death as it is to expect that the stars will again rise in the east." This idea appears in the writings of Hugh of St. Victor, who states in the *De arca Noë morali* [113] that the order of places and the order of time run in series; that whatever happened in the beginning of time happened in the Orient and that henceforth the course of events has gradually been moving westward, until now it has reached the end of the earth and we must face the fact that we are approaching the end of the ages (*saeculi*). Shortly after the Deluge the most important kingdoms and the capitol of the world were in the East, in the lands of the Assyrians, Chaldeans, and Medes; then the supreme power passed to the Greeks; and finally, towards the end of the ages, to the Romans who dwell on the confines of the world. In the *De arca Noë mystica* the front of the ark is said to face the east and the rear the west "in order that the position of places shall correspond with the order of time and the end of the world shall be at the end of the centuries." [114] The ark is here supposed to represent a map of the world, and the segment of the circle of the *orbis terrarum* cut by the ark and facing the east is the location of Paradise; the segment facing the west will be the place of universal resurrection. Ideas very similar to this are also found in the *De vanitate mundi* of Hugh of St. Victor.[115]

Though it cannot be proved that Otto of Freising made use of these works, nevertheless his philosophy of history is to a large extent based on the theory of the westward flow of civilization.[116] In the prologue to his *Chronicon* he queries, "Who can wonder that human power is changeable, when mortal wisdom also is unstable (*labilis*)? What great learning there was in Egypt and among the Chaldeans, from whom Abraham derived his knowledge! But what now is Babylon, once famous for its science and its power? A shrine of sirens, a home of lizards and ostriches, a den of serpents! And Egypt is now in large part a trackless and uninhabitable waste, whence science was transferred to the Greeks, then to the Romans, and finally to the Gauls and Spaniards. And," he concludes, "let it be observed that because all human power or wisdom began in the Orient and will end in the Occident, the mutability and disappearance of all things is demonstrated. This I propose, with God's aid, to make clear in the work which follows." Otto again hammers on this theme in the prologue of his fifth book [117] and finally, near the close of the same book,[118] remarks, "For behold, as I have explained above, just as the heavens turn from east to west, so we behold worldly affairs and powers revolving." If human power is so changeable, he asks, who can expect that the Kingdom of the Franks will last very long?

The idea that "westward the course of empire takes its way" was thus raised in the Middle Ages to a position of theological doctrine and philosophical principle.

FEELING FOR LANDSCAPE AND SCENERY

The pagan, or classical, attitude toward nature was characterized by a subjective and esthetic enjoyment of beautiful scenery; the Christian saw in nature the symbol and manifestation of the divinity.[119] Both points of view were represented in the literature of our age.

Spiritual Feeling for Nature

The more spiritual feeling found its expression in the writings of men like Bernard of Clairvaux, Hugh of St. Victor, Francis of Assisi, Alexander Neckam, and many others.[120] Bernard of Clairvaux believed that a man could learn more of the eternal verities through a reverent contemplation of nature than through the study of books. He wrote to Master Henry Murdach, an Englishman who afterwards became a monk of Clairvaux: "Believe one who has tried: you shall find a fuller satisfaction in the woods than in books. The trees and the rocks will teach you that which you cannot hear from the masters. Do you think that you cannot draw honey from the rock and oil from the hardest flint? Do not our mountains drop sweetness? the hills flow with milk and honey? and the valleys stand thick with corn?" (Eales's translation).[121] Bernard was fond of complex and detailed allegorical comparisons of the aspects of nature with the theological or spiritual concepts which he believed they symbolize. In a sermon on Benedict he said: "St. Benedict was a mighty fruit tree, like a tree planted by a watercourse. Where are the watercourses? Truly they are in the valleys, because midway between the mountains the water flows down. Who may not perceive that the streams retreat from the steep slopes of the mountains and make their way straight to the lowly midst of the valleys? Thus does God repulse the haughty and give grace to the humble. Here you may set foot in safety. Whoever of you are of the flock of Christ, place your trust in his staff and follow the footpath in the valley. On the hillsides that ancient serpent has ever chosen his abode which bites the horse's hoof and makes the rider fall back. Select rather the valley for your wanderings and plantings. Do not seek the dry and rocky mountain side to set out trees. In the valleys is abundance. There plants thrive, the grass is lush, fruits grow, and, according to the words of Scripture, 'the vales shall abound with corn.'" [122]

It was in much the same vein that Bernard spoke of the sea as the origin of all springs and rivers and compared it with Christ, the fount of all virtue and wisdom.[123] It was a wish to find an allegorical meaning in the phenomena of nature that induced Abelard to compare the flood of the Nile with the spread of Christian grace throughout the world.[124] These and the many other similar allegorical comparisons that are so frequent in the literature of our period are not mere juxtapositions of things that were seen to be alike. Bernard did more than liken the valley to the humble of spirit. He implied that the valley itself partook of the quality of humility and was thereby in some way more divine than the mountain. But, if Bernard believed that mountains were symbolical of pride and arrogance, others, like

Altmann of Passau, Anselm of Canterbury, and Francis of Assisi, were lovers of mountains in a truly spiritual sense. To the twelfth-century mystic the beauty of nature was more than a symbol of the divinity: it drew its very essence from God. The love that St. Francis bore towards birds and animals, mountains and fellow man was a love that arose out of his regarding all of these as creatures of God impregnated with something of the divine.

Esthetic Love of Nature

The esthetic love of nature that existed during our period was very different. It had its roots in a movement of protest and rebellion against the austerity of the Christian life and ideals. Men wished to enjoy the things of this world without thought of the next. What is more, they sometimes actually dared to write about their pleasures. These early stirrings of the humanistic spirit, the spirit of the Great Renaissance, brought forth troubled protests and angry remonstrances from men like Bernard and other reformers; but none the less love poems were often composed in the monasteries, and vagrant poets wandered over Europe singing the praises of earthly love, rejoicing in the spring-time, with little heed for aught but the beauty of the world. Popular wherever they went, these wanderers exerted a great influence, and something of their joyous, pagan spirit crept into more serious writings of the age.

It would be possible to quote at some length texts testifying to the presence of an esthetic feeling for nature in the twelfth and early thirteenth centuries.[125] Two or three examples must here suffice.

One of the most enthusiastic observers of natural scenery was Guy of Bazoches. He describes the environs of the castle of St. Gilles in southern France about as follows: [126] "Here smile cultivated and fertile fields, and here the sides of the hills are adorned with vineyards. The pleasing aspect of the shrubbery and the beauty of gardens meets the eye, and oh! how the sweet smell of the grass fills the air! Fruit trees groan under their load and lament their fertility, and the warbling birds in the branches send forth rich harmonies. If we look in a different direction we see the plain stretching out its level lap covered with green meadows and alluring us with its beauty. The Rhone, disdainfully cutting through the midst of the fields, rolls down proud waters and, reaching its place of birth, flows forth into the neighboring sea."

Even more striking is a passage from a poem that has been ascribed to Marbod of Rennes. "My uncle owns an estate in the forest where I am in the habit of going to leave care behind and all that may trouble one. The green grass, the silent woods, the soft and festive breezes, and a lively spring in the meadow revive my tired spirit: they give me back to myself and enable me to regain my poise (me mihi reddunt et faciunt in me consistere). For who is not robbed of himself in the restless city, roaring with a multitude of noises?"[127] The writer goes on to meditate in truly Roman fashion on the transitory character of all things of this earth. Ganzenmüller comments on the subjective character of these sentiments: "What a distance separates this from the attitude towards nature of a Bernard of Clairvaux! Bernard ascribes loneliness to God, our poet to himself. No longer did one seek in nature for God but for one's own self."[128]

Practical Interest in Countrysides

On the whole, however, the passages just quoted are more or less exceptional. The majority of descriptions of countrysides that date from our period reveal neither highly developed esthetic feeling nor transcendental emotion. What they do reveal is the prevalence of keen intellectual interest in detail. If a region was in any way unusual either by reason of the richness of its produce or the marvelous tales that were in circulation about it, that region was held to be worthy of comment.

Dreesbach has clearly pointed out[129] that the passages from the French literature of the Crusading period which describe the Orient show that the things which impressed themselves on the minds of historian and chronicler and poet were the richness of gardens and orchards and the fertility of the fields. Her fecundity, not her romantic or esthetic qualities, made the average man of the Middle Ages love nature; and a country not rich and prosperous hardly deserved any particular notice, in his way of thinking. The descriptions of Syria in William of Tyre's history reveal a great number of observations like the following: "The plain of Antioch, full of many rich fields for the raising of wheat and abounding in springs and rivulets," [130] or the neighborhood of Damascus, "where there are a great number of trees bearing fruits of all kinds and growing up to the very walls of the city and where everybody has a garden of his own." [131] Elsewhere William of Tyre emphasizes the contrast between the sterility of the desert and the marvelous fertility of Egypt, with its abundance of wheat.[132] The same interest in the economic qualities of the land appears in the few local descriptions that we find in the writings of Otto of Freising. Otto speaks [133] of the forested region about the Rhine, near Worms, as being "rich in produce and wine, abundant in hunting and fishing," and for this reason, he adds, the region was pleasing to the princes who came from across the Alps to take part in the Diet at Worms. In detailing the life of Corbianus, founder of the church at Freising, he gives us a topographical account of the vicinity of this city.[134] A hill, he says, situated in a most beautiful and delicious spot, overlooks like a watchtower the whole region, through which can be seen the swift stream of the Isar. In the days of Corbianus (about 745 A. D.) this territory was said to have been covered with woods and was a haunt of game; traces of these woods were still to be found in the ancient tree trunks among the thickets of the plains, and to Otto's own day immense quantities of deer and goats ran wild there. In the northern part of the district by no means inconsiderable tracts of woodland, commonly called "the forest," were still in existence, and from them much useful building material and fuel could be procured. The land contiguous to the hill was inclosed by the rivers Isar on the south and Amper on the north, and between the two streams it extended four German miles in the form of a very fertile peninsula. At the end of this, where the two rivers come together, was a place called Moosburg, beautiful and delightful, the site of a congregation of clergy connected with the church of the blessed Castulus.

Giraldus Cambrensis' Eye for Local Topography

Giraldus Cambrensis, more than his contemporaries, had an eye for local topography. In spite of his taste for the marvelous, this impelled him now and then to paint a fairly clear word picture of the appearance of the countryside. He notes many things of a sort that do not usually occur in other medieval works; for instance, the fact that in fair weather it is possible to see the hills of Ireland from St. David's Head in Wales; [135] that the fertility of the Irish soil lies in its grassland rather than in its grain; [136] that Ireland is rugged and hilly, very damp and watery, full of woods, swamps, and trackless wastes, with lakes at the foot of the hills and pools and bogs even on the highest summits; that here and there one sees beautiful plains, but in general open surfaces are of limited extent in comparison to woodland; that the seacoasts are low, that hills and mountains are restricted to the interior, and that both inland and along the shores there is more sandy than rocky country.[137] He was also impressed by the barren and desolate character of many parts of Wales; [138] the "angle" of the land near St. David's, he says, has a rocky, sterile soil, with neither woods, nor rivers, nor orchards, but is open and exposed to winds and storms. Mona also is arid and rocky, deformed in appearance, and generally unpromising, though as a matter of fact vastly more fertile and opulent than the adjacent portion of the Welsh mainland.[139]

CHAPTER X

THE ASTRONOMICAL GEOGRAPHY OF THE KNOWN WORLD

We have already examined the broader theories of astronomical geography whereby the relation of the globe to the remainder of the universe was explained. In this chapter we shall speak only of those aspects of astronomical geography which were intimately connected with man's knowledge of the various parts of the known world, or *oikoumene*, as distinguished from the sphere as a whole.

Phenomena Resulting From Differences in Latitude

Within the *oikoumene* the phenomena resulting from varying elevations of the ecliptic in different latitudes were fairly well understood. The facts that there are two summers between the tropics (particularly in India) and that the sun there passes vertically overhead twice a year had been commented on by Pliny and Solinus, whose observations in this connection found their way into Isidore's *Etymologiae* [1] and thus to the works of the plagiarists of Isidore in our period. The *De imagine mundi*,[2] the *Image du monde*,[3] Gervase of Tilbury,[4] and John of Holywood [5] all tell us that the same phenomenon was said to occur in Arabia which lies between the tropics. Similarly the long days and nights of far northern latitudes were described on the authority of Solinus and Isidore. In the *De imagine mundi*,[6] from which Gervase copies, it is said that in the island of "Chili" (Thule) there are six months of daylight and summer and six of night and winter. Giraldus Cambrensis also quotes Solinus [7] and Isidore [8] to the same effect and adds a brief description of how the sun continuously circles around the horizon during the long Arctic day and how its light disappears completely when the luminary departs southward towards the Tropic of Capricorn.[9]

"CLIMATA"

The ancient geographers had divided the earth's surface into *climata*, or climates, which, as we have already seen,[10] were not atmospheric regions but mathematical strips running east and west and bounded by parallels of latitude. Pliny,[11] for instance, had conceived of seven climates, the first in the latitude of India, where the length of the longest day is fourteen hours, and the seventh in that of the Borysthenes (Dnieper) and of Venetia, Umbria, Milan, and Aquitania, where the longest day is fifteen and three-quarters hours. Martianus Capella[12] added an eighth climate in the north between the parallel of the Borysthenes and that of the Rhipaean Mountains. Furthermore, he applied names to the strips. It must be added, however, that neither Pliny nor Capella were precise in the data they gave, and neither indicated in degrees the latitude of the parallels which bound their climates.

More definite is the information we find in the two works of Ptolemy. The *Almagest*[13] and *Geography*[14] give accounts of the characteristic astronomical phenomena that occur along a series of parallels, thirty-eight in number according to the former, twenty-one according to the latter.[15] The positions of these were determined by the length of the longest day at each one. Though there is no explicit mention of the older division by climates in the text of either of Ptolemy's books, such a division not only appears upon the map of the world made by Agathodaemon on the basis of material supplied by Ptolemy but also upon certain of the special regional maps which were probably the work of Ptolemy himself.[16]

At all events, the conception of the seven or eight climates did not disappear but at a very early period, whether by Ptolemy or not, was correlated with the Ptolemaic parallels.[17] That is to say, certain of Ptolemy's parallels were used to designate the imaginary lines marking the centers and bounds of the climates. This practice was adopted by the Arabs and from them transferred to the knowledge of the Christian West in various astronomical treatises. Among the Latin manuscripts of the *Toledo Tables*,[18] for instance, there are series of astronomical tables for each of the seven climates, according to which the climates occupy the space between latitude 16° N., with a longest day of thirteen hours, and 48° N., with a longest day of sixteen hours. The length of the longest day and the latitude are given for each parallel that bounds the climates. Except that Ptolemy notes minutes as well as degrees and in the *Toledo Tables* the minutes have in most cases been omitted, the figures correspond essentially with those of the *Almagest* and *Geography*. Thus: Ptolemy's eleventh parallel according to the *Almagest* (or tenth according to the *Geography*) has a longest day of fourteen and a half hours and is at latitude 36°. In the *Tables* the southern edge of the fourth climate likewise has a longest day of fourteen and a half hours and is at latitude 36°.

Again, in John of Seville's translation of Al-Farghānī's *Astronomy* [19] and in the *De sphaera* [20] of John of Holywood, who had borrowed from Al-Farghānī in this matter, we find a similar correlation. In both cases the figures of latitude correspond essentially, though with slight divergences in detail, to those of Ptolemy. The boundaries of each climate, however, have here been displaced by one parallel to the south of the parallels used in the *Toledo Tables* and those which we may presume were the Ptolemaic boundaries of the climates.[21]

The table, Figure 11 (in the Notes to Ch. X), gives some idea of the relative degree of accuracy of these figures as they were employed in the West during the Middle Ages. But just as in the case of other figures for latitude and longitude, as we shall shortly have occasion to see, this material was not utilized for geographical purposes during our age.

Geographical Coördinates

At the present time the study of regional geography is largely dependent on a precise knowledge of the geographical coördinates of places. The foremost duty of the explorer is to know where he is from day to day and to find this out by astronomical means, if possible. In classical times and among the Moslems the importance of such observations was not only well understood, but several methods of carrying them through were described by astronomers and geographers, and the latitudes of a great many stations had been determined astronomically. Longitude, on the other hand, long remained a stumbling block, and before the twelfth century, certainly, no systematic attempts to ascertain the longitudes of any large number of places had ever met with success.

A few relics of classical and Moslem study in this field became familiar in the West as a result of the intense interest in Arabic astronomy prevailing in Europe between the tenth and thirteenth centuries.[22]

Various figures representing the results of Arabic corrections of and additions to the data given in Ptolemy's *Geography* found their way into Western astrological tables. The most interesting of these occur in a list of the latitudes and longitudes of some sixty odd cities appended to the Paris manuscript of the *Marseilles Tables* of Raymond of Marseilles [23] and also to most of the Latin versions of the *Toledo Tables*.[24] This list and certain figures scattered through the astrological tables and canons[25] reveal the results of the reductions made by Al-Khwārizmī and by Az-Zarqalī of Ptolemy's gross overestimate of the length of the Mediterranean, to which we have referred in a preceding chapter.[26] The European student of these astrological works might have drawn a by no means contemptible map from the figures to be found in them had he been interested in what these figures could teach him of geography. Figure 6 is a map compiled from the coördinates given in the Paris manuscript of the *Marseilles Tables*.

At the end of this list of geographical coördinates in many manuscripts additional figures not derived from Moslem sources are given. These show the positions of such points in Europe as London, Hereford, Paris, Toulouse, Barcelona, Marseilles, Novara, Cremona, Florence, and Naples[27] (see Fig. 12, in Notes to Ch. X). They were undoubtedly determined by observations made during our period or shortly after.

Methods of Finding Latitude and Longitude

That such observations were carried out is entirely possible, for there is absolutely no doubt that methods of finding latitudes and longitudes were well understood in theory and were sometimes put to practical use. Rules are given for finding latitude in Az-Zarqalī's *Canons*, in Plato of Tivoli's translation of the *Astronomy* of Al-Battānī, and in many other astronomical and

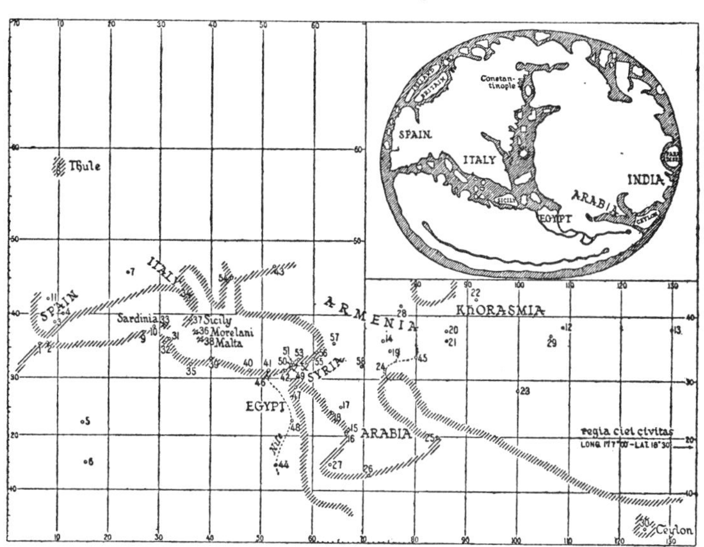

FIG. 6—Sketch map constructed from the list of geographical positions appended to the Paris manuscript of Raymond of Marseilles' *Marseilles Tables*. The outline of the coast, arbitrarily indicated by a shaded band, is shown merely to give some idea of the type of map that might have been constructed from the data given in the tables. This may be compared with the Henry of Mayence map (see above, p. 124) shown in outline in the inset. The original Henry of Mayence map reveals far greater detail and upon it east (not north, as in this figure) is at the top.

This list is based on the observations of the eleventh-century Arabic astronomers Al-Khwārizmī and Az-Zarqalī. Cities and other points have been plotted according to the coördinates of this list. The resulting map of the Mediterranean region and the Near East is remarkable for its comparative accuracy. For a key to the names represented by the numbers on the diagram and for the figures for the latitudes and longitudes, see J. K. Wright, *Knowledge of Latitudes and Longitudes*, 1923, pp. 87–88.

astrological treatises.[28] Two principal methods were recommended. You may either measure with the astrolabe the altitude of the sun above the horizon at noon at the spring or autumn equinox and find the latitude by subtracting this angle from 90° or you may measure the altitude of the celestial pole above the horizon, which is the same as the latitude. As to longitude, the fact that there are differences in local time between points east and west of each other was recognized and clearly explained by several writers of our age.[29] The *Marseilles Tables* give a rule for finding longitude by the observation of eclipses. Roger of Hereford indicates that he himself, by observing an eclipse in 1178, ascertained the positions of Hereford, Marseilles, and Toledo in relation to Arin, the world center of the Moslems.[30] Gerard of Cremona describes a method of finding longitude by noting the distance of the moon from a given point in the heavens and thereby dispensing with eclipses,[31] though it is doubtful whether this method was used until the sixteenth century. The lack of accurate instruments for ascertaining time must have rendered it extremely difficult to calculate longitude under any circumstances. Making allowances for this, it is surprising to find how accurate the few coördinates that have come down to us seem to be, if our interpretation of them is correct.[32]

The geographical interest of these figures and of investigations of this sort was not appreciated by the majority of the men of our age. The application of astronomical considerations to the problems of navigation was still in its infancy. The purpose of the investigator of the twelfth and early thirteenth century in finding geographical coördinates was astrological. He wished to make use of them to transpose tables made originally for the meridian and parallel of one station to the meridian and parallel of another. Their influence on the cartography of the age was absolutely *nil*. It is probably safe to make the categorical statement that the maps and geographical treatises of the century and a half preceding the year 1250 were drawn and written with almost complete disregard of any astronomical considerations whatsoever.

CHAPTER XI

CARTOGRAPHY

The maps of our period give us the most convincing possible illustrations of the geographical ideas that were current.[1] Their bright colors, naïve legends, childlike but often skillfully drawn vignettes, and preposterous inaccuracy take us back into the atmosphere of a credulous and uncritical age. We can catch much more of the flavor of the popular geography of the Middle Ages by a hasty glance at one of the crude Beatus representations of the world than by plowing through many of the dry pages of compilations like the *De imagine mundi.*

In this chapter there will be given a brief analysis of these maps as specimens of the cartographer's art and an explanation of certain points which all, or most, of them have in common.

INACCURACY

What strikes us first is their extraordinary inaccuracy. It is easy to laugh at this because subconsciously but inevitably we compare the outlines of seas, continents, and regions as represented in these maps with the outlines with which we have become familiar in modern atlases. We tend to forget that the contours of Europe, Asia, and Africa as we now know them are not images that have been stamped upon the minds of men at all times, that their accurate representation is the result of a series of long and laborious observations completed only at a relatively recent date. Hence it is somewhat unjust to reproach the medieval cartographer with his inaccuracy, for the reason that accuracy in the present-day sense was something impossible for him to achieve. The Greeks and Moslems, to be sure, had made far better maps than did the men of the Middle Ages; but, unfortunately, Greek maps had perished, few Arabic maps came through to the West, and the prevalent ignorance of Greek made it impossible for the Occidental scholar to gain inspiration from treatises on cartography written in that tongue.

Accuracy Not Deemed Necessary

Furthermore, it is a mistake to regard accuracy as the goal and ideal of the medieval map maker. To gain a sympathetic understanding of his work we must see what purposes he intended it to fulfill. He drew maps to accompany and clarify the written texts to which they were usually subsidiary. The maps were more or less in the nature of diagrammatic sketches on which the features of the earth's surface were shown in a general way, and the draftsman understood perfectly well that all he could hope to give was a rough approximation to relative positions. The medieval scribe and map maker was an artist who took pride in the beauty of his work. The same motives which impelled him to enliven his manuscript with a multitude of miniatures led him to relieve the coldly geometrical outlines of his map by lines and colors pleasing to the eye, by entertaining sketches and readable legends. He was creating something very different from the modern cartographic or topographic sheet that stands on its own merits as an independently useful, scientific document and from which we can get precise information about distances, heights, positions, and terrain. He would have branded any man a fool who thought that one could hope to determine from his map the distance from Jerusalem to England or from the mouth of the Ganges to the mouth of the Nile. In other words, most medieval maps—including wall maps—were nothing more than rough diagrams converted into works of art.

When, during the latter years of the thirteenth century, the sailors of the Mediterranean, driven by the necessity of securing reliable aids to navigation, began piece by piece to construct marine charts upon which the contours of the coasts were shown with an approach to modern correctness, we have indeed a revolution in cartographic art and geographical science.

Bearing in mind these considerations, we see that the major inaccuracies of medieval maps are (1) exaggeration in the scale of particular regions at the expense of others and (2) distortion, often amounting to a complete failure to show places in their proper relative positions. The first of these inaccuracies was usually deliberate, the second more or less unavoidable. Both are well-known characteristics of our modern American railway folder maps.

Exaggeration

The purpose of exaggeration was, of course, to emphasize the most interesting and significant localities. For example, on many maps of the world, Palestine—about which a good deal was known and in which interest naturally was centered—is shown to be almost as large as all the rest of Asia put together. The Jerome map of the East [2] exaggerates Asia Minor to an enormous size, making it a greater distance from Constantinople to Mount Ararat than from Armenia to Taprobane (Ceylon). On the other hand, the Jerome map of Palestine itself [3] would lead us to believe that the district lying between the Lebanon, the Jordan, and the sea is at least three times as large as the Anatolian peninsula. Certainly nobody ever thought that such proportions actually obtain in nature. Similarly, the plans of cities that are not infrequently included in maps are often immensely enlarged in relation to the surrounding country, as, for example, in the case of London, Rome, Acre, and Jerusalem on Matthew Paris' pictorial itinerary [4] and map of Palestine,[5] and Jerusalem on the "Situs Ierusalem" [6] (see Fig. 7).

Distortion

Errors arising from distortion were due partly to ignorance and partly to the necessity of making the map fit either the page upon which it was drawn or else a preconceived idea of an oval, or circular world. The "Cotton," or "Anglo-Saxon," map [7] several of the Beatus series,[8] and even Matthew Paris' maps of Britain [9] (the best of the whole period; see Fig. 9, p. 343, below) show a semi-rectangular land mass corresponding to the pages of the codices. On the latter a legend frankly admits that, if only the size of the page permitted, the island would be shown longer than it is ("Si pagine pateretur, haec totalis insula longior esse deberet").[10] The manner in which geography was forced to conform to a circular or oval world is admirably illustrated in the treatment of the islands of the ocean. On the Beatus series [11] and on Lambert's *mappaemundi*,[12] Britain and the other

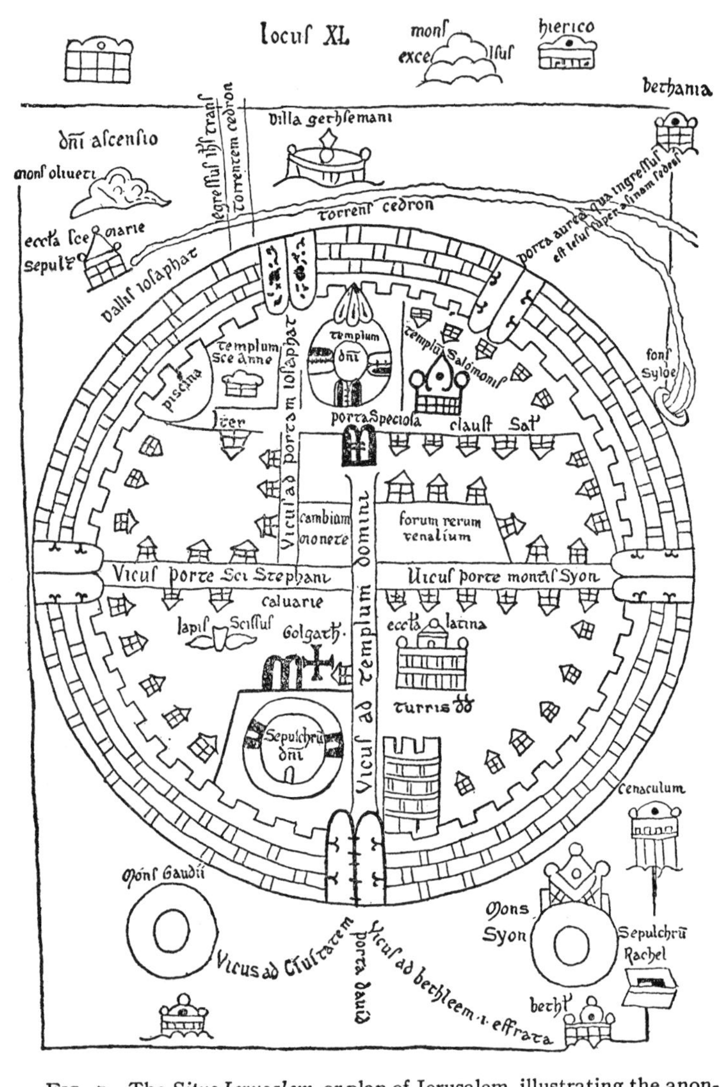

FIG. 7—The *Situs Ierusalem*, or plan of Jerusalem, illustrating the anonymous *Gesta Francorum Ierusalem expugnantium* as reproduced by Miller, *Mappaemundi*, vol. iii, 1895, fig. 14, from map in Codex of St. Omer.

islands appear as small, round, oval, or rectangular blocks more or less regularly spaced in the circumambient ocean. Other maps, like that of Henry of Mayence[13] (see inset of Fig. 6, p. 245, above), fit the islands into recesses in the oceanic shores of the continental areas so that the smooth outlines of the whole land mass are preserved.

An extreme of confusion and disregard for reality is found in one of the Beatus group[14] preserved in Paris. Here it is difficult to make out which continent is which. India, for instance, lies just across the Red Sea from Spain (it is doubtful in what direction); Arabia would seem to be in the farthest Orient, adjoined by Greece on one side and Thrace on the other. Such absurdities are unusual, but even the best maps of the period show serious errors when measured by modern standards. The "Cotton,"[15] for instance, in such a well-known part of the world as Italy, locates Ravenna on the Mediterranean shore southeast of Rome and shows an amazing eastward displacement of Arabia and the Red Sea, though in many other respects its geography, relatively speaking, is very good.

TECHNIQUE

The diagrammatic character of these maps is evident in the technique of their workmanship. They all show a tendency toward geometrical lines, curves, and symmetry. This is carried further on some than on others (as, for example, in the cruder specimens of the Beatus group[16]); but, in nearly all, the ocean is represented as a smooth circular band of even width; and, in many, rivers and mountains follow direct lines or regular curves. It is obvious that the ruler and compass were not neglected.

Conventions

Moreover, certain cartographic conventions were followed. In the great majority of cases east was placed at the top, and some authorities have endeavored to trace this convention back to the maps of the Romans.[17] While this explanation of its origin may be true, the traditions of the Church, which placed in the Orient the Garden of Eden together with the fountain of the waters of the world and of human life, must have had much to do toward perpetuating it. Conventions of a sort were also observed in the use of colors on colored maps: seas and rivers were nearly always blue or green, except for the Red Sea, which was invariably red. Less uniform was the color used for mountains: on the map of the world of Henry of Mayence[18] and on one of Lambert's *mappaemundi*[19] they are red; the "Cotton"[20] shows them a brilliant green; and one of the maps of Matthew Paris,[21] a yellow.

Symbols and Legends

Symbols representing the various features of the earth's surface were more or less conventionalized, though we can hardly say that any definitely developed "conventional signs" were in use. It is the usual intention of symbols as employed on modern maps to reproduce the appearance of the various features more or less as they look when viewed from above. This is relatively recent development; on medieval maps such elements as mountains, forests, and cities were shown as they appear from the side. In addition to symbols, legends were extensively employed to explain details of the map's surface, and sometimes these were expanded to considerable length to include historical data and other points of interest. A large variety of subjects were represented on these maps by symbols, vignettes, and legends.

The atmosphere figures in the Turin Beatus[22] in pictures at the four corners of wind blowers seated astride of wind bags. On the Jerome map of the East[23] the names of certain of the winds are written along the eastern border, and wind blowers were familiar figures in the cartography of a later period than ours.

The ocean and inland seas, usually tinted green or blue, are generally without symbols to emphasize their watery nature, except perhaps for pictures of fish. On two of the Beatus series,[24] however, lines are drawn running parallel to the coasts, showing that the medieval draftsman had hit upon and crudely executed a modern scheme of representing water. The Guido map of Italy[25] represents the sea by scalloped lines. On the Guido map of the world[26] the size of the Mediterranean and its branches is enormously enlarged;[27] whereas the worst examples of the Beatus group[28] show the inland seas as narrow channels bounded by straight shores.

The width of rivers is nearly always immensely exaggerated; on some maps rivers appear to be as wide as the seas themselves. Only the "Cotton"[29] forms an exception in representing them (except for the Nile) as single lines. On the whole, hydrography is drawn arbitrarily. Streams cross each other, separate, and connect one sea with another; though the Jerome maps,[30] certain of the Beatus series,[31] and the "Cotton"[32] place the headwaters of many of the rivers of Asia and Europe in mountain ranges.

Lakes are generally represented as bulb-shaped bodies from which rivers rise or into which they expand.

No attempt was made to show by symbols different kinds of land surface, except perhaps by Matthew Paris in one of his maps of Britain,[33] which differentiates the marshy country of the eastern shires from the rest of the island. On certain members of the Beatus group[34] we read legends in Africa and Asia calling the country "deserta et arenosa;" and legends appearing on Matthew Paris' maps[35] describe the boggy, wild, and mountainous country of northern Scotland and Wales. The Paris Beatus No. II[36] has a legend in a remote part of Asia indicating "land uninhabitable on account of the abundance of water."

Mountain ranges were generally represented by jagged, saw-tooth lines running parallel to straight lines;[37] particularly high or famous peaks, by a single great pyramid. Such pyramids are prominent features in the Beatus series,[38] where woods are often shown growing upon them. The Hyrcanian Forest is depicted and labeled on the Jerome map of Palestine,[39] and the pepper forests of India are indicated on the Jerome map of the East.[40]

Among the works of man cities and buildings take a foremost place, represented by vignettes of castles, towers, and churches. On several maps[40a] especially notable works are depicted, as the lighthouse of Alexandria, the tower of Babel, the columns of Alexander and Hercules; and the seas are sometimes filled with ships. As to men themselves, the legends give the names of cities, provinces, and countries. The Jerome maps[41] give a series of tribal names in Scythia. Adam and Eve with the serpent were stereotyped features enlivening the East on many but by no means all the maps of our age; and on the Osma Beatus[42] we see the uniformly gloomy features of the twelve apostles distributed over the earth's surface (see Fig. 4, p. 123, above).

The monsters of India were also represented by vignettes of a *skiapod*, or shadowfoot, on two of the Beatus group,[43] where this uncomfortable creature is shown as the most prominent inhabitant of the austral continent (see Fig. 4) and the existence of other monsters is hinted at by legends referring to griffons, cynocephali, and the like.

SUMMARY

In surveying the extant maps of our period as a whole, and in comparing them with one another, it is impossible to detect any appreciable development from worse cartography to better. To be sure, Matthew Paris' three maps of Britain[44] (Fig. 9, p. 343, below), made at the very end of our century and a half, are probably also the best. But they represent a limited area; and among the maps of the world the "Cotton," or Anglo-Saxon,[45] which possibly dates from the twelfth century but may be very much older, holds by all odds the highest rank so far as cartographic excellence goes. The complex and elaborate wall map of the late thirteenth century in Hereford Cathedral[46] and the immense Ebstorf map at Hanover (dated 1284)[47] represent the culmination of a process in the direction of increasing elaboration that had been in progress throughout the age. They do not indicate any improvement in cartographic standards but rather, as was the case with some of the great works of compilation of the time, a multiplication of fabulous and incongruous detail. Beazley dismisses them rather summarily as monstrosities. They are the cartographic counterparts of the *Image du monde* and the *Livre du trésor* of Brunetto Latino.

CHAPTER XII

REGIONAL GEOGRAPHY

We shall not attempt the thankless and impossible task of giving a complete conspectus of Western regional lore in the twelfth and early thirteenth centuries. This chapter, like its predecessors, consists largely of illustrative examples.

GENERAL CHARACTER OF REGIONAL KNOWLEDGE OF THE PERIOD

Geography of Tradition and Geography of Observation

We explained in the Introduction that there were two kinds of geographical information available in the Middle Ages—information derived from earlier literature and information derived from contemporary tradition and observation. In the period we are studying, these were found among men of very different interests and activities, and hence they usually failed to blend. It is true that now and then in a work of erudition of the time we come across a report of some original observation made by the writer himself or learned by him from a contemporary; but these data were seldom really assimilated into the body of the text, seldom used as a check on the assertions of older authorities. They seem to float like drops of oil on the deep, or shallow, waters of authoritative learning. Conversely, in works recording contemporary events—histories, chronicles, letters—we often come across facts and theories that were taken from older books; but these were infrequently subjected to critical examination in the light of contemporary knowledge. On the contrary, they were usually treated with indulgence or respect merely because they were old, even when observed phenomena seemed to prove them false.

In the present as in the foregoing parts of this book the attempt is made to distinguish between these two distinct types of geographical lore. For many regions the geographical ideas are indicated that were derived from Pliny, Solinus, Isidore, Bede, and other encyclopedists and that found expression in treatises like the *De imagine mundi*, the *Otia imperialia*, and the *Image du monde*. In contrast to these there is set forth the kind of information that was being gathered by contemporary eyewitnesses.

Gradations of Accuracy of Knowledge

Maps are sometimes drawn at the present day to show the state of progress of geographical knowledge. Upon these by various tints or shadings are indicated tracts that are accurately surveyed, partially surveyed, known only through route traverses, known only through reports from natives, or totally unknown. No such map could be constructed to show the character of regional knowledge in the Middle Ages, because our sources of information are not sufficiently complete and because the knowledge both actually and potentially available varied from country to country, from community to community, even from individual to individual. The printing press and facility of communication between the peoples of the world has rendered scientific knowledge or, at any rate, the possibility of obtaining scientific knowledge the common property of all modern civilizations. An Australian student, for instance, if he is willing to take the time and trouble, can learn through research virtually all that is known to Danish or Icelandic scholars about the geography of Greenland. In the Middle Ages, on the contrary, we may feel certain that the Danes and Norwegians had at hand much detailed information on Greenland and the Arctic shores of Europe that the Italian had no means whatever of obtaining. Correspondingly, the Italian trader of Genoa or Venice unquestionably knew a great deal about remote parts of Asia and North Africa that could never reach the ears of an author of a *De imagine mundi* or of a Lambert of St. Omer, writing in quiet cloisters of France or Belgium.

Yet if, for these reasons, we cannot show on a map the gradations in the character and accuracy of Western geographical knowledge in the age of the Crusades, such gradations nevertheless existed. From the point of view of Western Europe as a whole they might be grouped in a broad way as follows. First there were the well-known regions about which knowledge was derived and kept fresh through active commercial, diplomatic, ecclesiastical, military, and scholarly enterprise. These regions may be said to have included most of Europe west of the Elbe and Hungary. They also included the overland routes to Constantinople, the shores of the Mediterranean, and the Holy Land. From the point of view of the Scandinavian peoples, who were great travelers, they took in not only the foregoing regions but also the Baltic coasts, southern Norway and Sweden, and Iceland. Beyond the bounds of the well-known areas lay a second group of areas about which a fair amount of reasonably trustworthy information was at hand, derived from one of three sources: (1) reports of occasional travelers; (2) more or less reliable hearsay; (3) classical descriptions drawn from literary sources. Much of Western Asia and North Africa fell within this category and, for the Scandinavians, Greenland. Beyond lay the third group of regions known only through the vaguest of rumors—the domains of fabulous monsters and legendary men. To some writers India was such a land, to others Russia and northern Scandinavia, to still others the legendary isles that lay concealed in the Western Ocean. Finally, beyond them came those regions lying without the known world, about which the men of the Middle Ages themselves would have acknowledged that they knew nothing: the austral continent, the countries of the antipodeans, *antoikoi*, *antichthones*, which have been discussed in an earlier chapter. No boundaries could be drawn setting off these various tracts from one another; the well-known shaded off imperceptibly into the less well-known, and the vaguely known merged into fairyland; within each well-known tract were islands of doubt and mystery, and fabulous stories were told of even the most commonplace features of the landscape.

THE "OIKOUMENE" AS A WHOLE

Before turning to the various regions of the known world—the *oikoumene*, as the Greeks called it; the *orbis terrarum* or *habitatio* of the Romans—something must be said concerning theories about the *oikoumene* as a whole, about its center, and about Paradise and the four rivers of Paradise. It was usually supposed that the *oikoumene* itself occupies a relatively restricted part of the surface of the globe. The words of Seneca to the effect that there is only a short distance from Spain to India imply that the known world must stretch out over much more than a half of the circumference of the sphere.[1] Though these words were often read in our period, scant attention was paid either to them or to the Arabic interpretation of Aristotle's similar theory until a later date. Roger Bacon's specific explanation that the *habitatio* extends around much more than half the earth's circumference represents an opinion that was exceptional.[2] The majority of the thinkers of the twelfth and early thirteenth centuries who speculated on the subject at all were probably under the spell of the theory fostered by Macrobius, which made our habitable portion of the earth one of four similar regions separated from each other by two oceans.[3] This undoubtedly was the view most widely accepted, but in addition the idea was perhaps already being propounded early in the twelfth century that the lands of the known world form merely a small portion of the surface of the terrestrial sphere emerging above the surface of a larger, enveloping sphere of water.[4]

The "Oikoumene" Divided into Three Parts

The writers of the Crusading age were unanimous in dividing the *oikoumene* itself into three parts, Asia, Libya (or Africa), and Europe. Bernard Sylvester said: "In two parts the ether, and likewise in two parts the air, but in three parts you are to understand that the land is divided,"[5] almost as if a tripartite division of the lands were in accord with a law of nature. This division was inevitable in view of what was known of the arrangement of lands and seas. Orosius,[6] however, had spoken of certain writers who would split the known world in two, making Africa a part of Europe "because of its small size" and making Asia as large as Africa and Europe together. Those who had preferred to conceive of Africa as a separate continent, he had said, did so not on account of its size but because it is cut off from Europe by an arm of the sea. These words of Orosius were quoted by Otto of Freising[7] and by Gervase of Tilbury.[8] The theory that Asia is equal in size to Europe and Africa put together is reproduced by the author of the *De situ terrarum*,[9] and upon it was based that symmetrical division of the world's surface which we find depicted on the so-called T-O maps of the early Middle Ages.[10]

Isidore of Seville drew largely from Orosius in writing his chapters on geography. Theoretically he accepted the tripartite division,[11] but in his actual treatment of the countries of the world he appended a discussion of islands to his discussion of the continents. In this he was followed by the author of the *De imagine mundi* and by many other writers of the time,[12] all of whom declared that the earth's surface is divided in three, but added chapters on the islands after their descriptions of Asia, Africa, and Europe.

THE CENTER OF THE "OIKOUMENE"

Jerusalem as the Center

During the Middle Ages the idea that Jerusalem is at the center of the *oikoumene* seems gradually to have gained ground. Arculf, a bishop of an unknown see in Gaul and pilgrim to the Holy Land, so described it as early as the close of the seventh century;[13] but the tradition does not appear to have become established in the cartography of the West until the twelfth or even the thirteenth century.[14] To place Jerusalem at the center was to recognize the preëminence given that city in Scripture, not only in the New but also in the Old Testament.[15] It is natural for primitive peoples to think that the most holy of all places occupies a central position:[16] the Greeks believed that either Delphi or Olympus was the navel of the earth;[17] the Scandinavians thought the same was true of Asgard; the Hindus, of Mount Meru; the Babylonians, of Nippur.[18] Gervase of Tilbury argues in a confused, semi-theological manner on the position of Jerusalem:[19] Augustus, he believed, had thought that Judea was the heart of the earth because that Emperor had begun a survey of the provinces of the empire there; in addition, from texts of the

Bible Gervase attempted to demonstrate that Jerusalem is halfway between the North and the South, that by "antithesis" it must be halfway between the East and the West, and consequently must be at the center of the known world.

The Exact Position of the Earth's Center

There seems to have existed in the minds of writers some confusion as to the exact spot that marks the navel of the earth. A map of the year 1110 identifies it with Mount Zion.[20] The pilgrim Saewulf, who was in the Holy Land in 1102 and 1103, says:[21] "At the head of the Church of the Holy Sepulchre, in the wall outside, not far from the place called Calvary, is the place called Compas, which our Lord Jesus Christ himself signified and measured with his own hand as the middle of the world, according to the words of the Psalmist, 'For God is my king of old, working salvation in the midst of the earth.' But some say that this is the place where our Lord Jesus Christ first appeared to Mary Magdalene, while she sought him weeping and thought he had been a gardener, as is related in the Gospels" (Thomas Wright's translation).[22]

In certain astronomical notes of the early twelfth century an anonymous writer (possibly Adelard of Bath) asserts that Mount "Amor reorum" is the center of the earth and that he proved this to be the case by experiment.[23] It would seem that upon this mountain (possibly Mount Moriah) he hung a log, twelve cubits long by three in diameter, suspending it vertically in the air by means of a rope, and that at the time of the summer solstice he observed that the shadow of the log was directly beneath and circular in shape. This, he asserted, showed that Mount "Amor reorum" was the center of the earth. To clinch the veracity of his observation, he added that he had not been drinking wine and that his eyes were not satiated with sleep. Although the sun is not directly overhead at the summer solstice in Palestine, the same idea reappears in the *Otia imperialia* of Gervase of Tilbury.[24] Gervase seems to favor, as the center of the earth, the well where Christ spoke to the Samaritan woman.[25] He adds that this well has the characteristic that philosophers attribute to wells on the Tropic of Cancer at Syene in Africa, that is to say, that the sun shines directly into it at the summer solstice every year.

THE TERRESTRIAL PARADISE

Paradise in the East

Most medieval maps include in the eastern part of the world a picture of the Terrestrial Paradise,[26] surrounded by a high wall or mountain range and containing within it figures of Adam and Eve and the serpent[27] (see above, Fig. 2, p. 69). "The first place in the East is Paradise, a garden famous for its delights, where man can never go, for a fiery wall surrounds it and reaches to the sky. Here is the tree of life which gives immortality, here the fountain which divides into four streams that go forth and water the world."[28] "Around Paradise extends a savage, trackless waste, infested with wild beasts and serpents."[29]

This was the orthodox medieval view, to be found in Peter Abelard's commentary on the Works of the Six Days,[30] in the *De situ terrarum*,[31] and in the *Image du monde*.[31a] Gervase of Tilbury copies it word for word from the *De imagine mundi*[32] but gives additional details in another connection,[33] where he tells us that Paradise was the seat of the first of the four universal monarchies, that of Adam; that it was so called because of its delights, for "delight" is the meaning of the word "Eden," and that the Garden makes a spot of marvelous deliciousness, separated from our inhabited earth by a long tract of land and sea and elevated so high that it reaches the sphere of the moon, so high that the waters of the Deluge failed to disturb it.[34] Peter Lombard explained why it is thought that Paradise is in the East:[35] Scripture, he said, teaches us that God made man outside of Paradise and placed him ready-fashioned in the Garden of Delights which had been planted by the divine power at the beginning of time (*a principio*). In an old translation, Peter explained, instead of this phrase, *a principio*, the words *ad Orientem* were given, and consequently the earlier translator would have had us believe that Paradise was to be found in the eastern parts of the earth. Peter added that a long stretch of land and sea cut Paradise off from the regions inhabited by men and that it was situated on a height touching the circle of the moon's orbit, whence it came about that the waters of the Deluge could not penetrate thither.

It was generally agreed that Paradise is in Asia,[36] although this was not a universal belief. Hermann the Dalmatian in 1143 asserted that there was "no mean opinion" that Paradise lies beyond "Amphitrites," the ocean which encircles the earth from north to south, and that indications of its presence had been found both to eastward and to westward.[37] Gervase said that it could be forcibly argued that the Garden lies beyond the Torrid Zone and is inaccessible to man, though he did not commit himself either for or against this theory.[38] Robert Grosseteste speaks of theologians who would place Paradise under the equator.[39] Otto of Freising's words[40] also seem to imply indirectly that the Garden is not in Asia, for Otto tells us that Alexander the Great conquered the entire Orient from Scythia to the ends of the earth. The same idea may be gathered from the *De situ terrarum*,[41] which places the Seres and not Paradise in the farthest East, and also from the cycle of romances of Alexander, which relate how the Macedonian hero conquered all those Oriental regions where Paradise was usually supposed to be. The *mappaemundi* of Henry of Mayence[42] and of Lambert of St. Omer[43] place Paradise on an island beyond the easternmost limits of the habitable world; but St. Brandan found the Saint's Land of Promise (probably no other than Paradise) far out in the Western Ocean.[44] As a matter of fact there was no uniformity of opinion regarding the geographical position of the Happy Land: St. Augustine, whose works were read during our period, had even gone so far as to state that Paradise had no real existence at all but was merely an allegorical conception.[45] A child is not worried about the latitude and longitude of fairyland, and the average man of the Middle Ages was just as little worried about the exact whereabouts of the Garden of Eden.

Nevertheless, in one version of the Romance of Alexander a logical outcome of the conqueror's travels in the Far East was recognized. In the *Iter ad Paradisum*[46] Alexander is actually brought to the gates of Paradise. When he had subjugated

India he came to a broad river which he understood to be the Ganges; embarking with five hundred men on a ship that happened to be at hand, he arrived at the end of a month before an immense city surrounded by a wall on all sides. Here, after various adventures, he learned from a Jew that this city was the place where the souls of the just were sojourning until the Last Judgment or, in other words, that it was the Terrestrial Paradise.

JOURNEYS TO PARADISE

The *Iter ad Paradisum* and the various versions of the legend of St. Brandan's voyage are examples of a type of story very common in the Middle Ages, the story of actual journeys to Paradise by mortal men.[47] Among these we should include the account of the visit there of Adam's son, Seth, who brought back seeds from the tree of knowledge which were planted in Adam's mouth after the latter's death; the seeds ultimately sprouted into a great tree, the wood of which was used to make Christ's cross.[48] Tales were told of the sojourns of pious monks in Paradise and of how on their return to the homes of men they found that what had seemed only three days in the Garden of Delights was in reality a period of three hundred years. Godfrey of Viterbo in his *Pantheon*[49] relates a tale of a hundred brothers who, like St. Brandan, made widespread explorations in the ocean before coming to Paradise, a golden mountain redolent with wonderful odors and adorned with an image of the Virgin and Child. Another story, dating from an earlier time but undoubtedly well known during our period, was that of the fabulous St. Macarius.[50] Three brothers from a convent between the Tigris and Euphrates set out to find the place where "the earth joins the sky." After crossing Persia they entered India —a land of wonders, of cynocephali and of pygmies, of serpents and of darkness. Here they came upon the altars set up by Alexander the Great to mark the limits of his wanderings[51] and beyond them reached miraculous countries filled with giants and birds that talked. At last, about twenty miles from the Terrestrial Paradise, they found Macarius, a man of hoary age, dwelling in a cave on friendly terms with two lions. Macarius told them a romantic story, in the course of which he described the wonders of Paradise but, alas, emphasized the fact that this long-sought-for garden was absolutely inaccessible to human beings.

The Rivers of Paradise

The account of the four rivers of Paradise, like other passages in Scripture, was interpreted both allegorically and literally. In the religious art of our period these streams were often depicted in stone, glass, or miniature as symbolizing the four evangelists spreading the gospel throughout the world.[52] Neckam, after mentioning Paradise and the rivers, goes on to explain that, just as the world is watered by the four streams, so "by the gift of the Holy Ghost the garden of the Holy Church is irrigated by the four virtues, Justice, Temperance, Fortitude, and Prudence."[53] Literal interpretation of the passage, on the other hand, would present difficulties to the modern hydrographer, but these difficulties were easily overcome in the Middle Ages by appeal to the familiar theory of subterranean watercourses.[54]

The author of the *De imagine mundi*,[55] copying from Isidore,[56] makes the four rivers disappear into the ground, whence they spring forth in lands far distant; and some of the maps of our period represent all four rivers as rising from a central source within the Garden and vanishing into the earth at its walls or not far beyond. The Psalter map,[57] on the other hand, shows no less than five rivers issuing from an aperture leading out of Paradise and spreading out like a fan over the interior of Asia. Abelard[58] explains carefully that if we interpret the Bible correctly there can be but one river within Paradise, that this divides into four outside of the Garden, and that the names given to each of the four are applied to those parts only "which flow from their sources to the sea." We may assume that he refers here to the portions of the rivers between points where they issue from their subterranean passages and their mouths. Some writers would seem to imply, Abelard continues, that we cannot take literally the words of the Bible because the sources of some of the four streams are known and those of others are not. But, he asks, may not those streams, whose sources are supposedly known, in reality arise elsewhere far away and pass through numerous countries before issuing forth to the knowledge of mankind? There is no question but that this is the case with many streams, as is shown, he adds, by the statement in Boethius' *De consolatione philosophiae* (a famous work of the sixth century much read throughout the Middle Ages) that "the Tigris and the Euphrates spring from one source."

One version of the legend of Prester John informs us that the four rivers of Paradise all arise in a spring in the mountains of India and water the two Indias.[59] Like most rivers of Prester John's realm, they give forth quantities of gold and precious stones at regular intervals three times a year.

Discussion of the individual characteristics of each of the four rivers falls more logically with the treatment of the ideas concerning the countries through which they flow and will be reserved until later. In most of the geographical works of our period, however, the rivers receive special consideration immediately after the remarks on Paradise and before the description of the regions of Asia. Their unusual origin and character, as described in Scripture, entitled them to particular distinction: they were holy streams to Jew and Christian alike. It is, then, a peculiarly eloquent commentary on the paganism of Bernard Sylvester to find that he mentions and describes the Euphrates, Tigris, and Nile in his *De mundi universitate*[60] without referring to Paradise in connection with any of these three streams. To his thinking they would seem to have occupied no higher or holier place among streams than Tiber, Rhone, or Seine.

ASIA

There are no more absorbing chapters in the history of geography than those connected with the growth of European knowledge of Asia in antiquity and during the Middle Ages[61] and with its converse, the growth of Oriental knowledge of the Occident.[62] Of late years the historical and archeological investigations of Albert von Le Coq, Sir Aurel Stein, Edouard Chavannes, Paul Pelliot, and Albert Herrmann have thrown a flood of light on the connections that existed in the earlier medieval period between eastern and western Asia. While these early connections may have brought some vague information regarding the Far East to the Byzantine world, they probably exerted almost no influence upon the conceptions of Asia prevalent in Western Europe before the middle of the thirteenth century.

The Opening of Asia in the Thirteenth Century

Relations between the Far East and Far West, however, were profoundly modified by certain events that took place during the first half of the thirteenth century. As a result of these events, Farther Asia for the first time in history was opened to Occidental travelers. Beginning with the year 1245 no inconsiderable number of European missionaries and traders made their way overland through the hitherto unknown heart of the continent and penetrated to the mysterious region of Cathay (China) at the ultimate point of the world. For somewhat more than a century the veil of the Extreme Orient was drawn aside, but drawn aside only again to be closed when the disruption of the Mongol empires and the rise of the Ottoman Turks barred the overland routes. It remained for Portuguese and Spanish seafarers of the great age of maritime exploration to rediscover the Far East. The history of the earlier relations of eastern and western Asia and of the opening of that continent in the thirteenth and fourteenth centuries, however, falls outside our province and cannot be discussed in detail in the present volume. A few words, nevertheless, must be said on this subject in order that the traditional geographical lore of Asia in our period may be seen in its proper perspective.

The Mongol Conquests

The events that led to the overland journeys sprang from the establishment of what was probably the most extensive military empire the world has ever known.[63] Toward the end of the twelfth century, Temujin, chief of a small tribe dwelling near the headwaters of the Amur, consolidated his dominion over the neighboring Mongol peoples of the steppes north and northwest of China. Proclaimed "Chinkkis Khan" (Jenghiz Khan), or

"Inflexible Emperor," in 1206, he soon conquered northern China and turned his hordes to the west; Turkestan was subjugated, Persia was invaded, and in 1222–1224 a detachment overran southern Russia in the course of a great whirlwind raid that completely encircled the Caspian Sea. Jenghiz Khan died in 1227, but under his successors the wave of conquest swept still farther westward. Toward the close of the thirties the steppes of Russia were again overwhelmed, in 1240 Poland was devastated, and the Christian army of Henry of Silesia was defeated in 1241 at Liegnitz, near Breslau. Meanwhile another Mongol army was ravaging Hungary and had even driven the king of that country to seek refuge in an island off the Dalmatian coast. Relief to the stricken people of Central Europe came, however, in 1243 when news of the death of the Great Khan caused the invaders to withdraw to the plains of Russia, there to maintain their hold for many centuries to come.

These visitations of the Tatars, as the Mongols were called, took Europe unaware. "Barely a rumour" of the invasion of Russia in 1222 had "reached western Europe," writes Rockhill,[64] "and contemporary writers have left us but few brief references to it." The first full description of the Tatars is given in Matthew Paris' *Chronica maiora*[65] for the date 1240, the following extracts of which, as translated by Rockhill, are worth quoting: "That the joys of mortal men be not enduring, nor worldly happiness long lasting without lamentations, in this same year (*i.e.* 1240) a detestable nation of Satan, to wit, the countless army of the Tartars, broke loose from its mountain-environed home, and piercing the solid rocks (of the Caucasus), poured forth like devils from the Tartarus, so that they are rightly called Tartari or Tartarians. Swarming like locusts over the face of the earth, they have brought terrible devastation to the eastern parts (of Europe), laying it waste with fire and carnage. . . . They are inhuman and beastly, rather monsters than men, thirsting for and drinking blood, tearing and devouring the flesh of dogs and men, dressed in ox-hides, armed with plates of iron, short and stout, thickset, strong, invincible, indefatigable, their backs unprotected, their breasts covered with armour. . . . They are without human laws, know no comforts, are more ferocious than lions or bears, have boats made of ox-hides, which ten or twelve of them own in common: they are able to swim or to manage a boat, so that they can cross the largest and swiftest rivers without let or hindrance, drinking turbid or muddy water when blood fails them (as beverage). . . . They know no other language than their own, which no one else knows; for until now there has been no access to them, nor did they go forth (from their own country); . . . They wander about with their flocks and their wives, who are taught to fight like men. . . . It is believed that these Tartars, of cursed memory, are of the ten tribes who, having forsaken the Mosaic law, followed after the golden calves, and whom Alexander the Macedonian endeavoured at first to shut up in the rugged mountains of the Caspians with bitumen-covered rocks.[66] When he saw that the undertaking exceeded the power of man, he invoked the might of the God of Israel, and the tops of the mountains came together, and an inaccessible and impassable place was made. . . . It is written in sacred history that they shall come out toward the end of the world, and shall make a great slaughter of men. There arises, however, a doubt whether the Tartars now coming from there be really they, for they do not use the Hebrew tongue, neither do they know the laws of Moses, nor have they laws, nor are they governed by them. . . ."

Despite the impression of extreme ferocity reflected in this passage, after the warlike ardor of conquest had somewhat subsided, the Mongols showed themselves not intolerant in their attitude toward strangers and not unreceptive of foreign influence. The immediate result of their withdrawal from Hungary to Russia and the consequent removal of the direct menace to Central Europe was the dispatch of Christian ecclesiastics as ambassadors to the Mongol lords. Rumors had come to Europe that these nomads from the Far East were monotheists, and hope sprang up that they might be converted to Roman Catholic Christianity and used to offset the reviving Moslem power menacing the Christian states of the Holy Land.[67] The origin of the rumors which gave rise to this elusive hope is to be sought in the fact that the Nestorian form of Christianity had been firmly established among some of the Mongol tribes north of the Great Wall of China and was represented even in their ruling dynasty. Furthermore, these rumors seemed to confirm and be confirmed by the reports that had been in circulation since the twelfth century of the existence of a great Christian kingdom of Prester John in the remote interior of Asia.[68]

Thirteenth-Century Journeys

The journeys of the diplomatic missions sent out by Pope Innocent IV and by Louis IX, King of France, in 1245 and the years immediately following have often been described.[69] The Pope's envoy, John of Pian de Carpine,[70] and Louis' representative, William of Rubruck,[71] reached the Mongol capital at Karakorum, near Lake Baikal, and on their return wrote graphic narratives of their journeys, which have been preserved and which give full account of the Tatars and their customs. Many of the observations made by John of Pian de Carpine and by Simon of St. Quentin (who took part in an expedition under Friar Ascelin, or Anselm, sent by the Pope to a Mongol ruler in Persia in 1247) are included in the *Speculum historiale* of Vincent of Beauvais.[72] The geographical information acquired by Rubruck, although it was ignored by other writers of the period, found its way to Roger Bacon, who incorporated much of it in the *Opus majus*.[73]

The way shown by Pian de Carpine and Rubruck was soon followed by Nicolo and Maffeo Polo, whose incentive was commercial, and by their far more famous son and nephew, Marco.[74] Marco Polo's amazing wanderings were succeeded by the journeys of others, among them the wonderful missionary enterprises of John of Monte Corvino, Riccold of Monte Croce, and Orderic of Pordenone. The story of these and other travels of the period,[75] fascinatingly told in the third volume of Beazley's *Dawn of Modern Geography*, falls far beyond the limits of our subject. Suffice it to remark, however, that the wanderings of the adventurous traders and friars were generally forgotten in the West during the centuries that followed and were largely ignored, even in the literature of the time itself. Marco Polo was branded as an impostor, and the traditional lore of eastern Asia that had come down from the days of the Roman Empire, together with its accretions of legend and romance, was held to be more worthy of credence than the observations of eyewitnesses. We must now turn to this traditional lore as expressed in the writings of the time of the Crusades.

The Great Mountain System of Asia

Asia, the author of the *De imagine mundi* [76] tells us, quoting from Isidore,[77] derived its name from a queen of that name.

The great system of mountains which runs eastward through the heart of the continent—the Caucasus, the ranges of northern Persia, the Hindu Kush, the Himalayas—was well known to the Greek geographers, and the men of our time had acquired some hazy notions about it through reading Orosius and Isidore.[78] Gervase of Tilbury,[79] copying Orosius,[80] tells how the Caucasus, joined by the "Imabus" (Imaus), divides India from Scythia and extends the entire length of Asia as far east as the Seric Ocean, though bearing different names in its eastern parts. Several of the maps show a straight range of mountains running east and west across the continent and labeled with various names (Taurus, Caucasus, Ceraunius, Paropamisus).[81] The Jerome map [81a] reveals, on the other hand, many mountains in Asia but does not make them continuous.

According to the *De imagine mundi*, the Caucasus divides the countries of southern from those of northern Asia. Among the former were India, Parthia, Mesopotamia, and Palestine, reaching in a straight line from the Far East to the Mediterranean.[82] Egypt, which was regarded as belonging to Asia by the Greek geographers and by Isidore, was held to adjoin Palestine on the west, and to be part of this southern tier of countries. North of the Caucasus were the lands of the Seres, Bactria, Hyrcania, and Scythia, in the east, and in western Asia, Armenia, the country of Mount Ararat, Cappadocia ("where mares conceive through the wind alone and give birth to foals that live only three years"), and finally Asia Minor, almost completely surrounded by the sea.[83]

The Land of the "Seres"

At the eastern end of Asia, Gervase, following the Roman geographers, had placed the Seres on the shores of an ocean named after them.[84] "Seres" was a classical designation of the people of China in so far as that country was the terminus of the overland route toward the Far East described by Pliny and Ptolemy. Beyond vast solitudes, the former had said,[85] you come to this remote land, where the people comb silk from the trees; though they carry on an extensive trade in this commodity, they avoid all personal dealings with strangers (whose commercial morality must have been high) by leaving the silk on the banks of streams to be picked up by those who wish to procure it. Solinus[86] copied Pliny's account, but Isidore,[87] followed by the author of the *De imagine mundi*,[88] gives us less detail, merely stating that Seres is a city of the East, from which were named the Seric region, the people, and a kind of cloth. Pausanias first among classical writers had understood that silk comes from a worm. The silk manufacture was introduced into the Byzantine Empire in 552 A. D., and it may well be from Byzantine sources that there originated the more or less correct understanding of its production revealed in the *Letter of Prester John*,[89] where we are informed that the salamander is a worm which makes a sort of capsule (*pellicula*) around him, "as do the other worms that make silk."

China

If the land of the Seres lay at the end of the overland route eastward, the sea route ended, according to the *Periplus of the Erythraean Sea*, at the land of "Thin" (China), and according to Ptolemy's *Geography* at the country of the "Sinae."[90] Here we have the first use in the West of the word "China," knowledge of which had probably reached the Occident through Arabic channels, though not until the sixteenth century was it recognized that the land of the "Seres" (Cathay) and "China" were the same.[91] An indication of the Ptolemaic "Sinae" is found in Plato of Tivoli's translation of Al-Battānī's *Astronomy*:[92] here a branch of the Indian Ocean is described as reaching to the furthest point of India where lies "Thiema" (China).

Benjamin of Tudela also speaks of the country of "Zin," or China, in the uttermost East near the reputed Sea of Nikpa, where violent and stormy winds blow—possibly the typhoons of Far Eastern waters. Ships carried into this sea by the winds stick fast there; their supplies of food give out, and the crews often die of starvation. In order to avoid this fate, some of the men, armed with knives, throw themselves into the sea and are carried to shore in the talons of an enormous bird, the griffon. By slaying the griffon with their knives they are able to escape.[93] This story reminds us, on the one hand, of Western reports of the congealed sea[94] and, on the other, of Arabic tales of the Rukh, which reappear in Marco Polo's travels.[95]

India

Subdivisions

More abundant and somewhat more accurate information was to be had regarding India. This name was applied loosely to cover all of Farther Asia: the anonymous report of the visit of the Patriarch John of India to Rome in 1122 calls India the ultimate border of the world. The Pseudo-Abdias[96] had quoted "certain historiographers" as asserting that there are three Indias, the first facing Ethiopia, the second facing the country of the Medes, and the third occupying the end of the earth, with the realm of darkness on one side and the ocean on the other. The threefold division of India was found on many of the maps.[97] It was adopted by Ordericus Vitalis in his *Historia ecclesiastica.*[98] It undoubtedly inspired the declaration in the *Letter of Prester John*[99] that that potentate rules over the "three Indias," and probably with it in mind Gervase of Tilbury[100] spoke of "India superior," where St. Bartholomew, "India inferior," where St. Thomas, and "India meridiana," where St. Matthew preached. On the other hand, there is evidence of a twofold division of India in the *Elysaeus*[101] account of Prester John's kingdom. The broad and loose medieval usage of the term "India" is especially well shown in the *Image du monde*, where it comprises not only what we now know as Hindustan but also Persia.[102]

Limiting ourselves to the narrower definition of India, the

tract between the Himalayas and the ocean, let us see what was believed to exist there.

Facts Known About India

A few facts were known, many half-facts, and a great many more fables. This knowledge and misinformation was based to a very large extent on classical authority, for little new had been learned about these parts of the world since the days of Pliny. First let us examine the facts and half-facts.[103] It was known that much of India lies beyond the tropic so that the shadows fall south in summer and north in winter. It was known that a giant range of mountains encloses India on the north, and perhaps there was a hint of familiarity with the Himalayan forests in the old story of trees so lofty that they touch the skies. It was likewise known that the Ganges takes its rise in the mountains to the north and is joined by many streams. According to Isidore, who was followed by the *De imagine mundi*, Peter Abelard, Gervase of Tilbury, Peter Comestor, and a host of other plagiarizers,[104] the Ganges is no other than the Pison, one of the rivers of Paradise, which springs from Mount Orcobares and flows eastward to the ocean. Peter Comestor explains[105] that "Phison" may mean "flock," because ten rivers join to make this stream,[106] an interpretation in which we see perhaps a reflection of the true characteristics of the great stream of India, so strikingly different from the other three "rivers of Paradise" by reason of its multitude of tributaries. The same idea, or possibly even a suggestion of the Ganges delta with its many outlets, is found in the *Letter of Prester John*,[107] where the river Ydonus is mentioned as one of the streams of Paradise, flowing across a pagan province of the realm of the great Christian potentate and spreading its branches throughout the entire area. The "Ydonus" doubtless means the Pison, or Ganges. It was also known in the time we are studying that there are other mighty rivers of India, among them the Indus, sweeping into the ocean.[108] Likewise it was appreciated that India supports an immense population and enormous riches; that many of the people are Brahmins—though little enough was understood about their religion; and that some of them practiced the custom of suttee, which prescribed that wives burn themselves on the funeral pyres of their husbands.

Benjamin of Tudela acquired (probably in Mesopotamia) some information about Khulam, or Quilon, a great medieval seaport on the Malabar coast. He comments briefly on the honesty and dark complexions of the natives, the intense heat of the summer, the practices connected with the cultivation of pepper, the customs of embalming the dead, and the superstitions of sun worship.[109]

Marvels of India

But India was above all else a land of marvels (Fig. 8). Here were pygmies who fight with storks and giants who combat with griffons; here were "gymnosophists" who contemplate the sun all day, standing in the hot rays first on one leg and then on the other; here were men with feet turned backward and eight toes on each foot; *cynocephali*, or men with dogs' heads and claws, who bark and snarl; people whose women give birth to but one child and that one with white hair; races whose hair is white in youth but turns dark with age; one-eyed men; people who shade themselves from the sun by lying on their backs and holding up a single huge foot (*skiapodes*); persons who live on the smell of food alone; headless men with eyes in their stomachs; forest peoples with hairy bodies, dogs' teeth, and terrific voices; and a variety of horrible non-human monsters combining the parts of several animals.[110]

These marvels and more still are related by nearly all the Western writers of our period who concern themselves with India and the Orient. They originated, as we have seen, early in classical times. Collected by Ctesias,[111] Pliny, Solinus and others, they were passed on to our age, when we find them faithfully retold by the author of the *De imagine mundi*, by Gervase of Tilbury, by Rudolf of Hohen-Ems,[112] and in the *Image du monde*. They made their way into the Romance of Alexander as exemplified by the *Pseudo-Callisthenes* and the *Letter from Alexander to Aristotle*. In short, the "marvels of India" were a stock feature of medieval geography.[113] They figure on maps and in miniatures and even in architectural sculpture—a *skiapod* helps adorn the façade of Sens cathedral.

Two mythological personages and one historical character, the story of whose exploits became mythological in the Middle Ages, were supposed to have visited India. These were Bacchus (Liber Pater), Hercules, and Alexander the Great. The Altar of Liber and the Column of Hercules are shown on the Psalter map in the region between the Red Sea and Paradise.[114] On the Jerome map of Palestine two columns mark the ultimate limits of the journeys of Alexander and of Hercules.[115] The *Letter of Alexander to Aristotle* mentions the miraculous trees of the sun and moon, which spoke oracular words to the Macedonian conqueror and figured widely in the medieval geography of the Far East, appearing prominently on many of the maps.[116]

Legend of St. Thomas in India

Though classical antiquity was the main source of medieval knowledge and fancy concerning India, it was not the only source. The mysterious Ophir, whence came the gold and jewels of Solomon, was placed in India on the Lambert map [117] and on the Jerome map of the world.[118] There also early came into existence a well-rooted idea that this country was the home of a large and flourishing Christian colony. The origins of the latter belief are to be found in reports which had filtered through to Europe at an early date of St. Thomas the Apostle's preaching of the gospel in India and of the existence of Nestorian Christianity in southern Hindustan.[119] The story of St. Thomas contains some elements of geographical interest.[120] Christ was said to have sold Thomas to the merchant Habban in order that he might be taken to India to convert the people. Once arrived there by ship, having landed at a port of Sandaruk, or Andrapolis, he succeeded in gaining for the Christian religion the king, Gundophorus, and his brothers. The saint built for the king a palace in heaven. According to the original story, this palace was not a real structure but merely the symbol of a heavenly habitation for the monarch. As the legend was subsequently

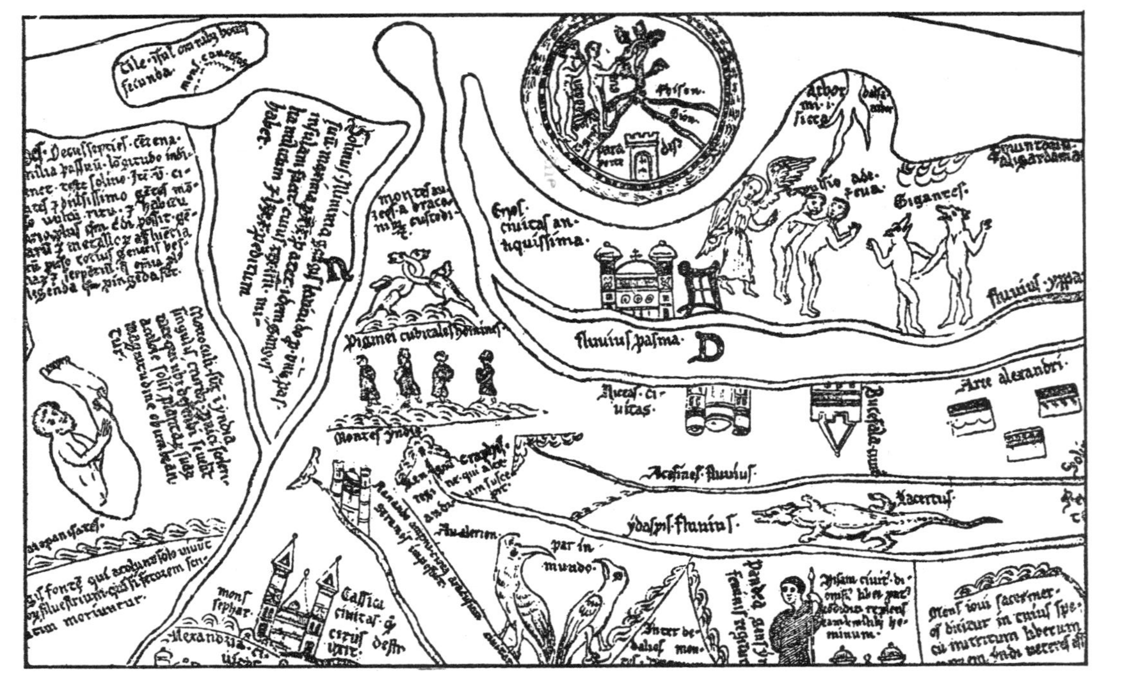

FIG. 8—Two sections from the Hereford map to illustrate the marvels of India. (From the reproduction accompanying Miller, *Mappaemundi*, vol. iv, 1896.)

In this first section are shown, among others, a *skiapod*, or sunshade-footed man (to the left), and *cynocephali*, or men with dogs' heads.

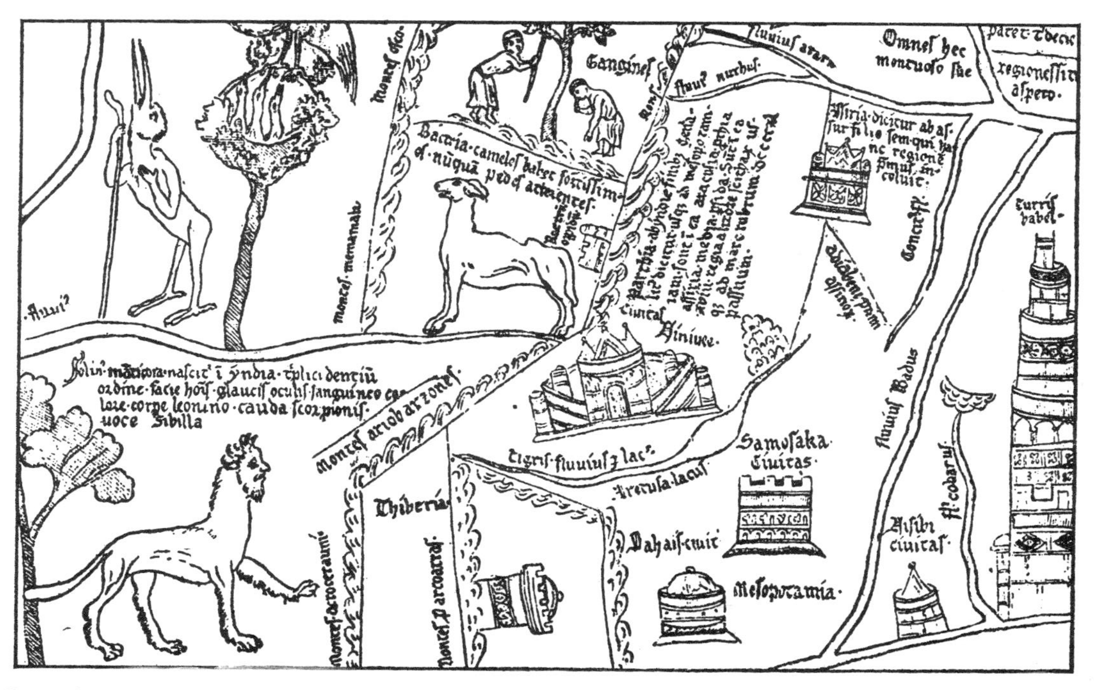

FIG. 8 (second section)—In this section is shown a *mantichora*, or beast with a man's head and a lion's body.

developed, St. Thomas was represented as an architect whom Gundophorus summoned to his court to build an actual dwelling, and one of the miracles by which the saint succeeded in converting the Indian potentate to Christianity was his almost instantaneous construction of the palace. The legend then proceeds to relate how St. Thomas was conducted by one Siphorius to the kingdom of a certain Mazdeus, of his martyrdom at the hands of the latter, and of the subsequent removal of his body to Edessa in Syria.

The stories of St. Thomas and St. Bartholomew were often retold during our period, notably, for instance, in the *Historia ecclesiastica* of Ordericus Vitalis.[121] The Osma Beatus map [122] shows heads representing the twelve apostles in the various countries of the world; that of St. Thomas is placed in India (see Fig. 4, p. 123, above). The unknown writer of the *Letter of Prester John* was undoubtedly familiar with the legend of St. Thomas, because he makes Prester John's palace correspond exactly to the palace built by the saint.[123] This legend was a favorite subject for representation in the sculptures of cathedrals and stained glass windows of the twelfth and thirteenth centuries.[124]

Visit of Patriarch John of India to Rome

Belief in the existence of a large Christian population in Asia was reënforced by an obscure event that took place in Rome in 1122. We have an anonymous account [125] of the visit of a certain Patriarch John of India in that year and of the stupendous sensation which it created in the Roman curia and throughout the whole of Italy. The narrator informs us that in the course of countless ages no native was ever known to have come from those distant and barbaric Oriental regions, nor had any one ever before been seen in Italy who had actually been there.[126] The purpose of the patriarch's visit to the West originally was to procure at Byzantium the pallium and the confirmation of his office, which he had recently assumed on the death of his predecessor. At Byzantium, however, being told that Rome was in reality the capital of the world,[127] he proceeded thither along with some homeward-bound Roman ambassadors and while in Rome gave a lecture about his native country before the papal curia. The principal city, he said, was Hulna, on the river Pison, one of the four rivers of Paradise; the city was of huge size, surrounded by gigantic walls and inhabited by faithful Christians. Outside the walls there was a mountain encircled by a very deep lake and on the top of the mountain was situated the Church of St. Thomas. Surrounding the lake were twelve monasteries erected in honor of the twelve apostles. The Church of St. Thomas was inaccessible except once a year, when the waters of the lake disappeared, allowing pilgrims to approach. The Patriarch John then went on to explain in considerable detail the marvels and miracles connected with the church.

We should be inclined—and justifiably—to reject the story of Patriarch John's visit as wholly fanciful, did it not seem to be confirmed by a letter [128] to a certain Count Thomas written by Odo, abbot of St. Remi in Rheims (1118–1151), who happened to be in Rome at the time John was there. The report of Odo about this event was probably not derived from the anonymous account, from which it differs in several minor details. Among other matters, according to Odo, John speaks of a river, not a lake, surrounding the shrine of St. Thomas and of how its waters diminished as a result of drought and became passable to a boy of seven years during eight days before and eight days after the festival of the apostle. The whole clergy and (Christian) people of India were said to gather here on this occasion.

We shall see shortly that these stories contributed to the formation of the curious medieval belief in the existence of a great Christian kingdom in the heart of Asia. First, however, we must consider what notions were current regarding the seas and islands to the south of India and the vast tracts to the northward beyond the Himalayan barrier.

Indian Ocean

A very brilliant feature on the maps of our period is the Red Sea, almost invariably colored red. This name was given to the entire Indian Ocean, and the red color was applied to the Persian Gulf as well as to the "Arabian Gulf," or Red Sea proper. The name "Indian Ocean" was also occasionally used, as, for example, on the Jerome map of the East.[129]

The Greeks had acquired some fairly correct information about the northwestern shores of the Indian Ocean and had heard vague rumors of the great peninsula and islands east and south of India: Malaya, Ceylon, Sumatra. Confused reports of the geography of Taprobane, or Ceylon, are found in classical works as far back as the time of the expedition of Alexander. Pliny, Solinus, Ptolemy, and others described Taprobane in some detail but exaggerated its dimensions to enormous proportions. Pomponius Mela had spoken of the islands of Chryse, lying off the eastern promontory of Asia, and Argyre, off the mouth of the Ganges. Perhaps these represented some vague knowledge of the Andamans or Nicobars or the Malay Peninsula; and certainly we recognize the last-named in the Aurea Chersonesus of Ptolemy.

Islands of the Indian Ocean

Some relics of this classical knowledge of Indian seas and isles was retained in the Middle Ages. Isidore[130] had spoken of "Chrisa" and "Argare" as full of gold and silver and perpetually blooming flowers, with mountains of gold guarded by dragons and griffons. This account found its way into the *De imagine mundi*[131] and was copied by Gervase of Tilbury;[132] the islands themselves, together with the "Island of the Sun" of Pliny, Mela, Solinus, and others, figured on many contemporary maps.[133] Orosius had said that in Taprobane there were ten cities.[134] Isidore, whom Gervase of Tilbury copied, added that the dimensions of the island were 875 by 625 miles, that it has two summers and two winters each year, and that the vegetation always remains green.[135] Solinus had described[136] Taprobane as being divided in two by a river; one half, he said, was full of wild beasts, but the other was inhabited by men. This division of the island is perpetuated on the Henry of Mayence,[137] Jerome,[138] Hereford,[139] and Ebstorf maps.[140]

Al-Battānī on the Indian Ocean

The geographical chapter in Al-Battānī's *Astronomy*, probably compiled from a redaction of Ptolemy's *Geography* and translated by Plato of Tivoli in our period, gave a description of the seas of the world.[141] The Indian Ocean, Al-Battānī said, extends from the land of the negroes to the exteme limits of India, a distance of 8000 miles. Its width was 2200 miles, of which 1900 (Plato of Tivoli mistakenly translated this 3900) reach south of the equator. What lands lay beyond are not specified. From this sea four gulfs run into the land: first the Barbaric Sea, which extends into the "land of the negroes," or Ethiopia, and may be the Gulf of Aden or possibly even Mozambique Channel; second, the Green Sea (Mare Viride), or our Red Sea, which reaches towards Hyla (Ailah?); third, the Persian Gulf (Mare Persicum); and, fourth, a second Green Sea, running out to the east towards China ("Thinae") and representing the Bay of Bengal or possibly the China Sea. In the Indian Ocean there are some 1370 islands, among them a very large one called "Tibiariae" (Taprobane), or Sarandib (Ceylon), opposite the eastern coast of India, 3000 miles in circumference, full of great mountains and rivers, quantities of rubies and hyacinths, and surrounded by fifty-nine lesser isles. The traditional account of the many isles of the Indian seas so persistent in Arabic literature arose unquestionably from familiarity with the vast Malay Archipelago or at least with its western portion. On the other hand, whether we may assume, as some have done, that the exaggerated classical and Arabic estimates of the size of Ceylon had their origin in rumors of the existence of Australia[142] is an obscure problem which we cannot attempt here to solve.

Scythia and Central Asia

North of the mountain barrier enclosing India lay lands about which Western medieval knowledge was equally vague. "Upper Scythia, stretching from the Caspian Sea to the Seric Ocean and southward to the Caucasus, includes much habitable land but also much that is sterile: gold and gems abound there, but men avoid them on account of the griffons. Lower Scythia adjoins Hyrcania, so called from the Hyrcanian Forest, where a marvelous bird is found whose plumage glows in the dark. Iranea, or Iran, is next to Scythia on the west: a region of nomads who wander widely because of the sterility of the soil and who are horrible and ferocious (*portentuosi ac truces*), eaters of human flesh and drinkers of human blood." In about these terms the author of the *De imagine mundi* and Gervase of Tilbury, borrowing from Isidore,[143] summed up very nearly all that was known of Central Asia before the great overland journeys of the thirteenth century to which brief reference has already been made.[144] Several of the maps show large rivers—Araxes, Oxus, Oscorus, and even Acheron, the stream of Tartarus—rising in the Caucasus and flowing northward into the Caspian.[145] The latter, in accordance with the usual classical tradition, is represented as a gulf of the encircling Ocean Stream.

Benjamin of Tudela on Central Asia

Benjamin of Tudela, who himself journeyed at least as far east as Baghdad, had opportunities for gaining information about Central and Northern Asia more favorable than those of his less traveled contemporaries. Samarkand he mentions briefly as a "great city on the confines of Persia" inhabited by 50,000 Jews. "Thence," he adds, "it is four days' journey to Tibet, the country in whose forests the musk is found" (Adler's translation).[146] He quotes the reports of Persian Jews that four of the lost ten tribes of Israel dwell in the mountains of Naisabur (in eastern Persia). These people were said to be independent and to dwell in a broad tract of land twenty days' journey in extent, with cities and large villages among the mountains.[147] Others associated the lost tribes with the abhorrent hordes of Gog and Magog.[148] Benjamin goes on to tell us that these Jews were in league with the "Kufar-al-Turak, who worship the wind and live in the wilderness and who do not eat bread nor drink wine but live on raw, uncooked meat. They have no noses, and in lieu thereof they have two small holes through which they breathe" (Adler's translation).[149] He relates the confused story of wars between these undeniably Turanian tribes of the steppes of Turkestan and the "King of Persia" (the Seljuk Sultan, Sanjar), events which perhaps gave rise to a legend that became widespread in twelfth-century Europe and to which we must now turn.

Prester John

The legend was the romantic story that in these far regions there lay a vast and powerful Christian kingdom ruled by a mighty potentate, Prester John. This tradition was the most important contribution of our period to regional geography, for, false as it was, it long persisted, became an integral part of late medieval geographical theory, and exerted in subsequent centuries a powerful influence on the course of exploration. The thirteenth-century Oriental travelers were constantly on the lookout for Prester John's kingdom and, when it finally became obvious that there was no such kingdom in Asia, Prester John was transferred to Africa, where he was sought for by the Portuguese navigators of the fourteenth and fifteenth centuries. How did this strange legend come into existence, and what did it contribute to Western notions of Asia?

Origins of the Legend

Various elements seem to have given rise to it. Perhaps rumors of the existence of a Christian nation in Abyssinia may at a very early period have fostered belief in the existence of a great Christian potentate in Asia. India in Asia and Ethiopia in Africa were often confused both in antiquity and during the Middle Ages. Furthermore, the story of the visit of the Indian archbishop or patriarch, already referred to, encouraged belief in a numerous Asiatic Christian population. Some of the elements of the patriarch's report became an integral part of one of the twelfth-century versions of the story of Prester John.

Then again, we have echoes of actual events in the East in Benjamin of Tudela's *Itinerary*, as we have just seen, and in Otto of Freising's *Chronicon*. Otto relates [150] that in 1145 the bishop of Gabala in Syria had come to Viterbo to report to Pope Eugenius III, among other things, the fall of Edessa. Here Otto met the bishop, and what he learned is recorded in the *Chronicon*. This was to the effect that, not very long before, a certain John, king and priest, who dwelt in the Far East beyond Persia and Armenia and who, together with his tribe (*gens*), was a Christian, waged war with the Samiards (Saniards), two brothers who were kings of the Medes and Persians. John captured Ecbatana, the capital of the Samiards' realm, defeated the brothers in battle, and put them to flight. He then proceeded to advance to the aid of the church at Jerusalem but was hindered from going very far by the river Tigris. Turning northwards in hope that the river would freeze over and thereby enable him to cross, he was finally constrained, after several years had elapsed, to give up the enterprise because continued warm weather prevented ice from forming. This John, Otto added, was said to have come of very ancient lineage, in fact, to have been one of the progeny of the Magi. The tribes under his command were perhaps the same as the "Kufar-al-Turak" of Benjamin of Tudela.[151]

Though the attempt has been made to identify the Christian potentate of the legend with a chieftain of the Caucasus,[152] the weight of evidence would seem to favor belief that the story in its more specific thirteenth-century form grew out of rumors of some Christian Mongol lord of Central Asia.[153] It is certain that the Nestorian form of Christianity was strongly represented in Central Asia during this period and that two powerful tribes of these distant regions, the Keraïts and the Onguts, formed outposts of this faith. But, as Pelliot writes, "whatever may have been the origin of the famous legend of Prester John, . . . it was to a prince of the Keraïts that the tradition was applied during the first half of the thirteenth century. All the Keraïts spoken of in the history of the Mongol dynasty seem to have been Christians; in any case this is true of the majority of them. In fact it was through marriage with Keraït princesses that Christianity penetrated even into the family of Jenghiz Khan."[154] Many of these Asiatic Christians bore Christian names preserved in Chinese forms, such as Yao-su-mu for Joseph or K'wo-li-ki-ssö for George.[155] We learn from Marco Polo and other thirteenth-century travelers that Mongol princes often submitted to baptism, though this was probably done out of indifference to religion rather than as the expression of any deep-seated convictions.

On such slender foundations as the report in Otto's *Chronicon* or the anonymous account of the visit of the Patriarch John to

Rome or on other rumors of events in the heart of Asia of which no record has been preserved, there was erected an elaborate, detailed, and wholly fanciful series of descriptions of Prester John and his realm, embellished by borrowings from the Romance of Alexander, from the legend of St. Thomas, and from that world of fable which constituted the medieval European conception of the Orient.

Prester John's Kingdom As Described in His "Letter"

The most important description of Prester John's kingdom is contained in the famous *Letter*, addressed in some manuscripts to Manuel, the Byzantine Emperor, in others to Frederick, the Roman Emperor; in still others, to the Pope. In this letter,[156] the earliest version of which dates from before 1177, John tells that he is superior in wealth and power to all the kings of the world. His realm includes the three Indias and St. Thomas' shrine. It extends across the desert of Babylon to the tower of Babel and contains seventy-two provinces, each ruled over by a king. Prester John is lord of the Amazons and Brahmins. In one direction his territory reaches out four months' journey. In the other, no one can tell how far. "Only if you could count the stars of the heaven and the sands of the sea would you be able to form an estimate of our dominion and our power." Many are the extraordinary features of this realm which abounds in milk and honey: here is one of the rivers of Paradise; here are streams that give forth gold and jewels; here pepper is gathered; here is the fountain of youth; and here a mysterious sea of sand fed by a river of rocks, beyond which dwell the ten tribes of the Jews, who, although they have their own kings, are nevertheless subject to the mighty Christian ruler. In one of the provinces near the torrid zone the salamander thrives, a "worm" which cannot live without fire and which makes a chrysalis about himself as do the silkworms (an interesting and unexpected bit of natural history embedded in the midst of fable). Prester John takes particular delight in expatiating on the enormous wealth of his country, on the virtues of its inhabitants—for among them there are neither liars nor adulterers nor indeed vice or crime of any description—and on their clemency and Christian piety. Every year the king makes a pilgrimage with his army across the serpent-infested Babylonian desert to the shrine of the prophet Daniel. A large part of the *Letter* is taken up with a minute description of the royal palace—exactly like that which St. Thomas built for the King Gundophorus, of the king's household, the grandees who wait upon him, the officials of the kingdom, etc., etc. In an early Latin version of the *Letter*, written probably in England, we are informed that there are people from all countries of the world at Prester John's court;[157] among the personal servants of the king there are Englishmen who wait upon him at table. No less than eleven thousand Englishmen are in his bodyguard, and every Englishman who comes to the court, whether clerk or knight, is invested with the order of knighthood. The French and Italian versions of the *Letter*, which were probably translated from this Latin text, substitute "François" and "Franceschi" for "Anglici."

Alliance With Prester John Desired

During the thirteenth century it was the vain hope of the Popes and of the Christian kings of Europe to gain the alliance of some great power in the East—either the Mongols or Prester John—as an offset to Turkish encroachments on the Crusaders' frontiers.[158] Perhaps we may detect the beginnings of this policy in a letter of Pope Alexander III (1177) to John, "Magnificus rex Indorum sacerdotum sanctissimus."[159] The Pope informs the great king that he has heard of his piety through a certain Master Philip, papal physician, who had held conversation with distinguished and honorable persons of his realm. Consequently Alexander was sending this Philip to expound to him the tenets of Western Christianity and to convert him to the true Catholic faith. It seems probable that Alexander was acquainted with the supposed letter of Prester John to the Byzantine Emperor, though there is also strong probability that he had confused the stories of the Asiatic Prester John with reports regarding the Christian kingdom of Abyssinia—a source of much confusion at a later period than ours.

Gog and Magog

The northern part of Asia was the reputed seat of the terrible tribes of Gog and Magog, whose eruption at the Last Day was destined to bring about the destruction of the human race. We have seen that Biblical prophecies were combined with the story of Alexander the Great's enclosing of these tribes behind great walls. The legend appears in our period under various forms. Most of the maps show Gog and Magog, usually surrounded by a wall; some add disparaging epithets, such as "gens immunda." Matthew Paris on his map of Palestine indicates in the north the walls whereby King Alexander the Great shut in Gog and Magog and states in the explanatory legend that from this same direction came the Tatars.[160] In the *De imagine mundi*[161] we find a simple statement that between the Caspian Mountains and the sea of that name dwelt those tribes who had been walled in by Alexander the Great, Gog and Magog, the fiercest of all peoples, eaters of the raw flesh of wild beasts and of human beings. The Moslems had placed Gog and Magog in the farthest corner of northeastern Asia: and in John of Seville's translation of Al-Farghānī's *Astronomy* we find the land of Gog at the easternmost extremity of the sixth and seventh "climates" (those farthest north).[162] Lambert li Tors speaks in the Romance of Alexander of "Gos et Magos" among the vassals of Porus: though they came forth with four hundred thousand men, Alexander, after he had defeated Porus, chased them back into the defiles of the mountains, where he shut them in with a great wall.[163] In a later part of the Romance, the subdivision of Alexander's kingdom at his death is explained: to Antigonus was given Syria and Persia as far as Mount Tus, together with the duty of standing guard over Gog and Magog.[164] Otto of Freising also mentions these tribes.[165] He derived his information from Frutolf's *Chronica*,[166] whence, in turn, it had come from the version of the Romance of Alexander known as the *Historia de praeliis*. In the days of Heraclius, Otto says, the "Agareni" (Saracens) devastated the lands of the empire and destroyed part of the army of Heraclius. In revenge the latter opened the Caspian Gates and let out those most savage tribes, which Alexander the

Great had enclosed along the Caspian Sea on account of their heinousness, and inaugurated a war against the Saracens. By night, as a punishment sent by the Deity for this sacrilegious act, fifty-two thousand of Heraclius' army were struck down by lightning, and, as a result of this terrible visitation, Heraclius himself died in the twenty-seventh year of his reign.

There were many variations of the legend of Gog and Magog. Elsewhere in Otto of Freising's *Chronicon*[167] we find an account, taken from Orosius, of the way in which Artaxerxes forced many of the Jews to dwell in Hyrcania near the Caspian Sea. It was believed that these people had multiplied greatly,[168] and they were expected to burst forth on the world in the days of Antichrist. Though not here expressly called Gog and Magog, the connection is plain; and Godfrey of Viterbo relates how Alexander enclosed Gog and Magog, the "eleven [*sic*] tribes of the Jews."[169] We have already quoted[170] Matthew Paris' description of the Tatars who, he said, might be the same as the tribes whom Alexander enclosed—the ten tribes of Israel.

Western Asia

When we turn from the remote parts of the Orient to Western Asia we find ourselves in regions much better known to the Western world, though the traditional geography of these regions, founded on classical and Biblical authority, persisted in encyclopedic writings hardly influenced at all by the contacts that in reality had been established. The *De imagine mundi*, Gervase of Tilbury's *Otia imperialia*, and other similar works add little to what Isidore and Orosius had written. Between the Indus and Tigris lie many countries, Arachosia, Parthia, Assyria, Persia, Media, all forming a harsh and mountainous tract called in Scripture "India" but more generally known as Parthia. Fire had been discovered in Persia.[171] The Tigris, so called because it is as swift as a tiger, rises from a common source with the Euphrates in the mountains of Armenia.[172] Thence the two rivers separate, leaving a long space between them known as Mesopotamia; the Tigris encircles Assyria and empties into the Dead Sea! Peter Comestor and the author of the *De imagine mundi* accepted the views of Isidore regarding the source of the Tigris in the highlands of Armenia,[173] but the latter adds to the already prevailing confusion by stating that both rivers of Mesopotamia debouch into the Mediterranean Sea. Gervase, on the other hand, corrects the error of the author of the *De imagine mundi* by making them flow into the Red Sea (or Indian Ocean),[174] as was depicted on most maps.

Mesopotamia

Mesopotamia was said to be famous as the site of Nineveh and of Chaldea, where astronomy was discovered;[175] and Gervase of Tilbury dilates on the immense size of the walls of Babylon.[176] Regarding Babylon, it is refreshing to find in Otto of Freising's *Chronicon* some really up-to-date information which he had derived from Frutolf.[177] In the first place, he makes a careful distinction between Babylon and Cairo, to which the name of Babylon was commonly given. "Old Babylon," he added, "as we learn from reliable men from across the seas, is partly inhabited at the present day and now called Baldach [Baghdad]. Part, however, as you would expect from the words of prophecy, is a desert waste extending for ten miles as far as the tower of Babel. The part which is inhabited and called Baldach is very large and populous." He explains that here is the seat of the greatest priest of the Persians, whom they call "Caliph," and who holds in some respects a position among these pagans parallel to that which the Pope at Rome holds among Christians.

With Baghdad we have at last come to a city that was actually visited and described during our period by Western Europeans whose descriptions have come down to us. The Jewish travelers, Benjamin of Tudela and Petachia of Ratisbon, appear to have sojourned in the Mesopotamian city in the seventh and ninth decades of the twelfth century respectively.

Benjamin of Tudela on Baghdad

Benjamin's personal familiarity with Baghdad saved him from making Frutolf's and Otto's mistake of confusing the Abbasid capital with old Babylon. We gather from Benjamin's *Itinerary* that the latter is three days' journey distant and that "the ruins of the palace of Nebuchadnezzar are still to be seen there, but people are afraid to enter them on account of serpents and scorpions" (Adler's translation).[178]

Baghdad, Benjamin writes (our quotations are from Adler's translation), "is on the River Tigris," which "divides the metropolis in two parts." The city "is twenty miles in circumference, situated in a land of palms, gardens, and plantations, the like of which is not to be found in the whole land of Shinar. People come thither with merchandise from all lands. Wise men live there, philosophers who know all manner of wisdom, and magicians expert in all manner of witchcraft."[179] Benjamin was particularly interested in the Caliph, of whose palace, park, family, and widespread authority he writes in no little detail and in highly commendatory terms,[180] for it seems that the Caliphs were more tolerant toward the Jews than were most Christian monarchs of the age. Besides treating of the Caliph, Benjamin tells about the "Head of the Captivity," another powerful ruler whose headquarters were Baghdad and in whom the Caliph had vested authority over all the Jewish communities throughout the eastern Moslem world. A descendant of David, King of Israel, he was a man of great dignity and rank, held high in the esteem of the Mohammedans. His power extended "over all the communities of Shinar, Persia, Khurasan, and Sheba, which is El-Yemen, and Diyar Kalach (Bekr) and the land of Aram Naharaim (Mesopotamia) and over the dwellers in the mountains of Ararat and the land of the Alans, which is a land surrounded by mountains and has no outlet except by the iron gates which Alexander made but which were afterwards broken. Here are the people called Alani. His authority extends also over the land of Siberia [Sikbia?] and the communities in the land of Togarmim[181] unto the mountains of Asveh and the land of Gurgan, the inhabitants of which are called Gurganim who dwell by the river Gihon (Oxus?); and these are the Girgashites who follow the Christian religion. Further it extends to the gates of Samarkand, the land of Tibet, and the land of India. In respect of all these countries the Head of the Captivity gives the communities power to appoint Rabbis and Ministers who come unto him to be consecrated and to receive his authority. They bring him offerings and gifts from the ends of the earth."[182]

Whether or not Benjamin was personally presented to the Head of the Captivity we are not informed. In any case he undoubtedly came into contact at Baghdad with Jews from all over Central and Western Asia and from them was able to gather those details regarding the Jewish communities which form such an important and interesting part of his *Itinerary*. Most striking in this connection are the data which he furnishes us about the Jews of Arabia.

Benjamin of Tudela on Arabia

The interior of that great peninsula until recently has remained very vaguely known to Western Christians, and in the Middle Ages there reigned almost complete ignorance regarding it. Gervase of Tilbury tells us (from Orosius) that Arabia lies between two seas and is the country of Mount Sinai, of the Queen of Sheba, and of frankincense.[183] Beyond this and a few details about the Bedouins picked up by the Crusaders, nothing was known. Hence the information which Benjamin gives on the Jewish communities is of exceptional importance. If we may trust his figures, it would seem that there was at this time a large Jewish population both in Yemen and farther north. Benjamin's conception of the geography of the peninsula, however, is remarkably confused. He tells us that at a distance of twenty-one days' journey through the deserts from Hillah in Mesopotamia one comes to the land of Saba, or El-Yemen. Here he places the great Jewish cities of Tanai, Tilmas, Teima, and Kheibar. Neither Tilmas nor Tanai have been definitely identified. To the former Benjamin assigned a population of 100,000 Jews; to the latter, with the district surrounding, a population of no less than 300,000 Jews. They may represent Jewish settlements in Yemen, though Benjamin's statement that Tilmas is only three days from Kheibar would seem to preclude this possibility. Tanai, on the other hand, has been thought to be Sanaa. Kheibar (to which Benjamin assigns 50,000 Jews) and Teima have long been well-known towns of northern Arabia not far from Medina. Now inhabited by half-breed negroes, these places were the centers of a Jewish population from before the times of Mohammed until as late as the sixteenth century.[184]

In a totally different connection Benjamin refers to Jews of the "land of Aden," which he believed to be part of India, taking India to include southern Arabia and Ethiopia. Their country he describes as mountainous. The Jewish element in the population, he adds, "are not under the yoke of the Gentiles but possess castles on the summits of the mountains from which they make descents into the plain country called Libya, which is a Christian empire" (Adler's translation).[185] This is indeed confusing. If by Libya Abyssinia is meant—which is likely, for Abyssinia was a Christian kingdom from very early times—it seems peculiar that Benjamin makes no mention of the Red Sea intervening between the land of Aden in Arabia Felix and the African coasts which would have to be crossed by Jews of the Aden highlands in making war on the Abyssinians. Possibly Benjamin, like Marco Polo a century later, conceived of Aden as lying in Africa.[186]

Syria and Palestine

Unlike all the rest of Asia, Syria and Palestine were well known at first hand to many European Christians. Yet, in writing about them, the makers of compilations like the *De imagine mundi* and the *Otia imperialia* were content to do little more than copy Isidore's dry catalogue of the names of places rendered famous through Scriptural associations.[187] The Dead Sea with its sinister neighborhood was the only natural feature of this part of the world which seems to have made a strong enough appeal to the imagination of these writers to impel them to add anything to what Isidore had said long before.[188]

Geographical Knowledge Enlarged by the Crusades

On the other hand, the Levantine countries were familiar through the journeys of Western travelers, though their observations were not incorporated into the works of the scholarly compilers. Many were the motives that induced men of the West to visit the Nearer East. Religious enthusiasm and the desire for commercial gain, however, were paramount. The Crusades contributed more than any great series of events between the time of Claudius Ptolemy and the middle of the thirteenth century to the broadening of man's geographical horizon, and, with it, the broadening of the whole range of human activity. We cannot attempt to discuss these wider aspects of the Crusading movement in any detail, but a few words must be said about the dissemination of regional knowledge that resulted from it. Feudal nobility, soldiers, pilgrims, and adventurers of all sorts and from all parts of the West were joined by Italian merchants in the great enterprise, the object of which was not only to redeem the holy places from the infidel but also to profit from the Levantine trade. Men of all ranks and callings, coming from every part of Christendom, made their way by land and sea to the Holy Land. Peasant, serf, and petty townsman, as well as powerful noble and church dignitary, were torn from old and familiar environments to wander through countries about which they had hitherto known next to nothing. In some cases the stories of their travels and adventures were preserved in chronicles and poems, but in most no permanent record was left. Nevertheless, the geographical knowledge of the average man was widened to an extent which we can scarcely appreciate at the present day. Before the Crusades communities throughout the greater part of Europe had lived very much to themselves, in limited contact with the outside world; but by the year 1200 it is safe to infer that practically every town and village of France, England, Germany, and Italy held someone who had visited the East and was not unready to tell about what he had seen there and on his way out and back. Just as the War of 1914–1918 has taught the world much European geography, so the Crusades taught all classes of Europe about the Holy Land and the routes thither. But the Crusades did more than give the people a wider knowledge of places: they brought them into contact with new customs, new religions, new ideals and modes of life, as well as with new types of landscape and terrain. All this tended to displace men from habitual and local modes of thought; Europe became more cosmopolitan, and the way was prepared for that profound change in man's entire attitude towards life which we now call the Renaissance.

Occidental Population of the Levant

We can merely hint at these general results of the extension of geographical contact with the Levantine world and turn to the more specific problem of the limits to which Western penetration was actually pushed. The Occidental population of the states established after the First Crusade along the eastern border of the Mediterranean was composed primarily of the Frankish nobility and soldiery and of Italian traders.[189] The former had established themselves in castles and garrisons, from which they ruled over widespread manorial estates tilled by native Syrians. The traders occupied large foreign quarters in such commercial centers as Acre, Jaffa, Ascalon, Tyre, and Tripoli on the coasts, and in the interior at Jerusalem. Trading privileges and the right to build up commercial colonies in the towns were granted to Genoese, Pisans, Venetians, and others in return for services rendered the Crusading armies by the Italian navies in the conquest of the coast towns and in the transportation of military forces. Through the reports brought back to Europe by returning soldiers, adventurers, and merchants, Syria and Palestine became more widely and accurately known in the West than most parts of Europe itself.

European Occupation of Syria

First-hand acquaintance with the Levant, however, did not, either in the twelfth or in the thirteenth century, necessarily lead to first-hand acquaintance with the neighboring countries that still lay under the domination of the Turk. At the time of its greatest extent the Kingdom of Jerusalem reached eastward to the edge of the desert plateau beyond the Jordan and Dead Sea and southward to Ailah on the Gulf of Akaba. Northeastward the upper Tigris marked the frontier of the County of Edessa. Beyond these restricted borders lay Saracen territory into which traders from the West did not dare to venture. Southern Mesopotamia was virtually *terra incognita;* and the men who held the small garrison posts along the eastern border of the states of the Crusaders were not prone to undertake rash enterprises in the enemy's country.

The danger of such enterprises is illustrated by the fate of a

Christian naval expedition sent down the Red Sea from Akaba in 1182–1183.[190] A small fleet, fitted out by Reynauld of Châtillon, lord of the castle of Kerak beyond the Jordan, succeeded in getting almost as far as Yembo, the port of Medina. We are not told of its true purpose by the Arabic historians, who alone seem to have recorded this adventure, though the Arabs certainly believed that the Crusaders were bent upon plundering the tomb of the prophet at Medina. Perhaps its leaders harbored a fanatic hope of attacking the holy cities of Islam. At all events, the navy of Saladin, hastily summoned from Egypt, soon overtook and defeated the little squadron at Haura, and those of the Crusaders who escaped ashore were either killed by the Bedouins or sold into slavery.

But though, with a few exceptions, Europeans themselves did not go beyond these bounds of the Crusaders' states, commercial relations were established with the more eastern regions.[191] Antioch and Laodicea were the termini of two trade routes from Aleppo, whence came merchants from Rakka on the Euphrates and ultimately from Mesopotamia, Persia, and Central Asia. Asiatic goods were also sold at a great open fair in the Hauran country, at one time in the territory of the Kingdom of Jerusalem and undoubtedly frequented by Westerners. And the harbors of the kingdom were the *entrepôts* of an extensive traffic from Arabia Felix and India by the Red Sea and across the Isthmus of Suez. At all of these points the Italians established connections with the Oriental merchants and learned from them much about Oriental lands and their products.

Asia Minor

During the early thirteenth century Asia Minor also became familiar ground to the men of the West.[192] The establishment of the Latin Empire at Constantinople in 1204 during the Fourth Crusade was mainly responsible for this; but even before the close of the twelfth century the Venetians had become preponderant from a commercial point of view in the districts that had hitherto formed parts of the Byzantine Empire, and after 1204 they were in a position to conclude advantageous treaties with their Anatolian neighbors, Greek, Seljuk, and Armenian. Venetian merchants were to be seen in the important towns and along the highways of the peninsula. Italians, with Provençaux in their train, exploited the trade of the small Christian kingdom of Little Armenia (the ancient Cilicia) and penetrated from the Mediterranean into and across the Seljuk sultanate of Iconium, whose rulers were disposed to look with fairly friendly eyes on the Frankish trader. Even the Empire of Nicaea, a small remnant of the Greek dominions which had managed to preserve its independence after the Fourth Crusade, was constrained in 1219 to grant extensive trading privileges to the Venetians.

Western Asia As Described by the Crusaders

The knowledge of Western Asia acquired in these various ways was naturally enough reflected in the works of the historians, chroniclers, and poets of the Crusades, many of whom had themselves visited the places they describe. Their fresh and realistic accounts contrast strikingly with the sort of geographical writings we have so far been discussing in this chapter. From Dreesbach's study of the Orient as described in the early French Crusading literature we may gain a concise idea of the sort of thing that impressed itself on the mind of the Occidental.[193] His impressions of climate and landscape need not detain us here, as they have already been explained in early chapters.[194] Of the natural resources, the wealth of the fruits of Syria, grapes, figs, pomegranates, almonds, olives, and locusts, were often the subject of wonder and admiration, and William of Tyre speaks enthusiastically of the great sugar plantations at Sur.[195] Of the animals,[196] the Arab horse and the camel attracted most attention; and the usefulness of the latter was known both as a beast of burden and as a swift traveler through the desert. A lively sketch of a man leading a camel laden with a large cask figures prominently on one variant of the Matthew Paris map of Palestine, and a legend reads: "Here abound camels, buffaloes (*bubali*), mules, and asses, which are used by the merchants trading between the peoples of the Orient and of the Occident."[197] Bears and lions, serpents and tarantulas, and carrier pigeons also invited notice; and the mosquito is mentioned by Ambroise, who says that though very small it has a terribly poisonous bite, bad enough to make every one, old and young alike, appear to be leprous:

"Que chescons, vielz ou damoisels,
Sembloit a estre tut mesels." [198]

Concerning the people[199] of the Levant we find that the distinction between the nomadic desert-dwelling Bedouins and the bearded turban-wearing Saracens (townsfolk) was well understood. The Bedouins—contrary to their present reputation—were looked down upon as cowards in battle, and William of Tyre relates with some disgust that it was their custom to hang about on the outskirts of a fight until they saw which side was going to win and then to join the victors.[200]

In commenting on the religion [201] of the Saracens the medieval Christians made the fundamental error of supposing that Islam is an idolatrous cult and that Mohammed was worshipped as a god. Nevertheless they were far from inaccurate in their remarks on the various customs, habits, and minor beliefs of the Moslems, on such matters, for example, as the pilgrimage to Mecca, the prohibited eating of pork and drinking of wine, the importance of ablutions, polygamy, and the customs of divorce. William of Tyre describes [201a] the division of the Mohammedans into two great groups, Shiah and Sunni, and explains how the former held that Ali ("Haly") was the only true prophet and the latter that Mohammed was the one messenger of God. Baghdad was referred to as the seat of the great "apostle" of the Saracens, or caliph, whom William of Tyre spoke of as a sovereign prince and chieftain whom all must obey; Cairo in Egypt was recognized as the capital of the caliphs of the rival Shiah persuasion.

Benjamin of Tudela also acquired some fairly clear ideas of Islam during his visits to Baghdad and to Egypt. He states that the Abbasid Caliph at Baghdad "is head of the Mohammedan religion, and all the kings of Islam obey him" and likens his position to that of the Christian Pope.[202] In writing about Cairo he tells us that the subjects of the Emir were followers of Ali (hence Shiites), that they rose against the Abbasid Caliph of Baghdad, and that a lasting feud was kept up between the two factions.[203]

Particular terror was inspired in the hearts of the Crusaders by that strange sect of Assassins,[204] whose principal seat was at Alamut in Persia, the stronghold of the notorious Old Man of the Mountain, though most of the Crusaders mistakenly thought that the outlying fortress of Massiat in Syria was the abode of the Old Man. William of Tyre dilates [204a] on the treachery and murderous nature of this people; and in Ambroise's *Estoire* we find [204b] a vivid account of how the children of the Assassins were brought up to do the bidding of the Old Man in every detail and in particular to bring about the murder of his enemies.[205]

AFRICA

Egypt As Part of Asia

Both the author of the *De imagine mundi* and Gervase of Tilbury include an account of Egypt with their descriptions of the countries of Asia. They then take up the remainder of Asia and Europe before finally returning to Africa toward the close of the geographical parts of their books. This order of treatment, which accorded with classical traditions, usually included Egypt with Asia or at least, as in the *De imagine mundi*, made the Nile rather than the Red Sea the boundary between Asia and Africa.[206] Certainly from an historical and cultural point of view Egypt has been more closely related to the Asiatic than to the African continent, even though geographically it forms a portion of the latter.[207]

The description of Egypt in the *Otia imperialia* [208] was copied in large part from the *De imagine mundi*,[209] and this in turn had closely followed the words of Isidore.[210] It ran somewhat as follows. Surrounded by the course of the Nile, which forms a letter *delta*,[211] Lower Egypt comprises five thousand country estates; these are not watered by rainfall but by the floods of the river alone, for the skies of Egypt are never obscured by clouds. The capital of Egypt is Babylon (Cairo), built by Cambyses. Close to Thebes—a city founded by Cadmus, Agenor's son and founder of Boeotian Thebes as well—are vast solitudes where there used to dwell a great company of hermits. The *De imagine mundi* speaks of the island of Meroë and of Syene on the tropic in

Upper Egypt, the latter famous for the well built there by the philosophers, into which the sun shines directly in the month of June.[212] The Jerome map of Palestine also shows Egypt in considerable detail, one of the most important features being the lighthouse at Alexandria.[213]

Descriptions of Egypt

Egypt, like the Holy Land, was frequently visited by Western merchants throughout our entire period. Benjamin of Tudela testifies to the enormous trade carried on there with the West. Alexandria was the principal port whence the spices and luxuries of the Far East were transshipped to Europe. Benjamin spoke with high appreciation of the wide straight streets of the city and of the architectural beauty of its buildings. He was much impressed by the swarm of merchants from all over the world who congregated in its streets and markets.[214] William of Tyre enlarged on the commercial importance of the great port and explained that the peppers, spices, ointments, drugs, lectuaries, precious stones, and silks of the Orient were brought first to Aden on the Red Sea and thence transported direct to Alexandria. He pointed out that Alexandria was also important as the meeting place of the river and maritime trades, and he gave a description of the local topography of the city.[215] Merchants from various Occidental nations and city states of Italy had *fondachi*, or trading stations, in this cosmopolitan metropolis, which was, as Schaube says, more subjected to European influences than any other city of Islam.[216] The Church endeavored to place severe restrictions on commerce with the infidel, in particular by the prohibition of the importation into Egypt of wood and iron, two materials of vital importance to the Saracens and much in demand. The restrictions, however, were disregarded, and trade flourished between Southern Europe and Egypt throughout nearly the entire twelfth and early thirteenth centuries, except for a short interruption at the time of the Third Crusade. In 1215–1216 there were said to be no fewer than three thousand Frankish merchants in Alexandria.[217] Egypt was the objective of the Crusaders of the Fifth Crusade, who seized and held the city of Damietta from

1219 to 1221, and again under Louis IX of France, who held it from 1248 to 1249; but in the interval between these two Crusades the Emperor Frederick II was on friendly and even intimate terms with the sultans.[218]

William of Tyre, who knew Egypt at first hand, gives a vivid picture of the fertile strip of country, hemmed in on either side by two deserts "in which the land is so burned and sterile that it supports no herb and no manner of tree, except where the river Nile waters the ground when it is in flood; in these parts alone a great abundance of wheat can grow."[219] He speaks of the flood of the Nile, between the months of June and September, and how it leaves a rich deposit of silt; of the palm gardens like a forest along the banks of the stream; and of the extensive orchards of fruit trees in the neighborhood of Alexandria.[220] He also fully describes the caliph's palace at Cairo and the Mamelukes, or sultan's bodyguard, recruited from the children of captured enemies.[221]

Benjamin of Tudela also marveled at the agricultural wealth of the flood plain of the Nile. The river alone, he said, irrigates and fertilizes the land, for "no rain falls, neither is ice or snow ever seen" (Adler's translation). Among other curiosities he described the Nilometer, which measured the height of the flood waters, and he gave details regarding the agricultural crops and fruits. Benjamin quoted the correct explanation of the flood: "The Egyptians say that up the river, in the land of Al-Habash (Abyssinia), which is the land of Havilah, much rain descends at the time of the rising of the river, and this abundance of rain causes the river to rise and to cover the surface of the land" (Adler's translation).[222]

Africa West of Egypt

To the west of Egypt, according to the *De imagine mundi*, lies Africa, stretching from the Nile to the ocean. Here in order are the provinces of Libya, named from a queen of that name; Cyrenaica, called from the city of Cyrene; Pentapolis, from the five cities of Berenice, Arsinoë, Ptolemaïs, Apollonia, and Cyrene; Tripolis, from the three cities of Occasa, Berete, and Leptis Magna; Heusis, containing the site of Carthage; Getulia; Numidia, with Hippo, the home of St. Augustine; and Mauretania.[223] The two

Syrtes (Major and Minor), or shallow bays of the north coast of Africa, are shown on the Henry of Mayence map immediately to the west of Egypt.[224] In the extreme west of Africa the *De imagine mundi*, with characteristic confusion, places Gades (Cadiz), from which the adjacent sea is called the Sea of Gades; and, on the borders of the ocean, Mount Atlas, a mountain of immense height, named after Atlas, once a king of Africa.[225] These mountains also appear prominently on the St. Sever Beatus map as a long range running parallel to the Atlantic[226] (see Fig. 2, p. 69, above). Other maps of the same group[227] show two great peaks on the western coast of Africa, which seem to represent a confusion of the Atlas Mountains with the famous Pillars of Hercules. A legend on the St. Sever Beatus map in the neighborhood of Tangier (Tingi) draws attention to the fact that "this region produces monkeys and ostriches,"[228] true certainly at the present day in regard to the former.

In the fourth and fifth decades of the twelfth century the Norman king of Sicily, Roger II, the patron of Edrisi, conquered many of the seaport towns along what is now the coast of Tunis; and, though the Latins were expelled from this region by the powerful Moroccan dynasty of the Almohads,[229] who during the following decade came to supersede the Almoravids in the domination over North Africa and Spain, close commercial relations were maintained between the northern and southern coasts of the Mediterranean Sea throughout the century and a half with which we are concerned.[230] The Genoese held the foremost place in the North African trade; but Pisan, Venetian, Massiliot, and Catalan merchants also frequented the markets of the seaboard towns. Under the Almohads, Ceuta and Bugia were important *entrepôts* of Genoese trade; and when the Almohad dominions split up in the early years of the thirteenth century (1212–1238), these two towns fell into the hands of Genoa.[231] Genoese fleets also ventured through the Strait of Gibraltar and not only tapped the commerce of the western coasts of the Iberian Peninsula but penetrated as far as Saleh on the Moroccan shore. Christians also found their way in various capacities into the interior of Maghreb, as the Moslems termed these western territories of Islam. During the Crusading epoch many Christians were taken captive in the wars in Spain and by pirates on the high seas; most of these were sold into slavery in the markets of the sea ports of Morocco, Algeria, and Tunis and sent to drag out lives of suffering in the towns of the interior. Towards the close of the twelfth century a Christian religious order was formed for the purpose of ameliorating the sufferings of the captives and of bringing about their redemption by exchange with Moslem captives held in Christendom.[232] We have evidence that these "Redemptorists," and the Franciscan and Dominican friars who were soon to follow them in the same work and who also served as ministers of the Christian religion to the European merchants engaged in business in Moslem countries, were not at all inhospitably received.[233] Their work was facilitated by almost uniformly friendly relations between the papacy and the rulers of Morocco, and the number of Christians in this part of the world became so great by the fourth decade of the thirteenth century that an episcopal see was established in Fez (1233), subsequently to be removed to Morocco City.[234] Another tie between Morocco and the Latin West was created by the maintenance at the court of the Almohads and their successors of a mercenary force composed for the most part of Spanish Christians from Catalonia and Aragon.[235]

On certain of the Beatus maps a "sandy desert" is shown between Egypt, western Africa, and Ethiopia;[236] and on the Psalter map it appears as a well-defined strip of territory labeled "sandy and sterile land."[237] This of course is no other than the Sahara, [237a] of which little or nothing was known, except that the Henry of Mayence map shows, [238] far back in the desert, the Temple of Jupiter (Ammon), in the oasis of that name, known since antiquity, and the St. Sever Beatus map represents certain immense *salinae*, or salt pits (the two squares west of the Nile on Fig. 2, p. 69, above), said to wax and wane with the moon.[239]

Ethiopia

South of Egypt and the Sahara lies Ethiopia. In the minds of medieval writers this name was not restricted to the region beyond Upper Egypt but was applied to the entire southern part of the known world, just as "India" sometimes was applied to the entire Far East. Indeed, from early classical times Ethiopia had itself been confused with India, and some of the writers whose works we are studying believed that the two regions were coterminous.

Nearly all the maps of the period carried the extremities of Ethiopia far to the east and minimized the size of the Red Sea and Indian Ocean in such a way as to bring Central Africa within no great distance of India. On the Jerome map of Palestine two tracts called "India Egyptii" and "India Ethiopie" were placed along the shores of the Red Sea opposite the mouths of the Indus.[240] Gervase of Tilbury speaks of three peoples inhabiting Ethiopia: the Hesperi in the west, the Garamantes in the center, and the "Indians" in the east,[241] and adds that there are one hundred and twenty provinces "from India into Ethiopia."[242] The *De imagine mundi* places Saba, the city of the Queen of Sheba, in the easterly part of Ethiopia.[243] It was conceded that Ethiopia is terribly hot on account of the proximity of the sun and that the soil there for the most part is dry and desert. Gervase speaks of the mighty Mount Climax of Ptolemy, Orosius, and other ancient writers in the midst of Ethiopia, a home of bearded women and similar marvels.

Some of the Beatus maps designate Ethiopia as a country "where there are races horrible on account of their strange faces and monstrous appearance. It extends as far as the borders of Egypt. It also abounds in wild beasts and serpents; and precious stones, cinnamon, and balsam are found there."[244] In fact, all remote parts of the world were made the habitats of marvels in the Middle Ages, and few parts of the known world were more remote than Ethiopia. In addition, the intimate connection between India and Ethiopia, which had persisted in the minds of men throughout so many ages, seems to have brought about a transference thither of many of those marvels and monsters that originally had been placed in the Far East. A most entertaining example of the peopling of Ethiopia by monstrous creatures is provided by the Psalter map and by the Ebstorf map of a period later than ours.[245] On these the entire shore of the equatorial ocean along the southern border of the known world is lined with men that are tongueless, earless, noseless, or men that have four eyes or mouths and eyes on their breasts, and with cannibals, *cynocephali*, snake-eating troglodytes, and the like.

Sources of the Nile

The main interest in Ethiopia, however, lay in the fact that from this country comes that great river the problem of whose sources has puzzled mankind from the earliest ages down nearly to our own day. In classical times three theories had prevailed concerning the headwaters of the Nile.[246] The correct theory, that of Eratosthenes and of Ptolemy, that the river rises in Ethiopia itself but far to the south, met with no recognition in our period. The second theory placed the sources in India and was closely allied with the very old belief that tended to confuse Ethiopia itself with India and can be traced back to Homeric or even pre-Homeric times.[247] The third theory, which probably originated in vague rumors that reached the Carthaginians and later the Romans and still later the Moslems, of the eastward-flowing course of a great river south of the Sahara (a river which we now know to be the Niger), placed the headwaters of the Nile either in a great lake or else in the Atlas Mountains in western Africa close to the ocean.

Traces of each of the last two theories are to be found in the writings of our period. According to the accepted interpretation of Scripture, the Nile was the same as the Gihon, one of the four rivers of Paradise, and its ultimate source must therefore have been in the east, where Paradise was nearly always thought to be. It is also possible that early Christian monks in Abyssinia may have learned of the course of certain of the eastern tributaries of the Atbara which rise close to the Red Sea, and this information, in the devious course of its transmission to Western Europe, may have been confused in such a way as to foster belief that one of these minor streams was the headwaters of the main river itself.[248] In any case, Orosius,[249] whose words were copied by Gervase of

Tilbury,[250] made the Nile spring from the ground near Mossylon Emporium on the shores of the Red Sea and, after flowing westward for some distance, turn north to enter Egypt. But he also said that other authorities state that the river rises far in the west and that, after an underground course through the sands and thence through a great lake, it runs eastward across the Ethiopian desert even as far as the ocean and then turns to the left into Egypt. In any case, he adds, it is true that there is a large river which has exactly such a source and produces all the monsters that the Nile does. The barbarians who dwell near its source call this latter river the Dara, but other natives name it the Nuchul. The Dara is mentioned by Pliny and the Nuchul by Mela; perhaps they represent a reminiscence of the generally eastward-flowing Niger. Orosius suggested that this river, coming from the west, may well contribute by an underground channel to the westward-flowing stream that springs from the earth near the Red Sea. Isidore seems to have derived from Orosius the idea of a West African origin of the Nile, its disappearance under ground, and subsequent emergence on the shores of the Red Sea and thence of its encircling of Ethiopia before flowing down into Egypt,[251] and in this idea he was followed by the author of the *De imagine mundi*.[252]

Orosius' and Isidore's theories are graphically represented on the maps. Several of the Beatus maps simply show the river springing from mountains in the western part of the continent and swinging east and north into the Mediterranean.[253] The symbols and legends on the St. Sever Beatus[254] indicate (see Fig. 2, p. 69, above) that thê river originates in the neighborhood of the Atlas Mountains; thence, passing beneath the sands, it expands into a vast lake, whence it flows toward the east through an immense swamp, like the Maeotic Swamp, but surrounded by mountains. After this it turns to the left, envelops the Isle of Meroë, and flows down into Egypt. Other maps, like the Cotton, Henry of Mayence (inset on Fig. 6, p. 245, above), and Jerome map of Palestine are even more faithful to the Orosian description. The sources of the Nile proper are shown near the Red Sea in the eastern part of Ethiopia, but another large river is also depicted, coming from the far west near the Atlas range and emptying into a large lake not far from the sources of the Nile, with which the lake may communicate. The Cotton map [255] splits this river into two sections and calls the upper section "Dara" and the lower "Fluvius Nilus." On the Jerome map of Palestine [256] it is called "Nuchul" and made to flow into a lake of the same name. Henry of Mayence [257] names it "fl. Gion."

Traditional View of Central Africa

As a matter of fact, no new information about Central Africa was brought to light during our entire period or had been during many centuries before, and no new theories were propounded. Old and hackneyed notions were handed down from one writer to another. Simar, in a recent admirable study of the geographical ideas regarding Central Africa in antiquity and in the Middle Ages, trenchantly sums up the whole matter with the following words, which might equally well be applied to ideas regarding many other parts of the world: "These meager notions soon became stereotyped and were repeated by the scholars of the Middle Ages, who vied with each other in their unalterable ardor. From Martianus Capella in the fourth century to Honorius of Autun [here the author of the *De imagine mundi* is meant] in the twelfth, passing by Macrobius, Priscian, Saint Avitus, Gregory of Tours, Jornandes, the Venerable Bede, Raban Maur, Dicuil, Alfred the Great, Alfric, Adelbold, Richer, Asaph, Hermann Contractus, Robert of St. Martin of Auxerre, Otto of Freising, Hugh of St. Victor, and even, later, the historian Joinville, men copied Solinus, Orosius, and Isidore and adopted like them a round *oikoumene* separated from the *terra incognita* by an impassable equatorial ocean, the uninhabitability of the torrid zone, the limit of Africa this side of the equator, the sources of the Nile in Mauretania, its course through Ethiopia from west to east, its ultimate origin in the Terrestrial Paradise situated to the east of India, and its submarine course as far as its emergence in the western part of Libya." [258]

THE MEDITERRANEAN SEA

The Name "Mediterranean"

To the great chain of inland seas that lies between Africa, Asia, and Europe the Romans had applied the name of *mare internum* or *mare nostrum*. Solinus was probably the first to describe these as mediterranean seas, and Isidore the first to convert the term "mediterranean" into a proper name.[259] The authority of Isidore was sufficient to make this designation familiar to future ages; and it was used by the author of the *De imagine mundi* and by Gervase of Tilbury with the same connotation that it enjoys at the present day.[260] The term, however, was not firmly established in popular use in our period and is conspicuously absent from most of the maps, which as a rule either give no name at all for the sea as a whole or else employ some vague designation like *mare nostrum* or *mare magnum*.[261]

Gervase of Tilbury says [262] that the Mediterranean is shaped like a letter Y with two branches, a longer one extending from the entrance (Strait of Gibraltar) to the Hellespont, and a shorter one forming the Sea of Alexandria or of Syria. This comparison suggests that Gervase must have had before him a typical medieval map of the world with east at the top. More detailed is the account of the Mediterranean in Plato of Tivoli's translation of Al-Battānī's *Astronomy*.[263] Here the "Roman Sea" is described as extending a distance of 5000 miles [!] from the Isle of Gadir (Cadiz) to Tyre and Sidon; it has various branches, one running off towards the Narbonnese, one called Adriatic, another called Pontus; and it contains a total of one hundred and sixty-two inhabited islands, of which five are especially noteworthy on account of their size.

The Mediterranean During the Crusades

During the Crusades the Mediterranean served as one of the main highways from the West to the Holy Land, and hence the men of Europe were enabled to learn much of its waters and coasts. Though the principal armies of the First Crusade had proceeded overland, in the years that followed the establishment of the states of the Crusaders there was constant coming and going by sea between the Levant and the ports of Italy, France, and England. The sea route was the way taken by the armies of Philip Augustus and Richard Coeur-de-Lion in 1190; by the cosmopolitan army that captured Constantinople in 1204; by Frederick II and the ill-starred expedition of St. Louis to Egypt; as well as by innumerable pilgrims, soldiers, merchants, and other individuals unconnected with any definite Crusading enterprise.

Instructions for Navigation in the Mediterranean

Perhaps the most attractive account of the Mediterranean derived from the literature of the Crusaders is to be found in the chronicles and histories recording the expedition of Richard Coeur-de-Lion. The *Gesta regis Ricardi*, mistakenly attributed to Benedict of Peterborough, and the *Chronica* of Roger of Hoveden contain descriptions of routes and coasts, parts of which were undoubtedly drawn from manuals of navigation. Here we find much the same sort of data that at the present time is incorporated in our Coast Pilot books, a combination of practical advice to sailors with useful and interesting information about the waters, islands, and shores. Great care is taken to inform the navigator of the best and most practicable routes for him to follow. For example, two ways are mentioned of going from Marseilles to Acre, one through the open sea and the other near the coast.[264] If the wind is favorable you can proceed by the first, leaving Sardinia and Sicily out of sight to the left, though you must constantly be on your guard against running too far to the right and falling afoul of the barbarian shores.[265] With a good breeze this journey can be made in fifteen days,[266] and vessels are safer on it from the menace of pirates than when they follow the coastwise route. On the other hand, the navigation is more difficult, and under no circumstances should this route be attempted by galleys, which might easily be sunk if a storm should come up. In the account of the coastwise route various menaces and dangers to ships are carefully pointed out. For instance, off the coast of Greece, about twenty miles from land and fifty from Modon, there is a low round rock called Triffar; and in order to avoid it ships are warned not to stand too far out to sea. West-bound vessels, however, are advised, instead of passing through the channels between "Chefeline" (Cephalonia), "Fale de Campar" (Ithaca), and the neighboring islands to keep out to sea, placing these islands on the right. Navigators are cautioned to beware of a sand bar in Corfu harbor with only four and a half *ulnae* of water upon it. The dangers of the narrow and crooked channel between Corfu and the mainland make it advisable for vessels en route to Italy to avoid taking this passage and, by steering out to sea, to leave Corfu on the right. The harbor of Karentet (Santa Quaranta) is said to be a fine one, except for submerged reefs at the entrance and extending under about half of its area; the best approach for ships is not far from the Corfu side.

We find also many full and practical details regarding the distances between various points along the coasts, the width of straits, the length of islands; the names of seaport towns and now and then their products and other distinguishing features are mentioned, for example, the fact that Marseilles has an excellent harbor surrounded on all sides by hills, or that Almeria in Spain is far-famed for its manufacture of silk. Prominent landmarks are carefully pointed out: great mountains making promontories on the coast of Spain, sand banks, the mouths of rivers (like the Ebro, or the Salef in Asia Minor, "in which Frederick Barbarossa was drowned and from the neighborhood of the sources of which the three wise men were said to have come"), the high peaks in the interior of Crete, or the volcanoes of Sicily and the Lipari Isles. Marine life, such as the flying fish of the waters near Corsica and Sardinia as well as less credible monstrosities of the Gulf of Satalia on the southern coast of Asia Minor, also seems to have aroused the curiosity of the navigator and chronicler.[267]

Islands of the Mediterranean

Most medieval maps show the islands of the Mediterranean scattered about with scant respect for their actual locations and relative sizes. The Guido map of the world, for instance, indicates but one island by name in the entire Mediterranean, and that is "Baleares." [268] The most important islands are fairly well represented on the St. Sever Beatus [269] (Fig. 2, p. 69, above), but the draftsman of the Osma Beatus did not have room enough for Tenedos and Rhodes in the Mediterranean (Fig. 4, p. 123, above), and hence placed then in the circumambient ocean to the east of Taprobane! [270] In the *De imagine mundi* and in the *Otia imperialia* the islands are described in a dull and catalogue-like manner from the data given by Orosius and other classical authorities.[271] The accounts of the Mediterranean in the chronicles which we have just been discussing also add little beside scattering details on Corfu and Cyprus and a significant observation that, owing to the danger from pirates, a large number of the islands of the Greek archipelago had been deserted by their inhabitants.[272]

Guy of Bazoches, who journeyed overseas with the Crusaders to Syria in 1190, told in a letter to his nephews [273] that on the third morning out from Marseilles they were in sight of Corsica and the many and varied inlets and promontories of its broken coast. The following day Sardinia was visible, likewise on the left. Sardinia, Guy wrote, might almost have been called free from poisonous serpents, were it not for one variety, the *solifuga*, which took the place of all the others, since the poisonous virulence of all serpents was concentrated in this one. Besides this there was a violently poisonous plant in Sardinia. On the other hand, these pests were compensated for by the presence of hot springs in several parts of the island which prevailed against the *solifuga* and were good for broken bones and for the eyes. We have already spoken [274] of Guy's description of Sicily, which was reached soon after Sardinia was left behind. From Sicily Guy came to Crete, "a famous island and once powerful with a hundred cities." Crete was blessed with an absence of all kinds of serpents, though the place of serpents was taken by a small animal called a *spalangius*, the bite of which was deadly. In the sea where Crete lay were the Cyclades, forming a circle around Delos, and Cyprus, more pleasing to the eye because of the richness of its fields, the delights of its vineyards, and its far-famed fertility.

Sicily

The critical position of Sicily on the routes between East and West and North and South, its peculiar volcanic phenomena, as well as the establishment of a Norman kingdom there, brought that island to the attention of the outside world.[275] Sicily came inevitably to figure in the poetry and legend of the period both in France and in the isle itself. The song of Roland and the Breton cycle of legends of King Arthur were sung and related on Sicilian soil, and echoes of these popular romances found their way into the Latin literature of our age. One story had it that the peers of Charlemagne had passed through Sicily on their return from Jerusalem and had named mountains after Roland and Oliver. Godfrey of Viterbo wrote: "There stands a great mountain which was called Roland and another similarly called Oliver, and these names were applied by the bold dukes as memorials."[276] Gervase of Tilbury was inclined to treat skeptically the report of how, in his own day, King Arthur, said to have been enclosed within Mongibel (Etna), had appeared miraculously on the outside of the mountain.[277] King Arthur also was associated in a French poem, *Florian et Florete*, with a distinctively Sicilian fairy, Morgain—who gave her name to the *fata morgana*, or mirage, over the Strait of Messina, and with Mongibel, an abode of supernatural beings. French poets writing of Sicily from far away often revealed an amazing ignorance of the geography of the isle, as is well shown by the *Dolopathos* of Jean of Haute Seille, in which not only is the city of Mantua placed in Sicily but the insular character of the latter is entirely overlooked.[278]

The travelers Conrad of Querfurt and Guy of Bazoches both discuss the phenomena of Etna[279] and Scylla and Charybdis and refer to the stories of Arethusa and of the rape of Proserpina.[280] Conrad identifies Taormina with the home of the minotaur.[281] These twelfth-century travelers were well read in the classical mythology of the places they chose to visit.

With this mythical lore of the Mediterranean island should be contrasted a few excellent and graphic accounts given by eyewitnesses. The troubadour Ambroise, who sings of the expedition of Richard Coeur-de-Lion, tells us something of the contemporary population of Messina, consisting of Lombards, "Griffons" (or Greeks), and "persons of Saracen extraction."[282] The latter, he complained, treated the French pilgrims abominably, insulting them with evil gestures, calling them dogs, and acting in an especially objectionable manner when the Frenchmen tried to take liberties with the Saracens' wives, a naïve admission not to the credit of the Frenchmen. We have already alluded to the graphic descriptions of Etna in the letters of Guy of Bazoches and in the second redaction of the *Image du monde*.[283]

EUROPE

Northeastern Europe

Eastern and northeastern Europe were quite as shadowy and unfamiliar to the men of the West during our period as Central Asia or the heart of Africa. Classical tradition had placed in the northern part of Europe a range of mountains not far from the Ocean Stream, the Rhipaeans—perhaps an echo of some very early acquaintance with the Urals.[284] Between these and the Ocean, so Gervase of Tilbury [285] affirmed, there was a land in the vicinity of the "septentrional" circle (called thus from the "seven stars" and known to the Greeks as the "Arctic circle") so cold as to be constantly frozen and uninhabitable. Another tradition dating back to remote antiquity placed the Hyperboreans far north in a region of temperate climate. Robert Grosseteste and Roger Bacon tried to prove that such a climate might be produced by the character of the mountains at very high latitudes.[286] The rivers of Scythia, among them the Lentulus and the Tanaïs (Don), were said to have their sources in the Rhipaean Mountains, and of these the Tanaïs, which was the largest, after flowing past the altar of Augustus, constantly poured an immense volume of water into the Euxine (Black Sea) near Theodosia.[287]

Russia

More recent information about Russia had been acquired by men of the West, though it had not been widely disseminated. In regard to northern Russia the Northmen were in possession of much valuable knowledge. We have already mentioned their adventurous voyagings in the Baltic and around the North Cape into the White Sea to a region which they had called Biarma.[288] There is evidence that their trade with Biarmaland was maintained throughout our period, although only three actual voyages after the tenth century are recorded: one in 1090, one in 1217, and one in 1222.[289] A member of the expedition of 1217, however, crossed Russia to the Black Sea and penetrated ultimately to the Holy Land before returning to Norway.

Of southern Russia and the northern coasts of the Black Sea some slight knowledge had undoubtedly filtered into the West through the medium of the Italian merchants. Though Genoese, Pisans, and Venetians penetrated these regions in the twelfth century,[290] the great expansion of Occidental commerce into the steppes and thence into the heart of Asia came only after the establishment of the Latin Empire in Constantinople in 1204 and after the conquest of the Ukraine and Crimea by the Mongols, whose relatively tolerant rule was favorable to the presence of European colonies and mercantile enterprise. Otto of Freising mentions the tribes dwelling to the north and east of Hungary on the plains of Russia, Petchenegs and Komans, devourers of raw and foul meats, such as those of horses and cats—tribes who inhabited a land which, though rich in game, had never felt the plow or rake.[291] The Komans were also spoken of by Robert de Clari (died 1216) in his *Prise de Constantinople* as a tent-dwelling folk, living on cattle, cheese, and milk and possessed of large herds of horses.[292] We have already quoted from Matthew Paris' graphic description of the Mongols,[293] who swept into Russia in 1222–1224 and later, in 1240–1243, menaced Central Europe itself.

Poland

Northwest of these tribes lay Poland, of which Ragewin gave a brief description in his continuation of Otto's *Gesta Friderici*.[294] Dwelling in a country bounded by the Oder on the west, the Vistula on the east, the Ruthenians and the Scythian Ocean on the north, and the Bohemian Forest on the south, the Poles, he tells us, are well protected by the character of the land on which they live. They are almost a barbaric people and are very quick to fight, partly because of their own inherent ferocity but partly too because of contact with more ferocious neighbors on the shores of the sea that washes their coasts.[295]

Slavic Europe As Described by Benjamin of Tudela and Petachia of Ratisbon

The Hebrew travelers Benjamin of Tudela and Petachia of Ratisbon also wrote of Slavic Europe, the former from hearsay, the latter from personal observation. Benjamin stated that Russia was "a great empire stretching from the gate of Prague to the gates of Kieff, the large city which is at the extremity of that Empire. It is a land of mountains and forests, where there are to be found animals called *vair* [a species of marten], ermine, and sable"[296] (Adler's translation). It seems that Benjamin would include in Russia much of Bohemia, Galicia, and Poland, together with the Carpathian Mountains. Petachia, who traversed Russia, Caucasia, and Armenia on his way from Prague to Baghdad, was one of the few Occidental travelers of the Middle Ages who ventured into the land of the steppes before the overland journeys of John of Pian de Carpine, William of Rubruck,[297] and others to the Mongol court during the middle and closing years of the thirteenth century. Petachia commented on the absence of mountains in Russia. He described accurately the tent-dwellers of Kedar, or the Ukraine (Petchenegs and Komans), noting especially the horsehide rafts on which they cross the great rivers; their diet of rice and millet boiled in milk and of raw flesh which they warm under the saddles of their horses; their custom of drinking from vessels of copper cast in the shape of a human face; their government in the hands of princes and nobles rather than of kings. He gave some details about that portion of the Sea of Azov now known as the Putrid Sea, telling us that when the wind blows from its foul surface in the direction of the Black Sea it causes the death of many people![298]

Hungary

With Pannonia, or Hungary, Western Europe was in much more intimate contact than with Russia and Poland. Gervase of Tilbury, to be sure, adds little to what Orosius had told about this country,[299] but in Otto of Freising's *Gesta Friderici* there is a description of both land and people.[300] Otto writes that Pannonia is enclosed by woods and mountains, particularly by the range of the Apennines (*sic*); it forms a wide and well-watered plain, fed by springs and rivers; there are a great many woods stocked with game of every variety, and the land abounds in fields so rich and fertile that they can be likened either to the Paradise of God or else to Egypt. The aspect of the country is beautiful but rendered so rather by nature itself than by the work of man, for, owing to the barbaric state of civilization in which the people remain, walls and buildings are very rare. Boundaries are marked by the courses of great rivers and not by woods and hills. The names which Otto assigns to the borders of Pannonia have a distinctly modern sound, contrasting with the classical geographic nomenclature used by Gervase for all this part of the world. "Eastward, where the famous river Sawa (Save) is received by the Danube, Pannonia borders on Bulgaria; westward on Moravia and the eastern marches of the Teutons; southward on Croatia, Dalmatia, Hystria (Istria), or Carinthia; and northward on Boemia (Bohemia), Polimia (Poland), Ruthenia, etc.; to the northeast are the Pecenati (Petchenegs) and Falones (Komans), and to the southeast is Rama." Otto also describes rather fully the tent-dwellers of the Hungarian plain. The country, he says, has suffered much through the invasions of barbarians, and hence no wonder it remains a land where the people are of rough speech and little culture. First the Huns overran this region, then the Avars, eaters of raw and unclean meat, and finally the Hungarians from Scythia. The latter have deep-set eyes, are ugly and small, wild and barbaric in speech and customs; and one is constrained to wonder at the injustice of fate, or, even more, at the patience of God, for giving such a beautiful country to such a monstrous folk. Otto then adds further details about the customs of the people: their deliberation in council, their unlimited obedience to the tyrannical and arbitrary authority of their kings, the rigid requirements of their military system. Their dwellings in the villages and towns are primitive to an extreme, the houses nearly always built of reeds, rarely of wood, and almost never of stone. As a matter of fact, the majority of the people lived both winter and summer in tents.

Relations between France and Hungary were fairly close in the twelfth century.[301] Intermarriages between members of the reigning houses had induced many of the Hungarian nobles to imitate French manners and customs. French teaching monks and military orders (Templars and Hospitalers) had established themselves in the Danubian plain before the close of the century, and during the Crusades many Frenchmen found occasion to visit the eastern kingdom in one capacity or another.[302] In the thirteenth century the Gallic colonies in Hungary became even more numerous than previously, and French merchants and architects were well known among the Magyars.[303] Conversely, this French infiltration led to the dissemination of some knowledge of Hungary in France and to frequent mention of that country in the *chansons de geste*, though the phrase "to go to Hungary" was held to be synonymous with visiting any extremely distant and unknown region.[304] It was not in the nature of the *chansons de geste* to supply detailed geographical information, least of all about a remote country; and consequently the presence of any testimony at all of a geographical nature in them justifies our belief that the troubadours knew more of Hungary than their songs at first glance would seem to indicate. We are told that among the products of the Magyar kingdom were horses, mules, and donkeys, which were exported to France; that the gold of Hungary was well known in the West; and that there were many cities in this realm, though only one of these, Striguus, is mentioned by name.

Balkan Peninsula

Quite characteristically, in dealing with Hungary and the Balkan Peninsula, such writers as the author of the *De imagine mundi*[305] and Gervase of Tilbury[306] merely copied from Isidore and Orosius, who in turn had derived their knowledge from much earlier sources. The accounts of this part of Europe in these standard authorities of our period, though fairly full, were nearly a thousand years out of date. Even so, it comes as something of a shock to find that on the Jerome map of the East, drawn as late as 1150, a legend near the Ister (Danube) informs us that in this locality "the pygmies fight with the cranes." [307]

More recent information seems to have been gathered by Arnold of Lübeck. In the *Chronica Slavorum* [308] he speaks of a city of Ravenelle,[309] where the river Ravana flows into the Morava. This city, he says, lies in the midst of a wood, and its inhabitants are called Servi. They are sons of the devil, heathens, ravenous for meat, and worthy of their name, for they are the slaves of all low and foul passions and live like beasts but are even wilder than beasts. In such uncomplimentary terms Arnold describes the ancestors of the modern Serbians and adds that they were subjects of the kings of the Greeks, i. e. the Byzantine emperors.

In regard to the Balkan Peninsula as well as to Hungary, however, much knowledge had undoubtedly been gained through the Crusaders. The main route from the West to Constantinople by way of the Morava and Maritsa valleys was taken in the First Crusade by Godfrey of Bouillon; in the Second by Louis VII and Conrad III (1147); and, in the Third, Frederick Barbarossa followed it as far as Adrianople, whence he made his way into Asia Minor through Gallipoli and across the Dardanelles. Other leaders of the First Crusade had traveled overland from the Adriatic at Durazzo and Avlona to Thessalonica and thence eastward along the shore to the Bosporus. During the Fourth Crusade the Latin fleet coasted Dalmatia, Greece, and the Archipelago; and the founding of the Latin Empire, with its petty Frankish principalities in Greece and among the isles, inevitably established a connection between those parts of the world and Europe beyond the Alps.

Knowledge of Balkan countries was also derived from trade as well as from the enterprise of the Crusaders. In the twelfth century, Occidental colonies were to be found in practically all the important cities of the Byzantine Empire. Heyd in his *Histoire du commerce du Levant* [310] gives a summary of the evidence on this subject, which shows that before the Fourth Crusade (1203–1204) there were in existence colonies, mostly of Italians from Genoa, Venice, and Pisa. Thessalonica harbored in its foreign quarter not only Italians, but Spaniards, Portuguese, and French. As commerce went mainly by sea, an important traffic had sprung up among the islands of the Archipelago and especially between Euboea, Crete, Rhodes, Lemnos, and the West, though prior to the Fourth Crusade Western merchants avoided penetrating the interior of Greece.

Constantinople

Constantinople was a great meeting place of merchants from all quarters of the known world and consequently a very important center for the dispersal of geographical knowledge. During the twelfth century Pisan, Venetian, and Genoese colonies flourished together there unharmoniously and vied with each other for trade privileges, but after 1204 the Venetians had matters very much in their own hands. Eustathius, archbishop of Thessalonica, says[311] that in 1180 there were no fewer than 60,000 Latins in Constantinople and that the majority of these were Italians. Benjamin of Tudela[312] and other writers also tell of merchants here from Babylon, Mesopotamia, Media, Persia, Armenia, Iberia (in the Caucasus), Egypt, Palestine, Russia, Hungary, the country of the Petchenegs, Bulgaria, Spain, France, and Germany, though the Latins were by all odds the most numerous among this multitude. After the establishment of the Latin Empire in 1204 we hear of the presence of Provençaux, Spaniards, citizens of Ancona, and even Danes and English,[313] though the latter were probably mercenaries rather than traders. With this motley population Constantinople was preëminently the great cosmopolitan city of the world and as such served as a vast clearing house for geographical information brought thither from all four corners of the earth.

Benjamin of Tudela described the Constantinople of his day in graphic terms,[314] alluding especially to the busy activity of its merchants, the costly magnificence of its buildings (notably the Church of Santa Sophia and the Palace of Blachernae), as well as to the wealth of its Greek inhabitants, who "go clothed in garments of silk with gold embroidery and ride horses and look like princes" (Adler's translation). He was impressed by the great shows given annually on Christmas Day at the Hippodrome, the like of which were to be seen in no other land; here, in accord with the old Roman custom, lions, leopards, bears, and wild asses were made to engage in combat. The Jews of Constantinople were segregated in the quarter of Pera, where their condition was very miserable, and they were subjected to many indignities. "Yet," Benjamin adds, "the Jews are rich and good, kindly and charitable, and bear their lot with cheerfulness."

Italy

Otto of Freising's *Gesta Friderici*[315] probably contains one of the best general descriptions of Italy dating from the time of the Crusades.[316] Otto says that the Italian peninsula as a whole is divided into three parts. The districts that once constituted the Roman *colonia* form *ulterior Italia*, which consists of Venetia, Emilia, and Liguria, with Aquileia, Ravenna, and Milan respectively as capitals. The part "within" the Apennines, where Rome and Tuscany are situated, is known as *interior Italia*. Beyond these mountains (to the south) are the fields from which Campania derives its name. This part of the peninsula extends as far as the Faro, or strait cutting off Sicily from the mainland—Sicily itself being counted with Sardinia and other neighboring isles as a part of Italy—and is known as *citerior Italia*, or Magna Graecia. In Otto's day this third portion was more commonly called Apulia or Calabria. In conclusion Otto adds that some authorities preferred to divide Italy into two parts only, *ulterior* and *citerior*, the latter consisting of the above-mentioned middle and southern districts together.[317]

Otto waxes particularly enthusiastic about Northern Italy, a region which he conceived of as bordered or hedged in by the high and craggy ranges of the Apennines and "Pyrenean" (*sic*) Alps, stretching out in either direction, enclosing the region in their midst. Like a "garden of delights" (the term frequently used to describe Paradise), this district is bounded by the Pyrenean Alps on the north, the Apennines (vulgarly called Mount Bardo) on the south, the Tyrrhenian Sea on the west, and the Adriatic on the east. Watered by the course of the great river Po, or Eridanus (which topographers considered one of the three most famous streams of Europe, says Otto), and by other rivers, blessed with a rich soil and a temperate climate, this land is most fertile in grain, in the vine and olive, and produces such a variety of fruit trees—especially chestnuts, figs, and olives—that it resembles an immense grove.[318]

To the world beyond the Alps, Lombardy was the best-known part of Italy. Godfrey of Viterbo [319] dilates on its immense potential strength, with thirty cities, the equal of any one of which could scarcely be found elsewhere in the world. The population of Lombardy is thicker than the hair on a woman's head, and rare are the times when a ship cannot be seen on the Po. Otto of Freising [320] gives an account of the Lombard invasion of Northern Italy, of the founding of Milan and its neighboring cities, and of the free government and liberal democratic institutions of the Italian city states.

Gunther of Pairis amplified and made more picturesque Otto of Freising's description of Italy, but it is doubtful whether he added any observations resulting from first-hand acquaintance with the peninsula. Whatever the sources from which he derived his descriptions of Lombardy and Apulia—his own imagination, personal experience, the inspiration of classical poetry, or the *Gesta Friderici*—if we compare them, we find that the differences between the inhabitants of the northern and southern parts of the peninsula were fully appreciated in the twelfth century. The Lombards, Gunther says,[321] are a keen, skillful, and active people, foresighted in counsel, expert in justice, strong in body and spirit, full of life and handsome to look upon, with light, supple bodies that give them great powers of endurance, economical and always moderate in eating and drinking, masters of their hands and mouths, honorable in every business transaction, mighty in the arts and always eagerly striving for the new. Lovers of freedom and ready to face death for freedom's sake, these people have never been willing to submit to kings.

Apulia in the south, Gunther goes on to say, is also a fair country, rich in all the blessings of this earth:[322] fruit trees, vineyards, pasture lands, towns and cities, all of which make a gloriously beautiful prospect. But what a contrast its people present to the Lombards, dirty, lazy, weak, good-for-nothing idlers that they are!

Rome

Rome must have been in a sad state of decay and dilapidation, if we can place any trust in the picturesque accounts of the city given by Otto and Gunther.[323] From our period there also dates a little booklet on the topography and monuments of Rome, which exerted wide influence and enjoyed great popularity during the thirteenth and later centuries. This work, the *Mirabilia urbis Romae*, contains a discourse on the antiquities and architecture of the Eternal City. It is in three parts. Part One treats of "the foundation of Rome and of her chief monuments, with chapters on the town walls, gates, arches, hills, baths, palaces, theaters, bridges, cemeteries, places where the saints suffered martyrdom," and so on; Part Two contains "divers histories touching certain famous places and images in Rome," that is legends of both classical and Christian origin; and Part Three is a "perambulation of the city," like Baedeker in its fullness of topographical and architectural detail. Though this book is a dry catalogue, its very existence and popularity are significant of the fact that antiquities aroused interest in the twelfth century and that the archeological tourist was not altogether a product of the days of the Renaissance. Gregorovius, the historian of medieval Rome, says of the *Mirabilia:* "In this curious composition . . . Roman archeology, which has now attained such appalling proportions, puts forth its earliest shoots in a naïve and barbarous form and in a Latin as ruinous as its subject."[324]

Another contemporary writer on Roman monuments, an unknown Master Gregory, includes a description of six out of the seven wonders of the world in his short tract on the marvels of the Eternal City![325]

Antiquities

In a letter of the traveler Conrad of Querfurt describing a journey through Italy[326] we also find a strongly antiquarian interest in evidence. Conrad's primary concern was for the mythological and historical associations of the places he visited, and he took a genuine tourist's pride in being able to say that he had seen with his own eyes spots made famous by the poets. His route carried him over the Alps to Mantua, thence down the length of the peninsula to the Strait of Messina and into Sicily. He tells us that he would have been amazed at the smallness of the famous Rubicon and that such a paltry stream could have presented any kind of obstacle to Caesar, had not a native informed him that in rainy weather the river was much wider. In the vicinity of Naples he noted, besides the baths of Virgil at Baiae, certain natural features: Mount "Veseus" (Vesuvius), which every ten years sends out flames and stinking ashes, and the subterranean passages under Monte Barbaro. Calabria, he says, is a rough and trackless country through which it is necessary to pass in order to reach Sicily.

Spain

Gervase of Tilbury [327] adds little besides a list of the archiepiscopal sees and their suffragans to the dry details which Orosius [328] and the *De imagine mundi* [329] had furnished concerning Spain. In the *Chronica* [330] of Roger of Hoveden the story of the passage of Richard Coeur-de-Lion's fleet around the coasts of the Iberian Peninsula was the occasion for a discussion of the geography of that part of the world, together with a list of the towns of the coast. Roger [331] enumerates the bishoprics of Spain and, in his description of Castile, mentions Toledo as the seat of the primate, under whom there were twenty-one bishops. He says that there were two hundred castles in Castile and, furthermore, that Castile contained a mountain from which were taken daily many thousand camel-loads of earth. No matter how big an excavation was made, if rain fell it was always filled up again on the following day. This earth was sold in the surrounding countries for washing the heads and garments of Christians and pagans alike. Roger also is careful to bring out the distinction between Christian Spain, consisting of Navarre, Castile, Portugal, Aragon, and the "lands of the kings of St. James" (Leon), on the one hand, and Saracenic Spain, comprising the kingdoms of Cordova, "Gahang" (Jaén), Murcia, and Valencia, on the other.

The Alps

Otto of Freising asserted that the Alps and Apennines join near Tortona,[332] though he was not inclined to dispute a prevalent belief that these two mountain systems form in effect one continuous range.[333] In order to demonstrate this, he says people assert that, as viewed from the deck of a vessel lying off Genoa, the two systems appear to be continuous and to constitute the same mountain range and that, according to Isidore, Pannonia was enclosed by the Apennines, from which it took its name. He argues that the portion of the Apennines which encloses Pannonia certainly cannot be the same as that part which is to be found in peninsular Italy and is there called Mount Bardo, but must be a continuation of the "Pyrenean Alps."

The Alps themselves not only are a great, wall-like barrier—broken, to be sure, by relatively low breaches—between Italy and the North, but themselves constitute a broad band of territory which until comparatively recent times has been difficult of access and during the Middle Ages was for the most part virtually *terra incognita* to the outside world. The existence of thickly populated centers of civilized life on either side had, however, long before our age led to familiarity with the main routes through the mountains. There were four or five motives which induced men to cross the Alps in the Middle Ages. Ecclesiastics traversed them when bound to and from Rome on official missions. German emperors en route to Italy to be crowned and to attempt to regulate Italian affairs led their armies over their defiles. Pilgrims and Crusaders toiled painfully through their passes towards Rome and the East; and merchants brought their wares across the snows back and forth from the busy cities of Northern Italy. Taking it all in all, there must have been a large number of men scattered throughout Germany, France, England, and the Scandinavian countries who were acquainted with the appearance of Alpine scenery and the difficulties of Alpine travel. Between 1100 and 1250 seven emperors made no less than thirty-nine journeys over Alpine passes.[334] The size of their armies varied greatly. The numbers given for the immense concourse (30,000) which Henry V is said to have mustered in 1110 at Roncaglia after conducting them through the mountains were undoubtedly exaggerated.[335] At all events, the army was so great that Henry had to divide it and send part over the Brenner Pass and part over the Great St. Bernard. The numbers of Frederick Barbarossa's armies probably ranged from 10,000 to 15,000. The time of year chosen for undertaking the journey by those among the medieval travelers who were free to make their own plans—notably the pilgrims—was usually the month of August. Albert of Stade near Hamburg, writing in his chronicle early in the thirteenth century, says that the journey should be undertaken "about the middle of August, since the air is then temperate, the roads dry, there is no excess of water, the days are sufficiently long for traveling and the nights for rest, and you will find at this time the storehouses full of fresh fruits." [336] Political exigencies, however, forced the emperors to conduct their hosts across at all seasons and under all conditions of weather.[337]

Of the many Transalpine routes, the Mont Cenis, Great St. Bernard, Septimer, and Brenner were the most frequented during our period. These were the passes over which trade flowed back and forth between Italy and the North.[338] English and North German pilgrims made frequent use of the Mont Cenis route because it offered an easy way, a long and simple ascent to and descent from the crest of the ridge, and no subsidiary passes to surmount.[339] Pilgrims from Iceland, though they also used the Mont Cenis, seem to have preferred the Great St. Bernard;[340] but when bound for the Holy Land they would sometimes traverse the Carnic Alps and embark from Venice.[341] The Brenner Pass was, of course, most used by the Germans and formed the grand highway of the imperial expeditions. Out of the thirty-nine imperial crossings between 1100 and 1250 nearly half were made by the Brenner, four by the Great St. Bernard, six by the Septimer, three by the Mont Cenis, two by the Lukmanier, and six by other passes.[342]

Use of Terms "Transalpine" and "Cisalpine"

In classical times the terms *trans Alpes* and *transalpinus* always referred to Gaul, Germany, and regions north of the mountains, for these countries were beyond the Alps as viewed from Italy. This usage was continued in the Middle Ages by writers who themselves dwelt north of the Alps, and we find in our period that Otto of Freising speaks of Germany as *trans Alpes* and of Italy as *cis Alpes.*[343] Ragewin, Otto's continuator, wrote more avowedly from the Germanic point of view and on several occasions refers to Italy as *trans Alpes.*[344]

"Alemannia"

The name "Alemannia" as applied to the whole of Germany was also in use in our period, although in the opinion of Otto it ought not to have been so used. Otto says that the city of Turegum (Zurich) is situated on a lake from which the river Lemannus flows and that from this river the province of Swabia is sometimes called Alemannia. "From this circumstance, some have come to think that the whole Teutonic land is called 'Alemannia,' whereas this province only [i.e. Swabia] should be called Alemannia, and its inhabitants only should be spoken of as 'Alemanni.'"[345] The question of the true etymology of the word Alemanni is one that lies beyond our field.

Germany

Though the author of the *De imagine mundi*[346] follows Isidore and classical tradition in dividing Germany into two parts, "Germania superior" and "Germania inferior," in the description of this part of the world he departs from his usual slavish habit of copying the words of Isidore and actually gives us a little information derived from a later source or, perhaps, even representing the result of personal and original observation. "Germania superior," he says, extends between the Danube and the Alps and westward to the Rhine. Called also Rhaetia, it is the land in which the Danube takes its rise (a river which, enlarged by the junction of sixty great streams, discharges its waters into the Pontic Sea through seven mouths, as does the Nile). Suevia (Swabia), Alemannia (so called from Lake Leman), and Noricum (or Bavaria), in which is the city of Ratisbon, are all parts of "Germania superior." It would almost seem as if the author of the *De imagine mundi* goes out of his way to mention Ratisbon, a fact that has been cited[347] as evidence (very slender evidence, it is true) that he may have been a native of this city or was at least personally acquainted with Germany. He carefully refrained from placing Isidore's marvelous bird with luminous plumage in the Hercynian Forest, but removed it to Hyrcania in Central Asia, which seems to show that he was skeptical about the possibility of such a bird being found in Germany.[348] Yet, though less lacking in originality than other parts of the work, the chapters on Germany in the *De imagine mundi* can hardly stand comparison with the information to be found in Otto of Freising's *Gesta Friderici* and in Gunther of Pairis' *Ligurinus*, both of which bespeak undeniable personal familiarity with the country. We have already noticed Otto's description of the local topography in the vicinity of Freising.[349] Elsewhere he mentions such matters as the good hunting and fishing in the neighborhood of Worms, enjoyed by the Italian princes who came over the Alps to take part in a diet held there.[350] This territory, he said, was divided by the Rhine, with Gaul on one bank and the confines of Germany on the other. On the Gallic side stood the Vosges and Ardennes; on the German, forests of considerable extent, which to Otto's day retained their barbaric place names ("barbara adhuc nomina retinentes"). Godfrey of Viterbo[351] also enlarges on the beauties of the region about Worms, the wealth and numbers of its population, the fields and the fish-filled streams which water them, flowing down from wooded places.

Gunther's description of the Main, Rhine, and Moselle country show that he probably was better acquainted with this district than with any of the other territories described in his poem.[352] He cites, among specific details concerning Mayence, the fact that the city is situated on the Rhine a few leagues below the junction of the Main with that stream and not at the junction, as had usually been stated previously.[353]

Hildegard of Bingen includes in her *Subtilitates*[354] remarks about the rivers of her native country, with cautions regarding their use. Her introductory statement in this connection, that the sea sends forth rivers by which the land is irrigated as is the human body by the blood in the veins, should be interpreted in the sense we have already explained in Chapter VIII.[355] She writes of the Seh (possibly the Selz, a stream that flows into the Rhine near Bingen), Rhine, Main, Danube, Moselle, Glan, Nahe, and other rivers, repeating in each case the assertion that the river arises from the sea. The bed of the Seh and its sands, she says, are polluted like a swamp because the stream rises and falls with the storms. Its waters should not be taken raw, nor even cooked in food, for, since they come from the foam of the sea, they are bad for the digestion and generally unsanitary. The Rhine is clear and flows through sandy country; but its water, when drunk unboiled, causes noxious blue fluids in the body. The sands of the Danube are clean and beautiful, its waters clear and harsh but not very good for drinking; the waters of the Main are insipid (*pinguis*); those of the Moselle light and transparent; and so on.

We find in the German chronicles of the time of the Crusades and of the century immediately preceding, some detailed notices about the northern parts of Germany and the shores of the Baltic not to be found in earlier works. In the middle of the eleventh century Adam of Bremen had described Saxony as a generally flat, low region of roughly triangular shape, lying between the lower Elbe and Rhine.[356] The rivers Elbe and Oder, he said, rise near each other in the forested mountains of Moravia but flow off in opposite directions, the former to the northern sea, the latter to the Scythian swamp, or Baltic.[357] Saxo Grammaticus in the geographical introduction to his *Gesta Danorum* gives some fairly full remarks on the configuration of the German Baltic coast and on the peninsulas and islands of Denmark. The latter country, he says, is so intersected and broken by arms and channels of the sea that it contains few continuous tracts of land of any great size.[358] Frisia Minor, adjacent to Denmark, is so low that it is often swept by violent storms and inundations which ruin the fields and destroy the houses.[359]

Baltic Regions

Adam of Bremen's foremost interest was not Germany, however, but the Scandinavian North and the wilder and little-known lands beyond the Elbe, into which the frontier of Teutonic civilization was at this time gradually being pushed eastward. Adam mentions Jumna,[359a] at the mouth of the Oder, a great commercial city and gathering place of heathens and Greeks, and adds that according to some authorities Jumna was the largest city in Europe.[360] Farther east lay various nations of Slavonia —Pomeranians and Prussians—and beyond them other "islands," Samland, Kurland, and "Ehstland" (Estonia), peopled by heathens. Traveling still more remotely in this direction one came to Russia and the fabulous regions of the North. Adam speaks well of the Prussians,[361] for though heathen, he said, they were good men, ready to come to the aid of ships beset by pirates or in danger from the sea. Blue-eyed, with red skins and thick hair, eaters of horseflesh and drinkers of mare's blood, they dwell in the midst of almost impenetrable swamps. Helmold, a chronicler of the twelfth century, copies extensively from Adam but adds many details regarding the religion and customs of the Slavs and, in particular, describes their worship of a great idol of the God Svantevith.[362]

Saxo Grammaticus was better informed than Adam on the countries bordering upon the southern and southeastern coasts of the Baltic, and about them he supplies more or less extensive details.[363] Though the Greeks and Romans alike had believed that on the north of Germany lies the ocean, in the midst of which are various islands—including Scandia and Scandinavia, about which little was known—they certainly had no adequate conception of the peninsular nature of Norway and Sweden. In the ninth century Einhard had described the Baltic as a bay, and Adam of Bremen quoted Einhard to this effect[364] and it is also possible that Adam may have learned something of the Gulf of Bothnia.[365] Adam, however, had no clear knowledge of the geography of this part of the world for "he speaks of the countries of the North as islands, and he seems to draw no sharp distinction between island and peninsula."[366] Saxo, on the other hand, writing over a century later, harbored no doubts whatever of the peninsular character of Scandinavia. He maintained that the sea swings around the north side of Norway and with constantly increasing breadth ends finally in a curved shore.

This sea was here called by the ancients Gandvic (the White Sea). A narrow isthmus separates Gandvic from the sea to the south (the Baltic), and if the isthmus did not exist, Saxo said, Norway and Sweden would be an island.[367]

Scandinavia

Adam of Bremen enjoyed peculiar opportunities for gathering information about the lands immediately to the north of Denmark through his association with archbishop Adalbert of Bremen.[368] Beyond Denmark, he wrote, a new world was opened up. Norway, he believed, extended northward to the limits of the known world, to the Rhipaean Mountains.[369] Through a second of his patrons, King Svend Estridsson of Denmark, who had spent no less than twelve years in these parts, Adam was enabled to learn something of the remote land of Sweden: a rich country, the principal towns of which were Birka and Upsala, the latter possessing a heathen temple, the scene of human sacrifices. Northward of Sweden were regions inhabited by tribes of Finns of marvelous swiftness of foot. These so-called "Finns"—probably in reality Lapps—are frequently mentioned in medieval literature on Scandinavia and the North.[370] They are sometimes called "Scritefinns," "Skritofinns," or "Skridfinns." Saxo Grammaticus spoke of them as great hunters who can climb over the rocky crags of the mountains to the very summits.[371] In the *Historia Norwegiae* we are told that they "fasten smoothed pieces of wood [literally, balks, stakes] under their feet, which appliances they call 'ondrer,' and, while the deer [i.e. reindeer] gallop along carrying their wives and children over the deep snow and precipitous mountains, they dash on more swiftly than the birds" (Nansen's translation).[372] Here we have one of the earliest accounts of the use of skis.

Beyond the Finns Adam of Bremen placed the realm of fable that encircled the medieval world,[373] where were to be found a race of dwarfs and bearded women inhabiting the Rhipaean Mountains; where were also Amazons, Cyclopes, and monsters like those which other writers of our age placed in the heart of Asia or of Africa.

Adam of Bremen, Saxo Grammaticus, and the author of the *Historia Norwegiae*, though they included much that is fanciful in their geographical chapters, also provided reliable data regarding the peoples of the North. Ragewin, on the other hand, in the continuation of the *Gesta Friderici*, and Gunther of Pairis give an account which undoubtedly represented a more usual idea of these people in the minds of Western Europeans. These northern folk aroused Ragewin's disgust, for, he said, they devour each other in time of famine. Owing to perpetual frosts, agriculture is impossible in their country, and their lives consequently are given over to hunting and killing. Well versed in the arts of piracy, these treacherous tribes infest the shores and isles of the ocean, Hibernia, Britain, Denmark, and other coasts.[374] Gunther in the *Ligurinus* [375] enlarges and amplifies this uncomplimentary description by drawing on his own imagination. He says that the inhabitants of the isles of the "Scythian Sea" are strong in the arm but weak in the head. They neither plow a soil made sterile by the perpetual cold nor harrow their uncultivated fields. Neither do they couple the vine to the elm, nor gather in the fruits of the trees, autumn's gifts, but seek their food by the chase and by frequent forays and grow old in piracy on the tireless waves of the sea. And when long privation aggravates a famine—horrible to relate and scarce to be believed, though report would have it so!—these miserable creatures bite and lacerate their own limbs. Father does not know enough to spare his son, nor brother his brother, and the daughter finds refreshment by devouring the boiled body of her mother!

We certainly must not take this effusion as a literally exact account of the customs of the Scandinavians at a time when they were far from being sunk in the abject state of savagery which Gunther pictures; but it shows the terror which the Vikings had instilled into the consciousness of Europe and also the very vague and hazy kind of reports which an intelligent German of the twelfth century received in regard to regions not very distant from his home. Furthermore, it is not at all improbable that the story of cannibalism among these people may have arisen from an actually existing practice of human sacrifice coupled with cannibalistic rites at an earlier date.[376]

France

Otto of Freising regarded the Rhine as the boundary between Germany and Gaul. Though he had studied at Paris, he used Orosius as the main source for the description of Gaul in his *Chronicon*[377] and discussed the various parts of this country and the proper manner in which it ought to be subdivided in a way that reminds us of Caesar. Authorities, he said, declare that there are two main subdivisions; Gallia Cisalpina and Gallia Transalpina. The former lies in Italy between the Po and the Alps; the latter —our France—in turn may be divided into three parts (the three parts made famous by Caesar), Belgian, Lugdunensian, and Aquitanian. Otto then proceeds to a dry and technical discussion of how these parts should be properly grouped in relation to an ill-defined Celtic Gaul.

Paris

More full of color than the pedantic discussion of Otto is a picturesque description of the Paris of the last half of the twelfth century in one of the letters of Guy of Bazoches.[378] "The city," Guy writes, "lies in the lap of a delightful valley crowned on both sides by hills which Ceres and Bacchus make beautiful, striving with one another in their eagerness. The Seine, by no means a humble stream among a host of rivers, takes its rise in the east and in mid-course divides its proud current into two branches, thus making an island out of the center of the city. Two suburbs stretch forth on either side, and even the lesser of these arouses the envy of many an envious town which it surpasses. Connecting each suburb with the island is a bridge of stone, the name of which is derived from the amount of traffic that falls to its lot. The bridge facing the north, the sea, and England is styled the 'great bridge' and the one which faces the Loire on the opposite side is called the 'little bridge.'" The so-called great bridge—

"Densely crowded with a wealthy, bargaining throng,

. . . . .

Swarms with boats, groans under riches, overflows
With merchandise: for lo! there is nowhere its equal!"

The little bridge, on the other hand, is given over to walkers, strollers, and disputers of logic. On the narrow strip of land that forms the island the royal palace towers up to lofty heights and audaciously overlooks with its shoulders the roofs of the whole city. Reverence for it is commanded not so much by the marvelous structure of the building as by the noble authority of its rule.

"This is that house, the glory of the Franks, whose
Praises the eternal centuries will sing.
This is that house which holds in its power
Gaul mighty in war, Flanders magnificent in wealth.
This is that house whose scepter the Burgundian,
Whose mandate the Norman, and whose arms the Briton
fears."

The description of Paris closes with a tribute to the island, from ancient times the home of philosophy and of the seven sisters—the liberal arts.

Alsace

Godfrey of Viterbo seems to have known something of Alsace, whose attractions and beauties he highly praised.[379] The Rhine, he said, is enlivened with shipping. Flowing into Alsace from Basel it laves with its waters wide fields through varied stretches of landscape and traverses a rich countryside. To cross this region takes a traveler three beautiful days' journey, and such vineyards as flourish there the poet sees nowhere else in the world, and the grainfields are marvelous in their fertility. It is a land that can be aptly compared with "Liguria" (Lombardy), for in like manner it is naturally defended by rivers and mountains. The Lord, in his special love for Alsace, had made its plain stand preëminent in beauty among the plains of the world. The population is extremely numerous, and so great are the riches of the people that England and Denmark look thither for markets. Dominating the whole country is the city of Argentina (Strasburg), through which flows the river Ill, rushing to pour forth its water into the Rhine.

Southern France

We find various passages in the *Otia imperialia* of Gervase of Tilbury revealing his familiarity with the south of France. On two different occasions Gervase speaks of the three mouths of the Rhone, which enclose the Sucades (or Sicades) Islands, "commonly called the Camargae."[380] The earth here is rich in salt of a high quality, and the region as a whole is incomparable for its sea and pond fishing, for the hunting of game and birds, and for its pastures.[381] Orosius[382] and Isidore[383] had mentioned the Sicades, undoubtedly having in mind the Stoechades of the ancient geographers, or what are now either the Îles d'Hyères or else, possibly, the small islets just outside the harbor of Marseilles. Gervase, on the other hand, identifies them undeniably with the flat alluvial islands of the Rhone delta, the largest of which is now called Camargue, as in Gervase's day. He also mentions the famous church of Saints Martha and Mary Magdalene on this isle, then, as at present, a much frequented shrine of pilgrimage.[384]

Gervase knew something of the Narbonnese.[385] On the authority of the *De imagine mundi*[386] he states that this province was called *togata* because of the length of the togas worn there, but adds that the description was no longer apt, because in his time the natives wore shorter garments.

Concerning Provence, Gervase made observations intended to impress on the Emperor Otto some idea of the strategic importance of this territory to his empire.[387] We have here an example of medieval political and strategic geography, based in this case not on classical authority but on what the writer actually had observed and thought. The argument, curiously enough, arose out of the discussion we have already mentioned[388] of the effects of the *mistral* on the character of the people of the lower Rhone valley. Gervase concluded that not only does the atmosphere exert an influence on everything upon which it bears down but also that every weight, whether material or spiritual, affects in some manner the objects upon which it rests. This led him to warn Otto that it would be advisable to moderate his *imperium* over Provence in order to propitiate the people. This should be done because the strategic position of that country—the old Kingdom of Arles—is of such nature that it might prove either a great menace or else a great benefit to the unity of the empire. Though admirably situated to threaten France, Gervase explained that Provence is subject to easy invasion by land from Spain, by sea from Africa, or across the Alpine passes from Italy. The character of the people, furthermore, makes it particularly important that they should be handled with circumspection. The Provençaux are shrewd in council and effective in whatever enterprise they undertake but false to their promises and without military strength; owing to their poverty largely dependent on charity (*pro sua paupertate in cibando larga*); insidious in crime (*nocenda*); but calm in the face of trouble. If they have a stable ruler whom they honor, no race is more quickly turned by good impulses, but no other race is more prone to evil when not blessed by such a ruler. In addition, their land is worth holding for its own sake, fruitful as it is above all countries in its seas, fish, meats, and all kinds of hunting, precious stones, swamps, lakes, mountains, rivers, springs and groves, and delicious in its woods and pastures.[389]

ISLANDS OF THE ATLANTIC OCEAN

The Romans had discovered the Canary and Madeira groups and, owing to the mild climate and favorable conditions, had associated them with the "Islands of the Blest" of Greek mythology and hence had come to call them the "Fortunate Isles." In the Middle Ages these isles passed again into the realm of the unknown, though their memory lingered on to adorn the Western Ocean on the Beatus maps, together with more fabulous isles and to serve as the datum point for the western prime meridian. The Cape Verde group and the Azores were utterly unknown.

On most of the maps of the world of our period the islands are arbitrarily squeezed within narrow confines of the encircling ocean, and no attempt is made to represent them in their relative positions or to indicate their distinctive shapes. On the St. Sever Beatus map[390] all islands are shaped like sausages (see Fig. 2, p. 69, above), whether in the Mediterranean or in the ocean. Ireland lies off the coast of Spain and is designated as "Insula Hibernia ab Scotorum gentibus colitur;" Britain, separated from the coasts of Frisia, Gaul, Aquitania, and Gascony by an "Oceanus Britannicus," is said to be 800 miles long by 200 broad—figures taken from Orosius,[391] who got them from Pliny.[392] Five cities are equally spaced from north to south, London, Lincoln, Wroxeter, Seaton, and "Condeaco" (?). Indeed, among the maps of the world the only one which represents the British Isles in recognizable outline is the Cotton,[393] and this probably dates from long before our period. Here we may note, in pleasing contrast to the absurdities we find elsewhere, such features as the westward extension of Cornwall and Devon and of Scotland; Ireland in its correct position and approximately its correct size; the Orkneys to the north of Scotland, and even Man and the Scilly Isles.

British Isles

The medieval reader of the *De imagine mundi* could certainly have gained no very accurate impression from the chapter devoted to the British Isles. This is worth translation in order to demonstrate the utter futility and antiquated character of this much-quoted and at one time, perhaps, unduly popular work:[394]

"Over against Spain toward the setting sun are the following islands in the ocean: Britain, England, Hibernia, Thanet—the earth of which, wherever it may be carried, will destroy serpents —the thirty-three Orkneys on the Arctic Circle where the solstice occurs, Scotia and Chile (Thule) . . . " This is all the *De imagine mundi* tells us of the British Isles!

For more ample data we must look to such native authorities as Giraldus Cambrensis, Alexander Neckam, Gervase of Tilbury, Matthew Paris, and the various British historians and chroniclers.

Gervase of Tilbury adds some details from Geoffrey of Monmouth to the brief notices which he took from Orosius on the dimensions of Britannia Major.[395] His account, though not thoroughly up-to-date in any sense of the term, is fuller and less misleading than that of the *De imagine mundi;* and we certainly do not gain from it any impression like the one we derive from the latter work, that Britain, England, and Scotland are three distinct islands. Geoffrey of Monmouth had told how Great Britain—as distinguished from Britannia Minor, or Armorica (Brittany) on the Gallic side of the Britannic sea—was divided in ancient times into four parts: Cornwall (Cornubia) to the west; Cambria, called vulgarly Wallia, to the north of this; Albania, called also Scotia, in the far north; and Loegria, or Loegrino, called also Anglia, in the middle and south; and that the rivers dividing these provinces were the Waja (Wye), Sabrinus (Severn), Boecura (?), and Deia (Dee).

Cities of Britain

Alexander Neckam, in the *De laudibus divinae sapientiae,* also regales us with a rambling poetical description of the marvels of Britain and of its principal cities.[396] Fame, he says, rejoices in placing Exeter before all other cities: but as for himself he would give New Troy (London) the first place, on account of its glory, wealth, customs, charm, and situation. The walls of London, he adds, would be worthy to hold a Helen. Among other famous cities he mentions Winchester, known in early times for its wealth, and also Canterbury, York, Lincoln, Durham (famous for its associations with the Venerable Bede), Gloucester, Verolamia (St. Albans), where took place the martydom of St. Alban, and Colchester. In the same poem Neckam discourses on the streams of England and Ireland when discussing the principal rivers of the world.[397] In connection with the Thames, he retells the mythological story of the founding of London. The Severn, he says, delights in the cities of Worcester and Gloucester on its banks, and its waters are augmented by those of the Usk. He points out that Britain contains several streams named Avon besides the one upon which Bath stands; that the Trent sends its fish to London; and that the Humber, unsafe for shipping on account of its tides, disdains to see a city but flows through the open fields.

Giraldus Cambrensis on Ireland and Wales

Gervase of Tilbury and Alexander Neckam give us more or less hackneyed and stereotyped descriptions of the British Isles. Far greater originality is revealed in the works of Giraldus Cambrensis. In many other connections we have spoken of the *Topographia Hiberniae* and *Descriptio Kambriae*, which are the most complete and satisfactory geographical descriptions of limited regions dating from our period. The introduction of a long series of fables into the treatise on Ireland tends to blind us to the merits of those parts of the work that have real scientific or historical value. In the beginning of the second "Distinctio" of the *Topographia Hiberniae*, Giraldus says that, as the prodigies of the East have long since been made familiar by the writings of diligent authors, he proposes to throw some light on the prodigies of the West. This he proceeds to do in a highly competent manner, wholly in keeping with the style of Solinus, that master among the "diligent authors" to whom he refers. The Englishman of the time who sat down with Giraldus' work on Ireland before him gathered from it quite as much fabulous and fantastic lore as he could have gathered from the pages of Solinus, but in this case it was lore of countries near at hand. It would almost seem that Giraldus, like a novelist, deliberately set out to throw a glamour of romance over familiar scenes and places. But, however this may be, Giraldus, unlike his model, Solinus, was more than a mere spinner of yarns. His works show that in many respects he was a close and accurate, if not always critical, observer; and certainly he had a vivid and lively interest in nature and mankind.

Ireland

Ireland, he writes, after Britain is the largest of islands. It lies one rather short day's journey to the west of Wales. Between Ulster and Galloway in Scotland the intervening arm of the sea narrows to about half its average width, and the promontories on either side can be seen across the straits in clear weather. South of Ireland, at three days' sailing, is Spain; and northward at an equal distance, Iceland, the greatest of the northern isles.[398] Cut off by the sea, Ireland is almost like another world and contains many phenomena not found elsewhere.[399]

After discussing in detail various earlier theories about the dimensions of Ireland—what Solinus, Orosius, Isidore, and Bede had said [400]—Giraldus proceeds to give some observations of his own on the healthful qualities of the climate, the character of the terrain,[401] and the fertility [402] and products of the soil. Ireland is a land full of pastures and of rich meadows flowing with milk and honey; wine is drunk there, but, as there are no vineyards, it has to be imported from Poitou in exchange for oxhides and the skins of other cattle and of wild beasts. Owing to the presence of a certain poisonous wild yew tree and also to the violence of the rainy winds, not nearly so many bees are kept in Ireland as one would expect.[403] Giraldus also remarks that there are more lakes in Ireland than in any other country,[404] a statement which, though perhaps not true literally, shows that he was aware of one of the differences, if not of the reasons for the difference, between glaciated and nonglaciated countries. These lakes and the rivers abound in fish, many of which are peculiar to the island.[405]

Giraldus gives a legendary account of the clearing of the Irish forests in the days of Partholan,[406] who was supposed to have come there only three hundred years after the Deluge. At that time the whole landscape—with the exception of a few mountains—was covered by an immense forest; and even in his own time, Giraldus adds, the area under cultivation was very restricted in comparison with the woodlands.

His attitude toward the Irish people is neither sympathetic nor complimentary.[407] A rude and inhospitable race, he says, they live like beasts and have scarcely advanced beyond a primitive pastoral stage of civilization. Their fields are used only to a limited extent for pastures, even less for raising of flowers, and less still for the sowing and cultivation of crops. What cultivated fields there are, are very poor; but this condition is the fault of the farmers rather than the result of defects in the soil, which is extremely fertile. There are few fruit trees, the metallic veins of the country are not worked, and there are neither manufacturing, trade, nor mechanical arts. But the people are great musicians![408]

We ought not to place too much faith in the accuracy of this account of the Irish people. As Dimock points out in his introduction to the "Rolls Series" edition of the *Topographia*, Giraldus' acquaintance with them was in all probability limited to a few clergy and to those elements of the population who could still submit "to exist in degradation under the grinding rule of the English invaders."[409] Giraldus was also prejudiced by the feeling of contempt for a supposedly "inferior race" which nearly always results from the conquest of one people by another.

Though his travels in Ireland were not extensive, the Welshman had acquired a superficial and inexact acquaintance with the topographical features of the island and, in particular, with its river systems.[410] The existence of nine principal rivers, he says, dates back to the earliest times, although more recently other streams of no less size had sprung into being. The Shannon is by far the most important. Rising in a large and beautiful lake which divides Munster from Connaught, it separates into two branches that run off in opposite directions. One turns south and, forming the border between the two parts of Munster, flows into "St. Brandan's Sea." The other divides Meath and Connaught from Ulster and after a winding course debouches into the Northern Ocean. The western quarter of the island is thus separated from the other parts by this "mediterranean river" (*mediterraneum flumen*) from sea to sea. Giraldus was accused in the seventeenth century by a violent Irishman[411] of either "raving or dreaming" when he made the Shannon divide Ulster from Connaught. It has nevertheless been shown that, though the Welshman's hydrographic theories were false, there was some justification for his mistaken statements. Certainly, from very near the headwaters of the Shannon other rivers flow away to the north, and a hasty observer might easily have believed them to arise from the same source.[412]

Wales

Giraldus was far better acquainted with his native country, Wales, about which his two treatises give us much accurate information regarding the mountain ranges and river systems, the types of terrain, and the character and customs of the people. He brings out the contrast between North and South Wales.[413] South Wales, he says, is pleasanter by reason of its flat plains, but North Wales is stronger in its defenses, more productive of powerful men, and also more fertile. Merioneth, however, and the land of Canani are the roughest and most inaccessible of all parts of Wales.[414] The Welsh people dwell for the most part in sequestered isolation and not in cities, villages, or castles.[415] Their houses are of the simplest construction. They possess neither gardens nor orchards, and the land is little used for aught else than pasturage. The inequalities and natural defensive strength of the ground make Wales a very difficult region to conquer.

The character of the topographic detail which Giraldus gives reveals his extensive personal acquaintance with the country. We have already had occasion to mention[416] his graphic description of the mountains around the Lake of Brecknock, of the valley of Ewyas, of the quicksands and submerged forests along the southern coast, and of the pasturage on Snowdon. His knowledge of the Welsh rivers (Severn, Wye, Usk, Dee), the mountains in which they take their source, and their courses seaward was far more accurate than his knowledge of the streams of Ireland. Certainly among the works of our period there is none that vies with the *Descriptio Kambriae* either in richness and correctness of detail or in vividness of presentation.

We must say a few words about a chapter which Giraldus introduces on the dialects spoken in Wales,[417] the only discussion of linguistic geography that the writer has found in the literature of the time.[418] The Welshman points out that the British tongue spoken in North Wales is more delicate, beautiful, and generally more praiseworthy than that spoken elsewhere, because this region had been subjected to the intermixture of foreign peoples. The speech of Cardiganshire, however, though this province lies in the heart of South Wales, was also said to be very distinguished and praiseworthy. The natives of Cornwall and Brittany made use of tongues much alike and nearly always comprehensible to the Welsh, because originally the language of all these people was the same. Cornish and Breton, however, in so far as they were more lacking in delicacy and form than Welsh, approached more closely to the ancient British idiom. Similarly the English spoken in southern England, and especially in Devonshire, seemed to Giraldus to be far less correct and more archaic than the tongue of the northern parts of the island, which had been modified by the incursions of the Danes and Northmen. We thus see that Giraldus was broad-minded enough to grant that a language could be materially enriched by contact with alien speech and by the infusion of foreign expressions.

William Fitzstephen on London

Any discussion of the medieval geographical lore of the British Isles would be inadequate without some mention of a famous account of London that forms part of the preface of William Fitzstephen's life of Thomas à Becket.[419] The highly colored picture that William draws surpasses in superlatives Guy of Bazoches' contemporary description of Paris.[420] Even in the twelfth century local pride might lead to the innocent exaggeration of merit. William tells us that "among the noble cities of the world celebrated by Fame, the city of London in the kingdom of the English is the one seat that pours out its fame more widely, sends to farther lands its wealth and trade, lifts its head higher than the rest." He goes on to specify how fortunate is London in its mild climate, piety, fortifications, site, manners and customs, and the character of its citizens. London's piety is shown by the presence not only of an episcopal church but of no less than thirteen "larger conventual churches besides one hundred and twenty-six lesser parish churches." "Above all other citizens," he says, "the citizens of London are regarded as conspicuous and noteworthy for handsomeness of manners and of dress, at table and in the way of speaking. The city matrons are true Sabine women." The city is very well organized so that the different businesses are distributed in different quarters. In the suburbs are "spacious and beautiful gardens" "planted with trees." To the north lie pastures and meadowland with streams flowing through them, "where the turning wheels of mills are put in motion with a cheerful sound." "The tilled lands of the city are not barren gravel but fat plains of Asia that make crops luxuriant and fill their tillers' barns with Ceres' sheaves." Nevertheless "very near lies a great forest with woodland pasture, coverts of wild animals, stags, fallow deer, boars, and wild bulls" (Morley's translation).[421] In the long account of the sports of the London youth with which William Fitzstephen closes we see that even at this early period the English were devoted to outdoor athletics and games. Besides shows and cockfights we are told in detail of ball games, gymnastics, wrestling, dancing, and more strenuous horseback exercises, sham battles, tourneys, and combats in the water with lances. In winter, when the "great fen or moor which waters the walls of the city on the north side" was frozen, boys and girls engaged in sports upon the ice. Nor were young people alone interested in athletics, for in the twelfth, as in the twentieth century, "the ancient and wealthy men of the town came forth to see the sport of the young men and to take part of the pleasure in beholding their agility" (Stow's translation).[422]

Matthew Paris' Maps of Britain

If Giraldus Cambrensis' treatises are the best descriptions of regional geography in the literature of our period, the best regional maps were also the work of a native of the British Isles. In their relative accuracy and fullness of detail, as well as in their freedom from servile dependence on acknowledged authorities, Matthew Paris' three maps of Britain occupy a place by themselves in medieval cartography. By far the best way to gain an idea of what they are like is to examine them in reproduction[423] (one herewith in Fig. 9). It will not be amiss, however, to point out a few significant details.

On one map a legend in the middle informs us that "Britain,

FIG. 9—One of the three maps of Britain by Matthew Paris, that on London Codex Claud. D VI, folio 8 vo. (From Miller, ***Mappaemundi***, vol. iii, 1895, fig. 23).

which includes Scotia, Galloway, and Wales, is now called England."[424] Another legend on a different map gives the dimensions (800 miles in length from St. Michael in Cornwall to Caithness, and 300 miles from St. David's to Dover)[425] and says that there are two archiepiscopal and thirty-two episcopal sees. The outlines of the coasts are in general admirably shown, especially the west coast, with the westward-reaching promontories of Galloway, Wales, and Cornwall. The east coast is less satisfactory, for neither the indentation of the Wash nor the broad eastward projection of Norfolk appear, and by some confusion a point on the coast of Suffolk is taken as the southeastern corner of Britain, with the result that the Thames is shown as debouching into the English Channel. In the far north, the sketchy outlines of Scotland show that relatively little was known of this remote part of the island. Indeed, on two of the maps the Firths of Clyde and Forth join in such a way as to cut off "Scocia Ultramarina" from the remainder of Britain, with which it is connected by a bridge (see Fig. 9). The courses of the main rivers, Severn, Humber, Avon, Thames, on the whole are well delineated. A large tract in the east is labeled *mariscus* to designate the Fen country, and the mountains Snowdon, Plynlimon, and Cheviot appear in their correct positions.[426] The northern Scottish Highlands are described by long legends as mountainous and woody regions which generate an uncultivated and pastoral people, inasmuch as a great part of this area is boggy and full of reeds.[427] Argyll is a "trackless and watery district well adapted to cattle and pasturage,"[428] and South Wales is spoken of in much the same terms.[429] Among the islands off the coast we notice Sheppey, Thanet, Wight, possibly some of the Channel Islands, Portland Head, Scilly, Lundy, Anglesey, Man, Tiree, Iona, and, to the east of Scotland, the Orkneys.[430] The Hebrides are conspicuously absent, and in their place a legend reads "immense and trackless sea." A large number of cities are placed more or less in their proper positions, together with the names of counties and other territorial divisions; and finally the Roman walls from Forth to Clyde and from Carlisle to Newcastle make the most prominent feature among the works of man.

Orkneys and Shetlands

Returning to Giraldus, we find that among the islands in the neighborhood of Britain he mentions Man, Mona (or Anglesey), the Orkneys, and the Shetlands. Man, he remarks, should be considered as belonging to Britain and not to Ireland. His criterion for so assigning it was the fact that its earth does not resemble the earth of Ireland in the property of killing venomous reptiles.[431] The Orkneys and Shetlands,[432] in the northern ocean beyond Ulster and Galloway, were subject to the Norwegian king, through whose piracy and prowess at sea they were held in submission even though geographically they lay nearer the coasts of other countries. Giraldus quotes Orosius and Isidore to the effect that, of the thirty-three Orkneys, thirteen were inhabited and twenty deserted, and he added that in his day, also, the greater part of these isles were uninhabited.

ICELAND AND THULE

Giraldus writes of Iceland, three days' sail to the north of Ireland, and gives a few details regarding its people.[433] The speech of the Icelanders was brief and truthful and they rarely made oath; their king was the equivalent of a priest; and government was in the hands of a bishop. Though thunder and lightning were rare in this distant isle, there was another curse far more terrible: volcanic eruptions and lava flows.

Apparently Giraldus did not associate Iceland with the Thule of the ancients, an isle which he was at a loss to identify.[434] In regard to the latter, he remarked that it was strange that this island, the nature of which was so well known to the Orientals, should remain unknown to the people of the West. After quoting what Solinus and Isidore had written about it, he added that no island familiar to the men of the Occident partook of the qualities which these writers attributed to Thule and that consequently it must either be fabulous—as well as famous, he naïvely remarks—or else hidden away in the far corners of the Boreal Ocean under the Arctic Pole.

The Emperor Frederick II in his treatise on falconry says that the gerfalcons come from a certain island between Norway and Gallandia (Greenland) called in Teutonic "Islandia," which may be translated as "frozen" or "region of ice."[435]

Iceland in Icelandic Literature

Long prior to the beginning of our period Iceland had become the home of an enterprising and cultivated Scandinavian people. From its shores pilgrims found their way to Italy and the Holy Land, and navigators sailed westward into the more mysterious recesses of the ocean. The Sagas give us data regarding these voyages and incidentally throw light on the geographical concepts in the minds of the Northern peoples concerning the seas and islands of the North. The *Ílendingabók* of Ari Frodhi, dating from shortly after 1134, tells of the first Norse visit to Iceland in 870 by Ingolf. Ari mentions it as significant that "at that time Iceland was clothed with forest from the mountains to the strand," and that "there were Christian men here, whom the Norsemen called Papar" (Nansen's translation).[436] It was supposed that these men came from the British Isles because here were found Irish books, bells, and crooks. In the *Historia de antiquitate regum Norwagiensium* of the monk Theodricus we are told that certain merchants in the time of Harold Fairhair had sailed to the Faroes but were driven out to sea by storms and came "to a far distant land, which some think to have been the island of Thule; but I cannot either confirm or deny this, as I do not know the true state of the matter. They landed and wandered far and wide; but although they climbed mountains, they nowhere found trace of human habitation" (Nansen's translation).[437] In the *Historia Norwegiae*, dating probably from the thirteenth century, we are told that "next, to the west, comes the great island which by the Italians is called Ultima Tile; but now it is inhabited by a considerable multitude, while formerly it was waste land, and unknown to men, until the time of Harold Fairhair" (Nansen's translation).[438] In the *Landnámabók*, of about 1200, we have a vivid account of the first Norwegian discoverers' ascent of a high mountain in this remote land. They "looked around them, whether they could see smoke or any sign that the land was inhabited, and they saw nothing. . . . As they sailed from the land much snow fell upon the mountains, and therefore they called the land Snowland" (Nansen's translation).[439]

Greenland

Greenland had been discovered about the year 900. In our period the southwestern coast had become the seat of two small settlements, the ruins of which may be seen at the present time.[440] The population was not great (less than two thousand), and yet this far outpost of European civilization was large enough to be constituted an independent bishopric about the year 1110. From its settlements, certainly during and after the thirteenth century and probably in the course of our period as well, regular summer seal-hunting expeditions were made to the north along the coast, perhaps as far as Baffin's Bay. The icebound east coast of Greenland, on the other hand, was avoided by the Scandinavian seafarers, although we read of frequent shipwrecks there. There is also a report of a seal-hunting trip to this coast made in 1129. From the mid-thirteenth century dates the work called the *King's Mirror*, which gives us a vivid account of the ice floes and icebergs that beset the inhospitable eastern shore.

"Now in that same sea [i.e. the Greenland Sea] there are yet many more marvels, even though they cannot be accounted for by witchcraft [skrimslum]. So soon as the greater part of the sea has been traversed, there is found such a mass of ice as I know not the like of anywhere else in the world. This ice [i.e. the ice-floes] is some of it as flat as if it had frozen on the sea itself, four or five cubits thick, and lies so far from land [i.e. from the east coast of Greenland] that men may have four or five days' journey across the ice [to land]. But this ice lies off the land rather to the northeast (landnorr) or north than to the south, southwest, or west; and therefore anyone wishing to make the land should sail round it [i.e. round Cape Farewell] in a southwesterly and westerly direction, until he is past the danger of [encountering] all this ice, and then sail thence to land. But it has constantly happened that men have tried to make the land too soon, and so have been involved in these ice-floes; and some have perished in them; but others again have got out, and we have seen some of these and heard their tales and reports. . . . These ice-floes are strange in their nature; sometimes they lie as still as might be expected, separated by creeks or large fjords; but sometimes they move with as great rapidity as a ship with a fair wind, and when once they are under way they travel against the wind as often as with it. There are, indeed, some masses of ice in that sea of another shape, which the Greenlanders call 'fall-jökla.' Their appearance is that of a high mountain rising out of the sea, and they do not unite themselves to other masses of ice, but keep apart" (Nansen's translation).[441]

POLAR SEAS

In the boreal parts of the Atlantic the Northern writers of our period placed great whirlpools and fabulous countries peopled by monsters. Adam of Bremen tells of the explorations of certain noblemen of Friesland during the time of the predecessor of archbishop Adalbert of Bremen. Sailing beyond Iceland "towards the extreme axis of the north . . . they suddenly glided into the misty darkness of the stiffened ocean, which can scarcely be penetrated by the eye" (Nansen's translation).[442] Here they were caught by a terrible current and were almost sucked into the vortex of the deep, only to be thrown forth away from danger by a reverse tidal current. Thence they came to an island, fortified like a town, where they found a race of giants whom they called Cyclopes and from whom they barely were able to make their escape. Saxo Grammaticus, writing about 1200, tells of the voyage of a legendary King Gorm of Denmark and an Icelander Thorkill to an even more mysterious region called "Farther Biarmaland," north of Norway.[443] Here too were loathsome monsters, a river dividing the land of men from the land of spirits, and many other wonders. In the *Historia Norwegiae* we are also told of a fabulous coast in the North Atlantic upon which sailors had landed when on the way from Iceland to Norway. This country lay "between the Greenlanders and the Bjarmas," and the sailors "asserted that they had found people of extraordinary size and the land of virgins ['virginum terram'] who are said to conceive when they taste water. But Greenland is separated from these by ice-clad skerries ['scopulis']" (Nansen's translation).[444] Yet more full of color is another description in the same work. Beyond Norway "there is the very deep and northerly gulf which has in it Charybdis, Scylla, and unavoidable whirlpools; there are also ice-covered promontories which plunge into the sea immense masses of ice that have been increased by heaving floods and are frozen together by the winter cold; with these traders often collide against their will, when making for Greenland, and thus they suffer shipwreck and run into danger" (Nansen's translation).[445]

Possibly these accounts in the *Historia Norwegiae* refer to Svalbard, "the country of the cold coasts," mentioned in the *Landnámabôk*.[446] The discovery of Svalbard was placed by the *Icelandic Annals* in 1194,[447] and it may well be that sailors in that year were driven out of their course and landed on the inhospitable shores of Spitsbergen.[448]

Wineland the Good

The voyages of Leif Ericsson and others to the coasts of America, though they had taken place over a century earlier, were doubtless remembered by the Icelanders of the period we are studying. Ari Frodhi in the *Islendingabók*, written about 1134, refers to Wineland and to the Skraelings as if they were entirely familiar to his contemporaries.[449] There is also a record in the *Icelandic Annals*, under the date 1121, that the Bishop Eric of Greenland actually sought Wineland, though we are not told whether his search was successful or whether he made any important discoveries in prosecuting it.[450] The detailed stories of the Wineland voyages which were current in oral tradition during the eleventh century were undeniably put into written form long before 1250, although the versions in which we now have them, the *Saga of Eric the Red* and the *Flatey Book*, are of later date.[451]

The true position of Wineland has for many years been a matter of acrimonious dispute among historians and geographers, but it is beyond our province to enter upon this controversy. On the other hand, it is of interest to point out that the Icelanders themselves or some of them, at least, must have believed that Wineland lay in relatively southern latitudes, for an Icelandic geographical description of the world,[452] dating perhaps from our period, contains the following remark: Not far from Markland is "Wineland the Good, which some affirm extends from Africa; and, if this is so, an arm of the sea separates Wineland and Markland."[453] In Europe outside of the Scandinavian countries practically nothing was known of Wineland. The earliest mention of it is in the pages of Adam of Bremen's description of the North, where we read the following brief passages: "Moreover he [King Svend Estridsson] spoke of an island in that ocean discovered by many, which is called Wineland, for the reason that vines grow wild there, which yield the best of wine. Moreover, that grain unsown grows there abundantly is not a fabulous fancy, but from the accounts of the Danes we know to be a fact" (Reeves's translation).[454] Ordericus Vitalis in his *Historia ecclesiastica* includes Wineland in a list of countries made subject to the king of the Norsemen but gives no details.[455]

Adam of Bremen or a later interpolator[456] adds to the passage just quoted a description of the Northern Ocean, which he erroneously places beyond Wineland. He says: "Beyond this island, it is said that there is no habitable land in that ocean, but all those regions which are beyond are filled with unsupportable ice and boundless gloom, to which Marcian thus refers: 'One day's sail beyond Thile the sea is frozen.' This was essayed not long since by that very enterprising Northmen's prince, Harold, who explored the extent of the Northern Ocean with his ship but was scarcely able by retreating to escape in safety from the gulf's enormous abyss, where before his eyes the vanishing bounds of earth were hidden in gloom" (Reeves's translation).[457]

Fabulous Isles

Until modern times the Atlantic has been an ocean filled by the imaginations of the coast-dwelling peoples of the Old World with fabulous and fantastic isles. In the *De imagine mundi* we read of the Isle of the Gorgons and of the Hesperides,[458] "among which was that great land described by Plato as having been submerged beneath that part of the sea now coagulated—an isle greater in extent even than Africa and Europe." In this story we recognize the old legend of Atlantis which had been the subject of speculation and discussion ever since the time of Plato. The *De imagine mundi* then goes on to speak of "Perdita," or the Lost Island, which far exceeded all the surrounding countries in the delightfulness and fertility of all things to be found therein. Though as a general rule unknown to man, this isle was sometimes to be found by hazard, though never found when looked for. Hence it was called "Perdita," or "Lost." To it St. Brandan was said to have gone in the course of his wanderings.

St. Brandan's Isles

For a full account of the islands visited by St. Brandan we must look to the famous narration of his voyages. Ernest Renan poetically characterizes this legend as follows: "In the midst of these dreams there appears with surprising truth a feeling for the picturesque in polar navigations: the transparence of the sea, the aspects of the ice floes and icebergs melting in the sun, the volcanic phenomena of Iceland, the playing of the cetaceans, the characteristic appearance of the fiords of Norway, the sudden fogs, the milklike sea, green islands covered with grass which overhangs into the waves. . . . "[459] In the most widely known Latin version, which was translated into English and French during our period,[460] we are told[461] that Brandan, the abbot of a large monastery in Munster, received information from a certain Barinthus of marvelous isles that the latter had visited in the western seas and in particular of the "Terra repromissionis sanctorum," or Saints' Land of Promise. Taking seven companions, the saint set out in a ship built especially for the voyage and wandered for seven years from one marvelous isle to another. After forty days' sailing in a northerly direction they came to an islet, where they entered into a narrow harbor between high and precipitous rocks. This harbor mouth, just wide enough to admit a ship, was typical of the ragged western coasts of Ireland and Scotland and was doubtless suggested to the poet by some bleak cove among the rocks of St. Kilda or the Outer Hebrides.

After leaving the islet the wanderers reached an isle covered with sheep—perhaps a reminiscence of the Faroes, the sheep of which had long before been described by Dicuil.[462] Beyond this they came to a smooth islet lacking verdure and with no sand upon it; this turned out to be a sea monster, which dived beneath the waves when the saint and his companions tried to light a fire upon its back. Their fortunate escape from the monster was followed by wanderings that brought them to an isle full of birds in such numbers and of such brilliant plumage that the voyagers could scarce see the branches of the trees. Some of the birds could talk; and one spoke words of prophecy foretelling the future course of Brandan's journeys. Thence they came to yet another isle, where they entered a port with a narrow entrance and found a monastery; then to an isle with a fresh-water spring which put each brother to sleep for a period corresponding to the number of cups he drank. After that they made their way still farther north, where the sea was coagulated, and then returned to many of the isles already visited in the course of their earlier sailings and also to fresh marvels—seas of miraculous clearness, terrible volcanoes, Judas's rock, the islet of Paul the hermit.[463] Finally, after seven whole years, they attained a broad and spacious country full of trees bearing apples as if it were the autumn of the year, a land where no night was ever known. Here a youth greeted Brandan and said that this was the country for which he had been seeking. Then Brandan sailed back to Ireland, where he lived out the remainder of his earthly life, and, after his death, returned forthwith to this "land of promise of the saints," or Paradise, which for so long had been his goal.

CHAPTER XIII

CONCLUSION

It now remains for us to give a brief résumé of the outstanding elements which constituted the geographical lore of the time of the Crusades and to draw a few generalizations from the mass of details that have been set forth in the foregoing pages.

The Outstanding Elements of the Geographical Lore of the Time of the Crusades

The dangers of attempting to condense the geographical thought of a century and a half into the compass of a few pages are manifest, and yet some of the more significant ideas may perhaps be presented without running an undue risk of over-simplification.

According to the orthodox view of the ecclesiastics, the world was created by an arbitrary act of God at a certain definite point of time. Under the influence of classical thought, writers of the Chartres group of the early twelfth century worked out theories of the Creation according to which, though the initiative was attributed to God's act, the actual Works of the Six Days were ascribed to the unfolding of physical processes governed by the laws of nature. Such theories did not meet with general acceptance, though they were never wholly lost sight of. The ancient belief in an eternally existent, periodically re-formed universe was not given credence, though it was well known to the readers of the period with which we are concerned through classical works in their libraries and through translations from the Arabic.

It was probably the opinion of most scholars that the universe is a sphere in which the four elements are arranged concentrically. Furthermore, nearly all scholars argued that the earth likewise is a sphere and that they were acquainted with convincing proofs of this. Standing immobile in the center of the universe, the earth was usually supposed to be a small body in proportion to the entire cosmos. The surface of our globe was divided into five zones, two temperate, two polar—uninhabitable on account of the intense cold—and an equatorial zone, uninhabitable by reason of heat. The habitability of the equatorial zone, however, was affirmed by a few writers conversant with Arabic literature.

There was a great deal of speculation regarding the characteristics of those parts of the world which lay beyond the *oikoumene*, or quarter of the globe known to Europeans. The theories of Macrobius and of Martianus Capella, who had divided the earth's surface into four equal parts by two encircling bands of ocean, strongly influenced the thought of many. Macrobius and Martianus Capella had also believed that all of these quarters of the earth were inhabited but that three of them were unknown to members of our human race, who could not visit them owing to the heat of the equatorial zone and the terrors of the ocean. Though this theory could not be reconciled with Christian teachings and was strongly controverted, it nevertheless persisted, and many of the writers of the Crusading age undoubtedly shared it.

Something was known of the atmosphere. William of Conches wrote of its decreased density and temperature with increased altitude. Rainfall was explained as the result of many causes, among them evaporation of sea water and condensation of water vapor in the air, and topographic influences on rainfall were recognized by Giraldus Cambrensis. The winds, defined as air in motion, were also occasionally ascribed to the influence of topography. William of Conches worked out an elaborate theory of a general circulation of the atmosphere produced by the circulation of ocean currents. The impressions made upon men by the climatic conditions of various parts of the earth found expression in many passages. The cold of the North was contrasted with the heat of the South, and Giraldus Cambrensis gives a colorful comparison of the damp climate of Ireland with the noxious dryness of the East.

The aqueous element was supposed to be divided into two parts, the waters above and the waters below the firmament. Theodoric of Chartres and William of Conches tried to explain the waters above the firmament on rational grounds; others were inclined to take the Biblical assertions absolutely literally. The waters below the firmament were believed to form one unit or congregation of waters, and an unceasing circulation was thought to be maintained from the seas and oceans through subterranean channels and cavities of the earth to the sources of streams. As to the seas themselves, many ingenious explanations were brought forward to account for their salinity. It was understood that the tides are caused by the moon, though subsidiary causes, such as whirlpools and ocean currents, were also adduced to explain them. The most interesting tidal studies of the period, made by Giraldus Cambrensis on the shores of the Irish Sea and Bristol Channel, were undoubtedly the results of careful synchronous observations of the times of high and low water in different localities. Something of the spirit of the North Atlantic is conveyed through the pages of the legend of St. Brandan. Of the waters of the lands, rainfall was not usually thought sufficient to account for the flow of rivers, which were supposed to be fed by underground channels from the seas. Springs, wells, and fountains attracted much attention, and many are the marvels related about them in the literature of the age. Giraldus Cambrensis describes marvelous lakes in Ireland, and strange tales were told of lakes of Italy, Spain, and elsewhere, which, together with the Dead Sea and volcanic craters, were objects of fear, because some men believed them to be ways of ingress to the infernal regions.

The lands of the earth's surface were classified in various manners. The author of the *De imagine mundi* mentions no less than six types of land surface. Different regions were supposed to have different effects on life: Ireland was thought to be remarkably healthful, and its earth to have the property of destroying venomous reptiles; the East, Giraldus Cambrensis would have us believe, is a fountain of poisons. Many medieval writers had an eye for the spiritual and esthetic beauties of landscape, and picturesque descriptions of rich cultivated scenes are not rare. It is doubtful, however, to what extent the grandeur of wild nature and of mountains was appreciated. The great majority of men certainly regarded mountains as grim and horrible. Mountain climbing was not indulged in for pleasure, though we have an account of an ascent of Etna in the *Image du monde*. On the other hand, there date from this age several extremely vivid descriptions of the hardships encountered during journeys over the Alps, one of which was made in midwinter. Alfred of Sareshel gives in a translation from the Arabic a clear account of geologic processes by which mountains were formed. Volcanoes impressed the men of the Middle Ages. The volcanic regions of southern Italy and Sicily and of Iceland are frequently described, and St. Brandan's legend contains what can be nothing else than an account of a volcanic isle. Fiery mountains were associated in the popular mind with entrances to Hell. Scientific investigators usually attributed their fires to burning beds of sulphur and bitumen within the mountains or else to the outbursting of imprisoned winds. To the action of winds in subterranean caverns classical authorities had ascribed the cause of earthquakes, and this view was accepted throughout the Middle Ages. Other features of the land that attracted attention were the deserts of the East, vividly described by the historians of the Crusades and in the *Letter of Prester John*, and the fabulous islands of the sea, especially of the unknown Atlantic. Some peculiarities of the movement of ice in glaciers were noted by Saxo Grammaticus.

The influence of geographical environment on animals and on man was sometimes commented upon. Bernard Sylvester emphasizes the control of terrain over plant and animal life. Giraldus Cambrensis attributes the independence and audacity of the Welsh to the rugged character of their country. A fatalistic idea is expressed in the writings of Hugh of St. Victor and of Otto of Freising, to the effect that the course of science, empire, and civilization proceeds with the heavenly bodies across the surface of the earth from east to west and that, as it has reached the uttermost confines of the West, the power of the kingdom of the Franks is soon destined to disappear.

Within the field of astronomical geography several methods were known whereby latitudes may be determined, and also the use of observations of eclipses for ascertaining longitude was understood. Figures indicating the positions of points in many parts of the known world had been introduced to Western knowledge through the Moslems. It seems likely, furthermore, that not only were the Arabic figures borrowed by the astrological writers of our age but also that a new series of observations was made by which the latitudes as well as the longitudes of several stations in Western Europe were found with no small degree of accuracy. These figures, however, were intended to serve as aids for astrologers and astronomers in making their calculations, and we have no evidence that they were put to geographical use.

The cartography shows little originality. It was in no way corrected or checked up with reference to astronomical observations. Most of the maps were based on earlier models, and it is perhaps possible to trace their origins back to maps of the Roman Empire. Cartographic accuracy was not the aim of the map maker of the time, and we are not justified in criticizing his maps in the light of modern standards. They should be regarded rather as diagrammatic approximations. A number of conventions were followed, the most important of which was the representation of the east at the top. The maps were vividly colored; and mountains, rivers, and the works of man were shown by pictorial symbols.

We may conceive of the regional geographic knowledge of the age as comprised within two concentric circles: a very broad outer circle, which includes all those lands of which knowledge had been derived at second hand through literary sources; and a smaller inner circle including those lands which were known at first hand through actual travel.

The outer circle took in to the east the land of the Seres, or China, and the lost Atlantis to the west; to the north the regions of the Hyperboreans and the semi-mythical Rhipaean Mountains; and to the south the Mons Climax of Ptolemy and the mysterious upper reaches of the Nile. Nearly all that lies between the two circles was a vague region of fancy and fable, though ideas that were more or less correct prevailed about some parts of Western Asia, familiar ground to the men of ancient Greece and Rome.

The inner circle included on the east the shores of the Black Sea and the Holy Land; on the south, the Mediterranean fringe of Africa; westward it was bounded by the Atlantic coast; northwestward, warped somewhat out of shape, it enclosed Iceland and even the icy coasts of Greenland. To the north, it ran through Scandinavia and the Baltic. Within these bounds there were many gaps that were still utterly unknown; but, in general, politics, pilgrimage, war, and commerce had familiarized the men of the West with most parts of this tract. It seems a small area indeed compared with what is now known of the world's surface and small even compared with what Ptolemy and earlier Greeks had known. Only in the age that immediately follows ours was the circle enlarged, at first to the eastward by the great overland journeys of Marco Polo and the other Asiatic travelers of the late thirteenth and fourteenth centuries and then westward, southward, and northward during the Age of Discovery. Not until our own day has it at last come to comprise the entire earth.

Character of the Geographical Lore of the Time of the Crusades

Men have always respected tradition and learning inherited from former ages, but in some periods dependence on earlier authority has been more unquestioning than in others. In the Middle Ages, especially, an immense mass of knowledge and belief was handed down from generation to generation.

A portion of this inherited mass of knowledge and belief constituted the recognized and orthodox geographical lore of the Crusading age. This body of teachings—to be sure, not altogether uniform or consistent—had been built largely on a foundation of Biblical and classical doctrine. The early Church Fathers, taking the Bible as their authority, had leveled destructive criticism against those ideas of the Greeks and Romans which appeared to go counter to Scriptural texts, but in the course of time reconciliation of ancient science with Christianity was partly achieved and, as a consequence, the accepted scientific lore of the twelfth and early thirteenth centuries was only to a limited extent drawn from a literal interpretation of the Bible. Nevertheless, those theories of antiquity that were too diametrically hostile to the words of Scripture still remained tabooed, and, when Manegold, Peter Lombard, or Peter Comestor inveighed against belief in *hyle*, the Great Year, or the antipodes, they were merely echoing the arguments of their early Christian predecessors. Classical learning and Christian doctrine were sufficiently at one by the opening of the twelfth century to make it no longer heretical to believe in the sphericity of the earth, in the existence of antipodal regions (if not inhabitants), and in a physical explanation of many geographical processes that an earlier age might have ascribed to the direct intervention of the divine will.

The works of our period show all too plainly that they were written in a credulous age, for credulity is an inevitable concomitant of the undue respect for authority. Credulity and love of the marvelous—which is much the same thing—are in many ways the most characteristic and entertaining qualities of the geographical writers of the Middle Ages. Marvels of all kinds, located in all countries, are solemnly described as if they were truth. India, especially, was the scene of fabulous monsters and prodigies; but no country, no matter how well known, was wholly without them. Even the most serious writers mention them, and they enliven all the maps.

In contrast with this geography based on authority and tradition stood another great body of geographical lore derived not from books or tradition but from observation by eyewitnesses of the countries of the earth and the physical features of its surface. We may style this second body of geographical lore the "geography of observation." It is represented almost universally in the literature of the period, for no writer was so completely immersed in the learning of the past that he failed altogether to respond to the world of his day. Even in the most learned works there are occasional passages drawn from contemporary observation; but it is especially in histories, chronicles, letters, and other less formal writings that the "geography of observation" finds unhampered expression. The latter are among the most illuminating documents of the age, for they reveal to us those things which above all interested the average man in the material world around him.

Measured by modern standards, this "geography of observation" is the only kind of geography that rests on a sound and scientific footing. Modern science rejects theories, however old and hallowed they may be, which cannot stand the test of an appeal to Nature herself. Precisely the opposite seems to have been the normal intellectual habit of the Middle Ages, when the prevailing tendency was if anything to put aside the evidence of Nature when contradicted by the classics, by the Church Fathers, or especially by the Bible. Logical impossibility or rational improbability did not usually bear much weight against a belief that had been approved by time.

And yet there were in the age of the Crusades numerous exceptions to this general rule. Never has there been a time when a few fore-reaching and individualistic spirits have not tried to search and see and think for themselves, to confront older teachings with new, to criticize established beliefs in the light of observed facts and reason. In the ardent, enthusiastic society of the twelfth and thirteenth centuries there was no lack of such spirits. Among the writers on geographical subjects we need but recall the names of the scholars of Chartres: Theodoric, who undertook to explain the Creation according to physical principles and specifically excluded from his discussion all moral and allegorical interpretations of the text of Genesis; or William of Conches, who argued that we may avoid irrational deductions from Scripture by an appeal to our own reason and who maintained that the animals of the earth and also Adam and Eve were produced through the interaction of the elements of fire, earth, air, and water. And this critical, inventive attitude reappears in the thirteenth century in the work of such men as Robert Grosseteste, Roger Bacon, and even Albertus Magnus.

We gain a deeper and more sympathetic understanding of the devious workings of the human mind when we trace in the geographical lore of the Middle Ages the persistence of old ideas and the transfer of prejudices and beliefs from age to age; but at best this is a disheartening study. On the other hand, there is always fascination in coming across oases of fresh observation and clear reason in the midst of the arid deserts of plagiarism that constitute so much of medieval literature. These oases mark the pathway of the history of science.

NOTES

NOTES

The numbers at the top of the inner margin of each page indicate on which pages of the text (pp. 1–361) the passages occur to which the notes on a given page refer.

For the works here cited in abbreviated form refer to the Bibliography. Works not listed in the Bibliography (these are relatively few) are here given with their full titles.

As a rule a work will be found in the Bibliography under its own author or, if anonymous, its own title. If not, the entry under which it will be found is generally here indicated. In the few cases where it is not the work should be looked for under the ancient or medieval author or title to which the work sought for relates.

Bible references and quotations throughout the present work, except where otherwise indicated, are based on the Douay and Rheims translation of the Vulgate.

CHAPTER I

THE CONTRIBUTION OF THE ANCIENT WORLD

[1] The *De caelo et mundo* should not be confused with the *De mundo* (*Περὶ κόσμου*), a spurious work ascribed to Aristotle and dating from about 100 B. C. See preface to E. S. Forster's translation of the *De mundo* in the Oxford translation of the works of Aristotle, vol. iii, 1914.

[2] On the geography of Posidonius see below, p. 371, note 55, and also the two important recent studies: Wilhelm Capelle, *Die griechische Erdkunde und Posidonius*, in: Neue Jahrbücher für das klassische Altertum, Jahrgang 23, vol. liv, Leipzig, 1920, pp. 305–323, and Karl Reinhardt, *Poseidonios*, Munich, 1921, especially pp. 59–135 for the geography and pp. 135–176 for the meteorology.

[3] For a brief general outline of the main trend of Greek geography see Berger, *Geschichte*, 1903, Überblick, pp. 1–24. See also Bunbury, *Ancient Geogr.*, 1879; Tozer, *Ancient Geogr.*, 1897; Tillinghast, *Geogr. Knowl.*, 1889. An extensive recent treatment of ancient geography has come to the attention of the writer as this book is going to press: Gisinger's article "Geographie" in *Paulys Real-Encyclopädie*, 1924. This contains many references to secondary works; it is particularly valuable as a synthesis of recent German research in the field.

[4] That Pliny's *Natural History* was extensively read in the Middle Ages is proved by the large number of times its title appears in medieval library catalogues. For example, in twelfth-century French catalogues alone it occurs in no less than six different places; in German catalogues in five different places before the twelfth century. Though at first glance

these figures do not appear large, when compared with similar figures for the works of other writers they show that, relatively speaking, Pliny was very popular. We are also confirmed in this opinion by the frequency of citations of Pliny (M. Manitius, *Philologisches*, 1892, pp. 59–60; idem, *Römische Prosaiker*, 1890, pp. 380–384). Furthermore, we have in manuscripts dating from the eighth century and onward a series of excerpts from Books II, III, IV, VI, and XVIII of the *Natural History*. These contain the outstanding geographical elements of Pliny's work and attest to its great popularity (see Rück, *Auszüge*, 1888; idem, *Exzerpt*, 1902; idem, *Naturalis Historia*, 1898, pp. 203–318). On p. 287 of the *Exzerpt* Rück writes that the existence of these excerpts forms "a weighty literary-historical proof of the continued life of Pliny in later centuries."

[5] The *Collectanea* is mentioned in France in one catalogue from before the twelfth century, in five from the twelfth, and in four from the thirteenth. In Germany it is mentioned in six catalogues from before the twelfth century, in four from the twelfth, and in two from the thirteenth. It is also mentioned in catalogues of British and Italian libraries. Its popularity was equal to that of Pliny and was perhaps even greater (see M. Manitius, *Philologisches*, pp. 78–79).

[6] Columba (*Questione soliniana*, 1920) holds that the materials in Solinus' *Collectanea* came in large part from a common source of Pliny's *Natural History* and Pomponius Mela's *Corographia*. This was a lost work which Columba styles *Corographia Varro-Sallustiana*. It was worked over (according to his theory) by an unknown compiler and reduced by Solinus into the form of a compendium, with borrowings here and there direct from Pliny. See note on Columba's monograph in Bollettino della Reale Società Geografica Italiana, vol. lviii, Rome, 1921, p. 44.

[7] Seneca's popularity as shown by the library catalogues was less than that of Pliny, though the *Quaestiones naturales* were read rather extensively in France in the twelfth century (M. Manitius, *Philologisches*, p. 42; idem, *Geschichte*, 1911, vol. i, p. 38).

[8] Capella merely followed the Latin tradition, which tended to restrict the field of geography and at the same time to limit the science of geometry to the art of measurements. The *De nuptiis Philologiae et Mercurii* served to pass on to the Middle Ages this attitude in regard to geography and geometry (Mori, *Misuraz. eratos.*, 1911, pp. 186–187; see also Haskins, *Studies*, 1924, p. 89).

[9] M. Manitius, *Philologisches*, p. 112, informs us that, next to Virgil and the Vulgate, the *De nuptiis Philologiae et Mercurii* was the most popular book of the Middle Ages. References to copies of it are found in nearly all medieval library catalogues. See also Mori, *Misuraz. eratos.*, pp. 388–391.

[10] Macrobius seems to have come next to Martianus Capella in popularity, particularly in the twelfth century, when his book finds mention

more than a dozen times in the catalogues of both French and German libraries of the period. It was also read in Italy, Spain, and Great Britain. In the latter country there are five entries from the early thirteenth century (M. Manitius, *Philologisches*, p. 106).

[11] Aristotle, *De caelo*, I, 3; Duhem, *Système*, vol. i, 1913, p. 173.

[12] Aristotle, *Meteor.*, I, 2; Duhem, *op. cit.*, vol. i, p. 164.

[13] These ideas are developed in Plato's *Timaeus* and in Aristotle's *De generatione et corruptione*, II, 11. See Duhem, *op. cit.*, vol. i, pp. 164–169.

[14] Berosus in the third century before Christ described Chaldean theories regarding the Great Year (Duhem, *op. cit.*, vol. i, p. 69).

[15] *ibid.*, vol. i, pp. 70–71.

[16] Notably Philolaus (*ibid.*, vol. i, p. 77).

[17] Seneca, *Quaest. nat.*, III, 28–29; Duhem, *op. cit.*, vol. i, p. 70.

[18] For example, Anaximander, Anaximenes, Heraclitus, Empedocles (Duhem, *op. cit.*, vol. i, pp. 70–71, 167).

[19] Aristotle, *De caelo*, I, 10; *Meteor.*, I, 14, as interpreted by Duhem, *Système*, vol. i, pp. 167–168.

[20] Günther, *Apokatastasis*, 1916, p. 85.

[21] See E. S. McCartney, *Fossil Lore in Greek and Latin Literature*, in: Proceedings of the Michigan Academy of Science, Arts, and Letters, vol. iii, New York, 1924, pp. 23–38, especially pp. 37–38.

[22] Aristotle, *Meteor.*, I, 14; Duhem, *op. cit.*, vol. i, p. 167. In the important paper cited in note 20 above, Günther traces the development in antiquity and during the Middle Ages of (1) theories of astronomical periods and (2) theories of the *apokatastasis*, or restoration of the earth to its previous condition after destruction by fire or by water. He shows that the ancient and medieval philosophers conceived of a complete parallelism between these two sets of phenomena. It is, however, difficult to follow his argument that they failed to recognize any causal relation whatsoever between the astronomical periods and the *apokatastasis*, although it is doubtless true that no attempt was made to explain in detail the manner in which celestial circumstances operated to produce effects upon the earth.

[23] See Duhem, *Système*, vol. i, pp. 65–85, 275–297.

[24] Cumont, *After Life*, 1922, pp. 12–13.

[25] Al-Mas'ūdī and Al-Bīrūnī describe the theory as it prevailed in India (Duhem, *op. cit.*, vol. i, pp. 67–69; vol. ii, pp. 213–220).

[26] Plato gives a formula from which it has been deduced that he believed the duration of the Great Year to be 760,000 terrestrial years. Aristotle explained that the figure could be found by determining the least common multiple of the periods of revolution of the various celestial bodies. Cicero calculated it at 12,954, and Macrobius at 15,000 years. See Duhem, *op. cit.*, vol. i, pp. 84, 165, 283, 288.

[27] Ptolemy describes Hipparchus' discovery of the precession of the equinoxes in the *Almagest*, VII, 2–3 (as cited by Duhem, *op. cit.*, vol. ii, [pp. 180–185).

[28] *Almagest*, VII, 2 (Duhem, *op. cit.*, vol. ii, p. 185).

[29] Duhem, *op. cit.*, vol. ii, pp. 212–223.

[30] ". . . l'évolution de la science hellène révèle non pas l'existence de luttes perpétuelles pour ou contre la sphéricité mais au contraire un accord, en somme assez rapide, établi avant la fin du ve siècle entre les penseurs de toutes écoles" (Thalamas, *Géogr. d'Ératosthène*, 1921, p. 103; see also the same, p. 99, note 3).

[31] Berger thinks that Anaximander may well have believed in a spherical earth (*Geschichte*, 1903, p. 32, note 2, and p. 34); this opinion has not been accepted by recent students, who ascribe to Anaximander participation in the older doctrine of a disk-shaped earth (Stegmann, *Anschauungen*, 1913, pp. 14–15; Heidel, *Anaximander*, 1921, p. 246; Gisinger, "Geographie" in: *Paulys Real-Encyclopädie*, 1924, p. 543). See also below, p. 372, note 61.

[32] *Phaedo*, 109. Plato thought that the universe, as well as the earth, is a sphere because the sphere is the most perfect of forms (*Timaeus*, 33). An obscure mathematical passage, *Timaeus*, 55, seems to liken the universe to a dodecahedron. See the *Dialogues*, Jowett's transl., 1892, vol. iii, p. 363, and Boffito, *Leggenda*, 1903, p. 584.

[33] These proofs were worked out by Aristotle in two ways (*De caelo*, II, 14). First he explained that physical laws require that the earth must be spherical; then he demonstrated that observation shows that it actually is a globe. Aristotle's physics were built upon a theory that superficially has been compared with the Newtonian theory of gravitation, although fundamentally it is entirely different. A principal law of Aristotelian physics is that all heavy bodies seek the center of the universe, whereas Newton's law is that all bodies, whether heavy or light, attract each other (see Duhem, *Système*, vol. i, p. 210). Aristotle (*De caelo*, II, 4) showed by mathematical argument that water, in obedience to his physical law, will, if unhindered, become a perfect sphere, with the center of the universe as its center, and that land, though it cannot become a perfect sphere owing to its rigidity, will tend to assume such a form.

That the earth actually is a globe, the Stagirite maintained, is revealed by the circular shadow it casts upon the moon in an eclipse. Furthermore, a traveler journeying from north to south sees new constellations appear above the southern horizon and vice versa, constellations that could only be hidden from him at his starting point by the curvature of a spherical earth (Duhem, *Système*, vol. i, pp. 211–215).

Adrastias of Aphrodisias, one of the Peripatetic school, adduced proofs similar to those of Aristotle (Duhem, *op. cit.*, vol. i, pp. 473–474), although he presented them with greater clarity. He showed by the argument of the appearance of new constellations to a traveler journeying north or south that the earth is convex from north to south. That it is also convex from east to west he proved from the observation that the same celestial body rises sooner in the eastern parts of the habitable world than it does in the western. This could be demonstrated by any eclipse of the moon: the eclipse appears at a later hour of the night and higher in the heavens to an observer in the east than it does to one in the west. As both observers see the same eclipse, it follows that the moon must in reality rise in the east before it rises farther west. If the earth were flat both observers would necessarily see the eclipse at the same hour of local time.

[34] *De motu corp. cael.*, I, 8 (as cited by Duhem, *Système*, vol. i, p. 471).

[35] *Hist. nat.*, II, 64. Both Cleomedes and Pliny demonstrated the sphericity of the sea by noting that mountains may be seen when the lower parts of the land are invisible and that shores become visible from the masthead of a ship before persons on deck can see them. Pliny (*op. cit.*, II, 65) had a theory to explain the sphericity of the sea that differed widely from that of Aristotle. The gist of this was that it is in the inherent nature of water to assume a spherical form. Traces of this view are to be found in the writings of Alexander Neckam in the thirteenth century. See below, p. 438, note 34.

[36] Ptolemy, *Almagest*, I, 4. Ptolemy's proofs were similar to those of Aristotle and Adrastias (see above, note 33). He neglected arguments of the physical necessity of a globular earth (Duhem, *Système*, vol. i, p. 480).

[37] *De nupt. Phil. et Merc.*, VI, 590–598. Martianus Capella brought together and vigorously presented many of the arguments of his predecessors: that of Aristotle that the shadow of the earth on the moon is curved, the argument of the different appearance of the heavens in different latitudes, and the argument from the eclipses (see above, note 33).

[38] On the heliocentric theory in antiquity see Duhem, *Système*, vol. i, pp. 399–426, and Heath, *Aristarchus*, 1913.

[39] Philolaus worked out an elaborate hypothesis which placed an immobile fire, the Hearth of the Universe, the seat of divinity, in the center of the cosmic system. Around this fire revolves our earth; an anti-earth counterbalances our earth on the opposite side of the fire, but man can never see either the Hearth or the anti-earth because he dwells on the side of our earth that is always turned outward from the center. See Duhem, *Système*, vol. i, pp. 11–21. Hicetas and Ecphantus modified the system of Philolaus by doing away with the anti-earth and placing our earth in the middle of the universe, enclosing the central fire within it. They accounted for day and night by a diurnal rotation of the earth around its axis (*ibid.*, vol. i, pp. 21–27).

[40] Some thought in antiquity that a passage in the *Timaeus*, 40, shows that Plato believed that the earth rotates on its axis; but this interpretation of the passage was disputed even in classical times, and other pas-

sages in Plato's works seem to confirm us in holding that he thought that the earth stands immobile (Duhem, *Système*, vol. i, p. 86). It should be noted that though Plato placed the World Soul in the center of the earth and of the universe, he was also convinced that great fires exist in the earth's interior. See above, p. 32.

[41] *Timaeus*, 34. See also Lutz, *Geographical Studies*, 1924, pp. 166–167.

[42] Aristotle's abstruse reasoning about the immobility of the earth is interpreted by Duhem, *Système*, vol. i, pp. 219–230. Duhem clarifies the arguments of the Stagirite by resolving them into four main propositions:

(1) "The movement of the heavens requires the existence of an immovable body distinct from the heavens at the center of the universe" (Duhem, *Système*, vol. i, p. 220). Why such an immovable body is necessary is explained in *De caelo*, I, 8, and in *Physics*, IV, 4 (cited by Duhem, *Système*, vol. i, pp. 198–210, 221). Later writers and commentators confused Aristotle's views here set forth with a theory which the philosopher—if he wrote it—presents in the *De motu animalium* and which is, in brief, as follows. "For every animal that moves there must be without it something immovable, but supporting itself upon which that which is moved moves. For were that something always to give way (as it does for mice walking in grain, or persons walking in sand) advance would be impossible, and neither would there be any walking unless the ground were to remain still" (*De motu anim.*, 2; translated by A. S. L. Farquharson in the *Works of Aristotle*, 1913, p. 698b). Although the writer of this passage expressly states that he does not intend this simple theory to be applied to the movements of the heaven in relation to the earth, it was, none the less, passed on by way of the Moslems to the West as an argument in favor of the immobility of the earth.

(2) "Physical reasons prove that it is not possible for the earth to move" with a circular motion. The normal motion of the particles which compose the earth is in a straight line toward the earth's center. Correspondingly "the movement which is natural to each part must also be natural to the whole, in such a way that the earth taken as a whole certainly has for its natural motion that movement in a straight line and directed toward the center which characterizes heavy bodies" (Duhem, *Système*, vol. i, p. 226). Any other movement, such as a movement of rotation, "being, then, constrained and unnatural . . . could not be eternal. But the order of the universe is eternal" (*De caelo*, II, 14; translated by J. L. Stocks in the *Works of Aristotle*, 1922, p. 296a).

(3) "Experiments show that as a matter of fact the earth does not move at all." If the earth moved "there would have to be passings and turnings of the fixed stars. Yet no such thing is observed" (*De caelo*, II, 14; Stocks's translation, p. 296b). In other words, if the earth moved one would expect to observe parallaxes of the fixed stars (Duhem, *Système*, vol. i, p. 227). "It is clear, then, that the earth must be at the center and immovable, not only for the reasons already given, but also because

heavy bodies thrown quite straight upward return to the point from which they started, even if they are thrown to an infinite distance" (*De caelo*, II, 14; Stocks's translation, p. 296b).

(4) "Physics teaches us the cause of the immobility of the earth." As all heavy bodies tend to seek the center of the universe, the various parts of the earth have arranged themselves around the center in such a manner that an equilibrium is established, and this equilibrium produces immobility (*De caelo*, II, 14, Stocks's translation, p. 297a; Duhem, *Système*, vol. i, pp. 216, 228–229).

[43] *Hist. nat.*, II, 5.

[44] Ptolemy (*Almagest*, I, 7) discussed the immobility of the earth in much the same manner as Plato and Aristotle. From Aristotle he derived the argument of the heavy body thrown into the air. See above, note 42, paragraph (3) and Duhem *op. cit.*, vol. i, pp. 480–484.

[45] *De caelo*, II, 14.

[46] *Hist. nat.*, II, 108.

[47] *De architectura*, I, 6 (edited by F. Krohn, Leipzig (Teubner), 1912; English translation by M. H. Morgan, Cambridge, Mass., 1914).

[48] *De nupt. Phil. et Merc.*, VI, 596.

[49] *In som. Scip. comm.*, I, 20, 20.

[50] *De motu corp. cael.*, I, 10.

[51] See Thalamas, *Géogr. d'Ératosthène*, 1921, pp. 162–163. Konrad Miller, *Erdmessung*, 1919, pp. 5–6, argued that Eratosthenes calculated the circumference at 252,000 stades, not 250,000. Even if, as Cleomedes tells us, he calculated it at 250,000 stades, it seems probable that it was Eratosthenes himself and not some later scientist who arbitrarily raised it to 252,000 in order to obtain a figure divisible by 60 or perhaps by 360.

[52] *De motu corp. cael.*, I, 10.

[53] Strabo, *Geogr.*, II, 2 (edited by A. Meincke, 3 vols., Leipzig (Teubner), 1904–1909; English translation by H. L. Jones, 2 vols., London, 1917–1923); Berger, *Geschichte*, 1903, pp. 579–582.

[54] Thalamas, *op. cit.*, p. 151.

[55] Miller, *Erdmessung*, pp. 12–14. For other possible explanations of Posidonius' figures, see Berger, *op. cit.*, pp. 579–582, and Oscar Viedebantt, *Eratosthenes, Hipparchos, Poseidonios: Ein Beitrag zur Geschichte des Erdmessungsproblems im Altertum*, in: Klio: Beiträge zur alten Geschichte, vol. xiv, Leipzig, 1914, pp. 208–256; idem, *Poseidonios, Marinos, Ptolemaios: Ein weiterer Beitrag zur Geschichte des Erdmessungsproblems im Altertum*, in: *ibid.*, vol. xvi, 1920, pp. 94–108.

[56] *De motu corp. cael.*, I, 10. See Thalamas' clear and reasonable discussion of Eratosthenes' measurement, *op. cit.*, pp. 128–164.

[57] *De nupt. Phil. et Merc.*, VI, 596. Capella's account of Eratosthenes' measurement differs slightly from that of Cleomedes (Mori, *Misuraz. eratos.*, 1911, p. 584; Thalamas, *op. cit.*, pp. 140–141).

[58] Miller, *op. cit.*, p. 7.

[59] Thalamas, *op. cit.*, pp. 158-159.

[60] *ibid.*, p. 170.

[61] See White, *Warfare*, 1920, vol. i, pp. 89-90. Lutz, *Geographical Studies*, 1924, p. 168, holds that "the fundamental notions of the Homeric poems, of Hesiod and Aeschylus regarding the earth [a disk surrounded by an ocean stream] are Babylonian in origin."

[62] Thales thought that the earth was created out of water (Norlind, *Problem*, 1918, p. 8).

[63] Berger, *Geschichte*, 1903, p. 285.

[64] Pliny gives details of explorations which he believed had proved the existence of connections between the Caspian Sea, the Atlantic, and the Indian Ocean (*Hist. nat.*, II, 167).

[65] Probably the best treatment of the history of theories of the antipodes is to be found in Rainaud, *Le continent austral*, 1893.

[66] *Meteor.*, II, 5. Pliny also thought that the polar and equatorial regions are uninhabitable, although he was aware of the fact that the northern boundary of the uninhabitable part of the equatorial regions must be well south of the Tropic of Cancer (*Hist. nat.*, II, 68, 74, 76, 108). See also below, p. 377, note 172.

[67] *De caelo*, II, 14.

[68] *Meteor.*, II, 5.

[69] "Quantum est enim, quod ab ultimis litoribus Hispaniae usque ad Indos iacet? Paucissimorum dierum spatium, si navem suus ferat ventus implebit" (*Quaest. nat.*, I, praef., 13). Doubt has been expressed by critics as to whether or not Seneca had in mind a passage westward across the Atlantic. See Edward Channing, *A History of the United States*, vol. i, New York, 1905, p. 31. Strabo discussed Eratosthenes' views on the possibility of sailing from Spain to India in his *Geography*, I, 64, 65. See Channing, *op. cit.*, p. 30.

[70] See Tillinghast, *Geogr. Knowl.*, 1889, pp. 6-12; Berger, *Geschichte*, 1903, p. 625; Norlind, *Problem*, 1918, *passim*, for discussions of the continental and oceanic theories in antiquity and in the Middle Ages. Roger Bacon (*Opus majus*, Bridges' edit., vol. i, 1897, p. 290) states that "Ptolemaeus vero in libro de dispositione sphaerae vult quod fere sexta pars terrae est habitabilis propter aquam, et totum residuum est coopertum aqua." That this should have been the opinion of Ptolemy is difficult to reconcile with his advocacy of unknown lands beyond the *oikoumene* enclosing the Indian and Atlantic Oceans (*Geogr.*, I, 17, 6; VII, 3, 6; VII, 5, 2; see Berger, *Geschichte*, pp. 625, 627, 629).

[71] See above, p. 187.

[72] For a summary of Aristotle's theories in regard to the elements, see Lippmann, *Chemisches*, 1910.

[73] Gilbert, *Meteorol. Theorien*, 1907.

[74] "Causas autem illi mutationis et inconstantiae alias terra praebet, cuius positiones, hoc et illo versae, magna ad aeris temperiem momenta

sunt. . . . " (*Quaest. nat.*, II, 11). Possibly "temperiem" should be translated "quality" rather than "temperature."

[75] *Meteor.*, I, 4; I, 7; II, 4. See Lones, *Arist. Researches*, 1912, pp. 30–33.

[76] *Meteor.*, I, 9–12. See also Lones, *op. cit.*, pp. 32–33, 42–45.

[77] See above, pp. 99–101, and below, p. 406, note 93.

[78] *Quaest. nat.*, V. See Gilbert, *Meteorol. Theorien*, 1907, pp. 537–539.

[79] Aristotle, *Meteor.*, II, 4–5; Seneca, *Quaest. nat.*, V, 7–14; Pliny, *Hist. nat.*, II, 44.

[80] Capelle, *Berges- und Wolkenhöhen*, 1916, pp. 1–2.

[81] *ibid.*, pp. 16–17, 28.

[82] *ibid.*, pp. 26–27.

[83] Posidonius understood, from observation of differences between the Indians and Ethiopians dwelling in the same latitude, that latitude was not the only determining element in the distribution of natural products and races of man but that other factors should also be given consideration (Berger, *Geschichte*, 1903, p. 557). Peschel, *Geschichte*, 1877, p. 226, wrote that in the Middle Ages Jordanus of Severac was the only man to recognize the fact that a meridian may mark the boundary between dissimilar areas of plant or of animal life. See, however, Giraldus Cambrensis' observations on this matter (see above, p. 177).

[84] For further discussion of ancient *climata*, see above, pp. 242–243.

[85] *Quaest. nat.*, III, 6; IVa, 2.

[86] The voyage of Pytheas of Marseilles was the source of the greater part of ancient beliefs in regard to high northern latitudes.

[87] *Hist. nat.*, II, 78.

[88] *Octavius*, 18. Minutius Felix was a Roman advocate, probably a contemporary of Marcus Aurelius. His dialogue *Octavius* (edited by C. Halm in: *Corpus script. eccles. lat.*, vol. ii; also in: Migne, *Pat. lat.*, vol. iii, cols. 231–360) is a defense of Christianity.

[89] *Meteor.*, II, 5.

[90] *Hist. nat.*, VI, 23.

[91] *Meteor.*, II, 4–5.

[92] *Quaest. nat.*, V, 18.

[93] *Hist. nat.*, II, 43–47.

[94] Modern meteorological studies would seem to show that the ancients were not far astray in associating the etesians of Greece with the monsoons of the Indian Ocean: "the etesiens [*sic*] are not local winds, due to limited and local causes; they belong to the great system of the proasiatic low pressure and are connected with the Indian monsoons" (J. S. Paraskévopoulos, *The Etesiens*, in: Monthly Weather Review, vol. 50, Washington, D. C., 1922, p. 420).

[95] *Quaest. nat.*, III, 22.

[96] *Meteor.*, II, 3.

[97] *Hist. nat.*, II, 100.

98 *Meteor.*, II, 1.

99 *Hist. nat.*, II, 102.

100 *loc. cit.*

101 *Meteor.*, I, 13.

102 The Coraxi inhabited the rugged coast where the Caucasus Mountains run parallel to the Euxine north of Colchis. Modern soundings show that the sea attains an average depth of 3000 feet within a dozen miles of the shore.

103 Tillinghast, *Geogr. Knowl.*, 1889, p. 28.

104 *Meteor.*, II, 1.

105 *In som. Scip. comm.*, II, 9.

106 Tozer, *Anc. Geogr.*, 1897, p. 185.

107 Probably the best work on ancient and medieval tide theories is Almagià, *Dottrina*, 1905. See also Duhem, *Système*, vol. ii, 1914, pp. 267–390. On the earliest Greek observations of the tides in the Mediterranean see Giorgio Pasquali, *''Αμπωτις und die ältesten Beobachtungen der Gezeiten im Mittelmeer*, in: *Festschrift für Wackernagel*, Göttingen, 1924, pp. 326–332 (not seen, title from review in: Rivista geografica italiana, vol. xxxi, Florence, 1924, pp. 86–88).

108 Strabo, *Geogr.*, I, 3.

109 Duhem, *op. cit.*, vol. ii, pp. 269–271.

110 Our knowledge of Posidonius' theory of the tides, which was explained in a treatise on the ocean, is derived from extracts from this treatise given in Strabo, *Geogr.*, III, 5, and from a Latin translation of Priscian of Lydia's *Solutiones* (citations from Duhem, *Système*, vol. ii, p. 280).

111 Strabo, *loc. cit.*, quotes Posidonius as stating that the ebb and flood are greatly increased at the time of the summer solstice, which, of course, is not so. Priscian, *op. cit.*, quaest. vi, gives a truer statement, that the greatest tides are those at the equinoxes (citations from Duhem, *Système*, vol. ii, p. 282).

112 *Hist. nat.*, II, 97.

113 Duhem, *Système*, vol. ii, p. 286.

114 Pliny, *loc. cit.*, also notes that there may be local differences in the period of the tides in different estuaries, although he explains this by differences in the times of the rising of the stars rather than as resulting from the influence of the configuration of the coast.

115 *Quaest. nat.*, III, 28.

116 *In som. Scip. comm.*, II, 9.

117 *Meteor.*, II, 2.

118 *Hist. nat.*, II, 65.

119 *Meteor.*, I, 13; II, 8; Seneca, *Quaest. nat.*, III, 15; III, 26; VI, *passim*. See Gilbert, *Meteorol. Theorien*, 1907, pp. 399–402.

120 Seneca, *Quaest. nat.*, III, 15. On the springs and fountains of the ancient world, many of which were believed to be the outlets of sub-

terranean water courses, see J. R. Smith, *Springs and Wells in Greek and Roman Literature: Their Legends and Locations*, New York and London, 1922 (on the Arethusa and Alpheus myth see pp. 669–672).

[121] Cumont, *After Life*, 1922, p. 78.

[122] *ibid.*, p. 79.

[123] *ibid.*, pp. 80–81.

[124] *ibid.*, pp. 7–12.

[125] *ibid.*, pp. 87–89.

[126] *ibid.*, p. 90.

[127] See above, p. 227, and below, p. 450, note 80.

[128] *Phaedo*, 112.

[129] *Meteor.*, I, 13.

[130] *Quaest. nat.*, III, 9–10.

[131] *Meteor.*, *loc. cit.*

[132] See Capelle, *Berges- und Wolkenhöhen*, 1916, pp. 2–12, for a full discussion of the sources of Aristotle's statements regarding the connection between mountains and the sources of rivers.

[133] Seneca, *Quaest. nat.*, III, 10. On Gregory's theory see Kretschmer, *Phys. Erdk.*, 1889, p. 93.

[134] See Khvostov, *Istoriya*, 1907, pp. 53–56; Langenmaier, *Alte Kenntnis*, 1916, *passim.*

[135] *Quaest. nat.*, IV, *passim.*

[136] These proofs were of two sorts: first, those which were intended to demonstrate the physical impossibility of there being any snow in Ethiopia; and, secondly, those which were intended to show that river floods actually known to be caused by melting snow do not come in midsummer but earlier in the year.

[137] See above, pp. 206–207.

[138] *Hist. nat.*, V, 9.

[139] *ibid.*, II, 86–92.

[140] *ibid.*, II, 90. Plato describes the disappearance of Atlantis in the *Timaeus* and in the *Critias;* he states that the story came from an Egyptian priest at Sais (*Dialogues*, Jowett's transl., 1892, vol. iii, pp. 429–433).

[141] *Phaedo*, 111. On ancient and medieval theories regarding the interior of the earth, see Stegmann, *Anschauungen*, 1913, *passim.*

[142] *Meteor.*, II, 7–8. "Aristotle sums up his views of the causes of winds, earthquakes, lightning, and thunder towards the end of *Meteor.*, II, 9, where he says that they all are essentially the same, viz. a dry exhalation which produces earthquakes when operating within the earth, winds when operating about the surface of the earth, and lightning and thunder when operating among the clouds" (Lones, *Arist. Researches*, 1912, p. 45).

[143] *Quaest. nat.*, VI, is devoted almost entirely to earthquakes.

[144] *Hist. nat.*, II, 79–80.

[145] *Meteor.*, II, 8.

[146] *Hist. nat.*, II, 106.

[147] See especially Capelle, *Berges- und Wolkenhöhen*, 1916. See also below, p. 447, note 27a.

[148] *Meteor.*, I, 13; Capelle, *op. cit.*, p. 3. See also Günther, *Optische Beweisung*, 1920, p. 374, note.

[149] "Dicaearchus, vir in primis eruditus, regum cura permensus montes, ex quibus altissimum prodidit Pelium MCCL passuum ratione perpendiculari" (*Hist. nat.*, II, 65). Dicaearchus also wrote a treatise on the mountains of the Peloponnesus and of other parts of Greece. See Günther, *Bergbesteigungen*, 1896.

[150] Capelle, *op. cit.*, p. 16.

[151] *ibid.*, p. 17.

[152] *ibid.*, pp. 19–20. See also Thalamas, *Géogr. d'Ératosthène*, 1921, pp. 104–110.

[153] See above, p. 214.

[154] Capelle, *op. cit.*, p. 24. For discussion of other figures regarding the heights of mountains as they were estimated in antiquity, see the same, pp. 30–31.

[155] Berger, *Geschichte*, 1903, p. 640.

[156] *ibid.*, p. 407.

[157] Peschel, *Geschichte*, 1877, pp. 43–44.

[158] The sun and the moon appear to revolve around the earth every twenty-four hours more or less. If the same eclipse of the moon is seen at A (to the west of B) one hour earlier than at B, obviously the difference in longitude between A and B will be 1/24 of the circumference of the earth, or 15°.

[159] Berger, *op. cit.*, pp. 18, 468–476.

[160] *Hist. nat.*, II, 70.

[161] *Geogr.*, I, 4.

[162] A useful general history of ancient cartography (i. e. of the Egyptians, Hebrews, Babylonians, Assyrians, and Greeks), though sometimes misleading in details, is Cebrian, *Geschichte der Kartographie*, 1923. This includes an appendix by Joseph Fischer, *Ptolemaios als Kartograph*, pp. 113–129. See also Kubitschek's important article "Karten" in *Paulys Real-Encyclopädie*, 1919.

[163] So called because it was discovered by Conrad Peutinger in 1507. Reproduced on two-thirds the scale of the original in colors by Konrad Miller in *Weltkarte des Castorius*, 1888; also a photographic reproduction by the Imperial Library, Vienna, 1888. See also more especially Miller, *Itin. rom.*, 1916. Miller (*Itin. rom.*, pp. xxvi–xxxvi) ascribes its composition to a certain Castorius of the fourth century of our era.

[164] The questions of whether or not Ptolemy drew maps to accompany the text of his *Geography*, whether or not the existing maps in Greek manuscripts and in printed fifteenth-century texts of Ptolemy's *Geography* can really be ascribed to Ptolemy, and whether they are more, or

less, authentic than the texts of the *Geography* are the subject of bitter controversies in the history of geography. For further discussion of this matter and for references to the literature dealing with it, see the works of Dinse, Schütte, Tudeer, and Fischer, cited in the Bibliography.

[165] See Detlefsen, *Ursprung*, 1906; Lessert, *L'oeuvre géogr.*, 1909.

[166] See Beazley, *Dawn*, vol. i, 1897, p. 379, note 2.

[167] Miller, *Mappaemundi*, vol. i, 1895, pp. 66–70, and vol. ii, 1895, *passim;* Beazley, *op. cit.*, vol. i, p. 378. The Roman maps would seem to be in turn related to Greek maps of the Eratosthenic school in general form and extent. Some of them showed, doubtless, in addition to the *orbis terrarum*, an austral continent beyond the equator (see below, p. 385, note 58). While in a broad way we may accept Miller's main conclusions that the cartography of imperial Rome exerted some influence over medieval cartography, it is not impossible that Miller is occasionally over-ingenious in his attempt to demonstrate specific relationships. See below, p. 458, note 17.

[168] These were the invention of Hipparchus (Avezac, *Projection*, 1863, pp. 16–20). The stereographic projection, called planisphere, was described by Ptolemy in a treatise entitled *Planisphere* which was translated into Latin from the Arabic during the time of the Crusades. See below, p. 398, note 36.

[169] Eratosthenes placed Meroë at 10,000 stades south of Alexandria and the limit of the *oikoumene* at 3400 stades south of Meroë (Strabo, *Geogr.*, I, 4, 2). He placed the tropic at Syene 5000 stades south of Alexandria (Cleomedes, *De motu corp. cael.*, I, 10). Therefore the limit of the *oikoumene* according to Eratosthenes must have been $10{,}000+3400-5000=8400$ stades south of the tropic. As Eratosthenes reckoned the circumference of the earth at 252,000 stades (see above, p. 371, note 51), 1° must have contained 700 stades, and the limit of the *oikoumene* must have fallen in his opinion $8400\div 700=12^\circ$ south of the tropic, or at approximately latitude $11^\circ\ 30'$ N.

[170] See Barthold, *Erforschung des Orients*, 1913, p. 10.

[171] On ancient theories regarding the sources of the Nile see Khvostov, *Istoriya*, 1907, pp. 53–68, and Langenmaier, *Alte Kenntnis*, 1916, pp. 1–144.

[172] Pliny says (*Hist. nat.*, II, 108) that the distance from the southernmost limits of the habitable world to Meroë in Ethiopia is 1000 Roman miles and that the distance by river from Syene, on the tropic, to Meroë was found by an expedition sent out by Nero to be 871 miles. If we make this arbitrarily 700 miles in order to take into account the windings of the river, we get a total of 1700 miles. In the same passage Pliny states that Eratosthenes found the circumference of the earth to be 252,000 stades, or 31,500 Roman miles. The 1700 miles which represent the distance south of the tropic at which Pliny places the Ethiopian Ocean are therefore equivalent to 13,600 stades, and these, in turn, to $19\,{}^3/_7{}^\circ$ (see

above, note 169, for method of calculating this figure). The southern limit of the *oikoumene* thus falls at about latitude 4° N. (23 1/2° — 19 3/7°).

[173] See Langenmaier, *op. cit.*, pp. 6–37, for the most recent and thorough attempt at an interpretation of the Ptolemaic geography of these parts of Africa.

[174] That Ptolemy's knowledge of the Central African lake region was derived from the east coast of Africa rather than from the upper Nile valley is shown by Langenmaier, *op. cit.*, and by Khvostov, *Istoriya*, 1907, pp. 65–66.

[175] "Nam Syene sub ipso tropico est, Meroe autem tribus milibus octingentis stadiis in perustam a Syene introrsum recedit, et ab illa usque ad terram cinnamoni feracem sunt stadia octingenta, et per haec omnia spatia perustae licet rari tamen vita fruuntur habitantes. Ultra vero jam inaccessum est propter nimium solis ardorem" (Macrobius, *In som. Scip. comm.*, II, 8, 3). In other words, the border of the habitable part of the world was placed by Macrobius 3800+800=4600 stades, or about 6 1/2°, south of the tropic, that is to say at about latitude 17° N.

NOTES

CHAPTER II

THE CONTRIBUTION OF WESTERN CHRISTENDOM BEFORE 1100 A. D.

[1] See above, pp. 41–42.

[2] On the geographical work of Byzantine writers, see Krumbacher *Geschichte*, 1897, pp. 409–427. Krumbacher distinguishes between tw types of Byzantine geographical treatise: (1) scientific or theoretical and (2) practical. The first consists almost exclusively of commentarie on, redactions of, or compilations of excerpts from earlier Byzantin works. The second type includes lists of ecclesiastical sees or provinces statistical lists for the use of government officials, itineraries, sailors manuals, pilgrims' handbooks, and the like. The *Christian Topograph* of Cosmas Indicopleustes, with its fantastic description of the world, i of the first type. It was held in high favor and became a principal sourc of geographical "knowledge" among the Slavic people of the early Middl Ages (*ibid.*, p. 35).

With the eleventh and twelfth centuries came a great literary reviv at Constantinople. Michael Psellos (born 1018) besides being a poe was a prolific writer on philosophy, philology, history, law, and natur science. Among his works on the last-named subject were a series essays on meteorology (*ibid.*, pp. 433–444, esp. bibliography, p. 442 Nikephoras Blemmydes (thirteenth century) also wrote on matters geographical interest (*ibid.*, p. 448).

[3] See above, pp. 48 and 75.

[4] Levantine traders were present in no inconsiderable numbers alon

the main avenues of commerce and in the larger towns of Italy, France, and England. The introduction of monachism into the West may be in part attributed to contacts with the Orient maintained in the early Middle Ages. Among the marvelous legends transmitted from the Levant to the Occident were the stories of St. Thomas' voyage to India and the Romance of Alexander (see above, pp. 49, 50, 73, 74, and also below, note 8; see also Bréhier, *Les colonies*, 1903). On diplomatic and political relations between Constantinople and the West during the early Middle Ages, see A. Gasquet, *L'Empire byzantin et la monarchie franque*, Paris, 1888. On Greek settlements in Magna Graecia and their influence upon Occidental culture, see Pierre Batiffol, *L'Abbaye de Rossano*, Paris, 1891, Introduction.

[4a] e. g. in: Müller(us), *Claudii Ptolemaei Geographia* (under "Ptolemy" in the Bibliography), atlas, 1901.

[4b] e. g. St. Sever Beatus map, reproduction accompanying Miller, *Mappaemundi*, vol. i, 1895 (our Fig. 2, p. 69, above).

[5] For example, those of Origen (second century) in the Eastern Church and of Ambrose (340–397) in the Western. On the hexaemeral exegesis see Zöckler, *Geschichte*, vol. i, 1877; Duhem, *Système*, vol. ii, 1914, pp. 393–501; Robbins, *Hexaemeral Lit.*, 1912.

[6] Exodus, xxvi.

[7] See above, pp. 72–73, 287–288.

[8] The Apocryphal Acts arose out of attempts of early heretical sects to provide apostolic authority for their beliefs. Ecclesiastical authorities complained most bitterly of a certain Manichaean, Lucius (or Leucius) Charinus, as the author of these documents. We do not possess any of Charinus' writings in the original. The most important collection of Apocryphal Acts was probably made in the seventh century and was commonly, though mistakenly, ascribed to Abdias, said to have been one of the Apostles who established himself as the first bishop of Babylon. Pseudo-Abdias drew from Charinus for the Acts of Andrew and Matthew. See Rudolf Hoffman's article on the New Testament Apocrypha in *Realenzyklopädie für protestantische Theologie und Kirche*, begründet von S. S. Herzog, 3rd edit., by Albert Hauck, vol. i, Leipzig, 1896, pp. 664–668.

The account of the Acts of St. Thomas in the Pseudo-Abdias version was probably originally composed in Syriac, translated later into Greek, and from Greek into Latin. From an analysis of the details of the story (particularly the plants and animals mentioned in it) Philipps concludes that the legend originated in the Euphrates valley and that St. Thomas was apostle of the Parthian empire and of India in the limited sense of that part of India which includes the Indus valley only (Philipps, *St. Thomas*, 1903). These conclusions are in the main borne out by Dahlmann in the latest and most satisfactory examination of the legend of St. Thomas. Dahlmann believes that within the story, to which many legendary elements became attached, may be found a kernel of fact.

He maintains that connections by sea were in existence in the first century after Christ between the Roman province of Syria and northern India and that by this route St. Thomas reached the court of Gundophorus, a Parthian king of the Kabul valley and of Peshawar. The second part of the story relates the martyrdom of Thomas at the court of a King Mazdai, or Mazdeus. Some have thought that the kingdom of Mazdeus may have been situated in southern India, where subsequently there grew up a large colony of Nestorian Christians who claimed that their church was founded by St. Thomas himself. What little evidence there is, Dahlmann believes, is against this identification. He holds that the death of Thomas occurred in northwestern India (Dahlmann, *Thomas-Legende*, 1912, *passim*).

[9] On the influence of the Bible in molding geographical theory and on the matter of interpretation, see Kretschmer, *Phys. Erdk.*, 1889, Einleitung, pp. 5-9.

[10] The great exponents of the allegorical and mystical method of exegesis during the early centuries of our era were the scholars of Alexandria; the literal method was primarily that of the Antiochians and Syrians (*ibid.*, pp. 17-20).

[11] Literal interpretation led men like Lactantius to the belief that the earth is flat. The pilgrim Theodosius, about 530 A. D., described the hills near the River Jordan which skipped like lambs when Christ came down to be baptized and added that when he was there the hills still appeared to be jumping (Beazley, *Dawn*, vol. i, 1897, p. 102). Peter Alphonsi in the twelfth century accused earlier Jewish doctors of going to extremes in their literal interpretation of Scripture, even to the extent of taking literally the words of the Psalm: "Flumina plaudent manibus, montes exsultabunt" (Migne, *Pat. lat.*, vol. clvii, col. 553).

Cosmas Indicopleustes' fantastic system of the world, based on the account of the Tabernacle of the Lord, is a famous and striking example of literal interpretation carried to an extreme. Cosmas was led by the Biblical text (and by his own imagination) to maintain aggressively that the universe is shaped like a strong-box with a semi-cylindrical cover.

[12] "Cum credimus, nihil desideramus ultra credere. Hoc enim prius credimus, non esse quod ultra credere debeamus." Quoted by Kretschmer, *Phys. Erdk.*, 1889, p. 2.

[13] *ibid.*, p. 22.

[14] On Platonism among the Church Fathers, see Duhem, *Système*, vol. ii, 1914, pp. 408-417. The combination of Neoplatonism with Christianity has been called Augustinianism (*ibid.*, vol. ii, p. 417).

[15] *ibid.*, vol. iii, 1915, pp. 44-47.

[16] *ibid.*, pp. 62-64.

[17] *ibid.*, pp. 64-67.

[18] *ibid.*, p. 9.

[19] *ibid.*, pp. 44-47. See *De div. nat.*, III, 33 (Migne, *Pat. lat.*, vol.

cxxii, col. 719). Stegmann, *Anschauungen*, 1913, p. 60, contrasts the speculative and critical mind of John Scot with the credulous spirit of Raban Maur, his contemporary.

[20] Mori, *Misuraz. eratos.*, 1911, p. 391.

[21] See Geidel, *Alfred der Grosse*, 1904.

[22] Aethicus of Istria was often confused in the Middle Ages with a so-called Julius Aethicus, who may have written a *Cosmographia* which probably dates from the sixth century and was edited in Riese, *Geogr. lat. min.*, 1878, pp. 71–103. See Beazley, *Dawn*, vol. i, 1897, pp. 355–362.

[23] The *Orbis descriptio* of Dionysius and Priscian's Latin version of it were edited by Müller in *Geogr. graeci min.*, vol. ii, 1882, pp. 103–176, 190–199.

[24] The unknown author most frequently cited is a Roman cosmographer of the name of Castorius. The citations, names, and extracts from Castorius correspond very closely to the legends on the Peutinger Table and have led Miller to the conclusion that the latter represents the work of Castorius. See Miller, *Weltkarte des Castorius*, 1888, pp. 36–47; the same, *Mappaemundi*, vol. vi, 1898, pp. 36–37; the same, *Itin. rom.*, 1916, pp. xxvi-xxxvi.

[25] See above, p. 104.

[26] The various Latin versions of the Romance of Alexander were destined to exert much influence on the form which the legend was to assume in the twelfth century and later. The earliest version of the Latin *Pseudo-Callisthenes* was made in the fourth century of our era by Julius Valerius; but this was little read in later centuries, and only three manuscripts of it are now extant. The work upon which most of the medieval versions of the Romance were based was an *Epitoma*, or abridgment, of Julius Valerius' translation, made perhaps in the ninth century. In addition to Valerius' version and the *Epitoma*, we have a *Letter from Alexander to Aristotle* describing the marvels of India. Longer, though corresponding essentially to chapter 17 of the third book of Valerius, it did not form part of the *Epitoma*, but was widely circulated as an independent booklet. A correspondence between Alexander and Dindimus concerning the Brahmins is also found in a ninth-century Latin form, perhaps translated by Alcuin from a Greek original. See Meyer, *Alexandre le grand*, 1886, vol. ii, *passim;* Thorndike, *Magic*, 1923, vol. i, pp. 551–557.

In the tenth century a wholly new version of the legend, also derived from the *Pseudo-Callisthenes*, appeared in the West. This was the *Historia de praeliis*, the Greek original of which was said to have been brought from Constantinople by a certain "Leo Archipresbyter" and translated by him into Latin. See Landgraf, *Die Vita Alexandri*, 1885, and Krumbacher, *Geschichte*, 1897, pp. 849–852.

[27] See below, p. 391, note 130.

[28] Much has been written on St. Brandan and his wanderings. The

Peregrinatio Sancti Brandani abbatis, or Latin version of the legend (also known as *Navigatio* or *Narratio*), the date of which is uncertain, was published by Schröder, *Sanct Brandan*, 1871. See also Beazley, *Dawn*, vol. i, 1897, pp. 230–240. More recent notable works dealing with Brandan's voyages and with other fabulous tales of the Atlantic are Westropp, *Brasil*, 1912; Babcock, *St. Brendan's Islands*, 1919; idem, *Legendary Islands*, 1922, pp. 34–49. That some of the stories of the St. Brandan legend were derived from Oriental sources (and not vice versa, as Schröder, *op. cit.*, pp. xii–xiii, attempted to show) was demonstrated by De Goeje, *St. Brandan*, 1890.

[29] T. D. Hardy, *Descriptive Catalogue of Materials Relating to the Early History of Great Britain*, London, 1862, vol. i, p. 159, cites a ninth-century manuscript in the Vatican (Regin. Christinae, 217). Hardy mentions five twelfth-century and ten thirteenth-century manuscripts of the *Vita S. Brendani*. This life of St. Brandan was printed by Jubinal, *Saint Brendaines*, 1836.

[30] Beazley, *op. cit.*, vol. i, 1897, pp. 186–188.

[31] See above, pp. 13–14.

[32] See above, p. 13, and Duhem, *Système*, vol. ii, 1914, pp. 447–449. Bible references and quotations throughout the present work, except where otherwise indicated, are based on the Douay and Rheims translation of the Vulgate.

[33] *ibid.*, p. 414. The similarities between the accounts of the Creation in the *Timaeus* and in Genesis were explained by ascribing to Plato knowledge of the Bible. Augustine was particularly struck by the resemblance of the Platonic and Scriptural doctrines. Peter Comestor in our period actually believed "that Plato read the Mosaic books in Egypt and confounded the spirit of God (Gen. i, 2) with the World Soul" (Robbins, *Hexaemeral Lit.*, 1912, pp. 12–13).

[34] Duhem, *op. cit.*, vol. ii, pp. 408, 454–460, 478–487.

[35] Augustine, *De civ. Dei*, XII, 13 (as cited by Duhem, *op. cit.*, vol. ii, pp. 452–453).

[36] Περὶ 'αρχῶν, II, 3, 4–5 (as cited by Duhem, *op. cit.*, vol. ii, p. 449).

[37] *ibid.*, vol. ii, pp. 462–471.

[38] *ibid.*, vol. ii, p. 464. It must be pointed out, however, that the Neoplatonic, as distinguished from the Peripatetic philosophers, believed in a creation (see above, note 33), even though they denied that there was a commencement of the world! A discussion of the highly abstract classical and medieval theories of time and space would lead us too far astray from the field of geography. Suffice it to remark that subsequent medieval commentators on the hexaemeron in general followed Augustine, who adopted the Platonic doctrine that God created the universe and time simultaneously. Augustine said: "Procul dubio, non est mundus factus in tempore, sed cum tempore" (*De civ. Dei*, XI, 6, as cited

by Duhem, *op. cit.*, vol. ii, p. 467; Robbins, *op. cit.*, pp. 7, 65–66, 82–83). See below, p. 418, note 26.

[39] See above, p. 145.

[40] Zöckler, *Geschichte*, vol. i, 1877, is devoted in the main to this subject. On Bede, see the same, pp. 246–252. See also Robbins, *op. cit.*, *passim*. For a discussion of theological, as distinguished from physical, concepts of the Creation among the early Christians, see A. C. McGiffert, *The God of the Early Christians*, New York, 1924, pp. 146–176.

[41] White, *Warfare*, 1920, vol. i, pp. 89–90.

[42] Günther, *Kosmogr. Ansch.*, 1882, discusses the influence of Jewish gnosticism and Aristotelianism on scholastic geography. Most of the early Jews conceived of a flat earth covered by a concave heaven through a window in which the sun and moon pass out in the west, whence they return to the east around the outside of the firmament.

[43] Sura, ii, 20; clxxi, 18; clxxviii, 6.

[44] From the King James version. One form of the Vulgate reads: "Qui sedet super gyrum terrae, et habitatores eius sunt quasi locustae: qui extendit velut nihilum caelos, et expandit eos sicut tabernaculum ad inhabitandum." The last phrase reads in another form used by the Church Fathers: "qui statuit velut fornicem coelum, et extendit velut tentorium" (Marinelli, *Scritti minori*, vol. i, [1908?], p. 326, note 2). The King James version renders the spirit of the Latin more accurately than the Douay and Rheims version, in which the word *gyrum* is translated "globe."

[45] Marinelli, *La geogr.*, 1882, p. 534 (also in *Scritti minori*, vol. i, [1908?], pp. 325–326, where there is an important footnote by Carlo Errera). See also Beazley, *Dawn*, vol. i, p. 275, note 1, and pp. 328–332.

[46] Marinelli, *op. cit.*, pp. 538–546 (also in *Scritti minori*, vol. i, [1908?], pp. 332–343); Beazley, *op. cit.*, pp. 273–303.

[47] *Div. institut.*, III, 24 (as cited by Kretschmer, *Phys. Erdk.*, 1889, pp. 37f.). Thorndike, however, believes that the "opposition of early Christian thought to natural science has been rather unduly exaggerated" and that Lactantius "should hardly be cited as typical of early Christian attitude in such matters" (*Magic*, 1923, vol. i, p. 480).

[48] The question of exactly what the early medieval thinkers in the West thought on this subject has been acrimoniously discussed from opposite points of view by Catholic and Protestant scholars. In the seventies of the last century Schneid (*Erdrundung*, 1877) defended the science of the Middle Ages against the attacks of Protestants like Whewell, Draper, and Günther, who accused the early ecclesiastical writers of servile dependence upon the letter of Scripture. Schneid's article is more particularly an indictment of another article of the same title by Siegmund Günther in: *Studien*, 1877–1879. Schneid believed that Günther, through insufficient acquaintance with the literature of the period, had been led to minimize the achievements and worth of patristic science. Augustine, declared Schneid, nowhere denied the sphericity of the earth,

and his mention of the antipodes shows that he was well acquainted with the theory. Isidore, Bede, Raban Maur, and Adam of Bremen, he maintained, were all firmly convinced that the earth is a sphere. While we may concede that Schneid was right in the case of Bede and Adam, that Isidore and Raban Maur held to the doctrine of a spherical earth is perhaps more doubtful. See below, note 51, and p. 385, note 53. Furthermore, it is a little difficult to understand Schneid's contention (p. 436) that Cosmas did not deny the sphericity of the earth through religious obscurantism but rather on the grounds of practical experience. See also below, p. 386, note 64, and p. 424, note 100.

More recently the Jesuit father, Reverend F. S. Betten, has contributed an article entitled *Knowledge of the Sphericity of the Earth During the Earlier Middle Ages* to the Catholic Historical Review, vol. iii (N. S.), Washington, D. C., 1923, pp. 74–90. In this he argues that "we have . . . at least one witness in every century to the tradition of the sphericity of the earth" (p. 86), and he cites as these witnesses Hilary of Poitiers (died 366), Ambrose of Milan (died 397), Augustine (died 430), Cassiodorus (died 575), and Isidore of Seville (died 636). Echoes of the Ptolemaic astronomy, to be sure, may be detected in the writings of these men. On the other hand, no one of them makes a clean-cut avowal of belief that the earth is a globe, and the passages quoted by Father Betten are not wholly irreconcilable with the doctrine of a flat earth. It is not enough, in dealing with the cosmographical opinions of the Church Fathers, to cite isolated remnants of classical science scattered through their works. Without taking into consideration all of a writer's assertions regarding a specific topic one can hardly arrive at safe conclusions regarding his opinions on that topic. Father Betten puts much stock in Isidore's supposed "faithful representation of the main tenets of Ptolemy's theory" (*ibid.*, p. 84). On the other hand he makes no mention of passages in Isidore which may be reconciled only with belief in a flat earth (see below, notes 50, and 51). We venture to hold that we are not as yet in a position to make any definite pronouncements upon the cosmographical opinions of the other writers cited by Father Betten. Such pronouncements should be made only after thorough investigation of *all* that these writers stated bearing directly or indirectly on matters of cosmography. Such an investigation has not been made as yet. Is it not, however, probable that the theories of a flat earth elaborated by the Eastern Fathers (see above, p. 383, note 45), theories built upon the interpretation of Scripture, were at least as influential in molding the early medieval cosmology of the Occident as the then often discredited relics of Greek science?

[49] Kretschmer, *Phys. Erdk.*, 1889, p. 50. See also the preceding note.

[50] *De nat. rer.*, 10. Why this passage should be interpreted to indicate belief in a flat earth is explained by Brehaut, *Isidore*, 1912, pp. 50–54.

[51] "The size of the sun is greater than that of the earth and so from the

moment when it rises it appears equally to east and west at the same time" (*Etym.*, III, 47; translated by Brehaut, *op. cit.*, p. 147). Gribaudi (*Isidoro*, 1905, p. 22) argued that Isidore of Seville held to the theory of sphericity.

[52] Bede, *De nat. rer.*, 46. Bede's proof was derived from Pliny, *Hist. nat.*, II, 64.

[53] See Mori, *Misuraz. eratos.*, 1911, pp. 390–391. C. B. Jourdain (*Infl. Arist.*, 1861, pp. 6–7) maintained that Raban Maur (*De universo*, XII, 2) inscribed the circumference of the terrestrial globe in an ideal cube, the angles of which correspond to the four cardinal points. Nothing in the text, however, would justify our supposing that Raban Maur had in mind either a globe or a cube. On the contrary he was doubtless thinking of the *orbis terrarum* in the Roman sense (see below, note 58), that is to say, of the circle of the known lands. Peschel (*Geschichte*, 1877, p. 100, note 3) and Marinelli (*La geogr.*, 1882, p. 552, note 5; *Scritti minori*, vol. i, [1908?], p. 352, note 1) tried to interpret the passage to mean that Raban Maur held that the *orbis terrarum* was square. Bertolini (*I quattro angoli*, 1910, pp. 1439–1441), however, has demonstrated conclusively that the text in question indicates that he thought it was a circle.

[54] *De div. nat.*, III, 33, in: Migne, *Pat. lat.*, vol. cxxii, cols. 716–718.

[55] *Gerberti opera*, Bubnov's edit., 1899, p. 362. See the same, pp. 310–313, note 1, for discussion of the reasons why it is not the work of Gerbert.

[56] Kretschmer, *Phys. Erdk.*, 1889, p. 61.

[57] Santarem, *Essai*, vol. i, 1849, Introduction, pp. 1–56; Simar, *Afrique centrale*, 1912, *passim*.

[58] The idea of antipodes in our modern sense of the term, as referring to regions on the opposite side of a spherical earth, came from the Greeks. Notably the doctrine of Crates of Mallos, it was adopted by Martianus Capella and Macrobius, who passed it on to the medieval West (see above, p. 18). Lactantius and Augustine argued against the possibility of such antipodes. The practical spirit of the Romans had not been interested in theoretical regions on the other side of the earth (see above, p. 10). Roman maps, we may infer, were usually circular and showed an ocean stream running around the *orbis terrarum*, or three known continents (Asia, Europe, Africa). Sometimes an unknown fourth continent beyond the impassable equatorial ocean was depicted (see Simar, *op. cit.*, p. 150). These Roman maps probably formed the basis of many maps of the early Middle Ages. But during the Middle Ages, as has been the case with modern attempts to interpret these theories, true antipodes became confused with the fourth, or austral, continent, belief in which did not necessitate belief in a spherical world. Isidore was probably referring merely to the austral continent when he wrote: "Extra tres partes orbis, quarta pars trans Oceanum interior est in meridie quae solis ardore nobis incognita est, in cujus finibus antipodas fabulose inhabitare produntur" (*Etym.*, XIV, 5).

Arguing thus, Simar contends, in his brilliant study of Central African geography in antiquity and the Middle Ages, that medieval discussions of the antipodes referred to the austral continent and did not necessarily have anything to do with the question of belief in the sphericity of the earth. While this may be true, he gives, in the opinion of the writer, a misleading impression that the doctrine of a spherical earth met with scant favor in the West until as late as the twelfth century (Simar, *op. cit.*, pp. 157–158). He tends to ignore the important influence of Macrobius and of Martianus Capella in keeping alive from the time of the Carolingian Renaissance onward the doctrine that the earth is a globe. On the influence of Macrobius, see Duhem, *Système*, vol. iii, 1915, pp. 62–71; and on Martianus Capella, see especially Mori, *Misuraz. eratos.*, 1911, pp. 390–391.

[59] *Div. instit.*, III, 24.

[60] *De civ. Dei*, XVI, 9. It should also be pointed out that Augustine (*loc. cit.*), in addition, objects to the possibility of there being inhabited antipodes on the purely rational grounds that it would be impossible for men to have reached such distant continents across the ocean. The Catholic father, P. Mandonnet (*Les idées cosmogr.*, 1893, p. 55), asserted that it was rather on the strength of physical argument than on that of Scriptural exegesis that Augustine based his opposition to antipodeans. At all events, Mandonnet admits that it was largely through Augustine's immense prestige that the theory of the possibility of inhabited antipodes was excluded from general acceptance throughout the Middle Ages (*ibid.*, p. 56).

[61] *Etym.*, IX, 2. See Boffito, *Leggenda*, 1903, p. 592, note 4.

[62] *De temporum ratione*, 34.

[63] "Absit ut nos quisquam vel hoc contentisse abstruere, vel antipodarum fabulas recipere arbitretur, quae sunt fidei Christianae omnino contraria [*sic*]" (*Classicorum auctorum e vaticanis codicibus editorum series*, vol. iii, edited by A. Mai, Rome, 1831, p. 337). For John Scot Erigena on the antipodes and for other texts dealing with the subject see Rand, *Johannes Scottus*, 1906, pp. 20–23.

[64] Migne, *Pat. lat.*, vol. vi, col. 426; vol. xli, col. 487; *Mon. Germ. hist.*, *Script. rerum merovingicarum*, vol. vi, 1913, pp. 517–520. Much has been written on Virgil of Salzburg and his relations to the ecclesiastical authorities of his time. Protestants like Draper, Whewell, White, and Siegmund Günther have looked upon Virgil as more or less a martyr to the cause of freedom of thought. Catholics, on the other hand, have tried to demonstrate that Virgil cleared himself of the charge of heresy and that as a bishop he was able to carry on valuable work for the church. See Krabbo, *Bischof Virgil*, 1903, and Van der Linden, *Virgile de Salzbourg*, 1914. The latter maintains that "contrairement à l'opinion reçue, Virgile de Salzbourg a été très probablement un simple commentateur et non un novateur . . . Sa théorie, au lieu de marquer le début d'une

ère de progrès dans les études cosmographiques, constitue l'un des derniers reflets de la culture classique avant la nuit du Xe siècle" (critique of Van der Linden, *op. cit.*, in Isis: International Review Devoted to the History of Science and Civilization, vol. ii, Brussels, Sept. 1919, pp. 437–438).

[65] See Marinelli, *Scritti minori*, vol. i, [1908?], pp. 331–332, note 4.

[66] Zöckler, *Geschichte*, vol. i, 1877, p. 340. See also White, *Warfare*, 1920, vol. i, pp. 106–107.

[67] "The influence of the Bible on the meteorological theories of the Church Fathers was very limited. Even when the attempt was made to hide the pagan influence in a Biblical shell, a close study reveals to us a truly pagan philosophical core" (Hoffmann, *Anschauungen*, 1907, p. 93).

[68] For texts of those parts of Isidore's *De natura rerum* (chs. 32–41), Bede's *De natura rerum* (chs. 25–36), and Raban Maur's *De universo* (IX, 17–20, 25–28) which deal with meteorology, see Hellmann, *Denkmäler*, 1904, pp. 1–19.

[69] *Liber contra insulsam vulgi opinionem de grandine et tonitruis* (Poole, *Illustrations*, 1920, p. 36).

[70] Poole, *loc. cit.*

[71] See J. C. Frazer, *The Golden Bough*, Part I, *The Magic Art and the Evolution of Kings*, London, 1911, vol. i, pp. 244–331.

[72] Poole, *op. cit.*, p. 37.

[73] For a discussion of various theories of the Church Fathers regarding the waters above the firmament, with references to the sources, see especially Hoffmann, *Anschauungen*, 1907, pp. 5–13.

[74] Duhem, *Système*, vol. ii, 1914, p. 489.

[75] Zöckler, *Geschichte*, vol. i, 1877, pp. 63, 226; Werner, *Kosm. Wilhelm von Conches*, 1873, p. 322.

[76] On the subject of the waters, Augustine made a statement which typifies the medieval attitude towards the authority of Scripture: "Proinde cum de isto fonte quaerimus quomodo id quod dictum est, *ascendebat de terra, et irrigabat omnem faciem terrae*, non impossibile videatur; si ea quae diximus impossibilia cuiquam videatur, quaerat ipse aliud, quo tamen verax ista Scriptura monstretur, quae procul dubio verax est, etiamsi non monstretur" (*De Genesi ad litteram*, V, 9, in: *Corpus script. eccles. lat.*, vol. xxviii, sect. 3, pt. 1, p. 152). See also Duhem, *op. cit.*, vol. ii, pp. 491–494

[77] *Hexaemeron*, II, 3, 9–11, in: *Corpus script. eccles. lat.*, vol. xxxii, sect. 1, pt. 1, pp. 47–50.

[78] Duhem, *op. cit.*, vol. ii, p. 489.

[79] This idea was expressed by Basil, Augustine, and by the author of the *De ordine creatorum liber*, a work sometimes attributed to Isidore (Migne, *Pat. lat.*, vol. lxxxiii, cols. 920–921; Robbins, *Hexaemeral Lit.*, 1912, p. 69; Duhem, *op. cit.* vol. iii, 1915, p. 15).

[80] This theory "avait été longuement exposée et discutée par Augustin

l'Hibernais" (Duhem, *loc. cit.*). See also Duhem, *op. cit.*, vol. iii, 1915, pp. 12-13, and below, p. 432, note 27.

[81] *Hexaemeron*, I, in: Migne, *Pat. lat.*, vol. xci, col. 20.

[82] "Abyssus profunditas aquarum impenetrabilis, sive speluncae aquarum latentium, e quibus fontes et flumina procedunt; vel quae occulte subtereunt, unde et Abyssus dictus. Nam omnes aquae, sive torrentes per occultas venas ad matricem abyssum revertuntur" (*Etym.*, XIII, 20). In the text is given the translation of Brehaut, *Isidore*, 1912, p. 241.

[83] Kretschmer, *op. cit.*, pp. 91-105.

[84] *De Genesi ad litteram*, V, 9-10, in: *Corpus script. eccles. lat.*, vol. xxviii, sect. 3, pt. 1, pp. 152-154.

[85] Kretschmer, *op. cit.*, p. 95.

[86] *ibid.*, pp. 93-94.

[87] Isidore, *De nat. rer.*, 43.

[88] Norlind, *Problem*, 1918, pp. 24-25.

[89] *De mens. orb. terr.*, Parthey's edit., p. 76 (as cited by Kretschmer, *op. cit.*, p. 106).

[90] *De nat. rer.*, 40.

[91] Duhem, *op. cit.*, vol. ii, 1914, p. 461.

[92] Augustine, *De civitate Dei*, V, 6, in: *Corpus script. eccles. lat.*, vol. xl, pt. 1, p. 218; Ambrose, *Hexaemeron*, IV, 7, 29-30, *ibid.*, vol. xxxii, sect. 1, pt. 1, pp. 134-136.

[93] Duhem, *op. cit.*, vol. iii, 1915, pp. 13-14. See Migne, *Pat. lat.*, vol. xxxv, col. 2159.

[94] Bede, *De nat. rer.*, 39; *De temporum ratione*, 28-29.

[95] *Hist. gentis Langobard.*, I, 6; (Duhem, *op. cit.*, vol. iii, pp. 113-115), It has been thought that Paul the Deacon's theory of the whirlpools was derived from Norse traditions, but Nansen suggests that it is just as probable that in this case "southern, originally classical ideas . . . have been localized in the Norse legends." Virgil mentions a gulf of the sea "which sucks the water into itself and sends it up again." Paul the Deacon speaks of whirlpools "not only in the north, and off the Hebrides, but also between Britain and Spain, and in the Strait of Messina." With Adam of Bremen the whirlpool becomes "exclusively northern, and later still we shall get it even at the North Pole itself" (Nansen, *Northern Mists*, 1911, vol. i, p. 159).

[96] See above, pp. 192 and 194.

[97] Kretschmer, *op. cit.*, pp. 133-135.

[98] Isidore, *Etym.*, XIX, 6; *De nat. rer.*, 47 (as cited by Stegmann. *Anschauungen*, 1913, p. 29).

[99] Stegmann, *op. cit.*, pp. 15-20.

[100] See above, pp. 28 and 29.

[101] For data on the Biblical origins of ideas of Hell, for early medieval conceptions of Hell, and for references on these subjects, see Stegmann, *op. cit.*, pp. 20-27.

[102] See Geikie, *Love of Nature Among the Romans*, 1912.

[103] Ganzenmüller, *Naturgefühl*, 1914, pp. 9–10.

[104] From Claudian's *Epithalamium*, verses 1 ff., and *De nuptiis Honorii Augusti*, verse 49 (as cited by Ganzenmüller, *op. cit.*, p. 10).

[105] Ganzenmüller, *op. cit.*, p. 10.

[106] *ibid.*, pp. 17–19.

[107] Dr. R. P. Blake of Harvard, specialist in Russian and Caucasian history, has been kind enough to furnish the writer with the following references on the love of nature in the medieval Orient: Krachkovskii, *The Divan of Abu'l-Wāwā, a Hamdanid Poet of the Eleventh Century*, text, translation, introduction, and commentary, Academy of Sciences, Petrograd, 1916 (in Russian); N. I. Marr, *Georgii Merchul, Zhitie sv. Grigorii Khandzt'iiskago* (*George Merchul, Life of St. Gregory of Khandzt'a*), text, translation, and introduction, with a diary of a journey to Klarjet'ia and Shavshet'ia, Teksti i Raziskaniya po Armyano-Gruzinskoi filologii (Texts and Studies in Armenian and Georgian Philology), vol. vii, Petrograd, 1911; *Life of St. Serapion*, published by M. Janashvili K'artuli Mcerloba, in vol. ii of his *Georgian Literature*, Tiflis, 1909 (in Georgian). Latin translations of the two latter texts, which testify to the love of wild nature, have been published by the Bollandist, Paul Peeters, in: Analecta Bollandiana, vol. xxxvi–xxxvii, for 1917–1919, Brussels and Paris, 1922, pp. 159–309.

[108] Ganzenmüller, *op. cit.*, pp. 116–118.

[109] *ibid.*, pp. 161–162.

[110] *Liber de astrolabio*, 19, in: *Gerberti opera*, Bubnov's edit., 1899, p. 142.

[111] See especially Miller, *Mappaemundi*, vol. vi, 1898; Beazley, *Dawn*, vol. i, 1897, pp. 387–391; Vidier, *Mappemonde de Théodulfe*, 1911, pp. 289–292.

[112] See above, pp. 35–36.

[113] Among these are notably the crude Albi map dating from the eighth century (Miller, *op. cit.*, vol. iii, 1895, pp. 57–59), the relatively accurate "Anglo-Saxon," or "Cotton," map dating probably from the mid-tenth but perhaps from as late as the twelfth century (Miller, *op. cit.*, vol. iii, p. 31; Beazley, *Dawn*, vol. ii, 1901, p. 560), and a map drawn at Ripoll in Catalonia during the eleventh century (Vidier, *op. cit.*, pp. 293–305).

[114] Simar, *Afrique centrale*, 1912, pp. 159–169, classifies these early maps as follows:

A. Maps derived from Roman representations of the *orbis terrarum*, or circle of known lands, and adapted to serve the immediate purpose of the cosmographer or historian whose works they were drawn to illustrate. To this group belong the Sallust maps, the T-O maps, and many maps in which the influence of Orosius appears to be predominant. Simar believes that he can detect evidences of Byzantine influence upon the latter, among which he includes the Albi and Cotton maps (see the preceding note), and, from the time of the Crusades, the maps of Guido (see above, p. 124), Henry of Mayence (see above, p. 124), and the "Jerome" maps (see above, pp. 125–126). To this group also belong the Psalter map, the Hereford and Ebstorf wall charts, and the maps in the Chronicle of Ralph Hygden (see above, p. 125)—all dating from the late thirteenth and fourteenth centuries.

B. Maps which aim to show the earth in its cosmographical relations, "the lamentable débris of Greek cosmography." To this group belong the Macrobian maps of the zones.

AB. Maps in which the purpose is a combination of the two elements shown in the maps of classes A and B above. These show the *orbis terrarum* but add a fourth, uninhabitable part of the world beyond the equator. To this class belong the Beatus maps (see above, pp. 122–124), the *mappaemundi* in Lambert's *Liber floridus* (see above, p. 124), (and, we may add, the Ripoll map described by Vidier, *op. cit.*).

[115] Beazley, *op. cit.*, vol. ii, 1901, p. 625; Miller, *op. cit.*, vol. iii, 1895, pp. 122–126.

[116] Beazley, *ibid.*, pp. 627–631; Miller, *ibid.*, pp. 116–122. T-O maps and maps of similar simple diagrammatic character accompany manuscripts of Isidore's *Etymologiae* and show the division of the countries of the earth among the children of Noah.

[117] Beazley, *ibid.*, pp. 631–632; Miller, *ibid.*, pp. 110–115.

[118] Miller, *op. cit.*, vol. i, 1895.

[119] See Yule, *Cathay*, vol. i, 1915, preliminary essay; Beazley, *op. cit.*, vol. i, 1897, pp. 176–194.

[120] See Tiander, *Poyezdki*, 1906.

[121] See Coli, *Il paradiso terrestre dantesco*, 1897.

[122] This is taken from the King James version, which here follows the version of the Septuagint. Jerome translated the Hebrew as follows: "And the Lord God had planted a paradise of pleasure from the beginning." Raban Maur pointed out the divergence between these two translations; likewise Peter Lombard in the twelfth century. See Coli, *op. cit.*, p. 68, and also below, p. 462, note 35.

[123] "Post eosdem montes [i. e. Rhipaean Mountains] trans aquilonem Hyperborei, apud quos mundi axis continua motione torquetur, gens moribus prolixitate vitae, deorum cultu, aeris clementia, sementri die, fine etiam habitationis humanae praedicanda" (*De nupt. Phil. et Merc.*, VI, 664). ". . . hinc Attagenus sinus Hyperboreis beatitate consimilis, quo incolae gratulantur qui circumactu vallium auras nesciunt pestilentes" (*ibid.*, VI, 693).

[124] See above, p. 63.

[125] Ganzenmüller, *Naturgefühl*, 1914, pp. 9–10, 87–88.

[126] Kretschmer, *Phys. Erdk.*, 1889, pp. 78–79.

[127] From the King James version (see above, note 122).

[128] On the river Pison see the description in Epiphanius, *Liber de XII*

gemmis rationalis summi sacerdotis Hebraeorum, in: *Corpus script. eccles. lat.*, vol. xxxv, pt. 2, pp. 747–748.

As this book is in press there has come to the writer's attention Lutz's interesting article, *Geographical Studies Among Babylonians and Egyptians*, 1924, which shows that some of the cosmographical ideas prevalent in the Christian Middle Ages may be traced back to Babylonian origins. The origins of the belief in the four rivers of Paradise, for instance, is unquestionably to be sought for in Babylonian astrology and geography, two sciences closely allied. One group among the Babylonians held that the earth's surface forms a quadrilateral, itself an exact counterpart of a portion of the firmament, Pegasus α-δ. "Andromeda . . . was identified with the Euphrates which flows south, while the Tigris was considered to flow parallel to the line between Pegasus α and δ. Two additional watercourses, which later tradition designated as Pison and Gihon, completed the watercourses around the trapezium. This view, however, must have gone back to a time when conditions as they existed in Babylonia were, *mutatis mutandis*, transferred to the sky; namely, it was ultimately based on the cultivated field surrounded by irrigation ditches" (*ibid.*, pp. 168–169).

[129] Kretschmer, *op. cit.*, pp. 80–91.

[130] On the legend of Gog and Magog see: Peschel, *Abhandlungen*, vol. i, 1877, pp. 28–35; Lenormant, *Magog*, 1882; Marinelli, *Gog e Magog*, 1882–1883 (also in *Scritti minori*, vol. i, [1908?], pp. 385–438); and Graf, *Roma*, vol. ii, 1883, Appendix, pp. 507–563.

[131] Lenormant, *Magog*, 1882, p. 10, note 2.

[132] Sura xxi, 95, 96; sura xviii. The latter sura describes the deeds of Alexander Dulkarnein, the two-horned—not Alexander the Great of Macedon but, according to Arabic tradition, an older Yemenic conqueror of the world (Peschel, *Abhandlungen*, vol. i, 1877, p. 30).

[133] Procopius, *De bello Persico*, I, 10 (complete works of Procopius edited by J. Haury, Leipzig, 1905).

[134] Sackur, *Sibyll. Texte*, 1898, p. 72.

[135] See above, p. 381, note 26. The connection of Alexander with Gog and Magog is found in the *Historia de praeliis*.

[136] See above, p. 381, note 26.

[137] See above, p. 379, note 8.

[138] *Anglo-Saxon Chron.*, sub anno 883, in: "Rolls series" edit., no. 23, edited by Benjamin Thorpe, London, 1861, vol. i, pp. 150–153.

[139] Tiander, *Poyezdki*, 1906.

[140] See especially the works of E. Bauvois, F. Michel, P. Gaffarel, and T. Stephens, to which references are given in: Geographisches Jahrbuch, vol. xviii, Gotha, 1895, pp. 5–10. For a critical study, see Zimmer, *Früheste Berührungen*, 1891.

[141] *De mens. orb. terr.*, VII, 2, 6.

[142] As is well known, the Icelandic discovery of America has been a

subject of constant discussion throughout the last century. Innumerable and often incredible theories have been propounded in an attempt to identify the places mentioned in the Sagas, and a large library of books, articles, and pamphlets has come into being relating to this subject. The sole aim in the present work is to give as brief as possible a statement of what countries the Icelanders of the twelfth and early thirteenth centuries believed to lie to the southwest of Greenland.

The sources for the Icelandic discovery of America are collected in: Rafn, *Antiq. americanae*, 1837, and Supplement, 1841. Icelandic texts are there given with Danish and Latin translations. For English translations of the Wineland Voyages, see Reeves, *Wineland*, 1890. The best bibliography is Hermannsson, *Northmen*, 1909. For references to recent studies on the subject see Geographisches Jahrbuch, vol. xxxix (1919-1923), Gotha, 1924, p. 277.

[143] Reeves, *op. cit.*, p. 11. In some Icelandic texts, *doegr* indicates twelve hours' sailing, though it probably did not always have this meaning. See *ibid.*, pp. 173-174.

[144] The Wineland voyages are described in detail in the *Saga of Eric the Red* and in the *Flateyjarbók*, dating from the end of the thirteenth and early fourteenth centuries (Reeves, *op. cit.*, *passim*).

NOTES

CHAPTER III

THE CONTRIBUTION OF THE MOSLEMS

[1] Duhem, *Système*, vol. ii, 1914, pp. 146-157.

[2] See above, pp. 98-102.

[3] On what follows concerning Moslem knowledge of Ptolemy's *Almagest* see the introduction to Karl Manitius' German translation of the *Almagest*, 1912. See also Haskins, *Studies*, 1924, pp. 103-104.

[4] See above, p. 96.

[5] Al-Battānī's *Astronomy*, Nallino's edit., pt. i, 1903, pp. 166-167; pt. ii, 1907, pp. 210-211; Al-Khwārizmī's *Kitāb ṣūrat al-arḍ*, Nallino's edit., 1894, p. 6. Ptolemy's *Geography* was translated into Arabic at least three times: (1) by Ibn Khurdādhbeh not earlier than about 846-847 A. D., but for private use alone; (2) by Ya'qūb ibn Isḥāq al-Kindī, before 874 A. D.; and (3) by Thābit ibn Qurra (826-901 A. D.).

[6] Al-Khwārizmī's *Kitāb ṣūrat al-arḍ* and its origins are of interest to us in view of the fact that certain of the figures there given for latitude and longitude found their way into the *Toledo Tables*, which were translated into Latin and enjoyed wide use in the West during the twelfth century and later (see above, pp. 243-244). Various figures given in the *Kitāb ṣūrat al-arḍ* were quoted by later Mohammedan writers, among them the fourteenth-century geographer Abū-l-Fidā. These formed the basis of

the discussion of Al-Khwārizmī's work in Lelewel's *Géographie du moyen âge*, vol. i, 1852, pp. 21–29; epilogue, 1857, pp. 47–60. A manuscript of the *Ṣūrat al-arḍ*, the only one in existence, was discovered by Wilhelm Spitta in Cairo in 1878 and described by him in an article entitled *Die Geographie des Ptolemäus bei den Arabern*, 1882. Spitta's article was completely superseded by Nallino's more critical study (*Al-Ḫuwârizmî e il suo rifacimento*, 1894). Nallino shows that Lelewel's theory, that the *Kitāb ṣūrat al-arḍ* is a translation of a work called *Oresmos* by a seventh-century Greek geographer, will not hold water. He suggested that the work was not a direct translation from Ptolemy but was composed to elucidate and explain a map which itself was compiled directly from a Greek, not Greco-Syrian, version of the *Geography*. The fact that Al-Khwārizmī's figures in many cases diverge slightly from those of Ptolemy may be explained by the supposition that they were reconstructed from data given on a map, rather than copied from the text of Ptolemy's *Geography*. Later and more thorough investigations into the *Kitāb ṣūrat al-arḍ* by Hans von Mžik confirm Nallino's opinion that the treatise was based upon a map but show that the map itself must have been compiled from a Syrian text. Al-Khwārizmī's work embodies the results of Moslem geographical calculations which had tended to correct Ptolemy's overestimate of the length of the Mediterranean Sea (von Mzik, *Ptolemaeus*, 1915, pp. 152–176; idem, *Afrika*, 1916).

[7] The *Astronomy* contains: (1) in the preamble, a chapter describing the world, first the earth as a whole and then the various seas; (2) among the astronomical tables, a table of the latitudes and longitudes of places in the *oikoumene*. The geographical chapter was edited and translated into French by Reinaud in the introduction to his *Géogr. d'Aboulféda*, vol. i, 1848 (pp. cclxxxiii–ccxc), and more recently into Latin by Nallino in his great edition of Al-Battānī's *Astronomy*. Nallino contends that it was drawn from a much altered version of a Greco-Syrian Ptolemy and that Lelewel and Reinaud were mistaken in thinking that its origin was non-Ptolemaic.

Al-Battānī says that he drew on a certain *Kitāb ṣūrat al-arḍ* for his astronomical tables. This was not the work of the same title by Al-Khwārizmī (see the preceding note), though its author undoubtedly derived some of his data from Al-Khwārizmī's *Kitāb* as well as from the Greco-Syrian version of Ptolemy (Al-Battānī's *Astronomy*, Nallino's edit., pt. ii, 1907, pp. 209–211).

[8] See above, pp. 97 and 244, and below, note 11.

[8a] See Haskins, *Studies*, 1924, pp. 3–19.

[9] The standard work on Az-Zarqalī is Steinschneider, *Études sur Zarkali*, 1881–1887, which deals almost exclusively with manuscripts, texts, and translations.

[10] Steinschneider, *op. cit.*, in: Bollettino, vol xx, 1887, p. 1.

[11] The writer has been unable to find that any detailed study has been

made of the sources of the *Toledo Tables* and of the *Canons* of Az-Zarqalī. Though these Spanish works in their geographical aspects undoubtedly owe much to Al-Khwārizmī, the exact relationship between them is an unsolved problem. As is explained in Chapter X, p. 244, above, most of the Latin translations of the *Toledo Tables* dating from the twelfth century and later are accompanied by a list of geographical coördinates obviously copied from a similar list in the original Arabic and Hebrew texts of the *Tables*. So far as the writer is aware no manuscripts of the original Arabic list are known. Consequently, if this is true, we can obtain no precise information regarding the connection between the earlier Arabic figures and those known in the West in our period. A superficial comparison, however, of the Latin list with the figures in Al-Khwārizmī's *Kitāb ṣūrat al-arḍ* suffices to show that there are many figures common to each and to establish the general thesis that the figures of the *Toledo Tables* are based on earlier Moslem figures, especially those of Al-Khwārizmī, which, in turn, were derived ultimately, though with many alterations, from Ptolemy's *Geography*.

[12] See above, pp. 97–98, and below, p. 400, note 45.

[13] Amari, *Musulmani di Sicilia*, vol. ii, 1858, ch. 13.

[14] This quotation is from the preface of Edrisi's *Geography*, Jaubert's translation (under Idrīsī in the Bibliography), p. xx.

[15] Dozy and De Goeje, *Description*, 1866 (under Idrīsī in the Bibliography), pp. ii, iv.

[16] 1154 is the date given in Edrisi's preface. See, however, note by G. Pardi in: Rivista geografica italiana, vol. xxiv, Florence, 1917, pp. 380–382.

[17] De La Roncière, *Marine française*, vol. i, 1909, p. 136.

[18] *ibid.*, pp. 136–137.

[19] See above, p. 95.

[20] It is uncertain whether the original tables of Al-Khwārizmī were known as the *Little Sindhind* or whether this title was given to another related work by the same author. See Suter, *Astron. Tafeln*, 1914, p. viii (under Khwārizmī, Al-, in the Bibliography), and also Nallino, *Al-Ḫuwârizmî e il suo rifacimento*, 1894, p. 10.

[21] Haskins, *Studies*, 1924, p. 45. This was published under the title *Introductorium in astronomiam* in Venice in 1506. See Duhem, *Système*, vol. iii, 1915, p. 174, note 6. This work was also translated by John of Seville (Haskins, *loc. cit.*).

[22] Duhem, *op. cit.*, vol. ii, 1914, p. 226.

[23] See above, pp. 14–15.

[24] Duhem, *ibid.*, p. 216.

[25] *ibid.*, pp. 218–220.

[26] See the German translation in Friedrich Dieterici's *Die Philosophie der Araber im ix. und x. Jahrhundert n. Chr.*, vol. v, Leipzig, 1876. The "Brothers of Piety and Sincerity" made some noteworthy con-

tributions to the science of geographical meteorology, but these were not passed on to the Western world. They understood, among other phenomena, the warming of the atmosphere by radiation from the earth's surface and its connection with the angle of incidence of the sun's rays; the influence of mountains upon precipitation; and the origin of springs and rivers (Hellmann, *Denkmäler*, 1904, pp. (18), 23–41).

[27] Dieterici, *op. cit.*, p. 100.

[28] Gregorius' edit., fol. 467 (367) (cited by Duhem, *ibid.*, p. 227).

[29] *ibid.*, p. 369.

[30] *Introductorium*, III, 4–9 (cited by Duhem, *ibid.*, pp. 377–386).

[31] Calonymos' edit.' fol. 5 (cited by Duhem, *ibid.*, p. 154).

[32] Duhem, *ibid.*, p. 388, cites this chapter as: Averroes Cordubensis, *In Aristotelis Meteora expositio media*, II, 1. This work was published in Venice in 1488.

[33] Moses Maimonides, the great Jewish astrologer of the twelfth century, on the other hand, ascribed the causes of the tides wholly to the moon (Duhem, *ibid.*, p. 388).

[34] Ibn Yūnūs, Abū-l-Fidā, and other Moslem geographers tell how, in the time of the Caliph Al-Ma'mūn, geographers were instructed to carry out this measurement on the plain of Sinjār, north of the Euphrates, and also in Syria near Tadmor (Palmyra) and that their results gave 57, 56¼, 56⅔, etc., Arabic miles for a degree. For translation of text of Ibn Yūnūs see *Notices et extraits des manuscrits de la Bibl. Natle.*, vol. vii, Paris, An XII [1803–1804], pp. 94, 96 footnote (2); for Abū-l-Fidā see Reinaud, *Géogr. d'Aboulféda*, vol. ii, pt. i, 1848, p. 17. See also Miller, *Erdmessung*, 1919, pp. 30–36, and Schoy, *Erdmessungen*, 1917, for other figures given by the Moslems and for a recent critical discussion of their measurement. Al-Bīrūnī describes a method of determining an arc of meridian by measuring the curvature of the earth from a mountain of known height. See Schoy, *Originalstudien aus "Al-Qânûn al-Mas'ûdî,"* 1923, pp. 69–74. See also Carra de Vaux, *Penseurs de l'Islam*, vol ii, 1921, p. 30.

[35] Miller, Erdmessung, 1919, p. 33.

[36] See above, pp. 243–246. On Moslem methods of determining latitude see Schoy, *Polhöhenbestimmung*, 1911; the same, *Über eine arabische Methode, die geographische Breite aus der Höhe der Sonne im 1. Vertikal ("Höhe ohne Azimut") zu bestimmen*, in: Annalen der Hydrographie und maritimen Meteorologie, vol. xlix, Hamburg, 1921, pp. 124–133; on longitudes, see the same, *Längenbestimmung*, 1915; *Originalstudien aus "Al-Qânûn al-Mas'ûdî,"* 1923; *Geography of the Moslems*, 1924, pp. 265–267.

[37] See above, p. 244.

[38] See J. K. Wright, *Knowledge of Latitudes and Longitudes*, 1923, pp. 89–91, and especially note (1) on p. 91.

[39] On Kang-Diz see Schoy, *Längenbestimmung*, 1915, pp. 47–48.

[40] Reinaud, *Géogr. d'Aboulféda*, vol. i, 1848, pp. ccxxxiii–ccxlvi.

Schoy, *Längenbestimmung*, 1915, pp. 45–57, discusses the question of the origins of the use of a central meridian for the measurement of longitude.

[41] See Schoy, *Geography of the Moslems*, 1924, for a general review of Arabic geography in the Middle Ages.

[42] Josef Marquart, *Osteuropäische und ostasiatische Streifzüge*, Leipzig, 1903, gives much important material, with excerpts from texts and translations, regarding Moslem descriptions of Slavic, Magyar, and Russian peoples in the ninth and tenth centuries of our era. There is included (*ibid.*, pp. 206–270) an Arabic description of Constantinople, of the road thence to Rome, and of Rome itself.

[43] Marquart, *op. cit.*, pp. 102, 145.

[44] Though the great, formal Arabic geographical works were not known in the West in the Middle Ages, legendary lore of the Moslems influenced European legends. The story of St. Brandan, for instance, undeniably owes much to Moslem romance. See De Goeje, *St. Brandan*, 1890.

NOTES

CHAPTER IV

THE SOURCES FOR THE PERIOD 1100–1250 A.D.

Note: See the Bibliography for references to editions of the original sources mentioned in the text of this chapter.

[1] De Wulf, *Medieval Philosophy*, 1909, p. 126.

[2] See above, pp. 2 and 52–53.

[3] Zöckler, *Geschichte*, vol. i, 1877, pp. 407–408.

[4] De Wulf, *op. cit.*, pp. 216–218.

[5] Hauréau, *Hugues de Saint-Victor*, 1886, p. vi.

[6] Hauréau (*op. cit.*, pp. 78–93) believed that these were all the work of Hugh.

[7] Another mystic of the early twelfth century was Rupert of Deutz, whose *De sancta trinitate et operibus eius* was written, according to Zöckler (*op. cit.*, vol. i, p. 393), about 1117.

[8] Some scholars, notably Singer, *Visions of Hildegard*, 1917, pp. 12–15, have cast doubt upon the genuineness of the *Subtilitates* and *Causae et curae*. See, however, Thorndike, *Magic*, 1923, vol. ii, pp. 128–129. See also below, pp. 423–424, notes 91–93.

The *Causae et curae* is the only one of the works which cannot be dated with considerable accuracy (see Thorndike, *op. cit.*, p. 127). The present writer, who has not studied the writings of Hildegard in any detail, hazards the following suggestion for what it is worth. Two passages in the *Causae et curae* can only be explained on the supposition that its author believed in a flat earth (see below, p. 425, note 101). Passages in the *Scivias* (written between 1141 and 1150) and in the *Liber divinorum operum* (written after 1163) speak explicitly of the earth as a globe (see below, p. 423, note 92). May it not be possible that the *Causae et curae* is an early work and that in the course of her subsequent life Hildegard gained a wider knowledge of current views of cosmology, which found their expression in the records of her visions?

[9] Thorndike, *op. cit.*, p. 131.

[10] See Masson, *Biblical Literature*, 1865.

[11] Clerval, *Écoles de Chartres*, 1895.

[12] The archives at Chartres show that a certain Bernard was *magister scholae* in 1119 and that a Bernard, chancellor in 1124, had been replaced by Gilbert de la Porrée in 1126 (C. V. Langlois, *Maître Bernard*, 1893, p. 242).

[13] "Perfectissimus inter Platonicos seculi nostri" (John of Salisbury, *Metalogicus*, iv, 35, in: Migne, *Pat. lat.*, vol. cxcix, col. 938). See also *Metalogicus*, I, 24, in: Migne, *op. cit.*, cols. 853–856.

[14] See above, p. 93.

[15] Hauréau, *Thierry de Chartres*, 1890, p. 50.

[16] Clerval, *Écoles de Chartres*, 1895, p. 172.

[17] Hauréau, *op. cit.*, pp. 52–70.

[18] Haskins, *Adelard*, 1911, pp. 491–498; *Studies*, 1924, pp. 20–42.

[19] Duhem at the time of the publication of vol. iii of *Le système du monde*, 1915, knew the text of the *Quaestiones naturales* only at second hand. (On the uncertainty of the date of the *Quaestiones naturales* see Haskins, *Studies*, 1924, pp. 26–27.) Adelard was also the author of *De eodem et diverso*, written probably in his youth (before 1109).

[20] The *De eodem et diverso* indicates that Adelard had already visited Salerno and Sicily at the time that it was written. In the *Quaestiones naturales* he mentions Tarsus and Antioch as places where he had been (Haskins, *Adelard*, 1911, pp. 492–493; *Studies*, 1924, p. 26).

[21] See above, pp. 95–96.

[22] See above, p. 97.

[23] Poole, *The Masters*, 1920, p. 330.

[24] This work consists of two parts, *Megacosmus* and *Microcosmus*. For an analysis of it see *Histoire littéraire de la France*, vol. xii, Paris, 1763, pp. 261–273, especially p. 267.

[25] The principal arguments against the identification of the two Bernards have been set forth by Hauréau (*Mémoire*, 1883, pp. 99–104), Clerval (*Écoles de Chartres*, 1895, pp. 158–163), and Sandys (*Hist. of Class. Schol.*, vol. i, 1921, p. 534, note 2). Hauréau and Clerval were followed by De Wulf, Duhem, and others. C. V. Langlois (*Maître Bernard*, 1893) championed the identification of the two. The most recent discussion of the problem, by R. L. Poole (*The Masters*, 1920), is convincing in so far as it demonstrates that the evidence now available tends to show that the two Bernards were not the same.

[26] Poole, *op. cit.*, pp. 333–335; Duhem, *Système*, vol. iii, 1915, p. 92.

[27] Hauréau, *Singularités*, 1861, p. 249.

[28] This work, written some time before 1145—for at about this date William, in a treatise called *Dragmaticon philosophiae*, retracted certain heretical doctrines which he had expressed in it—has been falsely attributed to Bede, to William of Hirschau, and to Honorius of Autun (see Poole, *Illustrations*, 1920, pp. 338-352, and Duhem, *Système*, vol. iii, 1915, pp. 90-93) and printed among the works of each of these. The text attributed to William of Hirschau was printed by Henricus Petrus at Basel in 1531 under the title *Philosophicarum et astronomicarum institutionum libri tres;* that attributed to Bede, under the title Περὶ διδαξέων *sive elementorum philosophiae libri IV*, in Migne, *Pat. lat.*, vol. xc, cols. 1127-1182; and that attributed to Honorius, under the title *De philosophia mundi*, in Migne, *op. cit.*, vol. clxxii, cols. 39-102.

On William of Conches as a scientist see especially Werner, *Kosm. Wilhelm von Conches*, 1873.

[29] See above, p. 143, and below, p. 419, note 38.

[30] See the preface to Thomas Wright's edition of the works of Neckam, 1863, pp. ix-xii, for a brief life of Alexander Neckam.

[31] On these and other works of Neckam, see Esposito, *Unpublished Poems*, 1915, pp. 460-471.

[32] On translators from the Greek, see Haskins, *Studies*, 1924, pp. 141-241. Shortly after the middle of the twelfth century a certain Sicilian, Henricus Aristippus, brought from Constantinople a copy of a Greek text of Ptolemy's *Almagest* as a present from the Byzantine Emperor for the Norman king, William I. Subsequently an anonymous medical student of Salerno made a Latin version of this work. Aristippus also distinguished himself at about the same time by turning into Latin from the Greek the fourth book of Aristotle's *Meteorology* (Haskins and Lockwood, *Sicilian Translators*, 1910, pp. 75-102; Haskins, *Further Notes*, 1912—under Haskins and Lockwood in the Bibliography—pp. 155-166; Haskins, *Studies*, 1924, pp. 155-168; on Aristippus' translation of the fourth book of the *Meteorology*, see also below, p. 401, note 60). A second translation of the *Meteorology* was made from Greek into Latin before 1260 (see Grabmann, *Forschungen*, 1916, p. 182; Fobes, *Mediaeval Versions*, 1915, p. 297). Translations from the Greek of the *Physics*, *De caelo*, and *De generatione et corruptione* were also known by the early thirteenth century (Grabmann, *op. cit.*, p. 178; Haskins, *Studies*, 1924, pp. 149, 224, and 225, note 8).

[32a] On translators from the Arabic, see Haskins, *Studies*, 1924, pp. 3-140.

[33] See above, p. 82.

[34] Haskins, *Adelard*, 1911, pp. 493-494; idem, *Studies*, 1924, pp. 22-23. There are at least five manuscripts of Adelard's translation.

[35] See Suter, *Astron. Tafeln*, 1914 (under Khwārizmī, Al-, in the Bibliography).

[36] This is indicated in the following note appended to a Latin translation

of Ptolemy's *Planisphere* made by Hermann the Dalmatian in 1143: "Quem locum a Ptolomeo minus diligenter perspectum cum Albateni miratur et Alchoarismus, quorum hunc quidem ope nostra Latium habet, illius vero comodissima translatione Roberti mei industria Latine orationis thesaurum accumulat nos discutiendi veri in libro nostro de circulis rationem damus" (*Ptolemaei opera omnia*, Heiberg's edit., vol. ii: *Opera astronomica minora*, 1907, p. clxxxvii). Some have sought to ascribe this Latin translation of the *Planisphere* to Rudolph of Bruges, a disciple of Hermann. Reasons why it cannot be the work of Rudolph are given by A. A. Björnbo in: Bibliotheca mathematica, 3rd series, vol. iv, Stockholm, 1903, pp. 130-133. See also Duhem, *Système*, vol. iii, 1915, p. 173. The note quoted above shows that a certain Robert (undoubtedly Robert of Chester—or, of Retines—whom we know to have been an associate of Hermann) had translated Al-Battānī's *Astronomy*. See also Suter, *Astron. Tafeln*, 1914 (under Khwārizmī, Al-, in the Bibliography), p. xiii.

[37] It is probable that the author of the *Dialogus* was also the writer of certain astronomical works from about the same period. On Peter Alphonsi see Haskins, *Reception*, 1915, pp. 60-61; the same, *Studies*, 1924, pp. 111-119.

[38] See above, p. 78. On the name "Johannes Hispanensis" see Duhem, *Système*, vol. iii, 1915, pp. 177-179. Duhem gives the date of the translation as 1134. He was apparently unfamiliar with Bibliothèque Nationale MSS., fonds St. Victor, no. 848, which establishes the date as March 11, 1135, and with an article on the subject by Woepcke: *Notice*, 1862, pp. 116-117. John of Seville's translation is found in many manuscripts and was printed at Ferrara in 1493 and Nuremberg in 1537. John of Seville also translated Abū Ma'shar's *The Great Book of the Introduction* (see Haskins, *Studies*, 1924, p. 45).

[39] Gerard's translation was entitled *Liber de aggregationibus scientiae stellarum* (Boncompagni, *Della vita*, 1851, fol. 442 (separate, pp. 58-59); Woepcke, *op. cit.*, p. 118).

[40] On the date of Plato of Tivoli, see C. H. Haskins, *The Translations of Hugo Sanctelliensis*, in: Romanic Review, vol. ii, New York, 1911, p. 2, note 5. On Al-Battānī, see above, p. 78.

[41] Bibliothèque Nationale MSS., fonds latin, no. 14704, fol. 110, col. a, to fol. 135vo. For the establishment of the date of these tables see Duhem, *Système*, vol. iii, 1915, pp. 203-204, and Haskins, *Studies*, 1924, pp. 96-98. The latter supplies the author's name from a fifteenth-century manuscript in Oxford of which Duhem was ignorant.

[42] See above, p. 79.

[43] See above, p. 244.

[44] Steinschneider, *Études sur Zarkali*, 1881-1887, discusses the various versions of Az-Zarqalī's *Canons* and of the *Toledo Tables*. The former were put into Hebrew, Spanish, Italian, and Latin; of the Latin versions,

the manuscripts are more numerous in England than elsewhere, but there are no fewer than nine in the Bibliothèque Nationale in Paris. The *Toledo Tables* probably did not become well known in the Latin West until the first half of the thirteenth century (see Duhem, *Système*, vol. iii, 1915, pp. 287–290), although they were probably known to Roger of Hereford (see Haskins, *Reception*, 1915, p. 66; the same, *Studies*, 1924, p. 95; and Duhem, *op. cit.*, pp. 520–521).

[45] Steinschneider (*op. cit.*, in: Bollettino, vol. xx, 1887, pp. 3–6) believed that there were two translations of the work of Az-Zarqalī because the manuscripts fall into two groups that differ markedly from each other. The manuscripts of one of these groups bear the name of Gerard of Cremona. Unfortunately, we lack confirmation of the attribution of this translation to Gerard in the list of seventy-four works of the great Cremonese discovered by Boncompagni in the Vatican (see Boncompagni, *Della vita*, 1851). Nevertheless it is highly probable that this list is incomplete, and there is no really good reason for supposing that Gerard was not the translator of the version in question.

[46] See above, p. 398, note 36.

[47] Haskins, *Reception*, 1915, p. 64; idem, *Studies*, 1924, p. 122.

[48] On the *De essentiis* see Haskins, *Studies*, 1924, pp. 48–49, 56–66. On pages 62–65 Haskins publishes for the first time the texts of two interesting geographical passages.

[49] Haskins, *Reception*, 1915, pp. 64–65; idem, *Studies*, 1924, p. 123.

[50] Haskins, *Reception*, 1915, p. 66; idem, *Studies*, 1924, p. 125; British Museum MSS., Arundel, no. 377.

[51] Haskins, *Reception*, 1915, pp. 67–68; idem, *Studies*, 1924, pp. 126–127. On Daniel of Morley, see also Thorndike, *Magic*, 1923, vol. ii, pp. 171–181.

[52] Duhem (*Système*, vol. iii, 1915, pp. 219–223) shows, conclusively the writer believes, both from external and internal evidence, that this work was by the twelfth-century Gerard of Cremona and not by the thirteenth-century Gerard of Sabbionetta, with whom the former was often confused. Boncompagni in his important work on Gerard (cited above, p. 399, note 39) made the mistake of attributing the *Theorica planetarum* to Gerard of Sabbionetta, in which error he was followed by the writer of the article on Gerard of Cremona in the *Encyclopaedia Britannica*, 11th edit.

[52a] See Haskins, *Studies*, 1924, pp. 104–110.

[53] Bibliothèque Nationale MSS., fonds latin, no. 7272, fol. 60, col. a to fol. 67, col. d; Duhem, *op. cit.*, p. 234.

[54] There is no modern critical edition of the *De sphaera*. Duhem (*op. cit.*, p. 239, note 4) cites seventeenth-century editions. The title of the fifteenth-century edition which has been used by the writer is given in the Bibliography.

[55] On the introduction of the writings of Aristotle to Western knowledge during the Middle Ages, see the modern works to which cross references

are given in the Bibliography under Aristotle. In the present work the attempt is merely made to indicate the dates at which those writings of Aristotle which contained materials of geographic importance became known in Western Europe.

[56] Steinschneider, *Europ. Übersetz.*, in: Sitzungsber., vol. cxlix, 1905, pp. 32, 42, 43. See also below, p. 402, note 61.

[57] Duhem, *Du temps*, 1909, pp. 163-178; idem, *Système*, vol. iii, 1915, pp. 181-193.

[58] Grabmann (*Forschungen*, 1916, pp. 16-17) argues that "this 'reflet de la *Physique* d'Aristote' which Duhem sees is in no way demonstrated by actual citations of Aristotle" but that it results from a general similarity of thought and ideas only. Grabmann believes that Alan of Lille, who appears to have known Aristotle's books on logic only, could not possibly have been ignorant of the *Physics* and *De caelo* if these two works had been known in the West before his time. While we may agree with Grabmann that it cannot be proved definitely that the Chartres scholars made direct use of Aristotle's *Physics*, his arguments should not be interpreted to mean that the scholars of the Chartres school were altogether uninfluenced by Peripatetic physical doctrines. Schneider (*Abendländische Spekulation*, 1915), though he holds that Duhem was mistaken in his interpretation of William of Conches' views regarding the Peripatetic physics (see below, p. 418, note 28), supports the French savant in maintaining that there was in existence "a specific Aristotelian trend in astronomic and cosmologic thought" at this period and that Theodoric and Gilbert may not have been uninfluenced by it. He maintains that the latter may well have been familiar with Aristotelian theories introduced through new Oriental sources and suggests as evidence of the probability of this the connections established by Hermann the Dalmatian and Rudolph of Bruges between the Chartres scholars and the group of translators at Toledo. He even goes so far as to add (p. 40): "Nicht ausgeschlossen ist, dass ihnen [Theodoric and Gilbert] als solche indirekte Quellen für die Kenntnis der aristotelischen Naturphilosophie die kurz gefassten und verhältnissmässig leicht verständlichen Paraphrasen Avicennas zur *Physik* und zur *De caelo et mundo* des Aristoteles gedient haben." See below, p. 419, note 32.

Aristotelian influence seems also to have been apparent in the *Quaestiones naturales* of Adelard of Bath (see above, p. 154-155, and below, p. 426, notes 110, 111). Adelard even cites "Aristoteles in phisicis et alii in tractatibus suis," though Grabmann and Haskins claim that this reference is too indefinite to be used to identify any particular works of the Stagirite or to indicate first-hand acquaintance with them (Grabmann, *op. cit.*, p. 16; Haskins, *Studies*, 1924, pp. 38-39).

[59] See Thorndike, *Magic*, 1923, vol. ii, p. 87, for references on Gerard.

[60] A marginal note in a Nuremberg manuscript of the *Meteorology*

indicates that the first three books were translated by Gerard of Cremona from the Arabic, the fourth by Henricus Aristippus (see above, p. 398, note 32) from the Greek, and the last three chapters by Alfred the Englishman (Alfred of Sareshel) from the Latin. See V. Rose, in: Hermes: Zeitschrift für classische Philologie, vol. i, Berlin, 1866, p. 385.

Another translation of the *Meteorology* was done entirely from the Greek and is dated 1260. See Fobes, *Mediaeval Versions*, 1915, pp. 297–314.

It is very doubtful whether the fourth book is really the work of the Stagirite. Hammer-Jensen (*Das sogenannte IV. Buch*, 1915) attributes it to Strato, a Greek Peripatetic philosopher of the third century before Christ. The last three chapters (those translated from the Arabic by Alfred of Sareshel) were referred to as *Liber de congelatis* by their translator and in printed editions (see Bibliography under Alfred of Sareshel, II, below) were ascribed either to Avicenna or to Geber (see Baeumker, *Alfred von Sareshel*, 1913, p. 26, note 2, and Hammer-Jensen, *op. cit.*, p. 131). These three chapters deal with: (1) the origins of stones, (2) the growth of mountains through earthquakes and through the influence of water and winds (see above, pp. 213–214), and (3) minerals.

Alfred of Sareshel was one of the most enthusiastic Aristotelians of the late twelfth and early thirteenth centuries. His *De motu cordis* "shows a wealth of Aristotelian citation such as we cannot find in any other Latin author of its time." Alfred was active in introducing a knowledge of Aristotle's natural science and metaphysics into England. See Haskins, *Reception*, 1915, pp. 68–69; the same, *Studies*, 1924, p. 129.

[61] *De caelo et mundo* was the title usually applied in the Middle Ages to the treatise in four books known in the Greek as Περὶ οὐρανοῦ (*De caelo*). It does not include the *De mundo* referred to above, p. 365, note 1. In the earlier part of the twelfth century Avicenna's version of the *De caelo et mundo* was translated into Latin by Dominicus Gondisalvi (Mandonnet, *Siger de Brabant*, vol. i, 1911, p. 15, note 1). The fifth book had been translated by Gerard of Cremona. On the work of Dominicus Gondisalvi and John of Seville (Johannes Hispanensis), see Duhem, *Système*, vol. iii, 1915, pp. 177–183; Thorndike, *Magic*, 1923, vol. ii, pp. 73–82. Versions of the *De caelo* from the Greek were also in existence before 1200 (Haskins, *Studies*, 1924, p. 149).

[62] On the manuscript list of the translations of Gerard of Cremona, see above, p. 400, note 45.

[63] Haskins, *Michael Scot*, 1921–1922, pp. 250–275; idem, *Science*, 1922, pp. 672, 684–686; idem, *Studies*, 1924, p. 276.

[64] See Haskins, *Michael Scot*, 1921–1922, pp. 268–270, and the same, *Studies*, 1924, pp. 292–294, for the Latin text of the questionnaire; the same, *Science*, 1922, pp. 689–691, *Studies*, 1924, pp. 266–267, for translation.

[65] Haskins, *Michael Scot*, 1921–1922, p. 270; idem, *Studies*, 1924, p. 294.

[66] In the same, *Michael Scot*, 1921–1922, pp. 272–275, and *Studies*, 1924, pp. 296–297, will be found the Latin text of the part dealing with hot springs and volcanoes.

[67] Stange, *Arnoldus Saxo*, 1885, pp. 26–31.

[68] Mandonnet, *Siger de Brabant*, vol. i, 1911, p. 17, note 1; Grabmann, *Forschungen*, 1916, p. 18.

[69] On Averroës, on his influence upon European thought, and on his various medieval adherents and opponents, see Renan, *Averroès*, 1866. As a general rule the great Dominican scholars of the thirteenth century (as Albertus Magnus and Thomas Aquinas) were determined opponents of the Averroïstic theology and philosophy. The Franciscans, on the other hand, were more ready to adopt these heretical teachings.

[70] Duhem, *Système*, vol. iii, 1915, p. 251.

[71] See below, p. 408, note 97.

[72] See especially C. V. Langlois, *La connaissance*, 1911, introduction.

[73] In the earliest printed editions the *De imagine mundi* is attributed to "Honorius Inclusus." In an edition of 1497 we are told that the work is sometimes ascribed to St. Anselm and sometimes to Honorius Inclusus. For the first time in 1544 it was attributed to the well-known Honorius of Autun and included among his works. This was also done subsequently in Migne, *Pat. lat.*, vol. clxxii, cols. 115–188. The attribution to Honorius of Autun was based on a note in the last chapter of that author's *De luminaribus ecclesiae* which gives a list of his writings: among them *Imago mundi de dispositione mundi*. It can be shown, however, that this chapter was added to the *De luminaribus ecclesiae* by a later compiler, who may well have confused Honorius of Autun with Honorius Inclusus. On an extremely shaky foundation the German scholar, J. A. Endres, in his *Honorius Augustodunensis: Beitrag zur Geschichte des geistigen Lebens im 12. Jahrhundert*, Kempten and Munich, 1906, has erected a theory that the author was a German, who lived at Ratisbon. For the whole question, see the clear and just discussion by Duhem (*Système*, vol. iii, 1915, pp. 24–31), who tends to favor the attribution of the work to the virtually unknown Honorius Inclusus and who says of the elaborate German argument: "Un loyal et modeste aveu d'ignorance ne vaudrait-il pas mieux que de tels raisonnements?" (*ibid.*, p. 31).

[74] "Hic nihil autem in eo pono, nisi majorum commendat traditio" (Migne, *Pat. lat.*, vol. clxxii, cols. 119–120).

[75] For a full discussion of the *De imagine mundi*, its sources, and its influence upon future literature, see Doberentz, *Erd- und Völkerkunde*, 1881–1882.

[76] *ibid.*, in: Zeitschrift, vol. xiii, 1881, p. 54.

[77] *ibid.*, p. 41.

[78] In the prologue of the *Liber floridus* the author refers to himself as

"Lambert, son of Onulph, canon of St. Omer." See Migne, *Pat. lat.*, vol. clxiii, col. 1003.

[79] See Miller, *Mappaemundi*, vol. iii, 1895, pp. 43-53.

[80] Six manuscripts of Guido's work are known (Miller, *ibid.*, p. 54).

[81] Doberentz, *op. cit.*, in: Zeitschrift, vol. xii, 1880, pp. 392-393.

[82] Hellmann, *Denkmäler*, 1904, p. (23). Hellmann warns against confusion of the German *Lucidarius* and its translations, on the one hand, with the French popular encyclopedia *Lucidaire* and the English *Lucydary*, on the other. The two latter are not translations from the German but are independent works.

[83] Le Noble, *Notice*, 1839, p. 243. The only known manuscript of the *Hortus deliciarum*, which contained a large number of magnificent miniatures, was destroyed during the bombardment of Strasburg in 1870. See, however, the edition of Straub and Keller, 1879-1899.

[84] The *Otia imperialia* is divided into three parts, or "decisiones." The first deals with theological and cosmological questions and is in the main derived from Peter Comestor. The second treats of geography, and the third of "mirabilia uniuscuiusque provinciae, non omnia, sed ex omnibus aliqua."

[85] See Doberentz, *ibid.*, vol. xii, pp. 412-419. Miller implies that the general description of the geography of the world which Gervase of Tilbury gives at the beginning of Decis. II was taken from a map drawn by Gervase himself (*Itin. rom.*, 1916, p. xxxvii).

[86] Doberentz, *ibid.*, vol. xii, pp. 426-428.

[87] C. V. Langlois, *La connaissance*, 1911, pp. 49-113. On the sources of the *Image du monde*, see the works of Fant, Fritsche, and Le Clerc, referred to in the Bibliography under these names. The poem in the first redaction was divided into three main parts: first, the part dealing with cosmogony, in fourteen chapters; second, that dealing with geography, in eighteen chapters; third, that dealing with astronomy, in twenty-two chapters. The second part, on geography, follows the *De imagine mundi* very closely, with additions from Jacques de Vitry. Fritsche, *Untersuchung*, 1880, gives an analysis of the work chapter by chapter. The "mediocrity" of Fritsche's book, which Langlois asserts, is illustrated by its author's inability to identify the city of "Aaron"—obviously the world center, Arin (Fritsche, *op. cit.*, p. 23).

[88] According to Prior (*L'Image du monde*, 1913) the first verse redaction dates from 1246. To this 4000 verses were later added, including a life of St. Brandan, an account of Seth's visit to Paradise, and details of the author's journey to Sicily and Syria and of his ascent of Mount Etna. The original poem with these additional parts constituted the second redaction, dating from 1248. A prose redaction was apparently composed on the basis of the first verse redaction but before the second verse redaction was made. See the discussion of the problem of dates by Prior, *op. cit.* (under "Image du Monde" in the Bibliography), pp. 7-9.

[89] Three manuscripts of the poem contain the assertion that its author was one Gossouin of Metz; only one manuscript of the poem complete with all the additions, alterations, etc., of the second verse redaction mentions Walter of Metz as the author. C. V. Langlois (*op. cit.*, pp. 63–65) believed that both verse redactions must have been the work of Gossouin; Prior (*op. cit.*, pp. 12–15) that the first verse redaction and the prose form were the work of Gossouin and that the second verse redaction may well have been the work of Walter. Uncertainty still prevails regarding the whole matter.

[90] The *King's Mirror* treats, among many other subjects, of the following matters of geographical interest: the moon, the ebb and flood, streams, climates, differences in the length of days and of summer and winter in northern Norway, marvels of India, marvels of Norway, snowshoes, Iceland, Greenland, whales, earthquakes and ice fields in Iceland, flora and fauna of Greenland, volcanic phenomena in Iceland and Sicily, subterranean fire in Iceland, the small extent of habitable land in Greenland, climatic phenomena, the northern lights and noises accompanying them, a cooler zone to the south of the hot equatorial zone where it is summer during our winter. This synopsis is based on portions of the *King's Mirror* as given in translation in Nansen's *In Northern Mists*, 1911.

Another Icelandic geographical description of the world, which probably dates from our period, besides drawing on well-known earlier authorities, also gives some idea of the Icelandic conception of geography and furnishes details of the itinerary of a certain Abbot Nicholas to Rome and the Holy Land. See above, p. 115, and also, Nansen, *op. cit.*, vol. ii, p. 237 and reference in note 1 regarding the identity of the author of this work, probably Abbot Nikulás Bergsson of Thverá (died 1159), though believed by Storm to be an Abbot Nikulás of Thingeyre. See also K. Kålund, *En islandsk vejviser for pilgrimme fra 12. århundrede*, in: Aarböger for Nordisk Oldkyndighed og Historie, series 3, vol. iii, Copenhagen, 1913, pp. 51–105.

[91] In addition to the general works discussed above, mention must be made of a geographical treatise of minor importance dating from our period. Book III of the *Tractatus excerptionum*, printed among the works of Hugh of St. Victor in Migne, *Pat. lat.*, vol. clxxvii, cols. 209–216, is entitled *De situ terrarum*. This contains chapters on the three parts of the earth, on Asia, Africa, and Europe, on mountains, rivers, islands, and cities. Its attribution to Hugh of St. Victor is extremely doubtful. See Santarem, *Essai*, vol. i, 1849, p. 66, note 2.

[92] The monumental *Speculum mundi* of the Dominican, Vincent of Beauvais, which probably cannot have been written much before 1250, is divided into three parts: *Speculum naturale*, *Speculum doctrinale*, and *Speculum historiale*. There is no complete modern edition. Copies of incunabula and of sixteenth- and seventeenth-century editions are not

rare. The work is a gigantic compilation drawn from a great multitude of sources, all of which were carefully indicated by the diligent compiler, together with additions by the compiler himself. Most novel from the geographical point of view are the data on Asia taken from Simon of St. Quentin and from John of Pian de Carpine, which are to be found in *Speculum historiale* (see above, pp. 269–270). *Speculum naturale* discusses the various features of the world in the order of their creation. It is in the nature of a vast commentary on the first chapter of Genesis. The following books are of especial geographical significance: II, consisting of metaphysical and theological material on the Creation; IV, dealing with the firmament, and the heavens; V, with meteorology; VI, with the waters; VII, with the lands; XXXIII, with regions habitable by man. The last is a typical cosmography, made up largely of fragments from Isidore, in which chapters are devoted to a discussion of the tripartite division of the earth, Asia and Paradise, India and its marvels, Asia Minor, Europe, Greece, other parts of Europe, Africa, the islands of the ocean which encircles the earth, the islands of the Mediterranean Sea, the Cyclades, etc.

[93]Most of Albertus Magnus' (1193–1280) many and voluminous works, the greatest repertory of Aristotelian science of the Christian Middle Ages, constitute an immense paraphrase of and commentary on all the writings of Aristotle that were available in the mid-thirteenth century. Albert used many of the titles that were applied in the period to Aristotle's works and the customary division into books and chapters. Of particular interest from the geographical point of view are: *De caelo et mundo* (Jammy edit., 1651, vol. ii); *Libri meteorum* (*ibid.*, vol. ii); *De natura locorum* (*ibid.*, vol. v), and *De proprietatibus elementorum* (*ibid.*, vol. v). Kretschmer, *Phys. Erdk.*, 1889, *passim*, and Werner, *Kosm. Wilhelm von Conches*, 1873, *passim*, give a fairly satisfactory general idea of the more important contributions of Albert to cosmology and physical geography.

In the second book of the *De caelo et mundo* Albert declares that the earth is spherical because the particles which compose it are drawn toward the center of the universe and, in striving to attain that point, arrange themselves symmetrically in the form of a sphere. He gives as proofs of the sphericity of the earth arguments that were familiar to writers of antiquity (see above, p. 368, note 33).

In the *Libri meteorum* (*Meteorology*) much material will be found on the atmosphere, on the waters, and on earthquakes. Albert thought that the winds are caused by an earthy humor raised by the sun (Werner, *op. cit.*, pp. 351–352; compare this theory with the theory of Seneca and of William of Conches, pp. 171–172, above). He thought that the areas of the earth's surface covered by water are much more extensive than those represented by land and that large rivers spring from great cavities in the interior of the earth. These cavities, he maintained, usually correspond in position to the major mountain ranges.

Points of physical geography are also treated at some length in the *De proprietatibus elementorum* (based upon the pseudo-Aristotelian work of the same title): hot springs, volcanoes, tides, the Deluge, the origin of mountains by earthquakes and by erosion. Albert expresses vigorous opposition to the theory of the periodic rotation of land and sea around the earth's surface under astrological influences (see above, pp. 14 and 83), but he believed, none the less, that the heavenly bodies through their varying motions and conjunctions may bring to bear powerful local changes in conditions of dampness and dryness which in turn may even produce interchanges of areas of land and sea. He refers to the discovery of the rudder of a great ship when a certain well was dug in muddy ground as evidence of gradual alterations in the relative level of land and sea (Kretschmer, *op. cit.*, p. 125).

In a great many respects the *De natura locorum* is the most valuable of Albert's books from the geographical point of view. Kretschmer goes so far as to declare that this work reveals to us in Albert the first great geographer since antiquity (*ibid.*, p. 139). Tractatus I treats, among other matters, of latitudes and longitudes, of the habitable and uninhabitable parts of the earth's surface, and of climates. Albert denies the older view that the equatorial regions are totally uninhabitable on the ground that people were actually known to dwell therein. Moreover, he was inclined to the belief that the countries near the equator are more temperate and pleasant than those nearer the tropics (see above, p. 164). Albert's "climatic observations in the *Liber de natura locorum* have at all times aroused undivided admiration, and we find in them the first attempt at a comparative geography" (Kretschmer, *op. cit.*, p. 139). This applies more especially to his observations regarding the influences of mountains, seas, woods, and other topographic features upon climate. These would well repay careful comparison with the views of William of Conches upon the same topics (see above, p. 178). Tractatus III of the *De natura locorum* is a "cosmographia," or description of the regions of the world, following the usual medieval scheme.

[94] Bartholomew Anglicus, author of the *De proprietatibus rerum*, "belonged probably to the circle of insular [British] clerics who were ardently interested in experimental researches and in natural history; of whom the encyclopedist Alexander Neckam was in a measure the precursor, and of whom the Franciscan Roger Bacon was the most illustrious representative" (C. V. Langlois, *La connaissance*, 1911, p. 117). It has so far been impossible accurately to determine the date of the *De proprietatibus rerum*, though it falls probably before the middle of the thirteenth century (*ibid.*, p. 118, note 2). This work was a compilation from many different sources and was intended for less educated readers. Book XI is devoted to the phenomena of the air, XIII to the waters,

XIV to the earth, and XV to a *mappamundi*, or description of the various "provinces" of the earth in alphabetical order. There is no modern edition. A summary of the contents will be found in C. V. Langlois, *op. cit.*, pp. 128–179, and a discussion of Bartholomew's geography is given by Thorndike, *Magic*, 1923, vol. ii, p. 424–429. Extracts from an English translation of Berthelet, 1535, are given in Steele, *Mediaeval Lore*, 1907 (under Bartholomew Anglicus in the Bibliography). The future influence of the work was very far-reaching, especially upon English literature of the Elizabethan period (see Steele, *op. cit.*, pp. 2–4; C. V. Langlois, *op. cit.*, pp. 126–127).

95 The Florentine Brunetto Latino died in 1295. He composed his great *Livre du trésor* in French during a period of exile in France between 1260 and 1266 (C. V. Langlois, *op. cit.*, p. 328). This work met with a wide success. It is divided into three parts, the first of which is devoted to geography and cosmography. Much of the material here was derived ultimately from Solinus. The *Trésor* was edited by P. Chabaille in 1863, but a definitive critical edition has not yet appeared. For a criticism of Chabaille's edition and for a summary of the contents of the first part, see C. V. Langlois, *op. cit.*, pp. 333–391.

96 Among these must be mentioned the following:

1. An unpublished encyclopedia by an otherwise unknown Arnold the Saxon. This dates from between 1210 and 1250 and is preserved in a manuscript in Erfurt. Rose's edition, 1875, pp. 447–454, gives a summary of the titles of chapters and prints the prologues of each book. Some idea of the character of the work may be gained from Stange's dissertation and article, both listed in the Bibliography. The first book, entitled *De caelo et mundo*, and the fourth, *De virtute universali*, include data on physical geography, meteorology, earthquakes, the sea, rivers, hot springs, and mineralogy (Stange, *Arnoldus Saxo*, 1885, p. 18) derived in part from Aristotle's *Meteorology* (*ibid.* and Rose, *op. cit.*, p. 450). It has been claimed that Arnold the Saxon's encyclopedia was used by Vincent of Beauvais, Albertus Magnus, and Bartholomew Anglicus, but this is probably erroneous (see Thorndike, *Magic*, 1923, vol. ii, p. 430).

2. The *De natura rerum* of Thomas of Cantimpré, in twenty books, written between 1228 and 1244 and as yet unedited in a modern edition. Thomas' work was especially popular in Germany (see C. V. Langlois, *op. cit.*, p. 118, note 2; also Thorndike, *Magic*, 1923, vol. ii, pp. 372–398).

3. A work of encyclopedic scope entitled *Summa philosophiae*, which has erroneously been attributed to Robert Grosseteste but which cannot possibly date from before 1250 and may be as late as 1270. It contains chapters on meteorology, tides, and minerals. The full text is given in Baur, *Philos. Werke Grossetestes*, 1912, pp. 275–643, with a critical discussion of its authorship, pp. 126*–141*.

97 Roger Bacon, one of the most original thinkers of the entire medieval

period in matters of natural science, was the last of a series of Englishmen who devoted themselves to these interests. In this group may be counted Adelard of Bath and, at a much later date, Alexander Neckam, Alfred of Sareshel, Daniel of Morley, and Robert Grosseteste (see above, p. 407, note 94). For the last-named, whose teachings in many particulars he adopted and elaborated upon, Bacon had the highest admiration.

Born about 1210–1215, Roger Bacon became a Franciscan between 1245 and 1250. His more important works were completed before 1266 and were condemned as heretical in 1278. He died in the last decade of the century. See Bridges, *Life of Bacon*, 1914, and Thorndike, *Magic*, 1923, vol. ii, pp. 616–691.

From the geographical point of view beyond all question the most important of Bacon's writings was the *Opus majus*, which sets forth his fundamental ideas in the realms of natural and physical science. Bridges' edition of this contains a full introduction and a detailed analysis of the text, chapter by chapter. The geographical material will be found in Part IV, on mathematical science. Distinctio ii of Part IV (Bridges' edit., vol. i, 1897, pp. 109–119) is devoted to the subject of rays of light and emanations from the heavenly bodies and to the problem of the sphericity of the universe. Elsewhere in Part IV the influences of the heavenly rays upon the earth, especially in respect to zones, tides, and the healthfulness of situations, are brought out. Bacon here is largely indebted to Robert Grosseteste (see above, pp. 163–165). These theories are also worked out in some detail in the chapters of Part V (on optics) devoted to the multiplication of species (Bridges' edit., vol. ii, 1897, pp. 539–543; Werner, *Kosm. Roger Baco*, 1879, pp. 597–599).

The last portion of Part IV (Bridges' edit., vol. i, 1897, pp. 175–404), not divided into chapters, is a treatment of two broad subjects:

1. The importance of mathematics in relation to theology. Under this heading, among other points, there is given an explanation of how mathematics aids us in acquiring knowledge of the heavens, of the location of Paradise and of Hell, of sacred geography (that is of the positions and physical conditions of places spoken of in Scripture), of geometry (here the influence of mountains in reflecting the sun's rays is elucidated; see above, pp. 179–180; Werner, *op. cit.*, p. 599; Duhem, *Système*, vol. iii, 1915, p. 418), and of numbers (here are explained the size, distance, and relative magnitude of the heavenly bodies in relation to the earth and to the heavenly spheres).

2. The influence of the heavens on things terrestrial (Bridges' edit., vol. i, 1897, pp. 286–403). According to Bacon geographic conditions are governed by astronomical and astrological forces. This part of the *Opus majus* shows first how the latter are effective in determining the conditions of habitability on the earth's surface; it closes with a general description of the habitable earth (see especially Werner, *op. cit.*, p. 545, note 4, and pp. 546–550, on Bacon's astrological geography, and pp.

600-606, on Bacon's regional geography). *Climata* and the practical utility of knowledge of geography and of climates to the missionary are discussed. The description of the habitable earth is particularly full for Egypt, the Holy Land, India, Eastern Europe, Central Asia, and Cathay. Much fresh material regarding the Mongols and the Far East was derived from Bacon's contemporaries, the Franciscan travelers John of Pian de Carpine and William Rubruck (see above, pp. 269-270). Bacon dismisses the geography of Western Europe as too familiar to require special treatment.

Besides the *Opus majus*, Bacon's *Communia naturalium* and commentary on the *Secretum secretorum* include a few passages of interest to us. In the former the finite character of the universe is explained (Oxford edit., fasc. iv, pp. 369-373; see also, *Opus tertium*, Brewer's edit., pp. 140-141), together with some consideration of the dimensions of heaven and of earth (Oxford edit., fasc. iv, pp. 414-418). In the latter (a book of miscellaneous precepts for the guidance of human affairs, which was many times translated from the Arabic during the Middle Ages and which was altered, augmented, and edited by Bacon) there is material on astronomy, on the size and sphericity of the earth, and on the relative extent of land and sea (Oxford edit., fasc. v).

[98] Dante treats incidentally of the traditional geography and astronomy of his period in the *Convito* and in numerous references in the *Divine Comedy*. His sources were mainly Orosius, Isidore, Albertus Magnus, and Brunetto Latino (see Moore, *Studies in Dante: Third Series*, 1903, pp. 110-111). A most interesting and original discussion of linguistic geography will be found in the *De vulgari eloquentia* (see Mori, *La geogr.*, 1922, pp. 289-292; Andriani, *La carta dialettologica*, 1923, pp. 255-263). The *Quaestio de aqua et terra*, frequently ascribed to Dante, is of doubtful authenticity. Moore, *Studies in Dante: Second Series*, 1899, pp. 303-374, Shadwell in his edition of the *Quaestio de aqua et terra*, 1909, and Mori, *op. cit.*, p. 285, hold it to be a genuine work of the poet; Boffito, *Intorno alla "Quaestio de aqua et terra,"* Memoria I, 1902, believed it to be spurious; serious objections to Boffito's arguments, however, were raised by V. Biagi in a review of the former's work (Bollettino della Società Dantesca, vol. x, Florence, 1903) with the "result that Boffito himself appears to be less resolved to maintain his thesis in his latest publication, *La "Quaestio de aqua et terra" di D. A., ed. principe del 1508 riprod. in facsimile, etc.*, Florence, 1905" (Marinelli, *Scritti minori*, vol. i, [1908?], p. 196, note 3, p. 219, note 1). See also Arnold Norlind: *Dante som geograf och medeltidens behandling av frågan om vatten och land*, in: Ymer: Tidskrift utgiven av Svenska Sällskapet för Antropologi och Geografi, vol. xliv, Stockholm, 1924, pp. 260-278.

For references to an edition of the text of Dante and to English translations of his various works see the Bibliography under Dante.

[99] For the latest and most authoritative study of Otto, his works and

his place among the literary men of the period, see Hofmeister, *Otto von Freisingen*, 1911–1912.

[100] The continuation to 1160 is surely, and that from 1160 to 1170 possibly, the work of Ragewin, Otto's pupil and notary (Potthast, *Wegweiser*, vol. ii, 1896, p. 886).

[101] *Gesta Frid.*, II, 13, 43. See Hofmeister, *op. cit.*, p. 734.

[102] The genuineness of the *Ligurinus*, which had long been suspected of being an imposture, was established after 1870 by two scholars working simultaneously and independently, Pannenborg and Gaston Paris. Pannenborg, who at first thought that the author of this poem was an Italian, was subsequently converted to the opinion that he was a German by the arguments of Paris. In 1883 Pannenborg definitely established the thesis that the *Ligurinus* was the work of Gunther of Pairis. See Pannenborg, *Über den Ligurinus*, 1871; the same, *Magister Guntherus*, 1873; the same, *Der Verfasser*, 1884; Gaston Paris, *Dissertation critique*, 1872; Vulpinus, *Der Ligurinus*, 1889 (under Gunther of Pairis in the Bibliography), introduction.

[103] Pannenborg, *Über den Ligurinus*, 1871, p. 254.

[104] See, for example, the description of the spring, Bk. VI, lines 481–485.

[105] Gaston Paris, *op. cit.*, pp. 85–86.

[106] See below, p. 412, note 131.

[107] See Delaborde's introduction to the *Philippis* in: *Oeuvres de Rigord*, vol. i, 1882, pp. lxxii–lxxiii (under William the Breton in the Bibliography).

[108] A thorough study of the geographical ideas expressed in the historical epics of the twelfth and early thirteenth centuries would undoubtedly yield fruitful results.

[109] The Nearer East as pictured in the old French Crusading literature is discussed by Dreesbach, *Der Orient*, 1901.

[110] *ibid.*, pp. 69–73.

[111] *ibid.*, p. 70.

[112] See preface to Stubbs's edition of the works of Benedict of Peterborough, vol. i, 1867, pp. ix–lxvii.

[113] *ibid.*, vol. ii, p. 122.

[114] *Chronica*, Stubbs's edit., vol. iii, 1870, pp. 47–55.

[115] Dreesbach, *Der Orient*, 1901, pp. 73–75.

[116] *ibid.*, pp. 79–83.

[117] *ibid.*, pp. 88–89.

[118] See Hermannsson, *Bibl. Icelandic Sagas*, 1908; the same, *Northmen*, 1909; the same, *Bibl. Sagas Kings*, 1910.

[119] See the same, *Bibl. Eddas*, 1920.

[120] On the *Saga of Eric the Red* and on the *Flateyjarbók*, see Reeves, *Wineland*, 1890, *passim*.

[121] Virtually nothing is known of Ari Frodhi. The *Íslendingabók* was "written probably shortly after 1134" (Hermannsson, *Bibl. Icelandic Sagas*, 1908, p. 56).

[122] The discovery of Iceland is also described in a Latin work written by "Theodricus monachus," probably toward the close of the twelfth century and bearing the title *Historia de antiquitate regum norwagiensium.* Nansen dates this work about 1180 (*Northern Mists,* 1911, vol. i, p. 254). See Hermannsson, *Bibl. Sagas Kings,* 1910, p. 67.

[123] Hermannsson, *Northmen,* 1909, pp. 5–6; Reeves, *op. cit.,* pp. 79–83.

[124] Nansen, *op. cit.,* vol. i, p. 263. The *Greenland Annals* were compiled by Björn Jonsson (1574–1656).

[125] Beazley, *Dawn,* vol. ii, 1901, p. 517.

[126] This manuscript was discovered in Scotland in 1849. See Hermannsson, *Bibl. Sagas Kings,* 1910, p. 31.

[127] See above, pp. 49–50 and 73–74.

[128] The fundamental work on the Romance of Alexander during our period is Meyer, *Alexandre le Grand,* 1886.

[129] The *Historia de praeliis,* for instance, the tenth-century work of Leo Archipresbyter (see above, p. 381, note 26), was the text from which Frutolf of Michaelsberg derived the version of the Romance of Alexander which he inserted in his chronicle and which thus found its way to the chronicle of Otto of Freising (Meyer, *op. cit.,* vol. ii, p. 39). That the chronicle from which Otto drew was by Frutolf and not by Ekkehard of Aura was shown by Bresslau, *Die Chroniken,* 1895.

[130] This probably dates from the beginning of the twelfth century (Meyer, *op. cit.,* vol. ii, p. 49).

[131] On the sources of the *Alexandreis,* see Francke, *Geschichte,* 1879, pp. 89–107, and Giordano, *Alexandreis,* 1917, *passim.*

[132] Meyer, *op. cit.,* pp. 69–101.

[133] *ibid.,* pp. 102–132.

[134] *ibid.,* pp. 133–253.

[135] Meyer, *loc. cit.,* has worked out the probable authorship and derivation of the various parts of the poem. He divides the work as a whole into four consecutive sections or "branches." Of these the oldest is the third in order and is by Lambert li Tors; this branch contains those parts of the Romance which are concerned with Alexander's adventures in the heart of Asia and in India; in fact those parts of the work which contain the majority of the elements of geographic interest. To this third branch, the first, second, and fourth were added at a later date. These were the work of Alexandre de Bernai and Pierre de St. Cloud. There are also a number of interpolations into the body of the poem which may not be attributed to any of the three writers named.

[136] This poem was entitled *Le Roman de toute chevalerie.* Meyer (*op. cit.,* vol. ii, p. 275) knew of four manuscripts. In one of these, in Paris, the *Roman* is ascribed to Thomas of Kent, and in a manuscript in Cambridge it is attributed to Eustace of Kent—Meyer holding that the latter is correct. There is much of geographical interest in the poem. The following are some of the chapter headings of parts dealing with

material of geographic significance (from a manuscript in Durham, Library of the Chapter of Durham, C. iv, 27b, as cited by Meyer, *op. cit.*, vol. i, pp. 177–190).

".i. Le proloug
.ij. La descripcion del mond . . ."
".lxxxiiij. De genz de grant age en Inde.
.lxxxv. De Gangarides l'idle e de son poeple.
.lxxxvj. De Polibatre e de son poeple.
.lxxxvii. Del mont Malens le plus haut del mond.
.lxxxviij. De genz qe vivent de veneison et de pesson . . ."
[Further details of races and marvels of India follow.]
".cxlviij. De Gog et Magog qui mangerent la gent . . ."
".ccxxxij. Del pople qu'est apellés Serres et de lur dreiture."

[137] Zarncke, *Priester Johannes* (under Prester John in the Bibliography), in: Abhandl.,vol. vii, 1879, pp. 832–846.

[138] Zarncke, *op. cit.*, p. 878. In some manuscripts this *Letter* is said to be a Latin translation by Archbishop Christian of Mainz; Thorndike, however, observes that it seems "even in its earliest and briefest form without doubt a Western forgery and bears the marks of its Latin origin" (Thorndike, *Magic*, vol. ii, 1923, p. 240).

[139] Edited by Zarncke, *op. cit.*, pp. 872–934.

[140] Zarncke, *op. cit.*. in: Abhandl., vol. viii, 1876, pp. 120–127.

[141] See Zarncke's observations regarding the French text (Berichte, vol. xxix, 1877, p. 135) and his edition of the English text (Berichte, vol. xxx, 1878, pp. 41–46). French, English, and Italian texts are addressed to the Emperor Frederick and not to Manuel.

[142] See above, p. 50; also pp. 381–382, notes 28, 29.

[143] Beazley (*Dawn*, vol. ii, 1901, pp. 112–217) gives an excellent summary of the history of pilgrim travel throughout the Middle Ages, with a résumé of the most important sources. For the bibliography of this subject see especially Röhricht, *Bibliotheca*, 1890. For English translations of the pilgrims' accounts of the Holy Land see the publications constituting *The Library of the Palestine Pilgrims' Text Society*, 1897 (see the Bibliography under Palestine Pilgrims' Text Society).

[144] Beazley, *op. cit.*, pp. 139–155. See also Bibliography under Saewulf.

[145] *ibid.*, pp. 190–195. See also Bibliography under John of Würzburg.

[146] *ibid.*, pp. 195–199. See also Bibliography under Theoderic (Pilgrim).

[147] From internal evidence the itinerary of Abbot Nikulás can be shown to date from the twelfth century. See above, p. 405, note 90.

[148] Beazley, *Dawn*, vol. ii, 1901, p. 184.

[149] *ibid.*, pp. 186–189. See also Bibliography under Fetellus.

[150] *ibid.*, pp. 203–207.

[151] See especially Ganzenmüller, *Naturgefühl*, 1914, pp. 202–216, for citations and translations (into German) of portions of letters which throw light on the medieval feeling for nature.

[152] Wattenbach, *Guido von Bazoches*, 1891 (under Guy of Bazoches in the Bibliography). Wattenbach (*op. cit.*, p. 71) refers to a *Libellus de regionibus mundi* by Guy of Bazoches now in Paris, Bibliothèque Nationale MSS., fonds latin, no. 4998.

[153] *Chronica Slavorum*, V, 19, in: *Mon. Germ. hist.*, Scriptores, vol. xxi, pp. 192-196.

[154] See Carmoly, *Itinéraires*, 1847, pp. 115-168, for text and commentary on the itinerary of Samuel bar Simson, 1211, and pp. 171-216, for Jacob of Paris' description of the holy tombs, 1258. The other itineraries in Carmoly's volume fall in a period later than that covered by the present study.

[155] Benjamin of Tudela, *Itinerary*, Adler's edit., 1907, p. xiii.

[156] On Benjamin of Tudela, see Adler's edition of the *Itinerary* and Beazley, *Dawn*, vol. ii, 1901, pp. 224-264. For a useful general introduction to the geographical literature of the Jews, see Zunz, *Essay*, 1841.

As the manuscript of this book was about to go to press there came to the writer's attention the brief note by Paul Borchardt, *L'itinéraire de Rabbi Benjamin de Tudèle*, 1924. Borchardt wrote (p. 31): "En différents travaux j'ai prouvé que le célèbre Rabbi Benjamin ne mérite pas le reproche d'inexactitude, même en ce qui concerne la route de Chine. . . . J'espère prouver par ce qui suit que R. Benjamin mérite comme Marco Polo le nom d'un homme digne de foi." References are given in footnote 1, p. 31, of Borchardt's note to other studies by Borchardt relating to Benjamin. [See Paul Borchardt, *Der Reiseweg des R. Benjamin von Tudela und des R. Petachia von Regensburg in Mesopotamien und Persien: Ein Versuch* (Sonderabdruck aus dem Jahrbuch der jüdisch-literarischen Gesellschaft), Frankfurt-am-Main, 1924; *Karawanenstrassen in Arabien nach R. Benjamin von Tudela*, Anthropos, 1922-23 (4-6), pp. 1056-1057; and *Der Faladschajuden in Abessinien im Mittelalter*, Anthropos, 1923-24 (1-3).] See also below, p. 474, note 237a.

[157] Petachia of Ratisbon, *Travels*, Benisch and Ainsworth's transl., 1856; Beazley, *op. cit.*, pp. 264-274.

[158] This poem is inserted at fol. 13 of Bibliothèque Nationale MSS., fonds latin, nouvelles acquisitions, no. 299, in the midst of the *Speculum regum* of Godfrey of Viterbo. Delisle, its editor, explains why it should be attributed to Godfrey (*Littérature latine*, 1890, p. 41; listed under Godfrey of Viterbo in the Bibliography).

[159] "Praelia regnorum non hic, set fastus eorum
Scribitur, aut fluvius, orbes speciesque locorum
Aut series morum, norma colenda, forum."
—*Denumeratio*, Delisle's edit., p. 44.

[160] Stubbs's edition of the works of Gervase of Canterbury, vol. i, 1879, p. xxi.

[161] On the dimensions of Britain he quotes from Henry of Huntingdon, *Historia Anglorum*, I.

[162] On the work of Giraldus as a whole see preface to vol. i (pp. i–xcv) of the Rolls Series edition (no. 21), London, 1861, and Lloyd, *History of Wales*, 1911, vol. i, pp. 554–564.

[163] *Giraldi Cambrensis opera* (Rolls Series No. 21), vol. i, edited by J. S. Brewer, London, 1861, Introduction, p. xl.

[164] *ibid.*, vol. vi, edited by J. F. Dimock, London, 1867, pp. xlvi–xlvii.

[165] In addition to the *Mirabilia*, there was written, probably in the twelfth century, a short tract by one Master Gregory, on the marvels of Rome, much of which was copied by Ranulph Higden in his *Polychronicon*. This appears to have been composed independently of the *Mirabilia*, although it deals with the same subject. The author may have been an Englishman. See James, *Magister Gregorius*, 1917 (under Gregory, Master, in the Bibliography), pp. 531–554.

[166] Miller's *Mappaemundi*, vol. i, 1895, deals with the Beatus maps and is accompanied by a colored reproduction of the St. Sever Beatus map (our Fig. 2, p. 69). Vol. ii, 1895, is an atlas of photographic reproductions of the Beatus and other maps of the world of the period. Vol. iii, 1895, contains explanatory text on the more important earlier maps, together with photographs and cuts. Vol. iv, 1896, and vol. v, 1896, are devoted to the Hereford and Ebstorf maps of the world from after our period, and vol. vi, 1898, to attempts at the reconstruction of lost *mappaemundi*. A word of caution is perhaps necessary against too ready acceptance of all of Miller's theories regarding the connections between maps and the influence of one type upon others. See above, p. 377, note 167, and below, p. 458, note 17.

[167] Beazley, *Dawn*, vol. ii, 1901, pp. 549–642.

[168] Miller, *op. cit.*, vol. iii, pp. 123–126. On p. 124 Miller states that "in the manuscript of the *Magna de naturis philosophia* of William of Conches . . . in the Stuttgart Library, three maps are included, described by Santarem." See Santarem, *Essai*, vol. iii, 1852, pp. 499–505. Beazley (*Dawn*, vol. ii, 1901, p. 626), following Miller, also ascribes these maps to a manuscript of the *Magna de naturis philosophia*. The manuscript in question, however, is of no other work than William of Conches' *De philosophia mundi*, which Santarem (*op. cit.*, pp. 499–500) ascribed wrongly to William of Hirschau (see above, p. 398, note 28). No manuscripts or copies of the *Magna de naturis philosophia* are extant, and Poole believes that if such a work ever existed it has been wrongly attributed to William of Conches (Poole, *Illustrations*, 1920, pp. 306–310).

[169] Miller, *op. cit.*, vol. iii, 1895, pp. 126–128.

[170] *ibid.*, pp. 118–120.

[171] *ibid.*, pp. 110–115.

[172] See above, p. 68. See also Miller, *op. cit.*, vol. i, 1895, *passim*.

[173] *ibid.*, vol. iii, 1895, pp. 43–53 and pl. 4.

[174] In this respect Lambert's map resembles a *mappamundi* made in the eleventh century at Ripoll in Catalonia. On this interesting map see Vidier, *Mappemonde de Théodulfe*, 1911, pp. 285-315.

[175] Miller, *op. cit.*, vol. iii, pp. 54-57.

[176] *ibid.*, vol. iii, pp. 21-29 and pl. 2; vol. ii, pl. 13.

[177] *ibid.*, vol. iii, pp. 71-73.

[178] *ibid.*, vol. iii, pp. 37-43 and pl. 3; vol. ii, pl. 1.

[179] *ibid.*, vol. iii, pp. 1-21 and pl. 1; vol. ii, pls. 11 and 12.

[180] *ibid.*, vol. iii, pp. 61-68.

[181] *ibid.*, pp. 68-94.

[182] Beazley, *Dawn*, vol. ii, 1901, p. 585.

NOTES

CHAPTER V

THE PLACE OF GEOGRAPHY IN THE MEDIEVAL CLASSIFICATION OF KNOWLEDGE

[1] Adam of Bremen, however, used the term "geography," applying it to the fourth section of his *Gesta Hammenburgensis ecclesiae pontificum*.

[2] Parker, *Seven Lib. Arts*, 1890, pp. 417-461.

[3] See above, p. 366, note 9.

[3a] *Fons philosophiae*, Charma's edit., 1868, Introduction, p. 11.

[4] *De eodem et diverso*, p. 28.

[5] ". . . qua ratione regulam omnibus saeculis perennam de terrae mensura habere posset" (*loc. cit.*).

[6] "Subsequenter ergo orbem in partes, partes in provincias, provincias in regiones, regiones in loca, loca in territoria, territoria in agros, agros in centurias, centurias in iugera divisit" (*loc. cit*).

[7] *De nupt. Phil. et Merc.*, VI, 580, 587. See Mâle, *Religious Art*, 1913, p. 78.

[8] *Anticlaudianus*, III, 6.

[9] Mâle, *op. cit.*, p. 114.

[10] *De div. phil.*, pp. 115-116.

[11] "Tercia vero inquirit de terra, de eo quod ipsa inhabitatur et quod non habitatur; et ostenditur quantum est illud, quod inhabitatur et quot sunt partes eius magne, que sunt climata; et comprehendit habitaciones, quas contingit esse in unaquaque illarum in illa hora, et ubi sit locus cuiusque habitacionis, et ordinem eorum ex mundo; inquirit de eo, quod sequitur necessario ut accidat unicuique climatum habitacionum de revolucione mundi continenti totio et est revolucio diei et noctis propter situm terre in loco, in quo sunt sicut ortus et occasus et longitudo diei et noctis et brevitas et alia hiis similia" (*ibid.*). This passage, together with the greater part of the *De divisione philosophiae*, is drawn from Al-Fārābī's book *On the Enumeration of the Sciences*. Al-Fārābī was a Moslem philosopher and Aristotelian of the tenth century. See Baur's edition of the *De div. phil.*, 1903, pp. 160, 314.

[12] See H. O. Taylor, *The Mediaeval Mind: A History of the Development of Thought and Emotion in the Middle Ages*, 2 vols., New York, 1914, vol. ii, pp. 312-313.

NOTES

CHAPTER VI

COSMOGONY, COSMOLOGY, AND COSMOGRAPHY

[1] On this rational spirit, see C. B. Jourdain, *Dissertation*, 1838, pp. 20ff.

[2] Poole, *Illustrations*, 1920, p. 148.

[3] ". . . secundum physicam et ad litteram" (*De sex d. op.*, p. 52).

[4] "Causas ex quibus habeat mundus existere et temporum ordinem in quibus idem mundus conditus et ornatus est rationabiliter ostendit" (*ibid.*). See C. B. Jourdain, *loc. cit.* On Adelard's rationalism, see the same, pp. 104ff.

[5] Hauréau, *Thierry de Chartres*, 1890, p. 51.

[5a] Haskins, *Studies*, 1924, pp. 40–41.

[5b] *Quaest. nat.*, ch. 6 in printed edit.; fol. 25v. in Bibliothèque Nationale MSS., fonds lat., no. 6415 (as cited by Haskins, *loc. cit.*).

[5c] *ibid.*, ch. 1 in printed edit.; fol. 24 in MS.

[5d] *ibid.*, ch. 4 in printed edit.; fol. 25 in MS.

[6] *De phil. mundi*, II, 3.

[7] ". . . principium a magistro, sed perfectio debet esse ab ingenio" (*ibid.*, I, 21; quoted by Duhem, *Système*, vol. iii, 1915, p. 99).

[8] *Entheticus*, 601–624, in: Migne, *Pat. lat.*, vol. cxcix, col. 978. See Ganzenmüller, *Naturgefühl*, 1914, p. 227.

[9] Translation from Moffat, *Complaint of Nature*, 1908 (in the Bibliography under Alan of Lille), p. 27. See also Ganzenmüller, *loc. cit.*

[10] See above, p. 223.

[11] *Historia Norwegiae*, Storm's edit., p. 95.

[12] *ibid.*, p. 96.

[13] Duhem, *Système*, vol. iii, 1915, p. 69.

[14] *Symb. elect.*, II, 1.

[15] *Topog. Hiber.*, I, 13.

[16] *De laud. div. sap.*, III, 97–98, 123–124. This point of view was also that of William the Breton, who, in more than one place in his *Philippis*, writes that it is enough for us to know the facts of such natural phenomena as tides, miraculous springs, and the like, but that the causes of them will forever remain hidden from men (*Philippis*, VI, 550–551; VIII, 82–90; see above, pp. 193–194).

[17] Haskins, *Michael Scot*, 1921–1922, pp. 271–272; idem, *Studies*, 1924, p. 295.

[18] *Otia imper.*, vol. i, pp. 885–890.

[19] See K. Werner, *Wilhelms von Auvergne Verhältniss zu den Platonikern des XII. Jahrhunderts*, in: Kaiserliche Akademie der Wissenschaften in Wien, Sitzungsberichte, Philosophisch-historische Classe, vol. lxxiv. Vienna, 1873, pp. 119–172.

[20] *De mundi univ.*, I, *passim*.

[21] *De sex d. op.*, pp. 52–54.

[22] *ibid.*, p. 60.

[23] *Sententiae*, II, 12, 1.

[24] Zöckler, *Geschichte*, vol. i, 1877, pp. 415–421.

[25] *Hist. schol.*, Gen. 1.

[26] Though Comestor here denies the teachings of Plato in regard to the existence of matter prior to the "Creation," he adopted a traditional medieval view based on the *Timaeus* of Plato and given expression by Augustine: that God created time and the universe simultaneously (see above, p. 52). How these two conceptions were reconciled is shown by Daniel of Morley where he writes: "Primus mundus est in eternitate figuratus, secundus cum tempore creatus, tercius in tempore formatus" (*De philosophia*, Sudhoff's edit., p. 8). (For Daniel of Morley's views on *hyle* see Singer, *Daniel of Morley*, 1920, p. 267.) Essentially the same Platonic doctrine was shared by Hugh of Amiens, archbishop of Rouen, who wrote in his *Tractatio in hexaemeron* that God precedes the world by eternity, not by time (Migne, *Pat. lat.*, vol. cxcii, col. 1249). The *De imagine mundi* (II, 1) applied the term *aevum* to God alone; *tempora aeterna*, beginning before the world and continuing with and after it, to the *architypus mundus* and to the angels; and *tempus* to the world (Robbins, *Hexaemeral Lit.*, 1912, p. 7, note 1).

[27] *De phil. mundi*, I, 21.

[28] Bede and Hugh of St. Victor also held that the elements were thus segregated at the moment they were called into existence by God (Zöckler, *op. cit.*, vol. i, 1877, pp. 248, 401).

William of Conches argues specifically against the Aristotelian doctrine of a fifth element of which the heavenly bodies are composed (*Dragmaticon philosophiae*, III, 80–83, cited by Schneider, *Abendländische Spekulation*, 1915, p. 40, note 1). Duhem (*Système*, vol. iii, 1915, pp. 105, 194) saw in William's *De philosophia mundi* what seemed to be a remarkable analogy between the ideas there expressed and those expressed by Aristotle in the fourth book of his *Physics*. Schneider (*op. cit.*, pp. 40–42) points out that Duhem, through failure to take into account the passage in the *Dragmaticon* to which we have just referred, was led to think that William was actually a believer in the main theories set forth in the *Physics*. On the contrary, in referring to the elements in the *Dragmaticon* William merely adopted the traditional Platonic doctrine, and he went on to explain Aristotle's theory of the fifth element and vigorously to denounce it. Though this shows that William may not have agreed with Aristotle in essentials, it would seem to be, nevertheless, an argument in favor of the existence of an Aristotelian trend of thought in William's time. See above, p. 401, note 58.

[29] Though William denied the possibility of chaos preëxisting the "Creation," he was none the less accused of heresy by Walter, prior of St. Victor in Paris during the last part of twelfth century, because of his failure to make it clear that God created everything out of nothing.

William's atomic theories suggest the possibility of belief in his mind that matter in the form of atoms had coexisted with God and that at the so-called "Creation" God had merely organized and arranged these atoms. See Hauréau, *Singularités*, 1861, p. 258; Poole, *Illustrations*, 1920, pp. 300–301.

30 *De sex d. op.*, p. 62.

31 See above, pp. 15–16. Belief in the World Soul (*anima mundi*) was a doctrine of Platonism. Theodoric of Chartres (*De sex d. op.*, pp. 60–62), Bernard Sylvester (*De mundi univ.*, *passim*), and William of Conches (see Poole, *op. cit.*, p. 151) shared it with Peter Abelard (Hauréau, *op. cit.*, p. 253). The two latter, like Theodoric, identified this mysterious unifying conscious spirit of all things with the Holy Ghost and maintained that belief in the World Soul was not inconsistent with the Christian teaching that each individual has a personal soul of his own. The personal soul in some way was thought to be merged with and to form a portion of the World Soul. The theory of the World Soul, however, could not be purged of an heretical taint. At the very beginning of our period Manegold argued as vigorously against it (*Contra Wolfelmum Coloniensem opusculum*, 1–3) as he argued against the possibility of antipodeans (see above, p. 161). It was also severely condemned by other defenders of more old-fashioned and orthodox beliefs. Peter Comestor says, for example: "Hunc locum male intellexit Plato, dictum hoc putans de anima mundi" (*Hist. schol.*, Gen. 1, 2), and Peter Lombard's whole treatment of the question of the Trinity in the *Sententiae* (II, 17) precludes the possibility of a World Soul. Peter Lombard specifically states that the soul of man is not of the same substance as the soul of God.

32 Theodoric adduced various reasons for the rotary motion of the heavens and gave explanations of this phenomenon which so closely resembled the arguments given by Aristotle in his *De caelo* (I, 8; II, 3), *Physics* (IV, 4), and *De motu animalium* (II, 698b) (see above, p. 370, note 42) that Duhem was led by them to the opinion that the Chartres scholar must have had direct access to Arabic translations of versions of Aristotle. See above, p. 154, and p. 401, notes 57, 58.

33 *De sex d. op.*, p. 54.

34 *ibid.*, p. 55.

35 *ibid.*, p. 57.

36 See above, p. 141.

37 *De phil. mundi*, I, 23; Werner, *Kosm. Wilhelm von Conches*, 1873, p. 320.

38 This curious opinion is expressed in *De phil. mundi*, I, 23. William retracted it in the preface to the sixth book of his *Dragmaticon philosophiae* on the ground that it contradicts the Scriptural account according to which Eve was made from Adam's rib. See above, p. 398, note 28.

[39] *De civitate Dei*, XI, 33, in: *Corpus script. eccl. lat.*, vol. xl, pt. 1, pp. 562–564. See also Zöckler, *Geschichte*, vol. i, 1877, p. 238.

[40] *Hexaemeron*, I, in: Migne, *Pat. lat.*, vol. xci, cols. 17–18. See also Zöckler, *op. cit.*, pp. 247–248.

[41] *De sacramentis*, bk. I, pt. 1, ch. 11, in: Migne, *Pat. lat.*, vol. clxxvi, col. 195. See also Zöckler, *op. cit.*, vol. i, p. 401.

[42] *Hist. schol.*, Gen. 1, 3. See also Zöckler, *op: cit.*, vol. i, p. 417.

[43] So Rupert of Deutz, Arnold of Chartres, Hugh of Rouen (*ibid.*, pp. 395, 405, 406).

[44] *Sententiae*, II, 13, 2–6. See also Zöckler, *op. cit.*, pp. 413–414.

[45] See Bauer, *Philos. Werke des Grosseteste*, 1912 (under Grosseteste in the Bibliography), p. 76*.

[46] *De luce seu de inchoatione formarum*, Baur's edit., pp. 51–59.

[47] See Duhem, *Système*, vol. iii, 1915, pp. 284–287, and vol. v, 1917, pp. 356–358.

[48] *De sex d. op.*, pp. 53–54.

[49] *Adnotat. elucidat. in Pentateuchon*, Gen. 6, in: Migne, *Pat. lat.*, vol. clxxv, cols. 34–37; *De sacramentis*, I, pt. 1, 1–16, in: Migne, *op. cit.*, vol. clxxvi, cols. 187–199. See also Zöckler, *op. cit.*, vol. i, p. 401.

[50] *De Genesi ad litteram*, V, 5, in Migne, *Pat. lat.*, vol. xxxiv, cols. 325–327. See also other passages in Augustine's works cited in Zöckler, *op. cit.*, pp. 236–237.

[51] Zöckler, *op. cit.*, p. 406.

[52] See above, p. 366, note 7.

[53] See above, p. 9.

[54] See above, p. 401, note 60.

[55] See above, p. 99.

[56] See above, p. 82.

[57] See above, p. 82.

[58] *De phil. mundi*, III, 19.

[59] Zöckler, *Geschichte*, vol. i, 1877, pp. 429–430. Averroës discussed the origin of matter in his commentary on Aristotle's *Metaphysics*, XII (Renan, *Averroès*, 1866, pp. 108–115). On medieval opposition to the Averroïstic doctrine of the eternity of the world, see the same, pp. 258, 274. On Michael Scot's denial of this doctrine see Haskins, *Michael Scot*, 1921–1922, pp. 260–261; the same, *Studies*, 1924, p. 285.

[60] Duhem, *Système*, vol. v, 1917, p. 277.

[61] Notably in the *De finitate motus et temporis* and in the unpublished *Hexaemeron;* see Baur, *Philos. Werke des Grosseteste*, 1912 (under Grosseteste in the Bibliography), pp. 19*–24*—especially p. 23*—93*–95*, 101–106). Robert Grosseteste's pupil, Roger Bacon, "believed that he was in a position to demonstrate by philosophical proofs that the world had a beginning; and besides he maintained that Aristotle never maintained a contrary doctrine" (Duhem, *op. cit.*, vol. v, p. 402). Albertus Magnus, on the other hand, did not categorically deny the truth of the Aristotelian

teaching, "but rather treated it as a theory that must be accepted from the philosophical point of view but rejected from the theological" (Zöckler, *op. cit.*, vol. i, p. 439). Bacon discussed this matter in an unpublished work now preserved in the Bibliothèque Municipale at Amiens, MS. no. 406, fol. 69, col. a; see Duhem, *op. cit.*, vol. iii, 1915, pp. 260–277. Albertus Magnus discussed the same subject in *Summa theologiae*, pt. II, tract. 11, and in *De quattuor coaevis*, both cited by Zöckler, *op. cit.*, vol. i, p. 436.

62 See the summary of the *De mundi univ.* in: *Histoire littéraire de la France*, vol. xii, Paris, 1763, pp. 267–269.

63 See Anderson, *Younger Edda*, 1880 (under Snorri Sturluson, II, in the Bibliography).

64 Ginungagap may be related to the great "northerly gulf" referred to above, p. 349.

65 Quotation is here from Anderson's paraphrase of the leading ideas of the *Edda* of Snorri Sturluson (Anderson, *op. cit.*, Preface, p. 5).

66 *Quod homo sit minor mundus*, Baur's edit., p. 59. See also Thorndike, *Magic*, 1923, vol. ii, p. 446.

67 See above, pp. 213–214.

68 Cumont, *After Life*, 1922, p. 12.

69 See above, p. 185, and also below, p. 436, note 17.

70 It is to be recalled that the *De mundi universitate* is divided into two books, *Megacosmus* and *Microcosmus*. See above, p. 146.

71 There are marked analogies between the theory of the microcosm as expounded by Herrad and by Hildegard of Bingen. Singer believes that "the theory, in the form in which these writers present it, reached the upper Rhineland somewhere about the middle or latter half of the twelfth century" (Singer, *Visions of Saint Hildegard*, 1917, p. 20).

72 See Singer, *op. cit.*, pp. 30–43, for a discussion of the theory of the macrocosm and microcosm according to Hildegard and for highly interesting reproductions of miniatures illustrating this theory. Singer, believing that the *Causae et curae* and *Subtilitates* are spurious (see above, p. 396, note 8), omits consideration of these works in this connection.

73 "In creatione hominis de terra alia terra sumpta est, quae homo est, et omnia elementa ei serviebant, quia eum vivere sentiebant, et obviam omnibus conversationibus ejus cum illo operabantur et ipse cum illis" (*Subtilitates*, I, praefatio, in: Migne, *Pat. lat.*, vol. cxcvii, col. 1125).

74 *Causae et curae*, I (Kaiser's edit., p. 2).

75 Thorndike, *Magic*, vol. ii, 1923, pp. 153–154.

76 *Subtilitates*, praef., in: Migne, *op. cit.*, vol. cxcvii, cols. 1125–1128.

77 "Terram centrum idest punctum vocamus eo quod sit media in spera." "Terra autem in medio celestris circuli per quem sol currit ut centro locata est" (Bibliothèque Nationale MSS., fonds latin, no. 8865, fol. 55vo).

78 Grosseteste, *De sphaera*, Baur's edit., pp. 12–13.

[79] *Im. du monde*, I, 13. See above, p. 15.

[80] John of Holywood, *De sphaera*, 1.

[81] Translation of Al-Farghānī's *Astronomy* by John of Seville (or Johannes Hispanensis, or John of Luna), Nuremberg edit., diff. iv, fol. 4ro. In the *De sphaera*, *loc. cit.*, John of Holywood stated that Ptolemy and all philosophers had declared that six signs and the middle of the heaven (*medietas caeli*)—by which he probably meant the celestial equator—were visible from any place whatsoever to which a man might go on the surface of the earth. If the earth were not at the center of the universe it would be impossible, he argued, to see the *medietas caeli* from those parts of the earth nearest the firmament: "aliquis existens in illa parte superficiei terrae quae magis accederet ad firmamentum non videret caeli medietatem."

Figure 10 illustrates what appears to have been John's line of reasoning as well as the flaws in it. With the earth in position I, not in the center of the universe, the celestial equator (E-E') is invisible from all points between x and y through N (the north pole), x and y being points at which tangents E-x and E'-y touch the earth's surface. If the earth is in the center of the universe and the sphere of the universe is incomparably great in relation to the size of the earth—something which John believed to be true (see above, p. 155)—the area between x' and y' will be reduced to a very small area around N'. John seems to have assumed that the universe is large enough to make this area negligible. Such an area must exist, nevertheless, with all but an infinitely great celestial sphere. But if the universe were of infinite dimensions, John's entire argument based on the invisibility of E-E' from an earth not in the center would fall to the ground, for all points may be deemed the center of an infinite universe. See also below, p. 426, note 118.

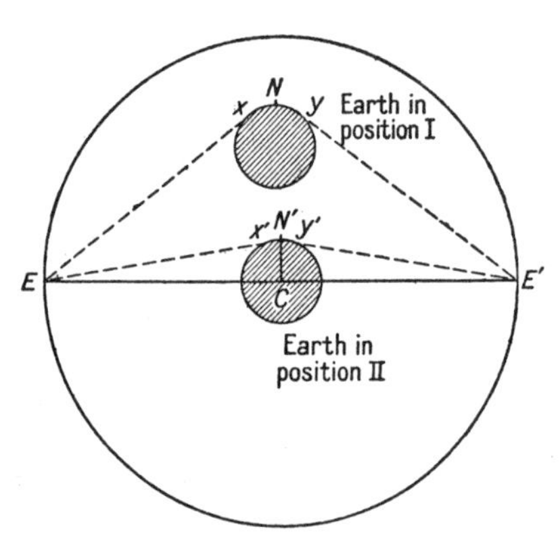

Fig. 10—Diagram to illustrate John of Holywood's reasoning that the earth is in the center of the universe.

Ptolemy's *Almagest*, I, 4, contains an argument aimed to demonstrate why the earth must be at the center of the universe. John of Holywood's reasoning is a confused attempt to condense the argument of Ptolemy into a short space.

[82] *De imag. mundi*, I, 5.

[83] *ibid.*, I, 1.

[84] *Otia imper.*, vol. i, p. 885.

[85] *Hist. schol.*, Gen. 1, 4.

[86] *Im. du monde*, I, 10.

[87] *Expos. in hex.*, cols. 735–736.

[88] *De phil. mundi*, IV, 1.

[89] Abelard (*loc. cit.*) and William of Conches (*loc. cit.*) compare the shell of the egg to the fire, the skin to the air, the white to the water, and the yolk to the earth. Daniel of Morley makes the same comparison, as follows: "Mundus vero ad similitudinem ovi factus est vel dispositus. Terra est in medio ut vitellum in ovo; circa hanc est aqua ut circa vitellum album; circa aquam aer ut panniculus continens album. Extra vero cetera concludens est ignis ad modum teste ovi" (*De philosophia*, Sudhoff's edit., p. 20).

[90] Haskins, *Michael Scot*, 1921–1922, pp. 271–272; idem, *Studies*, 1924, pp. 295–296.

[91] "Et terra modica est et prope fundum firmamenti est, quod si in medio firmamenti esset, tunc eam oporteret maiorem esse et tunc etiam facile caderet et dirumperetur, si tantam amplitudinem aeris sub se haberet, quantam super se habet. Sed et ipsa ad meridiem quasi descensus montis est, unde etiam ibi maiorem calorem de sole habet, quia sol et firmamentum ipsi viciniora ibi sunt. Ad aquilonem vero alta est adversum poenas, et etiam ibi maius frigus est, quia nec firmamentum nec sol ibi prope terram sunt, sed quaedam maior amplitudo firmamenti" (*Causae et curae*, II, Kaiser's edit., p. 49).

[92] *Liber div. op.*, pars I, visio II, in: Migne, *Pat. lat.*, vol. cxcvii, cols. 751–755, 759–760. In a previous vision referred to in the passage just cited and described in *Scivias*, I, visio III (Migne, *op. cit.*, col. 405), Hildegard saw the universe as an egg, in which the earth appeared as follows: "Et in medio istorum elementorum quidam arenosus globus plurimae magnitudinis erat; quem eadem elementa ita circumdederant, quod nec hac nec illac dilabi poterat. Sed dum interdum eadem elementa cum praedictis flatibus se invicem concuterent, eumdem globum sua fortitudine aliquantulum moveri. Et vidi inter aquilonem et orientem velut maximum montem, qui versus aquilonem multas tenebras et versus orientem multam lucem continebat; ita tamen quod nec lux illa ad tenebras, nec tenebrae ad lucem pertingere poterant."

Singer in his *Visions of Saint Hildegard*, 1917, pp. 22–30, discusses Hildegard's theories of the structure of the material universe as revealed in the records of her visions. Particularly striking are the colored illustrations taken from miniatures in manuscripts of her works. Singer asserts (p. 22) that "the concentric structure of the universe is a commonplace of mediaeval science, and is encountered, for instance, in the works of Bede, Isidore, Alexander of Neckam, Roger Bacon, Albertus Magnus, and Dante. To all these writers, however, the universe is spherical. The egg-shape is peculiar to Hildegard. Many of the *Mappaemundi* of the Beatus and other types exhibit the *surface* of the habitable earth itself as oval, and it was from such charts that Hildegard probably gained her conception of an oval universe. In her method of orientation also she follows these maps, placing east at the top of the page where we are accustomed to place the north." This statement would seem to be misleading if it means that the comparison of the universe with an egg is peculiar to Hildegard. As is shown by the texts cited above, p. 151, and below, note 100, *ad fin.*, this comparison was a frequent one throughout our period. It does not, however, necessarily imply belief that the universe is shaped like an egg, but merely that its concentric structure corresponds with that of the egg. Furthermore, in the opinion of the present writer, the fact that the Beatus and other maps of the period show the surface of the habitable earth as an oval or rectangle should not necessarily be taken as meaning that the draftsmen of the maps believed that the earth was oval or rectangular. The maps were highly conventionalized, and their shape was often determined by the shape of the page upon which they were drawn. On the other hand, Hildegard in her *Scivias* unquestionably meant to describe an egg-shaped universe. Otherwise she would not have been so careful to point out at the opening of the *Liber divinorum operum* that in the earlier vision described in *Scivias* the universe had appeared as an egg whereas in the vision she was about to describe it appeared as a wheel.

[93] "In medio quoque aeris terra posita est, ita scilicet ut aer aequali mensura super terram, ac sub terra, et in utraque partes terrae sit" (*Liber div. op.*, pars I, visio IV, cap. 63).

Doubts have been thrown on the authenticity of the *Causae et curae* as a work of Hildegard (see above, p. 396, note 8). The three passages quoted in this and the two preceding notes show that in both phrasing and substance the passage from the *Causae et curae* bears marked resemblances to the passages from the two other known works of Hildegard, even though there is inconsistency in regard to the central issue relating to the position of the earth. If the *Causae et curae* were not written by Hildegard, it was assuredly the work of someone thoroughly familiar with her writings.

[94] *De imag. mundi*, I, 5.

[95] *De phil. mundi*, IV, 2–3.

[96] See above, p. 368, note 33.

[97] John of Holywood, *De sphaera*, 1.

[98] Similar arguments are set forth in Robert Grosseteste's *De sphaera*, Baur's edit., p. 13.

[99] See Alexander Neckam, *De nat. rer.*, II, 14, where much the same argument is given. Neckam adds that the roundness of drops of dew is proof of the inherent tendency of water to assume a spherical shape.

[100] The text upon which this accusation is based is from *Otia imper.*,

II, 2, where Gervase says: "Nos tamen assignantes orbis divisionem distributioni filiorum Noë, a quibus summa totius orbis coepit partitio, orbem totius terrae Oceani limbo circumseptum et quadratum statuimus secundum Pauli Orosii sententiam, eiusque tres partes Asiam, Europam et Africam nominamus." This was interpreted by Daunou (*Discours*, 1824, p. 120)—who was followed by Santarem (*Essai*, vol. i, 1848, p. 107), C. B. Jourdain (*Infl. d'Arist.*, 1861, pp. 19–20), and others—as implying that Gervase believed the earth to be square. On the other hand, Lecoy de La Marche rallied to the defense of Gervase (*Connaiss. géogr.*, 1884, p. 208). He argued that the passage should be rendered thus: "Nous calculons, nous pensons, que le monde terrestre est entouré et encadré (*quadratum*) par une ceinture de mers" and that elsewhere Gervase asserts definitely that the earth is a sphere: "Forma eius (terrae) rotunda est ad modum pilae" (*Otia imper.*, vol. i, p. 885). As a matter of fact Gervase was speaking of the universe and not of the earth when he made this comparison with a ball, and Lecoy de La Marche would have been more correct if he had inserted *mundi* after *eius* instead of *terrae*. It seems, nevertheless, that we are justified in rejecting the text first quoted as furnishing any sure evidence that Gervase believed the earth to be square, especially since he also adopted the old comparison of the universe to an egg (*Otia imper.*, *loc. cit.*) with which it would have been difficult, though not impossible, to reconcile a theory of a square earth. Gervase, however, had an uncritical mind. His work was in large measure one of compilation from the writings of others, and it would not be surprising to find contradictory statements in it. Quite as contradictory passages on the same subject occur in Isidore and in most medieval writings of a similar encyclopedic character. See above, p. 54. Lecoy de La Marche, it would seem, tried to do the impossible when he attempted to show that Gervase had clear and consistent ideas of a scientific nature.

There is no question, however, but that belief in the sphericity of the earth was well grounded in the consciousness of many Western Europeans of the late twelfth century. Other evidence of this beside that already cited is furnished by the fact that in an ecstasy Alpis (or Alpäis) of Cudot, of the diocese of Sens, was said to have seen the entire world in the form of a globe, compact and united. The sun was larger than the earth; and the latter was suspended in the midst of the air like an egg surrounded by water on all sides (*Histoire littéraire de la France*, vol. ix, 1750, p. 155). This vision was much like those of Hildegard of Bingen; see above, p. 423, note 92.

[101] *Causae et curae*, II; Kaiser's edit., p. 49, quoted above, p. 423, note 91. The fact that Hildegard here states that if the earth were in the middle of the firmament it would have to be larger or else it would fall, would seem to necessitate belief in a flat earth contiguous with the firmament. The passage from *Causae et curae*, I, Kaiser's edit., p. 23, translated above, pp. 183–184, would also seem to require the same belief.

[102] See above, p. 54.

[103] See passages quoted above, p. 423, notes 91 and 92.

[104] *Scivias*, I, visio III, in: Migne, *Pat. lat.*, vol. cxcvii, col. 405; *Liber div. op.*, pars I, visio II, in: Migne, *op. cit.*, cols. 751–755, 759–760; pars I, visio IV, in: Migne, *op. cit.*, col. 869.

[105] *De arca Noë myst.*, 14. For a similar text see Daniel of Morley's *De philosophia*, Sudhoff's edit., pp. 9–10.

[106] See above, p. 369, notes 39 and 40.

[107] *De imag. mundi*, I, 5.

[108] *De sex d. op.*, p. 58.

[109] See above, p. 370, note 42; p. 401, note 58; p. 419, note 32.

[110] *Quaest. nat.*, 48 (49). Adelard's arguments resemble those of Aristotle in the *De caelo*. See above, p. 370, note 42; p. 401, note 58.

[111] Similar Aristotelian arguments are to be found in Alexander Neckam's *De nat. rer.*, I, 16. Neckam cites Aristotle as his authority.

[112] *De sphaera*, I.

[113] "Haec [i. e. terrae] centrum in medio mundi ut punctus in medio circuli aequaliter collocatur . . ." etc. (*De imag. mundi*, I, 5). "Tanta est firmamenti quantitas ut ipsi totalis terra collata quasi punctum esse videatur" (Alexander Neckam, *De nat. rer.*, I, 5). Michael Scot, however, believed that "the distance to the extreme of the waters beneath the earth equals the distance to the moon" (Haskins, *Michael Scot*, 1921–1922, p. 272; idem, *Studies*, 1924, pp. 295–296).

[114] "Cum ergo corpus solis et terrae aequalia non sunt, quippe cum sit sol octies major quam terra, umbram terrae *κυλίνδρος* esse non potest" (*De phil. mundi*, II, 32).

[115] *Im. du monde*, I, 14. This is based on Neckam, *loc. cit.*

[116] *Im. du monde*, III, 16. Neckam (*De nat. rer.*, I, 8), with whose text the *Image du monde* here corresponds, borrowed indirectly from Ptolemy via Al-Farghānī certain details in regard to the relative sizes of sun, earth, planets, and stars. The sun is by far the largest body in the universe, 166 and a fraction times larger than the earth. Next after the sun rank fifteen of the largest fixed stars; Jupiter ranks in the third place, Saturn in the fourth, the remainder of the fixed stars in the fifth, Mars in the sixth, the earth in the seventh, Venus in the eighth, the moon in the ninth, and Mercury in the tenth. See Ptolemy, *Almagest*, V, 16.

[117] *De sphaera*, I.

[118] "Item si intelligatur superficies plana super centrum terrae dividens eam in duo aequalia, et per consequens ipsum firmamentum, oculus igitur existens in centro terrae videret medietatem firmamenti; idemque existens in superficie terrae videret eandem medietatem. Ex his colligitur quod insensibilis est quantitas terrae quae est a superficie ad centrum et per consequens quantitas totius terrae insensibilis est respectu firmamenti" (*loc. cit.*).

John of Holywood's argument is here closely related to that employed by him to prove that the earth must be in the center of the universe as set forth above, p. 422, note 81. It would seem probable that by "an eye stationed in the center of the earth" he means an eye on a line between the center of the earth and the *medietas firmamenti*, and by "the same (eye) stationed on the surface of the earth" he means on the surface at a point where a line at right angles to the line from the center of the earth to the *medietas firmamenti* cuts the surface of the earth. Referring, then, to Figure 10, p. 422, above, let us assume that line *E-E'* represents the plane through the *medietas firmamenti* and the center of the earth (*C*). When the earth is at the center of the universe line *C-N'* will represent the line drawn at right angles to this plane. With a universe of infinite dimensions obviously *N'-E* and *N'-E'* would be parallel to *E-E'*, and the *medietas firmamenti* would be visible from *N'*. John assumes that the universe is so large in relation to the earth that the area around *N'* whence *E-E'* would be invisible is negligible.

[119] *Almagest*, I, 5.

[120] *De imag. mundi*, I, 5.

[121] *Im. du monde*, III, 15.

[122] *Liber floridus*, Bibliothèque Nationale MSS., fonds latin, no. 8865, fol. 55vo. A note illustrating a diagram on the same page of the same manuscript gives 240,000 stades for the circumference, one of the two figures of Posidonius. See above, p. 16.

[123] *De sphaera*, I.

[124] See the various works referred to on pp. 95–98, above. Robert Grosseteste's *De sphaera* includes a very clear discussion of the main elements of geocentric astronomy as taught in the early thirteenth century.

[125] See above, pp. 17–18.

[126] *De mundi univ.*, p. 17.

[127] *De imag. mundi*, I, 6.

[128] *Otia imper.*, vol. i, p. 892.

[129] *Etym.*, XIII, 6.

[129a] *De phil. mundi*, III, 2–3.

[130] "Extra tres autem partes orbis, quarta pars trans oceanum interior est in meridie, quae solis ardore incognita nobis est. In cuius finibus antipodas fabulosae inhabitare produntur." Text (not legible on our Fig. 2, p. 69) from Miller, *Mappaemundi*, vol. i, 1895, p. 58. See Isidore, *Etym.*, XIV, 5,17. Gervase of Tilbury describes the austral continent in similar terms: "Porro inter mare rubrum et Oceanum plaga torrida est, propter calorem nobis incognita, in cuius finibus antipodes esse dicuntur" (*Otia imper.*, vol. ii, p. 760).

[131] See above, p. 385, note 58.

[132] Miller, *op. cit.*, vol. iii, 1895, p. 50.

[133] "Hic antipodes nostri habitant, sed noctem diversam diesque contrarios perferunt . . . " (*loc. cit.*).

[134] See above, p. 185.

[135] *Microcosmus*, Bibliothèque Nationale MSS., fonds St. Victor, no. 738, fol. 18vo.

[136] *De sphaera*, Baur's edit., pp. 24–25. Amphitrite is also discussed in the *Liber de essentiis* of Hermann the Dalmatian, dating from 1143, in a geographical passage published recently by Haskins (*Studies*, 1924, pp. 62–64): "Hinc vero per Amphitritis sinus ab Athlante Libico Strixisque inflexu per littora Gaditana per confinia Thiles proprie Temiscirios campos e vicino portibus Caspiis usque ad Caucason et Ethiopici Gangis effluxus." In another passage of the same work quoted by Haskins (*op. cit.*, p. 64) Hermann indicates that in the latitude of Lisbon and Toledo eight equal land stages are the equivalent of 4° of longitude, that the width of Amphitrite is 44°, or the equivalent of eighty-eight equal land stages, and that there is an opinion that paradise lies beyond this ocean. ". . . spatium . . . dierum 44 que secundum quod ratio tribuit est dimidia latitudo Amphitritis, tota (totam) videlicet itineris terrestris equabilis dierum fere 88. Tantum ergo spatii vel etiam aliquanto plus que ratio hucusque transnatari prohibuit nondum audivimus nisi forte illa quam (que) exposuimus. In ea tamen parte non modica est opinio eam esse regionem quam paradisum vocant, cuius indicio sunt signa tam ab oriente quam ab occidente." In this same passage Hermann states that Toledo is 62° west of Arin (see above, p. 86). One would therefore expect the width of Amphitrite to be 44° in order to bring to 90° the total distance from Arin to the prime meridian in the midst of Amphitrite (Haskins, *op. cit.*, p. 64, note 202).

[137] *Im. du monde*, II, 1.

[138] "Quid significat globus aureus, qui regum manibus gestatur?

Aureus ille globus pomum vel palla vocatur,
Unde figuratum mundum gestare putatur,
  Quando coronatur, palla ferenda datur.
Significat mundum forma peribente rotundum,
Intus habet plenum terrestri pondere fundum,
  Quem tenet archanum palla ferenda manu.
Hec fuit ex terris mundi collecta quaternis;
Ut foret imperii manibus gestenda supernis,
  Hac tulit imperium Iulius arte suum.
Taliter hunc mundum gestat manus una rotundum,
Regius includit sic omnia climata pugnus,
  Taliter omne quod est regia pompa tenet."

—*Pantheon*, particula xxvi, 4; in: *Mon. Germ. hist.*, Scriptores, vol. xxii, pp. 274–275; pars 19 in Herold's edit., 1559, col. 620.

[139] Eugen Oberhummer, *Das britische Weltreich und die imperialistischen Staatenbildung früherer Zeit*, in: Mitteilungen der Geographischen Gesell-

schaft in Wien, vol. lxiii, 1920, pp. 108–109. See also Miller, *Mappaemundi*, vol. iii, 1895, pp. 129–131.

[140] "In den bûchen vant er ouch dô,
daz eine werlt wêre sô
gelegen under dirre erde:
swen ez hie naht werde,
daz ez danne dort tac sî."

Schröder, *Sanct Brandan*, 1871, p. 51.

[141] *De nupt. Phil. et Merc.*, VI, 602–608.

[142] The word *antipodes* as we employ it at the present time refers rather to the *antichthones* of Capella. These terms, however, were not used with consistency by classical and medieval writers.

[143] *In som. Scip. com.*, II, 5.

[144] *De phil. mundi*, IV, 3. Alexander Neckam also did not deny the abstract possibility of the existence of antipodeans: "Nonne enim et antipodes sub pedibus nostris esse dicuntur. Si tamen philosophice loqui volueris, non magis sunt sub pedibus nostris quam nos sub pedibus eorum. Sed numquid de primis parentibus descenderunt antipodes? Secundum Augustinum non sunt antipodes, sed doctrinae causa aut figmenti ita dici solet" (*De nat. rer.*, pp. 159–160).

[145] *Otia imper.*, vol. i, p. 975.

[146] "Mira res a messibus subterraneis veniens hyemalia frigora videt in nostro haemispherio perseverare, quod utique solis absentiae ac vicariae praesentiae merito adscribendum duxi" (*loc. cit.*).

[147] Duhem, *Système*, vol. iii, 1915, pp. 64–65. For data relating to another attack on Macrobius' cosmography preserved in a twelfth-century manuscript in Cambrai see Haskins, *Studies*, 1924, pp. 98–103.

[148] The Latin text of the passage of which this is a free paraphrase, runs as follows: "Suscepto enim semel, quatuor habitationes hominum esse, quorum ad se invicem nulla penitus possit esse per naturam commeandi licentia, dic age, quomodo verum erit, quod Sancta, & Apostolica rationalibiliter confitetur Ecclesia, Salvatorem videlicet, per primos Patres ab ipsis, ut ita dicam, huius Mundi cunabulis praesignatum, & a Patriarchis, & Prophetis consequenter multifarie, & multis evidentibus modis praefiguratum, tandem in plenitudine temporis, ineffabilibus humilitatis, & caritatis suae operibus cognitum, ac clarificatum, in salutem totius humani generis advenisse, si tria hominum genera excepta sunt, quae praedictus Macrobius praeter hanc habitabilem, quam incolumus, secundum zonarum Coeli, & terrae temperiem, posse esse persuadet, ad quae tantae salubritatis notitia pervenire non potuit? Ubi est, quod ille fidelis, quem invenit Dominus virum secundum cor suum, in spiritu veritatis clamat: 'Ante conspectum gentium revelavit justitiam suam Deus.' Et ibidem: 'Videbunt omnes fines terrae salutare Dei nostri,' si aliqui fines terrae sunt ab hominibus inhabitati, ad quos sonus Prophetarum, & Apostolorum nostrorum prohibente natura per inaccessibiles

aquarum, frigorum, calorumve distantias transire nequivit?" (Manegold, *Opusculum*, Muratori's edit., 1713, pp. 175–176.)

[149] Bibliothèque Nationale MSS., fonds latin, no. 14704, fol. 114vo. See also above, p. 96.

[150] *Dialogus*, I, in: Migne, *Pat. lat.*, vol. clvii, col. 547. Bibliothèque Nationale MSS., fonds latin, no. 10722, fol. 77ro, gives a diagram illustrating the eccentricity of the sun's orbit. In accord with the Moslem cartographic tradition, south is at the top.

[151] Plato of Tivoli's translation of Al-Bāttanī's *Astronomy*, Bologna edit., 1645, p. 26 (from *Opus astron.*, 6, Nallino's edit., pt. i, 1903, p. 14). Essentially the same ideas, though expressed in somewhat different terms, are to be found in the *Liber de essentiis* of Hermann the Dalmatian. See above, p. 400, note 48.

[152] *De lineis angulis*, etc., Baur's edit., p. 64. Roger Bacon's views on the influence of pyramidal rays as set forth in *Opus majus* (Bridges' edit., vol. i, 1897, pp. 117–143) are discussed in Werner, *Kosm. Roger Baco*, 1879, pp. 597–600. Bacon's indebtedness to Grosseteste, however, does not seem to be sufficiently emphasized by Werner. See above, pp. 179-180 and p. 408, note 97.

[153] *De natura locorum*, Baur's edit., pp. 66–67.

[154] *De sphaera*, Baur's edit., pp. 20–24.

[155] *De natura locorum*, Baur's edit., p. 69.

[156] Emmanuel de Martonne, *Traité de géographie physique*, 3rd edit., Paris, 1920, p. 40.

[157] *De sphaera*, Baur's edit., p. 25.

[158] *Opus majus*, Bridges' edit., vol. i, 1897, p. 192. See Duhem, *Système*, vol. iii, 1915, pp. 416–419.

[159] *De natura locorum*, Baur's edit., pp. 68–69.

[160] See above, pp. 179–180, and below, p. 431, note 7.

NOTES

CHAPTER VII

THE ATMOSPHERE

[1] Those parts of the *Dragmaticon philosophiae* and of the *De philosophia mundi* which deal with meteorology are conveniently available in Hellmann, *Denkmäler*, 1904, pp. 42–54, 69–75. See also the extensive discussion in Werner, *Kosm. Wilhelm von Conches*, 1873.

[2] *De phil. mundi*, I, 21; III, 1; III, 14. See also Werner, *op. cit.*, p. 318.

[3] *De phil. mundi*, I, 21. See also Werner, *op. cit.*, pp. 316–317.

[4] *De phil. mundi*, I, 17–21. See also Werner, *op. cit.*, pp. 313–315.

[5] These five regions were: (1) the celestial region, or sphere of the fixed stars; (2) the region of ether, which reaches from the sphere of the fixed stars down to that of the moon; (3) the upper air, clear and lucid; (4) the lower air, turbid and cloudy; and (5) the earth. (*De phil. mundi*, I, 16–21).

See Werner, *loc. cit.*, for discussion of these ideas, of their derivation from Plato's *Timaeus* and from later Platonists, and of the "demons" associated with each of the five regions.

[6] *De phil. mundi*, IV, 5; III, 5, 6.

[7] Robert Grosseteste believed that if you take into account the theoretical principles of the "pyramids" of rays alone (see above, pp. 163–164), mountain heights should be hotter than valleys because the pyramids striking the crests of mountains are shorter than those striking the floors of valleys (*De natura locorum*, Baur's edit., p. 66). In other words, mountain summits theoretically ought to be warmer because they are nearer the sun. In the *De natura locorum* Robert explains that accidental circumstances frequently cause a reversal of these conditions in such a way that the heights may be dominated by cold. Among these accidental circumstances are the winds and also the fact that peaks rise to the "middle space of the air or of the sphere where there is the greatest cold (medium interstitium aeris vel sphaerae, ubi est maxima frigiditas)."

[8] ". . . calor non provenit ex corpore solari, sed ex reflexione et condensatione radiorum" (*De impressionibus elementorum*, Baur's edit., p. 88).

[9] *ibid.*, pp. 87–88.

[10] See above, p. 23.

[11] "Triplex est universa dimensio, in longum, latum, et altum. Quoniam igitur omnis corporis sedes in fundamento suo terra vero tocius mundi fundamentum, multo pocius mundane prolis ex substantia collecte sedem terram esse necesse est. Eius pars quedam a terra in altum crescit, alia vero super terram in altum elevatur tocius fomentum hic spiritus terreni vapores pinguedine crassus, sine quo nulla huius geniture vita per aliquot horarum spacia possibilis. Hic autem vapor, ut per altitudinem Olimpi concipit Aristotiles, a terre superficie non plus quam .xvi. stadiis exaltatur. Hic ergo terminus videtur in altum omnis nostre habitabilis. Videtur fortasse huius altitudinis mensura sumi posse vel per arcum yris que secundum Ipparci descriptionem ab ipsis nubibus usque in superficiem terre perveniat. Sed quoniam nec ipsa descriptio constans nec ipsius arcus ad semicirculum habitudo, propterea nos id cuilibet probandum relinquimus" (*Liber de essentiis*, text from Haskins, *Studies*, 1924, p. 62, where variant readings from different manuscripts are given). Haskins points out that Aristotle (*Meteor.*, I, 13) omits Olympus from his list of the highest mountains.

[12] See above, p. 169, and below, p. 432, note 16.

[13] *Hist. schol.*, Gen. 34; copied in Gervase of Tilbury, *Otia imper.*, vol. i, p. 893.

[14] The origin of this story has not been traced by the present writer. It would certainly seem to be based on some actual knowledge of the physiological effects of lower air pressure at great heights.

According to Benini (*Origine del Monte del Purgatorio*, 1917,

p. 1085) Dante (*Purgatorio*, XXVIII, 103–112; see also *Inferno*, IV, 26–28, 149–150) held that the Mount of Purgatory reaches above the lower levels of the atmosphere, which are corrupted by the earth and where winds, clouds, rain, hail, and rainbows are to be found, into a realm of motionless air. The very summit of the mountain where the Terrestrial Paradise is situated is in a belt of air which moves from east to west with the motion of the ninth sphere.

[15] "Nos vero dicimus quod ille aer non spissatur, sed fumus humidus qui ex convallibus ascendit, ex frigiditate superiorum in nubes et nives constringitur" (*De phil. mundi*, IV, 5).

[16] *Dialogus*, IX, in: Migne, *Pat. lat.*, vol. clvii, col. 631.

[17] *De phil. mundi*, III, 4–8.

[18] Of the water drawn up by the sun, the lighter or "more liquid" (liquidius) portions were supposed actually to have been turned into fire and in this way to have served as a replenishment for the solar fires. The coarser portions fell back to the earth. A blood rain was caused by great heat.

[19] See E. W. Gudger, *Rains of Fishes*, in: Natural History: The Journal of the American Museum of Natural History, vol. xxi, 1921, New York, pp. 607–619.

[20] *De sex d. op.*, p. 54.

[21] William of Conches follows Theodoric in this explanation of snow and hail (*De phil. mundi*, III, 4, 8, 9). In the epic poem, *Philippis* (IX, 672–682), of William the Breton there is a remarkable description of a nocturnal fog lying over the humid and fertile ground near Lille, so thick that a rider could scarcely discern the ears of his horse in front of him. William attributed the fog to damp vapors rising from beneath the muddy surface of the plain rather than to a more probable cause: the cooling and condensation of water vapor in the lower strata of the atmosphere as a result of active radiation from the earth's surface.

[22] *Top. Hiber.*, I, 6. On the miraculous production of rain, see above, pp. 203–204, and below, p. 433, note 31.

[23] *De phil. mundi*, III, 7 (cited by Werner, *Kosm. Wilhelm von Conches*, 1873, p. 375). William discusses opposing views as to the end of the world, whether it will come by flood or by fire (see above, pp. 13–14). William himself was inclined to believe that it would be by fire.

[24] See above, p. 184.

[25] *Hist. schol.*, Gen. 34.

[26] *Otia imper.*, vol. i, p. 907. See below, p. 446, note 18.

[27] The presence of fossils on mountains was cited by early Christian writers as proof that the Deluge rose higher than the highest mountains. See references in E. S. McCartney, *Fossil Lore in Greek and Roman Literature*, in: Proceedings of the Michigan Academy of Science, Arts, and Letters, vol. iii, New York, 1924, pp. 23–38, references on p. 35.

[28] *Otia imper.*, vol. i, pp. 893–894.

[29] "'Non maledicam ultra terram, propter homines. Tempus sementis et messis, frigus et aestas, nox et dies requiescent.' Forte nondum ita plene distincta erant tempora quatuor, quia nec usque ad diluvium aquae collectae fuerant in nubes" (*loc. cit.*).

[30] *Liber div. op.*, pars III, visio VII, in: Migne, *Pat. lat.*, vol. cxcvii, col. 966. Quotation from Thorndike, *Magic*, 1923, vol. ii, p. 136.

[31] On the supernatural production of storms and wind, and on the belief that they are caused by magic and by evil spirits in the air, see White, *Warfare*, 1920, vol. i, pp. 336–350; Hoffmann, *Anschauungen*, 1907, pp. 85–91; and, especially, J. G. Frazer, *The Golden Bough*, Part I, *The Magic Art and the Evolution of Kings*, London, 1911, vol. i, pp. 244–331. See also above, pp. 203–204 and 209.

A characteristic story of this sort is related in the *Gesta regis Ricardi*, falsely ascribed to Benedict of Peterborough. Here we are told that a huge black dragon raises waterspouts in the Gulf of Satalia on the south coast of Asia Minor. The author adds, however: "Quidem autem dicunt quod hoc non est draco sed sol qui attrahit aquas maris ad se, quod plus verum videtur" (*Gesta regis Ricardi*, vol. ii, p. 197). The author is also skeptical towards a fantastic story of how storms are produced in the same gulf by the rising to the surface of the head of an abortive child that had been thrown into its waters (*ibid.*, p. 196).

[32] *De imag. mundi*, I, 54.

[33] "Ventus . . . est . . . aer commotus et agitatus" (*Otia imper.*, vol. i, p. 889).

[34] "Est igitur ventus aer densus usque ad offensionem (quidem) motus. Esse enim venti genus aerem estimo" (*Quaest. nat.*, 59 (60)). On references to the *Quaestiones naturales*, see the Bibliography under Adelard of Bath.

[35] "Ventus igitur est aer in unam partem flans" (*Dragmaticon philosophiae*, in: Hellmann, *Denkmäler*, 1904, p. 42).

[36] *Liber div. op.*, pars I, visio II, in: Migne, *Pat. lat.*, vol. cxcvii, col. 762; Thorndike, *Magic*, 1923, vol. ii, p. 132.

[37] *Causae et curae*, I, Kaiser's edit., p. 4.

[38] *ibid.*, p. 5.

[39] *De phil. mundi*, III, 15.

[40] *Quaest. nat.*, 59 (60); quotation is from Gollancz's translation, p. 145

[41] *Otia imper.*, vol. i, p. 922.

[42] *De phil. mundi*, III, 15.

[43] See above, pp. 192–193.

[44] *De phil. mundi*, III, 15.

[45] Gilbert, *Meteorol. Theorien*, 1907, pp. 539–557.

[46] *Quaest. nat.*, V, 17.

[47] On the names of the winds in medieval French literature, see Frahm, *Das Meer*, 1914, pp. 78–82.

[48] *Liber floridus*, Ghent MS., fol. 24, as cited in Migne, *Pat. lat.*, vol. clxiii, col. 1009.

[49] Einhard, the Frankish scholar, contemporary and biographer of Charlemagne, in his *Vita Caroli magni* so designates the winds (*Mon. Germ. hist.*, Scriptores, vol. ii, p. 459).

[50] Bertolini, *L'orologio*, 1916, p. 977.

[51] Cusa, *Denom. dei venti*, 1884, pp. 375-415.

[52] Alexander Neckam makes Boreas a bringer of hail and Auster a rainy wind (*De laud. div. sap.*, II, 85-92).

Bernard Sylvester writes:

> "Obriguit Boreas, maduit Notus, Auster et Eurus:
> Hic tempestates, ille serena facit."
> —*De mundi univ.*, p. 19.

Classical tradition, however, was apparently uniform in conceiving of Notus and Auster as the same. See table in Gilbert, *op. cit.*, pp. 550-551. William of Conches describes Boreas as a dry, as well as cold, wind "because it drives the clouds before it toward the mid region of the earth." But also, because of the very fact that it does so drive the clouds before it, it is a producer of rain along the borders of the torrid zone. "Siccus vero, quia nubes de hoc angulo terrae ad medium fugat, estque pluviosus juxta fines torridae zonae" (*De phil. mundi*, III, 15).

[53] *loc. cit.*

[54]
> "Arthous, Boreas, Boreae contrarius Auster,
> Sol oriens Eurum, vespera dat Zephyrum.
> Constringit Boreas, pluvius fert humidus Auster,
> Clara dies Euro, flos alitur Zephyro.
> Auctumno Boreas, aestati convenit Eurus;
> Auster hyemsque madent; ver Zephyrusque tepent."
> —*Symbolum electorum*, II, 1.

See also Giraldus Cambrensis, *Top. Hiber.*, I, 3, on Zephyr and Eurus, and I, 6, on Corus, the violent northwester which uproots or bends over trees in the west of Ireland. Corus was the favoring wind for voyagers from England to France, according to Willibald, an eighth century ecclesiastic, associate of Boniface, in his *Vita Bonifatii*, 5 (Migne, *Pat. lat.*, vol. lxxxix, col. 613). Alexander Neckam (*loc. cit.*) and Bernard Sylvester (*loc. cit.*) make Eurus a stormy wind. Neckam says that it disturbs the waters and is unwelcome to travelers; Zephyr, on the other hand, spreads the fields with flowers.

[55] *Otia imper.*, vol. i, p. 922.

[56] *ibid.*, p. 972.

[57] Liebrecht, *Gervasius von Tilbury*, 1856, p. 112.

[58] *Historia*, XIX, 16 (in medieval French transl., edited by Paulin Paris, vol. ii, 1880, p. 275; see also Dreesbach, *Der Orient*, 1901, p. 29). Walter of Châtillon describes vividly the drought, whirlwinds, and sand storms of the Libyan desert (*Alexandreis*, III, 374). See Ganzenmüller, *Naturgefühl*, 1914, p. 201.

[59] *De imag. mundi*, I, 31.

[60] *Collectanea*, Mommsen's edit., p. 236, translated in: Nansen, *Northern Mists*, 1911, vol. i, p. 193.

[61] *Top. Hiber.*, I, 3.

[62] Dreesbach, *op. cit.*, pp. 19–24.

[63] Ambroise, *Estoire de la guerre sainte*, verses 10610–10612, in: Gaston Paris' edit., col. 284; see also the same, verses 6303–6306 (Paris' edit., col. 168), and Dreesbach, *op. cit.*, p. 20. The last four words may be translated by "as is its wont."

[64] Benjamin of Tudela, *Itinerary*, Adler's transl., p. 81.

[65] *ibid.*, p. 64.

[66] *ibid.*, p. 38.

[67] *De phil. mundi*, IV, 3.

[68] *De prop. rerum*, XI, 3.

[69] *Top. Hiber.*, I, 33–40.

[70] *ibid.*, I, 35.

[71] Schröder, *Sanct Brandan*, 1871 (under Brandan in the Bibliography), p. 22.

[72] *Top. Hiber.*, I, 3, 6, etc.

[73] *ibid.*, I, 33.

[74] See above, p. 167.

[75] *De phil. mundi*, IV, 6.

[76] *Ligurinus*, II, 61–66, in: Migne, *Pat. lat.*, vol. ccxii, cols. 350–351.

[77] *Top. Hiber.*, I, 4.

[78] *Itin. Kamb.*, I, 2.

[79] *ibid.*, I, 3.

[80] *De natura locorum*, Baur's edit., pp. 68–69. See above, p. 165.

[81] *De natura locorum*, Baur's edit., pp. 68–69.

[82] *Otia imper.*, vol. i, p. 912.

[83] *ibid.*, p. 922.

[84] *Gesta Frid.*, II, 13.

[85] *Top. Hiber.*, I, 35–37.

[86] *Gesta Frid.*, II, 34.

[87] *Ligurinus*, IV, 179–220, in: Migne, *Pat. lat.*, vol. ccxii, cols. 381–382.

[88] Referring to Capua, Benjamin of Tudela wrote: "It is a fine city, but its water is bad and the country is fever-stricken" (Benjamin of Tudela, *Itinerary*, Adler's transl., p. 7).

NOTES

CHAPTER VIII

THE WATERS

[1] *Expos. in hex.*, in: Migne, *Pat. lat.*, vol. clxxviii, cols. 741–747.

[2] *De sex d. op.*, pp. 54–55.

[3] *De phil. mundi*, II, 2.

[4] William of Conches went on to explain in this connection (*De phil. mundi*, II, 4) why the heavens are blue, a phenomenon which some observers had attributed to the presence of waters. "What do we see up there, dense and the color of water? It is not fire, for if the air is invisible because of its great rarity (*subtilitas*), so also must fire be invisible, fire which is so much more rare than air. Furthermore, it is not the color of fire." William asserted that you see nothing at all and that the impression of seeing water is an optical illusion. Unless some other color interposes, a ray of light on entering the eye takes the color of water from the aqueous humor contained in the eye.

[5] Haskins, *Michael Scot*, 1921–1922, p. 272; idem, *Studies*, 1924, p. 296.

[6] *Otia imper.*, vol. i, p. 894.

[7] Paraphrase by White, *Warfare*, 1920, vol. i, p. 95, note.

[8] *De universo*, I, 38 (Orléans edit., 1674, p. 598, col. 2G, as cited and translated by Stegmann, *Anschauungen*, 1913, p. 19, note 3).

[9] *Causae et curae*, I (Kaiser's edit., p. 23). See above, p. 425, note 101.

[10] *Solutiones*, quaest. 2, in: Migne, *Pat. lat.*, vol. cxcvii, cols. 1040–1041.

[11] *Otia imper.*, vol. i, p. 893.

[12] *Expos. in hex.*, in: Migne, *Pat. lat.*, vol. clxxviii, cols. 743–744.

[13] Psalm cxlviii, 4–5.

[14] See above, pp. 186–187.

[15] *Hist. schol.*, Gen. 5. See Norlind, *Problem*, 1918, p. 39.

[16] *De sacramentis*, bk. I, pt. I, ch. 22. See Norlind, *op. cit.*, p. 44.

[17] *De imag. mundi*, I, 5. See also *Im. du monde*, II, 9; Bartholomew Anglicus, *De prop. rerum*, VIII, 3. The symbolism of the microcosm is in one instance curiously inverted in the *Causae et curae*, I (Kaiser's edit., p. 23) of Hildegard of Bingen, who compares the water with the body and the earth with the heart of man. On the other hand, in *Subtilitates*, II, 3 (in: Migne, *Pat. lat.*, vol. cxcvii, col. 1212) she asserts that "rivers are sent forth from the sea like the blood in the veins of the human body" (Thorndike, *Magic*, 1923, vol. ii, p. 132). See also above, pp. 147–150.

[18] *De imag. mundi*, I, 45.

[19] *De phil. mundi*, III, 14. See also Werner, *Kosm. Wilhelm von Conches*, 1873, p. 374.

[20] *Dialogus*, IX, in: Migne, *Pat. lat.*, vol. clvii, col. 631.

[21] *Hist. schol.*, Gen. 14.

[22] *Otia imper.*, vol. i, p. 892.

[23] See above, p. 60, and Norlind, *Problem*, 1918, pp. 38–40.

[24] Norlind, *op. cit.*, p. 38, notes, gives the following interesting quotations: "Quae videlicet aquae circumfusae globo terrae ipsum quodammodo sustentant, quod est mirabile in oculis nostris" (Gerhohus, *Expos. in psalmos*, ad Ps. cxxxv, 6, in: Migne, *op. cit.*, vol. cxciv, col. 901). "Quod autem terra super aquas fundata esse dicitur, nostram scientiam excedit. Mihi autem non videtur mirabilius, terram super aquas esse

fundatam, quam aquas, quae eiusdem ponderis sunt, super terras in aere volare" (Bruno Astensis, *Expos. in psalmos*, cxxxv, in: Migne, *op. cit.*, vol. clxiv, col. 1194). Bruno adds an allegorical explanation (*loc. cit.*): "Possumus autem per terram Ecclesiam intelligere quae super multos populos fundata est, qui per aquas significantur, etc."

[25] "Movebitur aliquis super hoc quod dicit propheta 'Dominum firmasse terram super aquas.' Ex hoc enim videbitur haberi posse aquas esse inferiores terra, cum tamen Alfraganus dicat, unam esse sphaeram aquarum et terrae. Sancti igitur expositores referunt illud prophetae ad cotidianum usum loquendi quo dici solet Parisius fundatam esse super Secanam. Rei tamen veritas est, quod paradisus terrestris superior est aquis, cum etiam lunari globo superior sit" (*De nat. rer.*, II, 49). See also below, p. 462, note 34.

[26] *Expos. in hex.*, in: Migne, *Pat. lat.*, vol. clxxviii, col. 748.

[27] See above, p. 151.

[28] "Verumtamen ut animalia terrena habitaculum et receptaculum haberent, aqua in concavitates terrae recessit et apparuit superficies terrae arida et separata. Estque terra cum aquis in se contentis sicut sphaera terrae solum" (*De sphaera*, Baur's edit., p. 12). Günther, *Studien*, vol. iii (?), 1879, p. 160, interpreted the last sentence to indicate that Robert believed that waters were contained in the interior of the earth and that it was to these waters that he here refers. Though this is possible, it is more likely from the context that the words "aquis in se contentis" are a reference to the seas (Stegmann, *Anschauungen*, 1913, p. 15).

[29] *Livre du trésor*, I, 35, 36, 39, as cited by Boffito, *Intorno alla "Quaestio de aqua et terra,"* Memoria I, *La controversia*, 1902, pp. 113–114.

The fact that the waters do not completely cover the lands also had puzzled the Moslems, who anticipated Robert Grosseteste in ascribing this apparent reversal of the normal operation of the laws of nature to God's wish to preserve a dry area whereon man and animals might thrive. Averroës had given a more proximate cause, maintaining that the stars are more numerous in the northern hemisphere than in the southern and that through their attraction of the land, as well as through the evaporative power of their heat and of that of the sun, the lands were uncovered. On the theory of eccentric spheres of earth and water see Kretschmer, *Phys. Erdk.*, 1889, pp. 67–74; Norlind, *Problem*, 1918, pp. 48–54; and more especially Boffito's elaborate discussion of the history of this theory and of ancient, Arabic, and Christian doctrines of the relations of land and water in general (Boffito, *op. cit.*). For the theory as developed in the sixteenth, seventeenth, and eighteenth centuries see Wisotzki, *Zeitströmungen*, 1897, pp. 39–57. The matter was discussed in a small treatise, *Quaestio de aqua et terra*, which has been attributed to Dante but is of doubtful authenticity (see above, p. 410, note 98). This is an argument against the possibility of eccentric spheres; the "emergent land" of the northern hemisphere is ascribed to the attractive force of the stars of that hemisphere.

[30] In *De imag. mundi*, I, 39, we find a definition of the word ocean: "Oceanus dicitur, quasi ocior annis, vel quasi zonarum limbus."

[31] II Esdras, vi, 42, 47, 50, 52.

[32] Roger Bacon, *Opus majus*, Bridges' edit., pt. iv, vol. 1, 1897, p. 291. See Kretschmer, *Phys. Erdk.*, 1889, pp. 141–142, for an explanation of Bacon's theory of the distribution of land and water.

[33] *De nat. rer.*, II, 16.

[34] Neckam believed that the level of the sea is higher than that of the lands, upon which the waters are prevented from encroaching only by the divine power. "Mare vero superius est litoribus, ut visus docet. Unde divinae jussioni attribuendum est, quod metas positas a Domino non transgreditur mare" (*De nat. rer.*, II, 49; *De laud. div. sap.*, III, 127–142). This curious doctrine persisted until the eighteenth century; see Wisotzki, *op. cit.*, pp. 39–57. "Mare etiam e litoribus ascendere videtur, secundum judicium visus. Fidem etiam facit proposito, videlicet quod aqua in sphericam formam tendat, guttae pluvialis concavatio in petra. Nisi enim rotunda esset gutta, non esset concavatio rotunda. Ros enim matutinus, qui rotundus est, verum esse docet quod diximus. Per rotunditatem autem perfectio intelligitur. Unde mens humana, per aquam designata, tendere habet ad perfectionem" (*De nat. rer.*, II, 14). See above, p. 369, note 35.

[35] Adelard of Bath, *Quaest. nat.*, 53 (54); *De imag. mundi*, I, 45, 47; Peter Alphonsi, *Dialogus*, IX, in: Migne, *Pat. lat.*, vol. clvii, col. 631.

[36] *Quaest. nat.*, 53 (54).

[37] *De imag. mundi*, I, 45.

[38] *loc. cit.*

[39] *Im. du monde*, II, 13.

[40] "Salsuginis causam in calore solis planetarumque pono. Cum enim per torridam mediamque zonam verus feratur occeanus perque eandem licet indirectus versetur cursus planetarum a tanto stellarum calore ipsum mare calefieri necesse est, ex quo et eiusdem caloris effectivam salsuginem accipere consequens est. Quod autem hec ita se habeant illud asserit quod in maritimis illis quae illi occeano propinquiora sunt, sine omni artificio aqua marina ad solem super rupes siccata in sal convertitur. In longinquioribus vero maribus ut sal habeas ipsam aquam marinam utpote iam a vi caloris remotam; ideoque minus coctam [*decoctam* in MS] igni adhibere et recoquere necesse est. Sed et dulces quasdam aquas in sal verti caloris artificiosa decoctione sepe visum est. Huc etiam [*Hinc et* in MS] illud accedit quod estate quidem omnis aqua [*aqua* omitted in MS] marina salsior est quam hyeme quod si quis operam dederit re ipsa experiri potit" (*Quaest. nat.*, 51 (52)).

[41] *De phil. mundi*, III, 16.

[42] *De nat. rer.*, II, 1; *De laud. div. sap.*, III, 75–80.

[43] *Otia imper.*, vol. i, p. 974.

[44] C. B. Jourdain, *Dissertation*, 1838, p. 75. Hildegard of Bingen speaks of the tides thus: "Et quoniam in oriente magna profunditas arenae et litoris est, idcirco mare superhabundando et se dilatando ibi non effluit; in occidente autem et in austro ac in aquilone tanta profunditas arenarum et litoris non est. Ideo ibi multotiens effluit magnas et latas effusiones ibi faciens, cum ab igne procellarum in insaniam commovetur, ut praedictum est. Unde ibi multa inutilia et sordida in se colligit atque putredines hominum, pecorum, avium et vermium sibi attrahit. Et idcirco fontes et flumina, quae de partibus istis de mari effluunt, tam sana et tam bona non sunt sicut illa, quae de orientali mari effluunt" (*Causae et curae*, I, Kaiser's edit., p. 24).

[44a] In this connection it is interesting to note that the Chinese in antiquity and during the Middle Ages had developed an understanding of the tides "in advance of anything that seems to have been known at that time in Europe" (A. C. Moule, *The Bore on the Ch'ien-T'ang River in China*, in: T'oung Pao, ou archives concernant l'histoire, les langues, la géographie, et l'ethnographie de l'Asie orientale, vol. xxii, Leiden, 1923, pp. 135–188, reference on p. 173).

[45] *De mundi univ.*, p. 19.

[46] *ibid.*, p. 46.

[47] *ibid.*, p. 47.

[48] Robert's theories of the tides are interpreted by Almagià, *Dottrina*, 1905, pp. 456–457. Almagià's exposition, though probably essentially correct, seems more clean-cut than the original upon which it is based.

[49] See above, p. 163.

[50] *De nat. locorum*, Baur's edit., pp. 69–70.

[51] *De impress. element.*, Baur's edit., p. 88.

[52] "Cuius summae difficultatis rationem multi astruere conantur per hoc, quod quartae mundi oppositae sunt eiusdem commixtionis, et ideo faciunt eosdem effectus. Sed ista ratio deficit tamen, quia falsa est, eo quod aliquae sunt imagines stellarum in una quarta et in alia, quoniam, quando planeta est super unam quartam mundi, tunc terra interponitur inter corpus eius et aliam quartam. Propterea, si hoc esset verum, peteretur principium. Quaeritur enim causa, quare sunt oppositae quartae eiusdem commixtionis et per consequens eiusdem effectus. Et ideo reflexio radiorum solvit istud, quoniam radii lunares multiplicantur ad caelum stellarum, quod est corpus densum. Ideoque per medium eius non possumus videre caelum, quod est valde luminosum, sicut dicit Alpetragius et Messalahe. Et alii radii reflexi cadunt in quartam oppositam ad angulos aequales" (*De nat. locorum*, Baur's edit., p. 70).

[53] See above, pp. 18–19 and, on William of Conches' related views, p. 173.

[54] Bibliothèque Nationale MSS., fonds latin, no. 8865, fol. 55vo.

[55] In the dialogue constituting the *Quaestiones naturales* Adelard's

nephew asks if the following theory is true: "Aiunt enim verum occeanum per torridam fluentem brachia immense quantitatis fluentia ab orientali et occidentali plaga in articam et in antarticam refundere regionem. Illis igitur vi magna confluentibus redundationem hanc fieri dicunt ut ictus nobis accessum pariat, cessio vero recessum." To this Adelard replies: "Philosophorum dictis invidere non ausim; illud tamen audacter affirmem: si ita ut aiunt maxima conveniunt brachia, semel comixtis undis secundo ictum non fieri neque enim convenit iterum eas separari; vel certe si iterum collidantur minor erit secundus ictus quam primus et tertius quam secundus itaque et quandoque minimus, deinde nullus. Videant igitur illi quid dixerint; ego pro me breviter respondebo. Recursus itaque brachiorum colligo; eorundem etiam obviationibus non contradico; non tamen ea conflui vel collidi concedo. Impotentie autem huius causam in ipsius terre situ facio. Cum enim ipsa brachia sibi obviare atque confluere impetuose festinent, fit tandem cum montium interpositione tum ipsius terre situ quodam elatiore ut ab eodem cursu dum deficiunt referantur. Itaque fit ut quo ea paternus motus ac naturalis impellit, ab eodem loci ipsius reducat situs. Licet non ignorem quosdam esse qui hunc motum nili mari idest caribdi dicant estuare. Quod si verum esset in maribus illis que torride zone viciniora sunt vis talis nec minus valeret; nunc vero illa omni fere tali carent agitatione; eo videlicet quod ab illa causa quam supra scripsimus procul remota sunt" (*Quaest. nat.*, 52 (53)).

It is not altogether clear as to what is meant by the last two sentences of this quotation, which is here given as in the printed text (see the Bibliography under Adelard, II) without collation from the manuscripts (see Haskins, *Studies*, 1924, p. 26). If the word *nili* is a corruption of *lunae*, they may possibly be interpreted as a denial of the lunar control theory of the tides. A passage from the *Disputationes adversus astrologos* of Giovanni Pico della Mirandola according to Duhem, *Système*, vol. iii, 1915, p. 116, cites a certain "Adelandus" as giving expression to views closely allied to those expressed in the preceding quotation. If Adelard is meant by "Adelandus," as Duhem assumes (*ibid.*, pp. 116–117), Pico's citation may well refer to this chapter of the *Quaestiones naturales*. Adelandus, in any case, is made categorically to deny the possibility of lunar control over the tides. Incidentally, it may be added that Duhem was unfamiliar with the text of the *Quaestiones naturales* at the time that he wrote the third volume of his *Système du monde* and that Almagià's otherwise exhaustive monograph on the history of theories of the tides gives us nothing on Adelard. Examination of the manuscripts (Haskins, *loc. cit.*) might throw light on the problem. The phrase "mari idest caribdi," in the next-to-the-last sentence of the quotation above, is not found in the manuscript copy of the *Quaestiones naturales* referred to in the Bibliography under Adelard, II. Gollancz's translation of this phrase, "one sea, the Caribbean" is an obvious absurdity (Gollancz, *Dodi ve-Nechdi*, 1920, p. 141).

[56] *De phil. mundi*, III, 14.

[57] See above, pp. 84–85.

[58] *De nat. rer.*, II, 17.

[59] In the *De imagine mundi*, I, 40, there is extraordinary confusion regarding the entire subject of the tides. There are said to be two tides daily, corresponding to the rising and setting of the moon. When the moon waxes, the height of the tides becomes greater; when it wanes, the height diminishes. When the moon at the time of the equinoxes is nearest to the earth, the floods rise to their highest; at the time of the solstices they rise less high on account of the distance of the moon. There is also said to be a tidal cycle of nineteen years. So far, these ideas were drawn from Bede; but in the succeeding chapter (41) there comes an echo of Paul the Deacon's description (*Hist. gentis Langobard.*, I, 6, as cited by Almagià, *La dottrina*, 1905, p. 51) of the great whirlpool, which "in exortu lunae majori aestu fluctus involvit et revomit."

[60] *Philippis*, VI, 500–551. See above, pp. 137–138.

[61] "Nobis humanam qui sortem vivimus infra,
Rem satis est sciri, nesciri causa sinatur."

—*Philippis*, VI, 550–551.

William the Breton in another connection (*Philippis*, VIII, 43–99) discusses the tides near Mont St. Michel in Brittany. His information appears to have been fairly correct, and he notes among other details that there is exceptionally high water at the times of the vernal and autumnal equinoxes. He makes no attempt to explain the cause of the ebb and flood, asserting that this transcends the knowledge of man. He puts forth, however, the singular suggestion that it is just as likely that the tides may cause the motion of the moon as vice versa, because the sea was created before the moon:

"Rursus an a luna maris hec inflatio fiat,
An magis a pelago fluat hec variatio lune,
Cum pelagus luna constet prius esse creatum,
Posteriusque sui nunquam sit causa prioris,
Nullaque res habitum trahat a non ente vel actum."

—*Philippis*, VIII, 73–77.

[62] *Top. Hiber.*, II, 3.

[63] *ibid.*, II, 14.

[64] *ibid.*, II, 1–2.

[65] See *United States Tide Tables* for 1919, also *British Islands Pilot*, U. S. Hydrographic Office [Publications] nos. 145, 146, Washington, D. C., 1917. See also: A. Defant, *Die Gezeiten und Gezeitenströmungen im Irischen Kanal*, Akademie der Wissenschaften in Wien, Sitzungsberichte, mathematisch-naturwissenschaftliche Klasse, Abteilung IIa, vol. cxxix, 1920, pp. 253–308.

[66] *Top. Hiber.*, II, 2.

[67] *ibid.*, II, 3.

[67a] "In the British Museum (Cotton MS. Julius D. 7, fol. 45vo) there is a tide table of the thirteenth century giving the time of 'fflod at london brigge' for each day of the lunar month, and the hours of moonlight (quantum luna lucet in nocte)" (A. C. Moule, *The Bore on the Ch'ien-T'ang River in China*, in: T'oung Pao, ou archives concernant l'histoire, les langues, la géographie, et l'ethnographie de l'Asie orientale, vol. xxii, Leiden, 1923, pp. 135–188, reference on p. 155).

[68] *Top. Hiber.*, II, 3.

[69] *ibid.*, II, 28.

[70] *Otia imper.*, vol. i, p. 1003.

[71] See above, p. 279.

[72] *Expug. Hiber.*, I, 36.

[73] See above, p. 351.

[74] Schröder, *Sanct Brandan*, 1871 (under Brandan in the Bibliography), p. 19.

[75] For references to the Liver Sea and to classical allusions to a clotted sea, see Moritz, *Geogr. Kenntnis*, 1904, p. 24, note 2; Konrad Kretschmer, *Die Entdeckung Amerika's in ihrer Bedeutung für die Geschichte des Weltbildes*, Berlin, 1892, p. 85, note 1; and more especially the full data in Graf, *Miti, leggende*, vol. i, 1892, p. 106 and notes on pp. 186–187, and in Nansen, *Northern Mists*, 1911, vol, i, pp. 181–182 and p. 182, note 1. Benjamin of Tudela places the clotted sea in the Far East (*Itinerary*, Adler's transl., 1907, p. 66, and above p. 272). In early French literature the sea is often referred to as *la mer betée* (see Frahm, *Das Meer*, 1914, pp. 76–77).

Many theories have been adduced to explain the origins of this persistent rumor of a clotted sea. It may have arisen through distorted reports of floating masses of seaweed or of the Sargasso Sea. It has also been suggested that experiences in dead water such as that described by Fridtjof Nansen (*Farthest North*, New York, 1897, vol. i, p. 196) may have contributed to the formation of the legend. Such dead water, Nansen explains, is caused by the presence of a layer of fresh water from melted ice over the surface of the sea water. See Frahm, *loc. cit.*; Koch, *Das Meer*, 1910, pp. 21–22. For another explanation see Paul Masson, *Pythéas et le poumon marin*, in: Bulletin de la Section de Géographie, vol. xxxvii, Paris, 1923, pp. 55–66.

[76] Schröder, *Sanct Brandan*, 1871 (under Brandan in the Bibliography), p. 27.

[77] Ezekiel, xl, xli.

[78] Revelation, xxi, 11.

[79] Schröder, *op. cit.*, p. 26.

[80] *Otia imper.*, vol. i, p. 921.

[81] Liebrecht, *Gervasius von Tilbury*, 1856, p. 94, note 24. Later tradi

tion sometimes had it that the Emperor Frederick II was the king who sent Nicholas the Fish to explore these waters. See Haskins, *Science*, 1922, p. 686; the same, *Studies*, 1924, p. 262; and Liebrecht, *loc. cit.*

[82] *Romans d'Alix.*, Michelant's edit., 1846, pp. 259–260. This is an interpolation into the part of the poem called by Meyer the "third branch." It is not by Lambert li Tors, author of the "third branch," but was derived from the *Historia de praeliis* (Meyer, *Alexandre le Grand*, 1886, vol. ii, p. 216). See above, p. 381, note 26. Alexander Neckam (*De nat. rer.*, II, 21) and Roger Bacon also refer to Alexander's visit to the sea floor. See Thorndike, *Magic*, 1923, vol. ii, pp. 263–264, 654–655.

[83] *De mundi univ.*, p. 22.

[84] *De phil. mundi*, III, 17–18.

[85] *Quaest. nat.*, 56 (57), 57 (58).

[86] *Sermones in cantica*, xiii; translation from Eales, *Life and Works of St. Bernard*, vol. iv, 1896, p. 67.

[87] Haskins, *Science*, 1922, p. 690; idem, *Studies*, 1924, p. 267. See above, p. 100 and p. 402, note 64.

[88] *Causae et curae*, I (Kaiser's edit., pp. 24–30).

[89] See above, pp. 185 and 326–327, p. 436, note 17, p. 439, note 44; also Thorndike, *Magic*, 1923, vol. ii, pp. 132–133.

[90] See above, p. 439, note 44.

[91] See above, pp. 211–212.

[92] *De phil. mundi*, III, 19. See also *De imag. mundi*, I, 47. Hildegard of Bingen also believed that the interior of the earth is warmer in winter than in summer. She attributed this circumstance, however, to the fact that "in hieme sol supra terram sterilis est et sub terram calorem suum figit, quatinus terra diversa germina servare possit" (*Causae et curae*, I, Kaiser's edit., p. 30). See also *Subtilitates*, II, 9, in: Migne, *Pat. lat.*, vol. cxcvii, col. 1213.

[93] *De imag. mundi*, I, 48.

[94] *ibid.*, I, 49.

[95] Haskins, *Michael Scot*, 1921–1922, pp. 272–273; idem, *Studies*, 1924, pp. 296–297.

[96] *Top. Hiber.*, II, 7.

[97] *Gesta Danorum*, Praefacio, Holder's edit., p. 6.

[98] *Otia imper.*, vol. i, p. 961.

[99] *Top. Hiber.*, II, 7.

[100] *loc. cit.*

[101] *Otia imper.*, vol. i, pp. 987, 990.

[102] J. G. Frazer, *The Golden Bough: A Study in Magic and Religion*, Part I, *The Magic Art and the Evolution of Kings*, London, 1911, vol. i, p. 301.

[103] *De nat. rer.*, II, 3–7; see also *De laud. div. sap.*, III, 171–328.

[104] "Sic et sapientia hujus saeculi mentes candore innocentiae fulgentes

nonnunquam in pejus commutat, sapientia autem vera mentes tenebris vitiorum involutas reddit serenas" (*De nat. rer.*, II, 3).

[105] *Gesta Danorum*, Praefacio, Holder's edit., p. 6.

[106] *Letter of Prester John*, 27–30, in: Zarncke, *Priester Johannes*, in: Abhandlungen, vol. vii, 1879, pp. 912–913.

[107] *Romans d'Alix.*, Michelant's edit., 1846, p. 350.

[108] *Otia imper.*, vol. i, p. 974.

[109] *ibid.*, p. 892.

[110] *Top. Hiber.*, I, 7. See above, p. 339.

[111] On another unusual type of river, the gold-bearing stream, as understood in the Middle Ages (but not discussed by Giraldus Cambrensis), see below, p. 479, note 318.

[112] *Top. Hiber.*, II, 2.

[113] *Itin. Kamb.*, I, 8.

[114] *ibid.*, I, 2.

[115] *ibid.*, II, 11.

[116] The *British Islands Pilot*, United States Hydrographic Office [Publication] no. 145, Washington, D. C., 1917, p. 375, testifies to the changeable character of the sands and channels of the Dee estuary.

[117] See above, pp. 235–237.

[118] Isidore, *De nat. rer.*, 43, in: Migne, *Pat. lat.*, vol. lxxxiii, col. 1013.

[119] Bede, *De nat. rer.*, 43 (Giles's edit., p. 117).

[120] *Expos. in hex.*, in: Migne, *Pat. lat.*, vol. clxxviii, cols. 779–780.

[121] *Sermo XXI in Feria quarta Pentecostes*, in: Migne, *Pat. lat.*, vol. clxxviii, cols. 518–521.

[122] On the flood of the Nile see also above, p. 300.

[123] *Top. Hiber.*, I, 8.

[124] *ibid.*, III, 2.

[125] *ibid.*, III, 3.

[126] *Itin. Kamb.*, I, 1.

[127] *ibid.*, I, 2.

[128] *loc. cit.*

[129] *ibid.*, II, 9.

[130] *Top. Hiber.*, II, 9.

[131] *Otia imper.*, vol. i, p. 1001.

[132] "Navim non patitur, quinimo tota supereminet nisi sit bituminata, et hoc forte propter homines intus viventes. Siquis vivum aliqua arte immiserit statim super exilit" (*loc. cit.*). Gervase seems here to have derived from Bede (*De locis sanctis*, 12, in Tobler, *Itinera*, vol. i, 1877, pp. 227–228) a hazy conception of the actual properties of the waters of the Dead Sea. The opposite theory, however, had been expressed by Antonius Martyr two centuries earlier than Bede: "Nor do sticks float, nor can a man swim, but whatever is cast into it sinks to the bottom" (White, *Warfare*, 1920, vol. ii, p. 228).

[133] *Otia imper.*, vol. i, p. 966.

[134] *ibid.*, p. 982. See below, p. 449, note 49.

NOTES
CHAPTER IX
THE LANDS

[1] *De eodem et diverso*, p. 28.

[2] *Etym.*, XIV, 1.

[3] *De imag. mundi*, I, 4.

[4] Peter Comestor stated that on the third day of the Creation the earth appeared and that it bears five names, the derivation of which he explained as follows: (1) *arida*, because the earth appeared (*quia apparuit*); (2) *humus*, because it was still humid; (3) *terra*, because it was trodden upon (*quia teritur*) by the feet of animals; (4) *solum*, because, of the four elements, it forms the one that is solid; and, finally, (5) *tellus*, because it endures (*quia tolerat*) the labors of man (*Hist. schol.*, Gen. 5). See Zöckler, *Geschichte*, vol. i, 1877, p. 418. These are typical examples of free etymology. For Hildegard of Bingen on qualities of different kinds of earth or soil, see above, p. 232.

[5] *Otia imper.*, vol. i, p. 966.

[6] *ibid.*, p. 895.

[7] Peter Comestor speaks of islands with the same characteristics: "Cum adhuc sint quedam insule viventium, in quibus nullus moretur" (*Hist. schol.*, Gen. 3, cited by Liebrecht, *Gervasius von Tilbury*, 1856, p. 62, note 6**).

[8] *Im. du monde*, I, 6.

[9] *Top. Hiber.*, II, 4.

[10] See above, p. 177; for Hildegard's corresponding views see above, p. 201.

[11] *Top. Hiber.*, I, 28.

[12] *ibid.*, I, 29.

[13] *ibid.*, I, 30. This legend regarding the properties of the earth of Ireland was very widespread in the Middle Ages. It is found in Bede's *Historia ecclesiastica*, I, 1 (Giles's edit., vol. ii, p. 34), which Giraldus goes on to quote at length on the subject (*Top. Hiber.*, I, 31). It also appears in Gervase of Tilbury's *Otia imperialia*, vol. i, p. 917 (see Liebrecht, *op. cit.*, p. 88, note 21). Solinus, *Collectanea*, 22 (Mommsen's edit., p. 101), and Isidore, *Etym.*, XIV, 6, ascribe similar properties to the earth of the Isle of Thanet. In his *Letter*, Prester John boasts that some of his territories are proof against poisonous snakes and animals. See *Letter of Prester John*, 21, in: Zarncke, *Priester Johannes*, in: Abhandlungen, vol. vii, 1879, p. 912.

[14] *Top. Hiber.*, I, 39.

[15] *ibid.*, I, 34–40.

[16] Benl, *Frühere und spätere Hypothesen*, 1905, pp. 1–14, discusses the origin and development in antiquity and the Middle Ages of theories regarding the distribution of the principal mountain systems of the known

world, the Taurus-Caucasus-Imaus range of Asia, the Rhipaean Mountains of the far north, and the Mountains of the Moon of Africa. The subsequent elaboration of these theories between the sixteenth and nineteenth centuries, when the conception was developed by some geographers of a symmetrical, rectilinear arrangement of the mountain ranges of the entire globe is treated by Wisotzki, *Zeitströmungen*, 1897, pp. 131–192, and by Benl, *op. cit.*, pp. 15–50.

[17] *Hist. schol.*, Gen. 34.

[18] Gervase said that the waters for the Flood came from the bowels of the earth and from the air above. They rose to a level of fifteen cubits above the summits of the mountains which are now in existence, "quia tunc terram dicunt in planitie factam" (*Otia imper.*, vol. i, p. 907). See above, pp. 170–171.

[19] *De prop. rerum*, XIV, 1.

[20] *Liber de congelatis*, 2. For the Latin text of this passage see Hammer-Jensen, *Sogen. IV. Buch*, 1915, pp. 132–133. See the next note and also above, p. 401, note 60.

[21] This translation is from Geikie, *Founders of Geology*, 1905, p. 43. The processes of erosion by winds and water as a cause for the inequalities of the earth's surface are much more in evidence in arid regions than in regions of dense vegetation. It is therefore not surprising that these processes were recognized by Moslems like Avicenna (if it be he from whom Alfred of Sareshel translated the above quotation) and Ḥamd-Allāh Mustaufī, a Persian writer of the early fourteenth century, who dwelt in the arid countries of the East. The latter writes: " . . . the sun's heat . . . beginning to act on the stone, this loses its hardness and is broken up; which process continually accelerated by the succession of many nights and days, cracks appear, splitting the rocks, which same are thus again turned to earth. Then by the action of earthquakes mountain peaks are demolished, while by the blowing of the winds and the running waters the soft earth is carried from one place to another, yet all that is rock and hard soil will remain fixed, whereby heights and hollows are formed, and it is these heights that are mountain ranges" (Guy Le Strange, transl., *The Geographical Part of the Nuzhat-al-Qulūb Composed by Ḥamd-Allāh Mustawfī of Qazwīn in 740 (1340)*, London and Leiden, 1919, p. 180).

[22] *De sancta trinitate*, Gen. I, 34; see also Zöckler, *Geschichte*, vol. i, 1877, p. 396. That teleological reasoning of this sort was not confined to the medieval period may be seen from the following paragraph from R. J. Sullivan, *A View of Nature in Letters to a Traveller Among the Alps*, London, 1794, vol. 1, p. 105: "On a cursory view it must be acknowledged, the surface of our earth exhibits no great regularity or order. In its outward appearance it strikes us with heighths, depths, plains, seas, marshes, rivers, caverns, gulfs, volcanoes, and a vast variety of other discordant objects; . . . Yet all these apparent deformities are abso-

lutely necessary to vegetation and animal existence. Were the earth's surface smooth and regular, we should not have those beautiful hills which furnish water. A dreary ocean would cover the globe, which would in such case be suited only for the habitation of fishes. As it is, the motions of the sea and the currents of the air are regulated by fixed laws. The returns of the seasons are uniform, and the rigour of Winter invariably gives place to the verdure of Spring. Men, animals, and plants consequently succeed one another, and flourish in their destined soils."

[23] *De imag. mundi*, I, 5.

[24] *Hist. schol.*, Gen. 34 (Gervase in: *Otia imper.*, vol. i, pp. 893, 972).

[25] *De phil. mundi*, IV, 5.

[26] *Otia imper.*, vol. i, p. 972. Gervase also said that Mount Atlas was so high that it was inaccessible (*ibid.*, p. 986).

[27] *Dialogus*, I, 17, in: Migne, *Pat. lat.*, vol. xx, col. 194.

[27a] Roger Bacon (*Opus majus*, part iv, Bridges' edit., vol. i, pp. 229–230) discusses classical and Arabic estimates of the heights of mountains. His own opinion was that the maximum height is eight miles. See the discussion of this topic included in Benini's interesting treatment of the altitude of Dante's Mount of Purgatory (*Origine del Monte del Purgatorio*, 1917, pp. 1056–1072, especially pp. 1057–1058).

[28] *Itin. Kamb.*, II, 7.

[29] *Otia imper.*, vol. i, p. 982. See Liebrecht, *Gervasius von Tilbury*, 1856, p. 139.

[30] *Romans d'Alix.*, Michelant's edit., pp. 70–71. This story is found in the "first branch" of the Romance. See above, p. 412, note 135. Meyer, *Alexandre le Grand*, 1886, vol. i, p. 151, did not know the origin of it.

[31] *Romans d'Alix.*, Michelant's edit., pp. 320–330. This story is an interpolation into the "third branch" (Meyer, *op. cit.*, pp. 172–174).

[32] *De mundi univ.*, p. 20.

[33] *Otia imper.*, vol. i, p. 986.

[34] *Descr. Kamb.*, I, 5.

[35] *Itin. Kamb.*, II, 5.

[36] *De mundi univ.*, p. 20.

[37] "Hic claustrales, in claustro sedentes, cum respirandi gratia forte suspiciunt, ad quascunque partes trans alta tectorum culmina, montium vertices quasi coelum tangentes, et ipsas plerumque feras, quarum hic copia, in summo pascentes, tamquam in ultimo visus horizonte prospiciunt. Hora vero diei quasi circa primam, vel parum ante, super montium cacumina vix emergens, etiam sereno tempore, corpus hic solare primo conspicitur" (*Itin. Kamb.*, I, 3).

[38] *Alexandreis*, I, 427–441. See Giordano, *Alexandreis*, 1917, pp. 40–41; Ganzenmüller, *Naturgefühl*, 1914, pp. 199–200.

[39] See above, p. 236.

[40] *Vita Altmanni*, 39, in: *Mon. Germ. hist.*, Scriptores, vol. xii, p. 238. See also *Vita Altmanni*, 26–29, for a vivid description of a mountain. See Ganzenmüller, *op. cit.*, p. 143.

[41] Eadmer, *Vita Sancti Anselmi*, II, 4, in: Migne, *Pat. lat.*, vol. clviii, col. 100. See Ganzenmüller, *op. cit.*, p. 173. Eadmer (1060–1124) was bishop of St. Andrew's in Scotland early in the twelfth century.

[41a] For an article on the Casentino, with photographs of La Verna, see Fulberto Vivaldi, *Casentino ignorato*, in: Le vie d'Italia: Rivista mensile del Touring Club Italiano, vol. xxx, Rome, 1924, pp. 1073–1082.

[42] *Gesta Frid.*, II, 40.

[43] *Ligurinus*, IV, 432–447. [vol. x, p. 307.

[44] *Gesta abbatum trudonensium*, xii, 6, in: *Mon. Germ. hist.*, Scriptores,

[45] "In quo loco tamquam in mortis faucibus coagulati, manebant nocte et die sub pericula mortis. Angustia villulae tota completa erat peregrinorum multitudine. Ex altissimis et scopulosis rupibus ruebant frequenter intolerabiles omni opposito nivium aggeres, ita ut aliis iam collocatis, aliis adhuc supersedentibus mensis domos iuxta, eos prorsus obruerent, et inventos in eis quosdam suffocarent, quosdam contritos inutiles redderent" (*loc. cit.*).

[46] Gribble, *Early Mountaineers*, 1899, p. 4. Quotation from John of Bremble's letter as translated by Gribble, *loc. cit.*

[47] *Gesta Danorum*, Praefacio, Holder's edit., p. 7.

[48] See Thoroddsen, *Gesch. isländ. Geogr.*, vol. i, 1897, p. 63.

[49] Peter Comestor speaks of certain philosophers who made the ascent of Mount Olympus (see above, p. 168). We have already mentioned St. Francis' visit to the mountain of La Verna (see above, p. 217).

Though not falling strictly within our period, several other medieval mountaineering exploits deserve notice. The anonymous *Chronicon novaliciense*, 5, written in the eleventh century, describes unsuccessful attempts at the ascent of the Rochemelon, near Susa in the Dora Riparia valley, in search of the treasure of a mythical King Romulus (from whom the mountain takes its name) supposed to be hidden there. In the fourteenth century the Rochemelon (11,605 feet high) was a place of pilgrimage (Gribble, *op. cit.*, pp. 5–13).

The *Heimskringla* (under Snorri Sturluson in the Bibliography) describes King Olaf Trygvasson's ascent of the Smalserhorn, now probably the Hornelen, in the year 1000. The feat was accomplished in a sporting, athletic spirit, and Olaf is said to have left his shield at the summit (H. Raeburn, *Mountaineering Art*, London, 1920, p. 6). Of this mountain, which overlooks the Fröj Fiord, Karl Baedeker's *Norway and Sweden*, Leipzig, 1909, p. 160, says: "Soon . . . to the left is seen the huge Hornelen (3002 feet) towering almost sheer, ascended on the E. side by K. Bing in 1897."

The *Chronicle* of Fra Salimbene of Parma (*Salimbene parmensis chronica*, Parma, 1857, p. 354, cited in: Geographisches Jahrbuch, vol. xviii, Gotha,

1895, p. 12) describes the ascent of Mount Canigou (9135 feet) in the latter half of the thirteenth century by Peter III of Aragon. This mountain lies "on the borders of the province of Spain," and the king found upon the summit a lake into which he threw a stone, whereupon "a horrible dragon of enormous size came out of it, and began to fly about in the air, and to darken the air with its breath" (Gribble, *op. cit.*, pp. 14–17, 262–263). Canigou is probably the Mount "Cavagum" described by Gervase of Tilbury as an abode of devils (see above, pp. 209 and 214). Curiosity as to what was on the top seems to have impelled Peter to make the climb.

S. Günther, in writing of scientific mountaineering before 1600 (*Wiss. Bergbesteigungen*, 1896), gives no details on mountaineering in the period between the ascent by Philip III of Macedon (181 B. C.) of a peak in the Rhodope Range and Petrarch's famous ascent of Mont Ventoux in 1336.

[50] Haskins and Lockwood, *Sicilian Trans.*, 1910, pp. 80, 89; Haskins, *Studies*, 1924, pp. 159, 191.

[51] Schröder, *Sanct Brandan*, 1871 (under Brandan in the Bibliography), p. 29.

[52] The passage describing the ascent of Etna is given in full by C. V. Langlois, *La connaissance*, 1911, pp. 57–58. We heartily agree with Langlois' view that this passage could only have been written by one who had personally visited the Sicilian volcano: "Aucun doute ne peut subsister sur ce point après avoir lu sa description, certainement directe et d'après nature." On the other hand, Fant, *L'image du monde*, 1886, p. 33, calls the assertions in the narrative "tout-à-fait fantastiques." See note in Langlois, *op. cit.*, p. 58.

[53] *Otia imper.*, vol. i, pp. 964–965.

[54] Virgil, about whom a cycle of legends grew up in the Middle Ages, was regarded as a prophet. Gervase of Tilbury tells of many marvels performed by him (Gregorovius, *City of Rome*, vol. iv, 1896, pp. 670-677).

[55] Liebrecht, *Gervasius von Tilbury*, 1856, p. 107, note, shows that this story and others like it were common in the Middle Ages. He cites an analogous South Russian legend of twelve miraculous wind-blown horns which keep Gog and Magog at bay and will continue to do so until the horns shall have been silenced either by birds building nests in them or else by falling to the ground. When this occurs the hordes of Gog and Magog will come forth and destroy the world.

[56] Conrad of Querfurt, *Letter*, in: Arnold of Lübeck, *Chron. Slavorum*, V, 19.

[57] Wattenbach, *Guido von Bazoches*, 1891 (under Guy of Bazoches in the Bibliography), p. 106.

[58] *ibid.*, p. 108. [*naissance* 1911, p. 57.

[59] Second verse redaction of *Im. du monde*, in: C. V. Langlois, *La con-*

[60] Haskins, *Michael Scot*, 1921–1922, p. 273; idem, *Studies*, 1924, pp. 296–297.

[61] *Top. Hiber.*, II, 13.

[62] *Collectanea*, Mommsen's edit., p. 236. Translated in: Nansen, *Northern Mists*, 1911, vol. i, p. 193, note 1.

[63] *Gesta Hammenb. eccles. pont.*, IV, 35.

[64] Nansen, *loc. cit.*

[65] *Gesta Danorum*, Praefacio, Holder's edit., p. 6.

[66] *Hist. Norweg.*, Storm's edit., pp. 93-95.

[67] Thoroddsen, *Gesch. isländ. Geogr.*, vol. i, 1897, p. 65.

[68] *Konungs-Skuggsjá*, 8 (Brenner's edit., pp. 30-31). See also Thoroddsen, *op. cit.*, p. 66.

[69] Schröder, *Sanct Brandan*, 1871 (under Brandan in the Bibliography), pp. 28-29.

[70] Haskins, *Michael Scot*, 1921-1922, p. 274; idem, *Studies*, 1924, p. 298. See below, note 80.

[71] Schröder, *op. cit.*, p. 30. This incident is the subject of Matthew Arnold's poem of St. Brandan.

[72] *Otia imper.*, vol. i, pp. 965-966.

[73] Liebrecht, *Gervasius von Tilbury*, 1856, pp. 108-109.

[74] *Konungs-Skuggsjá*, 9 (Brenner's edit., pp. 32-34). See also Thoroddsen, *op. cit.*, p. 66; Stegmann, *Anschauungen*, 1913, p. 38.

[75] *Gesta Danorum*, Praefacio, Holder's edit., p. 7.

[76] *De imag. mundi*, I, 35.

[77] *Otia imper.*, vol. i, p. 922.

[78] Haskins, *Michael Scot*, 1921-1922, pp. 272-274; idem, *Studies*, 1924, pp. 296-297. See also Geographical Review, vol. xiii, New York, 1923, pp. 141-142.

[79] "Vulcanus est iste ignis inferior, qui ideo dicitur claudus, quia quasi uno pede materiae adhaeret, altero quasi in altum prout flammae natura desiderat nititur" (*De nat. rer.*, I, 17; Stegmann, *op. cit.*, p. 39).

[80] See Stegmann, *op. cit.*, p. 22, note 5, for references to texts demonstrating the widespread belief in the Middle Ages that Hell is at the center of the earth. On the topography of Dante's Inferno, see Benini, *Origine del Monte del Purgatorio*, 1917, pp. 1080-1129.

[81] Hildegard of Bingen in the passage quoted above, p. 423, note 92, would seem to refer to blasts of wind as a cause of earthquakes.

[82] Other explanations of earthquakes were sometimes given. It was occasionally argued that seismic disturbances are not the result of purely physical causes but are punishments sent by God. It was also held by some that they are due to movements in the mass of waters which was thought to permeate the earth, or else to the collapse of subterranean cavities as a result of the erosion caused by these waters. See Stegmann's elaborate discussion of this matter and his many references, *op. cit.*, pp. 44-73.

[83] In the *De philosophia*, p. 21, Daniel of Morley expresses the same idea, that in earthquakes the earth moves *particulariter*, not *universaliter*.

[84] *Quaest. nat.*, 50 (51). See above, pp. 31–32.

[85] *De imag. mundi*, I, 42; *Im. du monde*, II, 12; *De prop. rerum*, XIV, 1.

[86] *Dragmaticon philosophiae*, Hellmann's edit., p. 43; *De phil. mundi*, III, 15. See also Werner, *Kosm. Wilhelm von Conches*, 1873, p. 35.

[87] *De nat. rer.*, II, 48.

[88] *Gesta regis Henrici Secundi*, Stubbs's edit., vol. i, p. 220 (in the Rolls Series, no. 49, 1867).

[89] *ibid.*, p. 337.

[90] See passages cited by Dreesbach, *Der Orient*, 1901, pp. 28–29.

[91] *Letter of Prester John*, 31–41, in: Zarncke, *Priester Johannes*, in: Abhandlungen, vol. vii, 1879, pp. 914–915.

[92] *Top. Hiber.*, II, 16.

[93] " . . . longe post diluvium, terra multiplicatis jam animantibus ubique repleta, non violenter et subito, sed paulatim et tamquam per eluvionem insulas natas fuisse" (*loc. cit.*).

[94] *Otia imper.*, vol. i, p. 983.

[95] *Itin. Kamb.*, II, 9.

[96] Schröder, *Sanct Brandan*, 1871 (under Brandan in the Bibliography), pp. 3–36.

[97] See below, p. 487, note 463.

[98] *Top. Hiber.*, II, 12.

[99] *De mundi univ.*, pp. 46–47.

[100] "Cepit enim fructosa lupos, deserta leones,
Arida serpentes, pars nemoralis apros."

—*ibid.*, p. 21.

[101] "Fronduit in plano platanus, convallibus alnus,
Rupe rigens buxus, littore lenta salix,
Monte cupressus olens, sacra vitis colle supino
Inque laborata Palladis arbor humo."

—*ibid.*, p. 23.

[102] *De nat. rer.*, II, 57.

[103] *Subtilitates*, I, 9; in: Migne, *Pat. lat.*, vol. cxcvii, col. 1214. See also above, p. 211.

[104] *Gesta Frid.*, II, 13.

[105] *Descr. Kamb.*, I, 6.

[106] *Ligurinus*, VI, 24–34, based on Ragewin's continuation of Otto of Freising, *Gesta Frid.*, III, 1.

[107] *Descr. Kamb.*, I, 1.

[108] *ibid.*, II, 8.

[109] *Otia imper.*, vol. i, p. 986.

[110] *Top. Hiber.*, I, 8.

[111] Ragewin's continuation of Otto of Freising, *Gesta Frid.*, IV, 12.

[112] *De mundi creatione*, 5, in: *Maxima bibliotheca veterum patrum*, vol. xxvii, Lyons, 1577, p. 118.

[113] *De arca Noë morali*, IV, 9.

114 "In hoc spatio mappa-mundi dipingitur ita ut caput arcae ad orientem convertitur, et finis ejus occidentem contingat, ut mirabile dispositione ab eodem principe decurrat situs locorum cum ordine temporum, et idem sit finis mundi, qui est finis saeculi" (*De arca Noë mystica*, 14).

115 *De vanitate mundi*, II.

116 On the relations of this theory to Otto's philosophy of history, on its origins, and on the bibliography of the subject, see I. Schmidlin, *Die geschichtsphilosophische und kirchenpolitische Weltanschauungen Ottos von Freisingen*, in: Studien und Darstellungen auf dem Gebiete der Geschichte, vol. iv, Freiburg-im-Breisgau, 1906, pts. 2 and 3; see especially pp. 20, 35ff.

117 Here he explains that science, invented in the East among the Babylonians, passed first to the Egyptians, thence to the Greeks, and thence to the Romans, notably Scipio, Cato, and Tully. Finally it was brought to the West, that is to Gaul and Spain, by Berengar, Manegold, and Anselm (of Canterbury).

Neckam (*De nat. rer.*, II, 174) traces the course of learning—i. e. the study of the liberal arts—among the Egyptians and Greeks and, in later days, in Italy and Spain, but he draws no moral from it as did Hugh of St. Victor and Otto of Freising.

118 *Chron.*, V, 36.

119 See above, p. 64. On this subject see Ganzenmüller, *Naturgefühl*, 1914, *passim*. Many of the references in this section are derived from Ganzenmüller's book.

120 *ibid.*, pp. 163–182.

121 *Epistola CVI ad Magistrum Henricum Murdach*, in Migne, *Pat. lat.*, vol. clxxxii, col. 242. Translation from Eales, *Life and Works*, vol. i, 1889, p. 353.

122 *Sermo in natali sancti Benedicti abbatis*, in Migne, *op. cit.*, vol. clxxxiii, col. 377.

123 *Sermo XIII in Cantica*, in: Migne, *op. cit.*, vol. clxxxiii, cols. 833–834; Ganzenmüller, *op. cit.*, pp. 170–171. See also above, p. 200.

124 See above, pp. 206–207.

125 See especially Ganzenmüller, *op. cit.*, pp. 182–241.

126 From a letter of Guy of Bazoches to his uncle, in: Wattenbach, *Guido von Bazoches*, 1891 (under Guy of Bazoches in the Bibliography), p. 78.

127 *Carmina varia*, xxviii, in: Migne, *op. cit.*, vol. clxxi, cols. 1665–1666; Ganzenmüller, *op. cit.*, pp. 224–225.

128 Ganzenmüller, *op. cit.*, p. 225.

129 Dreesbach, *Der Orient*, 1901, pp. 24–36.

130 *Historia*, IV, 10; Paulin Paris' edit., vol. i, pp. 134–135.

131 *ibid.*, XVII, 3; Paulin Paris' edit., vol. ii, p. 141.

132 *ibid.*, XIX, 15–16, 24; XIX, 14–15, 23, in: Paulin Paris' edit., vol ii, pp. 273–275, 288–289.

133 *Gesta Frid.*, II, 46.

[134] *Chron.*, V, 24.
[135] *Itin. Kamb.*, II, 1.
[136] *Top. Hiber.*, I, 5.
[137] *ibid.*, I, 4.
[138] *Itin. Kamb.*, II, 1.
[139] *ibid.*, II, 7.

NOTES

CHAPTER X

THE ASTRONOMICAL GEOGRAPHY OF THE KNOWN WORLD

[1] *Etym.*, XIV, 6.
[2] *De imag. mundi*, I, 11.
[3] *Im. du monde*, II, 2.
[4] *Otia imper.*, vol. i, p. 911.
[5] *De sphaera*, 3.
[6] *De imag. mundi*, I, 31.
[7] *Collectanea*, 22.
[8] *Etym.*, XIV, 6.
[9] *Top. Hiber.*, II, 17.
[10] See above, p. 23.
[11] *Hist. nat.*, VI, 33–34.
[12] *De nupt. Phil. et Merc.*, VIII, 876.
[13] *Almagest*, II, 6.
[14] *Geogr.*, I, 23.

[15] The relation between the parallels as given in the *Almagest, loc. cit.* and in the *Geography, loc. cit.*, are shown graphically in the adjoining table (Fig. 11, cols. I and II). In the text of the *Almagest* the parallels are not specifically named beyond the twenty-sixth. Each paragraph, however, is numbered to correspond to the parallel which it describes through the thirty-eighth. The thirty-ninth paragraph describes conditions at the pole.

[16] See Fischer, *Ptolemäus und Agathodämon*, 1916, pp. 89–93.

[17] On the famous Vatopedi manuscript map of the world ascribed to Agathodaemon by Fischer but, as Fischer claims, directly based upon material furnished by Ptolemy, the boundaries of the climates are expressly defined in relation to Ptolemy's parallels, as set forth in the *Geography*. The first climate begins with the parallel of Meroë, latitude 16°25′N., and extends to that of Syene, 23°50′N., there being a difference of half an hour between the length of the longest day at its northern and at its southern edge. The other six climates follow as shown on Figure 11, col. III. The same correlation is made in the anonymous Greek treatise *Διάγνωσις ἐν ἐπιτομῇ τῆς ἐν τῇ σφαίρᾳ γεωγραφίας* in: Müller, *Geogr. graeci min.*, 1882, vol. ii, pp. 491–493. See Fischer, *op. cit.*, pp. 90–91. See Figure 11, cols. III and IV.

Scale of Latitude	I Ptolemy's "Geography": Number of Parallel	I: Latitude	I: Length of Longest Day	II Ptolemy's "Almagest": Number of Parallel	II: Latitude	II: Length of Longest Day	II: Geographical Features on the Indicated Parallels	III Agathodaemon (Vatopedi Manuscript Map): Number of Parallel	III: Number of "Clima"	III: Latitude	III: Length of Longest Day	IV Anonymous Διάγνωσις τῆς ἐν τῇ σφαίρᾳ γεωγραφίας: Number of Parallel	IV: Number of "Clima"	IV: Latitude	IV: Length of Longest Day	IV: Geographical Features on the Indicated Parallels	V "Preceptum Canonis Ptolemei": Number of "Clima"	V: Latitude	V: Geographical Features on the Indicated Parallels	VI "Toledo Tables": Number of "Clima"	VI: Latitude	VI: Length of Longest Day	VII Al-Farghānī's "Elements of Astronomy" A John of Seville's Translation: Number of "Clima"	VII A: Latitude	VII A: Length of Longest Day	VII B John of Holywood's "De Sphaera": Number of "Clima"	VII B: Latitude	VII B: Length of Longest Day	VIII Al-Khwārizmī: Number of "Clima"	VIII: Latitude	IX Actual Latitudes of the Geographical Features Indicated: Latitude	IX: Geographical Features
				etc. to the Pole the parallels are indicated on which the longest day is respectively 2, 3, 4, and 5 months long																												
68				[34]	67°	1 MONTH	66 — 23																								66°18'	ARCTIC CIRCLE IN PTOLEMY'S TIME
66				[33]	66 8 40	24 H	65 30 — 22																									
			[32]																													
			[31]																													
64				[30]	64 30	21	SCYTHIANS																									
	21	63°	20 H	[29]	63	20	THULE					21		63°	20 H																	
62				[28]	62	19½	EBUDIC ISLES																									
	20	61	19	[27]	61	19	N. LESSER BRITAIN (IRELAND)					20		61	19																60 30	THULE (SHETLAND IS.)
60				26	59 30	18½	MIDDLE LESSER BRITAIN																									
58	19	58	18	25	58	18	SOUTHERN LESSER BRITAIN					19		58	18																57 30	EBUDIC IS. (OUTER HEBRIDES)
				24	57	17¾	CATURACTONIUM IN BRITAIN																									
56	18	56 10	17½	23	56	17½	MIDDLE GREATER BRITAIN					18		56	17½																	
				22	55	17¼	BRIGANTIUM IN G^TR BRITAIN																								54 23	SITE OF CATARACTONIUM (CATTERICK, YORKS)
54	17	54	17	21	54 1	17	MOUTHS OF TANAÏS (DON)					17		54	17																	
				20	52 50	16¾	MOUTHS OF RHINE																								52 20	S. LESSER BRITAIN (S. IRELAND)
52	16	51 30	16½	19	51 30	16½	SOUTHERNMOST BRITAIN					16		51	16½									50°30'	16½ H		50°30'	16½ H			51 50	MOUTHS OF RHINE
50				18	50 4	16¼	MAEOTIS LAKE		VII				VII				VII			VII												
48	15	48 30	16	17	48 32	16	MOUTHS OF BORYSTHENES	15		48°30'	16 H	15		48 30	16	BORYSTHENES		48°32'	BORYSTHENES		48°	16 H	VII	48 40	16	VII	48 40	16		48°		
																								47 15	15¾		47 15	15¾	VII		46 39	MOUTHS OF THE BORYSTHENES (DNIEPER) KHERSON
				16	46 51	15¾	SOURCES OF ISTER		VI				VI				VI			VI												
46	14	45	15½	15	45 1	15½	MIDDLE OF THE PONTUS	14		45	15½	14		45 1	15½	MIDDLE OF THE PONTUS		45 1	MIDDLE OF THE PONTUS		45°22'	15½	VI	45 24	15½	VI	45 24	15½		45		

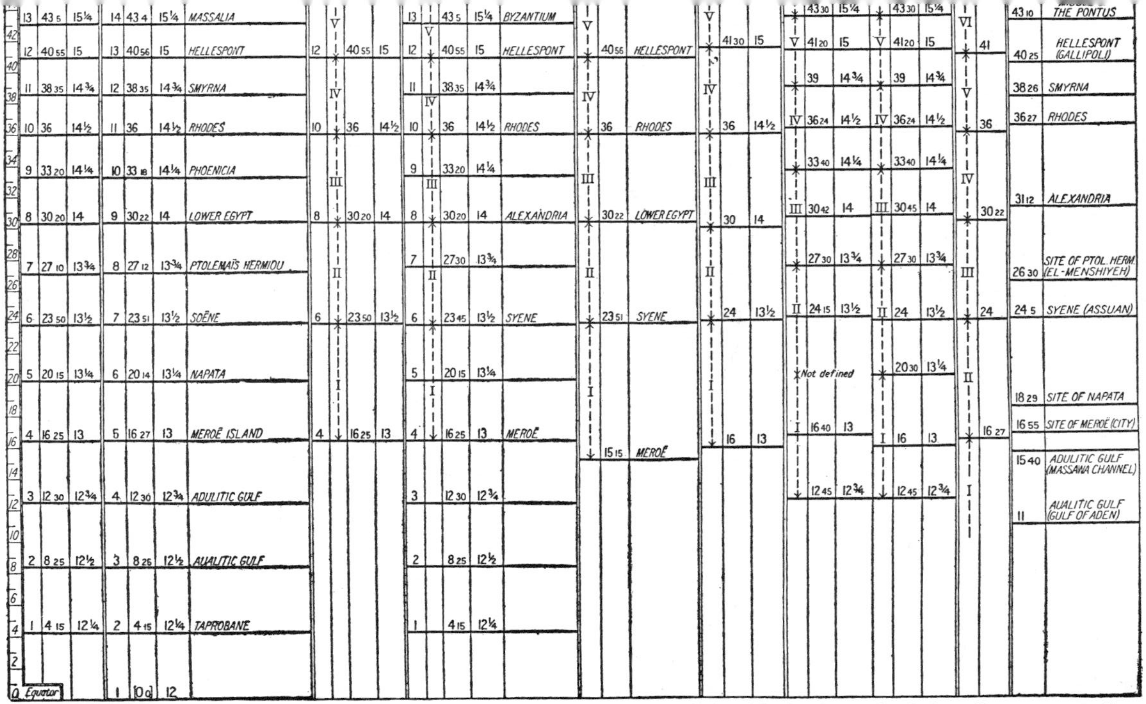

Latitude scale: 0 (Equator), 2, 4, 6, 8, 10, 12, 14, 16, 18, 20, 22, 24, 26, 28, 30, 32, 34, 36, 38, 40, 42

13	43 5	15¼
12	40 55	15
11	38 35	14¾
10	36	14½
9	33 20	14¼
8	30 20	14
7	27 10	13¾
6	23 50	13½
5	20 15	13¼
4	16 25	13
3	12 30	12¾
2	8 25	12½
1	4 15	12¼
Equator		

14	43 4	15¼	MASSALIA
13	40 56	15	HELLESPONT
12	38 35	14¾	SMYRNA
11	36	14½	RHODES
10	33 18	14¼	PHOENICIA
9	30 22	14	LOWER EGYPT
8	27 12	13¾	PTOLEMAÏS HERMIOU
7	23 51	13½	SOËNE
6	20 14	13¼	NAPATA
5	16 27	13	MEROË ISLAND
4	12 30	12¾	ADULITIC GULF
3	8 26	12½	AUALITIC GULF
2	4 15	12¼	TAPROBANE
1	[0 0]	12	

12	V	40 55	15
	IV		
10		36	14½
	III		
8		30 20	14
	II		
6		23 50	13½
	I		
4		16 25	13

13		43 5	15¼	BYZANTIUM
12	V	40 55	15	HELLESPONT
11	IV	38 35	14¾	
10		36	14½	RHODES
9	III	33 20	14¼	
8		30 20	14	ALEXANDRIA
7	II	27 30	13¾	
6		23 45	13½	SYENE
5	I	20 15	13¼	
4		16 25	13	MEROË
3		12 30	12¾	
2		8 25	12½	
1		4 15	12¼	

V		
	40 56	HELLESPONT
IV		
	36	RHODES
III		
	30 22	LOWER EGYPT
II		
	23 51	SYENE
I		
	15 15	MEROË

V	41 30	15
IV	36	14½
III	30	14
II	24	13½
I	16	13

	43 30	15¼
V	41 20	15
	39	14¾
IV	36 24	14½
	33 40	14¼
III	30 42	14
	27 30	13¾
II	24 15	13½
Not defined		
I	16 40	13
	12 45	12¾

	43 30	15¼
V	41 20	15
	39	14¾
IV	36 24	14½
	33 40	14¼
III	30 45	14
	27 30	13¾
II	24	13½
	20 30	13¼
I	16	13
	12 45	12¾

VI	
	41
V	
	36
IV	
	30 22
III	
	24
II	
	16 27
I	

43 10	THE PONTUS
40 25	HELLESPONT (GALLIPOLI)
38 26	SMYRNA
36 27	RHODES
31 12	ALEXANDRIA
26 30	SITE OF PTOL. HERM. (EL-MENSHIYEH)
24 5	SYENE (ASSUAN)
18 29	SITE OF NAPATA
16 55	SITE OF MEROË (CITY)
15 40	ADULITIC GULF (MASSAWA CHANNEL)
11	AUALITIC GULF (GULF OF ADEN)

FIG. 11 (in two sections)—Comparative diagram of certain parallels of latitude and of the *climata* according to various ancient and medieval geographers. For explanation see the text, pp. 242–243, and notes 15, 17, 18, and 21 of this chapter.

It may be added that in a work entitled *Preceptum canonis Ptolemei*, preserved in Chartres, Bibliothèque Publique, MS. No. 214, fol. 1ro., and dating perhaps from the sixth century, the writer found a description of the division of the world in seven climates. No mention is made of the parallels by number, but the boundaries of the climates, as there defined and as is shown on Figure 11, col. V, correspond to the figures for latitude assigned to the fifth, seventh, ninth, eleventh, thirteenth, fifteenth, and seventeenth parallels of Ptolemy's *Almagest*.

[18] The figures as given in Bibliothèque Nationale MSS., fonds latin, no. 16658, fol. 50ff., are shown in Figure 11, col. VI.

[19] *Rudimenta astronomica*, Nuremberg edit., 1537, fol. 8vo.

[20] *De sphaera*, 3. After giving a brief definition of the climates, John says: "Dicitur autem clima tantum spacium per quantum sensibiliter variatur horologium." In practice, this was always taken to be a difference of a half hour up to and including the sixth climate.

[21] The boundaries of Al-Farghānī's and John of Holywood's climates are one parallel south of those indicated in the various works referred to in note 17, p. 453, above, and those of the *Toledo Tables;* that is to say, the centers of the former are at the parallels of the northern borders of the latter (see Fig. 11, col. VII). According to Al-Khwārizmī, the figures for the parallels bounding the climates appear to have been derived from the *Almagest;* Al-Khwārizmī's second climate, however, corresponds to the first climate of Agathodaemon's map and of the other works derived from Ptolemy (see above, p. 453, note 17, and Fig. 11, cols. III–VI). The third climate of Al-Khwārizmī corresponds to the second climate in the works derived from Ptolemy, and so on. See Fischer, *op. cit.*, p. 92, and footnotes 1 and 2. See Figure 11, col. VIII.

[22] This subject has been discussed by me in greater detail in: J. K. Wright, *Knowledge of Latitudes and Longitudes*, 1923.

[23] Bibliothèque Nationale MSS., fonds latin, no. 14704, fol. 119vo. At the time of the publication of the article referred to in the preceding note, the writer was not aware of Professor Haskins' discovery of the name of the author of the *Marseilles Tables* (see Haskins, *Studies*, 1924, pp. 96–97).

[24] See, for example, Bibliothèque Nationale MSS., fonds latin, nos. 7198, fol. 90ro., 7406, fol. 58vo., 7421, fol. 203vo., 16211, fol. 93vo., 16658, fol. 113ro.

[25] J. K. Wright, *op. cit.*, pp. 84–85.

[26] See above, p. 86.

[27] J. K. Wright, *op. cit.*, pp. 91–96.

[28] *ibid.*, pp. 77–84.

[29] For texts illustrating this see Haskins, *Reception*, 1915, p. 57; the same, *Studies*, 1924, pp. 114–115. See also Peter Alphonsi, *Dialogus*, I, in: Migne, *Pat. lat.*, vol. clvii, cols. 543–547.

[30] See J. K. Wright, *op. cit.*, p. 85.

[31] *Theorica planetarum*, Renner's edit., fourth page before *explicit.* See also Bibliothèque Nationale MSS., fonds latin, no. 7421, fol. 133.

[32] See J. K. Wright, *op. cit.*, pp. 91–96, for discussion of the interpretation of these figures. In Figure 12 the circles show the relative positions of certain points in Europe as they actually are; the stars show them as

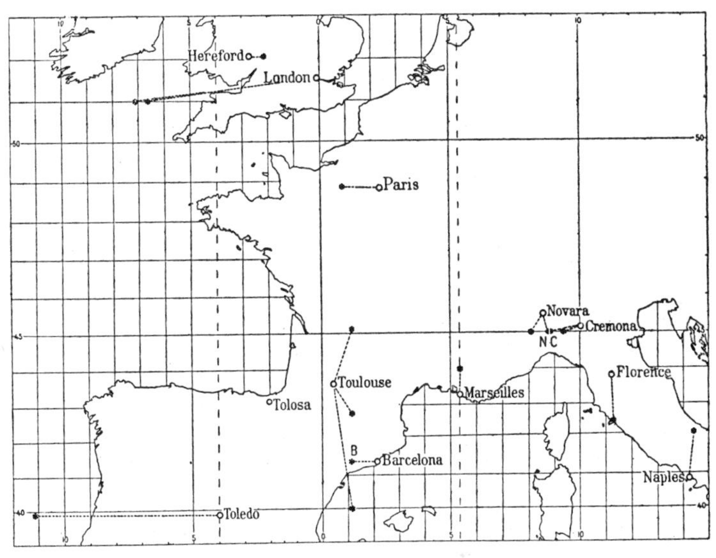

FIG. 12—Map showing the relative positions of certain points in Europe as indicated in astronomical tables of the twelfth and early thirteenth centuries. In the original tables a consistent error appears in the longitudes of all the cities in Italy. This has been corrected as discussed in the work cited in note 32 above.

given in the tables and referred to the meridian of Marseilles. It will readily be seen that the relative longitudes of all the points except London and Toledo are remarkably accurate when we consider the rough means of calculation at the disposal of twelfth- and thirteenth-century observers. London and Toledo are placed accurately in relation to each other though far astray in relation to Marseilles, probably as a result of a single initial error in the estimation of the number of degrees between the meridian of Toledo and that of some intermediate station (perhaps Marseilles) from which the positions of the remaining stations were calculated. The highly erroneous latitudes of Toulouse, Florence, and Naples are probably attributable to clerical errors. For a fuller discussion of this map see work cited, p. 95.

NOTES

CHAPTER XI

CARTOGRAPHY

[1] For facsimiles and texts of legends of the maps referred to in this chapter, see Miller, *Mappaemundi*, vols. i and ii, 1895, for the Beatus group, and vols. ii and iii, 1895, for other small maps of the world. Specific references are given in the notes that follow.

[2] Miller, *Mappaemundi*, vol. ii, 1895, pl. 11; vol. iii, 1895, pl. 1.

[3] *ibid.*, vol. ii, pl. 12; vol. iii, p. 14.

[4] *ibid.*, vol. iii, pp. 85–89.

[5] *ibid.*, pp. 91–92.

[6] *ibid.*, pp. 62–65.

[7] *ibid.*, vol. ii, p. 10; vol. iii, p. 33.

[8] *ibid.*, vol. ii, pls. 3a, 4, 5, 6, 7.

[9] *ibid.*, vol. iii, pp. 74, 76, 77.

[10] *ibid.*, p. 78.

[11] *ibid.*, vol. ii, pls. 3b (our Fig. 4, p. 123, above), 8, 9. See also Figure 2, p. 69, above.

[12] *ibid.*, vol. iii, p. 46 and pl. 4.

[13] *ibid.*, vol. ii, pl. 13; vol. iii, pl. 2.

[14] *ibid.*, vol. ii, pl. 2; vol. i, p. 31.

[15] *ibid.*, vol. ii, pl. 10; vol. iii, p. 33.

[16] *ibid.*, vol. ii, pls. 3–9.

[17] Notably Miller, *op. cit.*, vol. vi, 1898, pp. 143–145. Detlefsen, *Ursprung*, 1906, pp. 106–107, argues against this theory of Miller. See above, p. 377, note 167, p. 415, note 166.

[18] Miller, *op. cit.*, vol. iii, p. 23.

[19] On the Paris map (*ibid.*, p. 45). The St. Sever Beatus map shows some mountains in green and others in a dark tint, in both cases outlined with red (see reproduction, *ibid.*, vol. i, reduced in our Fig. 2, p. 69, above, where of course the difference in color cannot be distinguished).

[20] *ibid.*, vol. iii, p. 31.

[21] *ibid.*, vol. iii, p. 74.

[22] *ibid.*, vol. ii, pl. 8.

[23] *ibid.*, vol. ii, pl. 11; vol. iii, pl. 1.

[24] *ibid.*, vol. ii, pls. 2, 3b; vol. i, pp. 31, 35.

[25] *ibid.*, vol. iii, p. 56.

[26] *loc. cit.*

[27] The immense size of rivers and seas was characteristic of Moslem cartography. Pullé, *La cartog. antica*, pt. 2, 1905, pp. 21–22, points out the striking resemblances in this respect of the Guido map to contemporary specimens of Moslem cartography.

[28] Miller, *op. cit.*, vol. ii, pls. 3a, 4–9.

[29] *ibid.*, vol. ii, pl. 10; vol. iii, p. 33.

[30] *ibid.*, vol. ii, pls. 11, 12; vol. iii, pl. 1 and p. 14.

[31] *ibid.*, vol. ii, pls. 3–9. See also Figure 2, p. 69, above.

[32] *ibid.*, vol. ii, pl. 10; vol. iii, p. 33.

[33] *ibid.*, vol. iii, p. 76.

[34] *ibid.*, vol. i, pp. 53, 56, 58.

[35] *ibid.*, vol. iii, pp. 78–79.

[36] *ibid.*, vol. i, p. 32; see also reproductions, vol. i, p. 31, vol. ii, pl. 2.

[37] On the general arrangement of the mountains of the known world as shown on medieval maps see Benl, *Frühere und spätere Hypothesen*, 1905, pp. 8–14. See also above, p. 445, note 16.

[38] Miller, *op. cit.*, vol. ii, pls. 3–9. See also Figure 2, p. 69, above, where Mount Sinai (the black pinnacle in the southern part of the map) and Mount Olympus (the wooded pyramid in the northeastern part) are so represented.

[39] *ibid.*, vol. ii, pl. 12; vol. iii, pp. 13, 14.

[40] *ibid.*, vol. ii, pl. 11; vol. iii, p. 8 and pl. 1.

[40a] The lighthouse of Alexandria is shown on the Jerome map of Palestine (*ibid.*, vol. ii, pl. 12; vol. iii, pl. 1), the columns of Alexander and Hercules on the same map and on the Henry of Mayence map (*ibid.*, vol. ii, pl. 13; vol. iii, pl. 2), the tower of Babel on the Psalter map (*ibid.*, vol. ii, pl. 1; vol. iii, pl. 3) and the Ebstorf and Hereford maps (reproductions accompanying *ibid.*, vols. v and iv respectively).

[41] *ibid.*, vol. iii, pp. 5, 13.

[42] *ibid.*, vol. i, p. 35; vol. ii, pl. 3b.

[43] On Paris No. II (Miller, *op. cit.*, vol. ii, pl. 2; vol. i, p. 31), and on Osma (*ibid.*, vol. ii, pl. 3b; vol. i, p. 35).

[44] *ibid.*, vol. iii, pp. 74, 76, 77.

[45] *ibid.*, vol. ii, pl. 10; vol. iii, pp. 29–37.

[46] *ibid.*, vol. iv, 1896, with reproduction in colors accompanying the volume. Two sections are reproduced in Figure 8, pp. 276–277, above.

[47] *ibid.*, vol. v, 1896, with facsimile in colors accompanying the volume.

NOTES
CHAPTER XII
REGIONAL GEOGRAPHY

[1] See above, p. 19 and p. 372, note 69.

[2] *Opus majus*, Bridges' edit., vol. i, 1897, p. 292. Pierre d'Ailly (1350–1420), the famous French theologian, in his *Imago mundi*, an encyclopedic compilation of the same sort as the *De imagine mundi* of our period, plagiarized the work of Roger Bacon in this connection. The *Imago mundi* was read and annotated by Columbus, and in this way the idea that the eastern shores of Asia lie not far to the west of Spain was brought to the attention of the discoverer of America. See Henry Vignaud, *Histoire critique de la grande enterprise de Christophe Colomb*, 2 vols.,

reference in vol. i, Paris, 1911, pp. 315–316; Edward Channing, *A History of the United States*, vol. i, New York, 1905, p. 15.

[3] The Cratesian or Macrobian theory (see above, p. 18) would seem to have been accepted by William of Conches (*De phil. mundi*, IV, 3) and by Giraldus Cambrensis (*Top. Hiber.*, II, 3) as the basis of their explanation of the tides. See also *Im. du monde*, II, 1. The theory was set forth by Macrobius and by Martianus Capella and, as a result of the great popularity of both of these writers throughout the Middle Ages, was undoubtedly entirely familiar to scholars.

[4] See above, pp. 186–187.

[5] *De mundi univ.*, p. 48.

[6] *Hist. adv. pag.*, I, 2, 1.

[7] *Chron.*, I, 1.

[8] *Otia imper.*, vol. i, p. 910.

[9] *Tractatus excerptionum* (under Hugh of St. Victor in the Bibliography), III, 1, in: Migne, *Pat. lat.*, vol. clxxvii, col. 209.

[10] See above, pp. 66, 121–122, and Fig. 1 on p. 67.

[11] *Etym.*, XIV, 2.

[12] *De imag. mundi*, I, 7, I, 34; Gervase of Tilbury, *Otia imper.*, vol. i, p. 908; Rudolf of Hohen Ems, *Weltchronik*, cited by Doberentz, *Erd- und Völkerkunde*, in Zeitschr., vol. xiii, 1881, p. 171; *Im. du monde*, II, 5.

[13] Beazley, *Dawn*, vol. i, 1897, pp. 133, 338–339.

[14] Jerusalem is not at the center in the Beatus maps. Probably the earliest map now known which so places it is the T-O map of 1110 at Oxford, upon which a cross on "Mons Syon" marks the exact spot (Miller, *Mappaemundi*, vol. iii, 1895, p. 119). Jerusalem is at the center of the *oikoumene* on the Psalter (*ibid.*, vol. ii, 1895, pl. 1; vol. iii, 1895, pl. 3), Hereford, and Ebstorf maps (*ibid.*, accompanying vols. iv, 1896, and v, 1896, respectively) of the late thirteenth century. See below, p. 463, note 38.

[15] "Ista est Hierusalem, in medio gentium posui eam et in circuitu ejus terrae" (Ezekiel, v. 5). See also Ezekiel, xxxviii, 12. Jerome, *Commentarius in Ezechielem*, II (Migne, *Pat. lat.*, vol. xxv, col. 54), gives proofs that Jerusalem is the center of the earth. The Jews also identified Bethel and Mount Moriah, and the Samaritans Mount Gerizim with the center (Roscher, *Omphalos*, 1913, p. 27).

[16] On ancient and Scriptural theories concerning the center of the earth, see Liebrecht, *Gervasius von Tilbury*, 1856, p. 54, note 3a; Roscher, *Omphalos*, 1913, pp. 20–36; the same, *Neue Omphalosstudien*, 1915, pp. 12–28, 73–75; and A. I. Wensinck, *The Ideas of the Western Semites Concerning the Navel of the Earth*, in Verhandelingen der Koninklijke Akademie van Wetenschappen te Amsterdam, Afdeeling Letterkunde, N. S., vol. xvii, No. 1, 1916.

[17] White, *Warfare*, 1920, vol. i, p. 98.

[18] Liebrecht, *loc. cit.*

[19] *Otia imper.*, vol. i, p. 892. Gervase, *loc. cit.*, gives the following proof that there is as much land to the east as there is to the west of Jerusalem: "Unde tradunt, tantam terram a Jerusalem protendi ad Orientem, quantam ad Occidentem, quod probant ex eo, quod legitur: 'Deus ab austro veniet et sanctus de monte Pharaan' [Habakkuk, iii, 3]. Auster enim et Aquilo, qui pro Borea scribitur, ut ibi: 'ab Aquilone pandetur omne malum.' Et alibi: 'Ponam sedem meãm ab aquilone, & ero similis altissimo.' Per contrapositionem oppositi per effectum, & locorum distantiam objecti, aequaliter distant a centro, quod est inter Orientem et Occidentem." See below, p. 463, note 38.

[20] See above, p. 460, note 14.

[21] *De situ Hierusalem*, d'Avezac's edit., 1839, pp. 841–842; Wright's translation, 1848, p. 38.

[22] The cross of Calvary was usually supposed to mark the navel of the earth (White, *Warfare*, 1920, vol. i, p. 100).

[23] The manuscript in which the passage telling of this experiment is found is described in Sir G. F. Warner and J. P. Gilson's *Catalogue of Western Manuscripts in the Old Royal and King's Collections* [British Museum], vol. i, London, 1921, p. 193, under MS 7 D xxv (saec. xii). It is there suggested that the author may have been Adelard of Bath; Professor Haskins (*Studies*, 1924, p. 31) states that the manuscript "clearly represents Adelard's generation and circle of interests" and gives (*ibid.*, pp. 31–32) the following transcription of the text of the passage (from folio 66): "Mons Amor reorum est locus medius mundi, ubi apposui mensuras et probavi per multa loca et posui lignum rea [*sic*] rotundum habens. xii. cubitos longitudinis et grossitudo illi cubitus unus et suspendi illum per funem et tantum commutavi eum de loco in locum in medio eius. vii. kal. Iulii donec suspendi illud in loco medii diei et residit suum cum splendor solis ex omnibus partibus et facta est umbra ipsius subtus cum rotunda sicut rotunditas ipsius ligni quod suspenderam; et de ipsa mensura cognovi quod medius mundus est in Monte Amor reorum. Et tempore quo mensuravi hoc est annus . xxxviiii. et vinum non bibi, oculi mei somno satiati non fuerunt, ne exuperaveram in eo quod inquirebam." Haskins (*loc. cit.*) suggests that ".vii." should read ".xi." and "exuperaveram" should read "exuperarer."

[24] "Hoc autem circumferentiae centrum arbitrantur quidam in illo loco esse, ubi Dominus locutus est ad Samaritanam ad puteum, illic enim in solstitio aestivo monstrans, meridiana hora sol recto transite descendit in aquam putei umbram nullam aliqua parte monstrans, quod apud Syenem fieri tradunt philosophi . . . " (*Otia imper.*, vol. i, p. 892; Liebrecht, *Gervasius von Tilbury*, 1856, p. 1).

[25] This would seem to place the center of the earth, not at Jerusalem, but at Jacob's well on Mount Gerizim in Samaria. See John, iv, 6, 20, and above, p. 460, note 15.

[26] The most elaborate and scholarly monograph on the Terrestria

Paradise as it was conceived in the Middle Ages is Coli, *Il paradiso terrestre dantesco*, 1897. This treats in great detail the history of the legends of Paradise and the development of theories concerning the nature and location of the Garden of Delights. Special attention is given to the Terrestrial Paradise of Dante.

[27] On the St. Sever Beatus map, Paradise is enclosed by mountains, its northern border by the Montes Ceraunes, a continuation of the Taurus (see Fig. 2, p. 69, above). On the Beatus maps Paradise is rectangular (Miller, *Mappaemundi*, vol. ii, 1895, pls. 2–9); on the Psalter (*ibid.*, vol. ii, pl. 1; vol. iii, 1895, pl. 3) and Lambert *mappaemundi* (*ibid.*, vol. iii, p. 46 and pl. 4) it is circular; and on the Henry of Mayence map (*ibid.*, vol. iii, pl. 2) it is more or less circular and is placed on an island in the Eastern Sea. A few maps do not show it at all; as the Cotton, Jerome, Guido, some of the Sallust maps, and the Matthew Paris map of the world (*ibid.*, vol. ii, pls. 10, 11, 12; vol. iii, pp. 56, 70–71, 110–113).

[28] Paraphrased from *De imag. mundi*, I, 8, from Isidore, *Etym.*, XIV, 3.

[29] Paraphrased from *De imag. mundi*, I, 10; *Im. du monde*, II, 2.

[30] *Expos. in hex.*, in: Migne, *Pat. lat.*, vol. clxxviii, cols. 775–776.

[31] *Tractatus excerptionum* (under Hugh of St. Victor in the Bibliography), III, 2, in: Migne, *op. cit.*, vol. clxxvii, cols. 209–210.

[31a] *Im. du monde*, II, 2.

[32] *Otia imper.*, vol. i, p. 911.

[33] *ibid.*, p. 892.

[34] See also Alexander Neckam, *De nat. rer.*, II, 49: "Rei tamen veritas est, quod paradisus terrestris superior est aquis, cum etiam lunari globo superior sit. Unde et aquae cataclysmi paradiso nullam intulere molestiam. Enoc, qui in paradiso jam tunc erat collocatus, aquarum non sensit diluvii incrementa." See above, p. 437, note 25.

[35] *Sententiae*, II, 17, 5. Peter Lombard maintains that there were three *sententiae* concerning Paradise: (1) that of those who conceived of it in a spiritual sense, (2) that of those who conceived of it in a corporeal sense, and (3) that of those who conceived of it in both senses. The third method was the most pleasing to Peter, who says: "ut homo in corporali paradiso sit positus, qui ab illo principio plantatus accipi potest, quo terram omnem remotis aquis herbas et ligna producere jussit. Qui etsi praesentis Ecclesiae vel futurae typum tenet, ad litteram tamen intellegendum est esse locum amoenissimum fructuosis arboribus, magnum et magno fonte foecundum. Quod dicimus 'a principio,' antiqua translatio dicit 'ad Orientem.' Unde volunt in orientali parte esse paradisum, longo interjacente spatio vel maris vel terrae a regionibus quas incolunt homines, secretum, et in alto situm, usque ad lunarem circulem pertingentem, unde nec aquae diluvii illuc pervenerunt." The older translation referred to may have been the "Old Latin" translation of the Septuagint. See above, p. 390, note 122.

[36] The Beatus (Miller, *Mappaemundi*, vol. ii, 1895, pls. 3a, 3b—our Fig. 4

on p. 123, above—4–9; vol. i, 1895, pp. 35, 39, and accompanying reproduction—our Fig. 2 on p. 69 above) and Psalter (*ibid.*, vol. ii, pl. 1; vol. iii, pl. 3) maps show Paradise in Asia; those of Henry of Mayence (*ibid.*, vol. ii, pl. 13; vol. iii, pl. 2) and of Lambert (*ibid.*, vol. iii, pl. 4) place it on an island. On Paradise as represented on these and other medieval maps, see Coli, *Il paradiso terrestre*, 1897, pp. 100–122.

[37] See above, p. 428, note 136.

[38] *Otia imper.*, vol. i, p. 892. Dante also placed the Terrestrial Paradise in the southern hemisphere, at the summit of the Mount of Purgatory, which was the antipodes of "Mount Zion." This has usually been interpreted to mean the Mount Zion near Jerusalum. See Coli, *op. cit.*, pp. 185–207; Moore, *Studies in Dante, Third Series*, 1903, pp. 134–139; Mori, *La geogr.*, 1922, pp. 287–289. Benini (*Origine del Monte del Purgatorio*, 1917, pp. 1037–1055), however, maintains that the mountain to which Dante refers was to be associated with Sinai or with the Mount Pharaan of Habakkuk, iii, 3 (see above, p. 461, note 19; see also R. Benini, *Il grande Sion, il Sinai e il piccolo Sion* (*dove ha posto Dante l'entrata dell' inferno*), in: Rendiconti della Reale Accademia dei Lincei, Classe di scienze morali, storiche e filologiche, series 5, vol. xxiii, Rome, 1915, pp. 293–315). He argues that Dante believed this mountain to be on the Tropic of Cancer and that the Mount of Purgatory, its antipodes, was consequently on the Tropic of Capricorn.

[39] See above, p. 164.

[40] *Chron.*, II, 25.

[41] *Tractatus excerptionum* (under Hugh of St. Victor in the Bibliography), III, 2, in: Migne, *Pat. lat.*, vol. clxxvii, col. 211.

[42] Miller, *Mappaemundi*, vol. ii, 1895, pl. 13; vol. iii, 1895, pl. 2.

[43] *ibid.*, vol. iii, p. 46 and pl. 4.

[44] Schröder, *Sanct Brandan*, 1871 (under Brandan in the Bibliography), p. 36.

[45] Augustine, *De Genesi ad litteram*, VIII, 1, in: Migne, *Pat. lat.*, vol. xxxiv, cols. 371–373. On other medieval ideas concerning the location of Paradise, see Graf, *Miti, leggende*, vol. i, 1892, pp. 1–15.

[46] *Iter ad Paradisum*, edit. by J. Zacher, 1859 (under "Alexander the Great, Romance of, VI" in the Bibliography). See Meyer, *Alexandre le Grand*, vol. i, 1886, pp. 47–51.

[47] Graf, *op. cit.*, pp. 73–126, discusses these stories in detail. In his *La leggenda*, 1878, pp. 22–44, he shows that there were four types of Paradise legend in the Middle Ages: (1) legends which grew out of preexisting legendary themes, as, for example, the story of Seth's visit to Paradise; (2) those which developed out of a spirit of pure devotion and asceticism, such as certain of the stories of the visits of pious monks; (3) those which arose out of a spirit of exploration and adventure, as the story of St. Brandan's voyages or that given in the *Pantheon* of Godfrey of Viterbo; and, finally, (4) those which arose from a chivalric love of

adventure and conquest, as the *Iter ad Paradisum*, connected with the Romance of the conquests of Alexander the Great.

[48] On the story of Seth's visit to Paradise, see Graf, *Miti, leggende*, vol. i, 1892, pp. 76–84. This story was included in the second verse redaction of the *Image du monde*. See above, p. 404, note 88.

[49] *Pantheon*, pars 2, in: Pistorius' edit., 1726, pp. 58–60; see also Graf, *Miti, leggende*, vol. i, 1892, pp. 112–113.

[50] *Acta Sanctorum quotquot toto orbe coluntur. . . . Editio novissima*, Octobris vol. x, Paris and Rome, 1869, pp. 566–574 (see Potthast, *Wegweiser*, vol. i, 1896, p. xxxii–xxxiii).

[51] Hercules' and Alexander's columns are shown on the Jerome map of Palestine (Miller, *Mappaemundi*, vol. ii, 1895, pl. 13; vol. iii, 1895, pp. 13–14).

[52] Mâle, *L'art religieux*, 1898, p. 19. Cyprian, bishop of Carthage in the third century, had suggested this allegorical interpretation, and it was passed on to the Western world by Isidore. See Rahn, *Glasgemälde*, 1879, p. 42 (14).

[53] *De nat. rer.*, II, 2.

[54] See above, pp. 29–30, 59–60, 184–185, and 199–203.

[55] *De imag. mundi*, I, 10.

[56] *Etym.*, XIV, 3.

[57] Miller, *Mappaemundi*, vol. ii, 1895, pl. 1; vol. iii, 1895, pl. 3.

[58] *Expos. in hex.*, in: Migne, *Pat. lat.*, vol. clxxviii, col. 778.

[59] *Elysaeus*, 14, 26, in: Zarncke, *Priester Johannes*, in: Abhandlungen, vol. viii, 1876, pp. 123–124.

[60] *De mundi univ.*, p. 22.

[61] See the introduction to Yule, *Cathay and the Way Thither*, 2nd edit., vol. i, 1915.

[62] See Friedrich Hirth, *China and the Roman Orient*, Leipzig, 1885; an especially full study is Albert Herrmann, *Die Westländer in der chinesischen Kartographie*, forming vol. viii, pt. 2, of Sven Hedin, *Southern Tibet*, Stockholm, 1922. See also Albert Herrmann, *Die ältesten chinesischen Karten von Zentral- und Westasien*, in: Ostasiatische Zeitschrift, vol. viii, Berlin, 1919–1920, pp. 185–198, and note upon this monograph in: Geographical Review, vol. xiii, New York, 1923, pp. 311–313.

[63] See E. Bretschneider, *Mediaeval Researches from Eastern Asiatic Sources: Fragments Towards the Knowledge of the Geography and History of Central and Western Asia from the Thirteenth to the Seventeenth Century*, London, 1888, vol. i, pp. 275–344; Leon Cahun, *Introduction à l'histoire de l'Asie: Turcs et Mongols des origines à 1405*, Paris, 1896; René Grousset, *Histoire de l'Asie*, in 3 vols., Paris, 1922, vol. ii, pp. 12–160.

[64] W. W. Rockhill, translator and editor, *The Journey of William of Rubruck to the Eastern Parts of the World, 1253–55, As Narrated by Himself, With Two Accounts of the Earlier Journey of John of Pian de Carpine*, Hakluyt Society Publications, series 2, vol. iv, London, 1900, p. xiii.

[65] *Chron. maiora*, Rolls series edit., vol. iv, pp. 76–78; translated by Rockhill, *op. cit.*, pp. xiv–xvii.

[66] See above, pp. 287–288.

[67] See Beazley, *Dawn*, vol. ii, 1901, pp. 275–391; Bréhier, *L'Église et l'Orient*, 1911, pp. 219–221, 228–233. See also above, p. 286.

[68] See above, pp. 283–286.

[69] See especially Beazley, *Dawn*, vol. ii, 1901, pp. 275–391, vol. iii, 1906, pp. 15–381.

[70] For the Latin text of John of Pian de Carpine's travels edited by d'Avezac with extensive commentary see: Recueil de voyages et de mémoires publié par la Société de Géographie, vol. iv, Paris, 1839, pp. 397–779. English translation of a part of this in Rockhill, *op. cit.*, pp. 1–32. Professor Paul Pelliot of the Collège de France in a lecture delivered at Columbia University in 1923 announced that the original letter sent by Carpine from the Khan at Karakorum to the Pope had recently been discovered in the Vatican archives.

[71] For the Latin text of Rubruck's travels edited by d'Avezac see: Recueil de voyages et de mémoires publié par la Société de Géographie, vol. iv, Paris, 1839, pp. 213–396. English translation and commentary in Rockhill, *op. cit.*

[72] See above, p. 405, note 92.

[73] See above, p. 408, note 97.

[74] See Yule, *Marco Polo*, 3rd edit., 1903, with Cordier's supplement, *Ser Marco Polo*, 1920 (both under Polo, Marco, in the Bibliography).

[75] See especially vols. ii and iii of Yule's *Cathay*, 2nd edit. by Cordier, 1913–1914.

[76] *De imag. mundi*, I, 8.

[77] *Etym.*, XIV, 3.

[78] For a brief statement in regard to the origins of the conception of a great mountain range running east and west across Asia see Benl, *Frühere und spätere Hypothesen*, 1905, pp. 1–7.

[79] *Otia imper.*, vol. ii, p. 761.

[80] *Hist. adv. pag.*, I, 2

[81] St. Sever Beatus (see Miller, *Mappaemundi*, vol. i, 1895, p. 50, also reproduction accompanying volume—reduced in our Fig. 2, page 69, above), Osma Beatus (*ibid.*, vol. i, p. 35—our Fig. 4, p. 123, above—; vol. ii, 1895, pl. 3), Henry of Mayence (*ibid.*, vol. ii, pl. 13; vol. iii, 1895, pl. 2), Psalter (*ibid.*, vol. ii, pl. i, vol. iii, pl. 3). For "Paropanissade montes," see Jerome map of the East (*ibid.*, vol. ii, pl. 11; vol. iii, p. 8 and pl. 1).

[81a] Miller, *op. cit.*, vol. ii, pls. 11 and 12; vol. iii, pl. 1.

[82] "Hae superius dictae regiones, ab oriente incipientes, recta linea ad Mediterraneum mare extenditur" (*De imag. mundi*, I, 18). See Isidore, *Etym.*, XIV, 3; Gervase of Tilbury, *Otia imper.*, vol. ii, pp. 758–760.

83 *De imag. mundi*, I, 19; Isidore, *loc. cit.;* Gervase of Tilbury, *op. cit.*, vol. ii, p. 762.

84 Gervase, *loc. cit.*, says that all he remembers having read about the Seres are certain verses of Sidonius, which he quotes as follows:

"'Ergo ubi se mediam solio dedit (sc. Roma), advolat omnis
Terra simul, fert quaeque suos provincia fructus.'
Et post pauca:
'Ser vellera, thura Sabeus.'"

85 *Hist. nat.*, VI, 17, sect. 54.

86 *Collectanea*, 50.

87 *Etym.*, XIV, 3, 29.

88 *De imag. mundi*, I, 19.

89 *Letter of Prester John*, 42, in: Zarncke, *Priester Johannes*, in: Abhandlungen, vol. vii, 1879, p. 915.

90 Yule, *Cathay*, vol. i, 1915, pp. 11–13, 183–185, 187–196, especially p. 195. On the *Periplus* see above, p. 40.

91 See Yule, *op. cit.*, pp. 181–182.

92 *De scientia stellarum*, Bologna edit., 1645, p. 24.

93 Benjamin of Tudela, *Itinerary*, Adler's edit., pp. 66–67. See above, p. 414, note 156.

94 See above, p. 197, and p. 442, note 75; and Borchardt, *Itinéraire*, 1924, p. 33.

95 Marco Polo placed the griffon, or Rukh, in Madagascar and asserted that it could carry elephants in its talons (Yule, *Marco Polo*, 3rd edit., 1903 (under Polo, Marco, in the Bibliography), pp. 412, 415).

96 Pseudo-Abdias, *De historia certaminis apostolici*, VIII; edition of 1560, fol. 96a.

97 Guido's *mappamundi* of 1119 indicates "insunt tres Indiae" (Miller, *Mappaemundi*, vol. iii, 1895, p. 54). Lambert's map designates the three divisions as "India prima, hic pigmei et fauni et reges gentium," "India secunda," and "India ultima, hic arbores solis et lunae" (*ibid.*, p. 49). The Jerome map of the East represents "India ultima" as extending from the Indus to the "Hipanis," bordering on Persia and Carmania, and including the city of Ophir. "India inferior" lies between the "Hipanis" and the Ganges, and "India superior" to the northeast, between the Ganges and the Octorogorra, a river rising in the Caucasus (*ibid.*, pl. 1). Pullé, *La cartog. antica*, pt. 2, 1905, p. 31, conjectures plausibly that these three divisions may represent in order, Punjabic India, peninsular India, and Gangetic India.

98 *Hist. eccles.*, pt. I, bk. II, 15.

99 *Letter of Prester John*, 12, in: Zarncke, *Priester Johannes*, in: Abhandlungen, vol. vii, 1879, p. 910.

100 *Otia imper.*, vol. i, p. 911.

101 "Isti 4 rivuli fundunt his duabus Indiis. . . " *Elysaeus*, 14, in: Zarncke, *op. cit.*, vol. viii, 1876, p. 123.

[102] "En Ynde a maintes granz contrées qui sont pueploiées de genz et de grant plente de bestes. Une en y a que l'en apele Perse . . . " etc. (*Im. du monde*, II, 2). This shows that the writer considered Persia a part of India. A rubric in the manuscript of the *Image du monde* of the Bibliothèque Nationale, fonds français, no. 574, reads "Des contrées d'Ynde," and includes under it Babylonia, Chaldaea, Arabia, Phoenicia, Assyria, Palestine, and Armenia, showing that the scribe at least, if not the poet, believed that India comprises the greater part of Asia.

[103] See, on India, Isidore, *Etym.*, XIV, *passim; De imag. mundi*, I, 11, 12, 13; Gervase of Tilbury, *Otia imper.*, vol. i, p. 911; vol. ii, pp. 755, 756; *Im. du monde*, II, 2. Also see, for a study of India as delineated on medieval maps, Pullé, *La cartog. antica*, pt. 2, 1905.

[104] *Etym.*, XIII, 21; *De imag. mundi*, I, 10; Peter Abelard, *Expos. in hex.*, in: Migne, *Pat. lat.*, vol. clxxviii, col. 779; Peter Comestor, *Hist. schol.*, Gen. xiv; Gervase of Tilbury, *Otia imper.*, vol. i, p. 892.

[105] *Hist. schol.*, *loc. cit.*

[106] Peter Comestor gives an alternative suggestion that the word "Phison" may refer to the changeable appearance of the river.

[107] *Letter of Prester John*, 22, in: Zarncke, *Priester Johannes*, in: Abhandlungen, vol. vii, 1879, p. 912.

[108] The Jerome map of the East (Miller, *Mappaemundi*, vol. iii, 1895, pl. 1) and the Henry of Mayence map of the world (*ibid.*, pl. 2) show these rivers and give their Greek names, Hydaspes, Indus, and Hipanis. Pullé, *op. cit.*, pt. 2, pp. 28, 31, believes that the shape of the coast line, the Greek names of the rivers, the position of Taprobane, and other details on these maps strongly suggest the Ptolemaic representation of the East. The resemblances in form to the Ptolemaic map, however, are too doubtful to warrant us in assuming any direct Ptolemaic influence.

[109] Benjamin of Tudela, *Itinerary*, Adler's edit., pp. 63–65.

[110] These marvels were almost never arbitrary inventions. They can usually be traced back to a remote source which was itself an exaggeration or distortion of a true story. See Peschel, *Abhandlungen*, vol. i, 1877, pp. 9–19. Most of the marvels of India as set forth by Ctesias had their counterparts in Persian and Indian mythology and probably "originated in obscure and disfigured accounts of nature and man in the mountain chains between the upper Indus and the Ganges and on the high plateaus as far as the Tarim Basin" (Doberentz, *Erd- und Völkerkunde*, in: Zeitschr., vol. xiii, 1881, pp. 41–57).

[111] Many of the stories go back to Greek writers earlier even than Ctesias. The pygmies who fight with storks are found in Homer, the half-dog-half-men in Hesiod, the umbrella-footed men in Alcman, the gold-guarding griffons and the one-eyed Arimaspians in the writings of Aristeas of Proconnesus. Hecataeus, Scylax, Aeschylus, and, above all, Herodotus, repeat many of these yarns. Ctesias of Cnidus gathered together most of the earlier tales and added to them stories that he him-

self had heard in the Persian realm, or, perhaps, he wrote down descriptions of monsters that he had seen depicted or sculptured on the walls of the great palaces at Persepolis. Ctesias' book became the great reservoir to which later writers looked for their marvels. See Doberentz, *loc. cit.*

[112] The mantichora (see Fig. 8, p. 277 above) was a beast described by Pliny, *Hist. nat.*, VIII, 21, as follows (transl. in Bohn's edit., vol. ii, p. 280): "It has a triple row of teeth which fit into each other like those of a comb, the face and ears of a man, and azure eyes, is of the color of blood, has the body of a lion, and a tail ending in a sting, like that of a scorpion. Its voice resembles the union of the sound of the flute and the trumpet; it is of excessive swiftness, and is particularly fond of human flesh." Doberentz shows the route by which the story of this extraordinary combination found its way from its Oriental place of origin to the *Weltchronik* of Rudolf of Hohen-Ems.

This route was the same as that taken by most of the other marvels which came to this chronicle. The beast appears illustrated on the monuments of Persepolis; possibly it was thought to be the king of the evil beasts of Ahriman, the Zoroastrian god of darkness. Ctesias describes it in his *Indica;* thence it probably made its way to the *Historia animalium* of Aristotle, thence to the *Chorographia Pliniana*, thence to Solinus, thence to the *De imagine mundi*, and thence to Rudolf's chronicle (Doberentz, *op. cit.*, pp. 175-180).

[113] Peschel in his *Abhandlungen*, vol. i, 1877, p. 10, pointed out that some medieval commentators on the subject were disinclined to believe in the existence of these creatures because they were not included in Noah's ark. St. Augustine, *De civitate Dei*, XVI, 8, had said: "Either such monsters do not exist at all, or else they are in no wise men, for in the latter case they would be sprung from Adam." In the ninth century there was discussion as to whether or not the *cynocephali* in the north were descended from Adam. During our period no text that has been found by the writer questions their existence.

[114] Miller, *Mappaemundi*, vol. iii, 1895, p. 41 and pl. 3; vol. ii, 1895, pl. 1.

[115] *ibid.*, vol. iii, 1895, pp. 13 and 14; vol. ii, 1895, pl. 12.

[116] Lambert (*ibid.*, vol. iii, 1895, p. 49), Jerome (Palestine) (*ibid.*, p. 13), Psalter (*ibid.*, p. 38). On the Hereford map the legend reads: "Arbor balsami id est sicca" (*ibid.*, vol. iv, 1896, p. 8); on the Ebstorf map, "Oraculum solis et lune" (*ibid.*, vol. v, 1896, p. 48). See Yule, *Marco Polo*, 3rd edit., 1903, vol. i, pp. 128-138; Cordier, *Ser Marco Polo*, 1920, pp. 31-32 (both under Polo, Marco, in the Bibliography).

[117] Miller, *op. cit.*, vol. iii, p. 48 and pl. 4.

[118] *ibid.*, p. 8 and pl. 1.

[119] See above, p. 74.

[120] Philipps, *St. Thomas*, 1903, pp. 1-8.

[121] *Hist. eccles.*, pt. I, bk. II, 14. Ordericus drew from Pseudo-Abdias. See above, p. 379, note 8.

[122] Miller, *op. cit.*, vol. i, 1895, p. 35; vol. ii, 1895, pl. 3 (our Fig. 4 on p. 123 above).

[123] *Letter of Prester John*, 56–72, in: Zarncke, *Priester Johannes*, in: Abhandlungen, vol. vii, 1879, pp. 916–920.

[124] Mâle, *L'art religieux*, 1898, pp. 378–388.

[125] Zarncke, *op. cit.*, pp. 832–843.

[126] In writing of the journey of Sighelm, who was sent by King Alfred to the shrines of Saints Thomas and Bartholomew in India (see above, p. 74), William of Malmsbury remarks that the journey was made with great success, "at which everybody in this age wonders" (*Gesta regum Anglorum*, II, 122, edited by William Stubbs (Rolls Series, no. 90), 2 vols., London, 1887).

[127] *De adventu patriarchae Indorum ad urbem sub Callisto papa II*, 12, in: Zarncke, *op. cit.*, p. 838.

[128] See Zarncke, *op. cit.*, pp. 843–846.

[129] Miller, *Mappaemundi*, vol. iii, 1895, p. 12 and pl. 1; vol. ii, 1895, pl. 11.

[130] *Etym.*, XIV, 6.

[131] *De imag. mundi*, I, 11.

[132] *Otia imper.*, vol. i, p. 911.

[133] Jerome map of the East (Miller, *op. cit.*, vol. iii, p. 12 and pl. 1; vol. ii, pl. 11); Lambert map of the world (*ibid.*, p. 50 and pl. 4).

[134] *Hist. adv. pag.*, I, 2. This passage was copied in: *De imag. mundi*, I, 11.

[135] *Etym.* XIV, 6; *Otia imper.*, *loc. cit.* Copied from Orosius in: *De imag. mundi*, *loc. cit.*

[136] *Collectanea*, 53, 2–3.

[137] Miller, *op. cit.*, vol. ii, 1895, pl. 13; vol. iii, pl. 2.

[138] *ibid.*, vol. ii, pls. 11 and 12; vol. iii, pl. 1.

[139] *ibid.*, reproduction accompanying vol. iv, 1896.

[140] *ibid.*, reproduction accompanying vol. v, 1896.

[141] *De scientia stellarum*, Bologna edit., 1645, pp. 24ff.

[142] G. A. Wood in his *Discovery of Australia*, London, 1921, p. 28, writes that though the Arabs "knew Sumatra, and Java, and perhaps Timor, and though they must have shared whatever knowledge may have been possessed by the Malays or Hindus, there seems no evidence that they had heard of Australia."

[143] *Etym.*, XIV, 3, sects. 31–32; *De imag. mundi*, I, 19; *Otia imper.*, vol. ii, p. 756. A long legend on the St. Sever Beatus map describes "Scythia maior" in similar terms (Miller, *Mappaemundi*, vol. i, 1895, p. 49).

[144] See above, pp. 269–270.

[145] Notably on the Jerome map of the East (Miller, *op. cit.*, vol. iii,

pl. 1), the St. Sever Beatus (*ibid.*, reproduction accompanying vol. i, 1895; see Fig. 2, p. 69, above), the Osma Beatus (*ibid.*, reproduction in vol. ii, 1895, pl. 3; see also vol. i, p. 35, and Fig. 4, p. 123, above), and Henry of Mayence map (*ibid.*, vol. ii, 1895, pl. 13; vol. iii, 1895, pl. 2). Other significant features shown on contemporary maps in northern and central Asia are the Amazons, the Anthropophagi, the Caspian Gates, the Armenian Pillars, and the Hyperboreans. Beatus Paris No. II (*ibid.*, vol. i, pp. 31-32) shows a region in the vicinity of the Caspian Sea labeled "terra inhabitabilis propter habundanti[am] aqu[ae]," which does not appear on other maps.

[146] Benjamin of Tudela, *Itinerary*, Adler's edit., p. 59.

[147] *loc. cit.* See Neubauer, *Ten Tribes*, 1888-1889. Neubauer's article traces the history of speculations regarding the lost ten tribes from the earliest times and contains incidentally much important geographical lore.

[148] See above, pp. 287-288.

[149] Benjamin of Tudela, *Itinerary*, Adler's edit., p. 60.

[150] *Chron.*, VII, 33.

[151] Benjamin of Tudela, *Itinerary*, Adler's edit., pp. 60-61.

[152] See Yule, *Marco Polo*, 3rd edit., 1903 (under Polo, Marco, in the Bibliography), vol. i, pp. 234-235.

[153] Oppert, *Presbyter Johannes*, 1870, *passim;* Zarncke, *Priester Johannes* (under Prester John in the Bibliography), in: Abhandl., vol. vii, 1879, [pp. 847-871.

[154] Pelliot, *Chrétiens*, 1914, p. 627.

[155] *ibid.*, p. 629.

[156] Zarncke gives a critical Latin text of the *Letter* in *Priester Johannes*, in: Abhandl., vol. vii, 1879, pp. 909-924.

[157] Zarncke in: Berichte, vol. xxix, 1877, p. 151 and note 9.

[158] See above, pp. 268-269 and p. 465, note 67.

[159] The name "Prester John" was not used in early manuscripts of the *Letter of Prester John*. The letter of Pope Alexander III was discussed and edited critically by Zarncke in his *Priester Johannes*, in: Abhandlungen, vol. vii, 1879, pp. 935-946. See Yule, *Marco Polo*, 3rd edit., 1903 (under Polo, Marco, in the Bibliography), vol. i, p. 231.

[160] Miller, *Mappaemundi*, vol. iii, 1895, p. 93.

[161] *De imag. mundi*, I, 11.

[162] *Rudimenta astronomica*, Nuremberg edit., 1537, dif. ix, fol. 9ro.

[163] From Meyer's "third branch." See above, p. 412, note 135, and Meyer, *Alexandre le grand*, 1886, vol. ii, pp. 170, 217, 386-389.

[164] From Meyer's "fourth branch," by Alexandre de Bernay (de Paris). Meyer, *op. cit.*, vol. ii, p. 207.

[165] *Chron.*, V, 9. Godfrey of Viterbo incorporated this passage in his *Pantheon*, pars 16 (in Migne, *Pat. lat.*, vol. cxcviii, col. 913; also in *Mon. Germ. hist.*, Scriptores, vol. xxii, p. 196).

[166] *Chronicon Wirziburgense*, in: *Mon. Germ. hist.*, Scriptores, vol. vi, p. 25. See above, p. 412, note 129.

[167] *Chron.*, II, 23, from Orosius, *Hist. adv. pag.*, III, 7.

[168] This belief in the increase of Jewish population in these regions may possibly have been connected in some way with knowledge of the conversion of the Khazars to Judaism in the eighth century. See Carmoly, *Itinéraires*, 1847, pp. 3–112, and S. Schechter, *An Unknown Khazar Document*, in: Jewish Quarterly Review, vol. iii (N. S.), London, 1912, pp. 181–219.

[169] "Goth & Magoth, aeternaliter conclusit. Vndecim trib. Hebraeorum, montib. aeternaliter circumcinxit, de quibus omnibus in versibus plenius dicemus atque iocundius" (*Pantheon*, pars 11, Herold's edit., 1559, col. 262; for the poetic elaboration mentioned, see cols. 266–267; both of these passages of the *Pantheon* are omitted in the editions of Migne and of the *Mon. Germ. hist.*). Marinelli (*La geogr.*, 1882, p. 493; *Scritti minori*, vol. i, [1908?], p. 316, note 2, p. 415, note 2) knew of the passage in the *Pantheon* just quoted at second hand through a paraphrase in Giusto Grion, *I nobili fatti di Alessandro Magno: Romanzo storico tradotto dal francese nel buon secolo . . .* , Rome, 1872, p. cxxxii; not having the original text of the *Pantheon* at hand, Marinelli was in doubt as to whether the error in the statement that there were *eleven* tribes was to be imputed to Grion or to Godfrey. Marinelli cites this passage together with a passage from Albertus Magnus' *Compendium theologicae veritatis*, VII, 10, as evidence of the fact that the ten tribes of the Jews were associated with Gog and Magog as early as the twelfth and thirteenth centuries. See also the prophecy in the *Pantheon* within a longer prophecy of the Sibyl: "Et exurgent ab Aquilonae spurcissimae gentes, quas Alexander rex inclusit, Goth videlicet & Magoth. Haec duodecim [*sic*] regna, quorum numerus est sicut arena maris" (pars 10, Herold's edit., col. 257; *Mon. Germ. hist.*, Scriptores, vol. xxii, p. 147). See also above, p. 391, note 130, p. 470, note 147.

[170] See above, pp. 267–268.

[171] *De imag. mundi*, I, 14; *Otia imper.*, vol. ii, p. 756, from Orosius, *Hist. adv. pag.*, I, 2.

[172] *De imag. mundi* and *Otia imper.*, *loc. cit.*, from Isidore, *Etym.*, XIV, 3, sect. 13.

[173] *Hist. schol.*, Gen. 14; *De imag. mundi*, I, 10.

[174] *Otia imper.*, vol. i, p. 911. Most of the maps of the period correctly represent the Tigris as flowing into the Persian Gulf; the Jerome maps even show a common outlet for the two rivers (Miller, *Mappaemundi*, vol. ii, 1895, pl. 11; vol. iii, 1895, p. 14 and pl. 1). The Jerome map of the Orient, however, makes the Hydaspes a branch of the Tigris (*ibid.*, vol. iii, p. 14).

[175] *Otia imper.*, vol. ii, pp. 756–757; *De imag. mundi*, I, 15, from Isidore, *Etym.*, XIV, 3.

[176] *Otia imper.*, vol. ii, p. 757, from Orosius, *loc. cit.*

[177] Otto of Freising, *Chron.*, VII, 3.

[178] Benjamin of Tudela, *Itinerary*, Adler's edit., p. 42. See also above, p. 414, note 156.

[179] Benjamin of Tudela, *loc. cit.*

[180] *ibid.*, pp. 35–38.

[181] Some manuscripts give "Sikbia" rather than "Siberia." The "land of Togarmim" was Turkestan.

[182] Benjamin of Tudela, *Itinerary*, Adler's edit., pp. 40–41.

[183] *Otia imper.*, vol. ii, p. 757, from Orosius, *op. cit.*, I, 2. See also *De imag. mundi*, I, 16, from Isidore, *Etym.*, XIV, 3.

[184] Benjamin of Tudela, *Itinerary*, Adler's edit., pp. 47–51. See especially pp. 48–50, note 2. See also above, p. 414, note 156.

[185] Benjamin of Tudela, *op. cit.*, p. 67.

[186] Yule, *Marco Polo*, 3rd edit., 1903 (under Polo, Marco, in the Bibliography), vol. ii, p. 431.

[187] *Etym.*, xiv, 3; *De imag. mundi*, I, 16–17; *Otia imper.*, vol. ii, pp. 757–758.

[188] On the growth of the legends of the Dead Sea before and after our period and particularly on the supposed persistence of the pillar of salt into which Lot's wife was turned, see White, *Warfare*, 1920, vol. ii, pp. 221–235. See also above, pp. 208–209.

[189] See Rey, *Colonies franques*, 1883; Bréhier, *L'Église et l'Orient*, 1911, pp. 88–100; Heyd, *Commerce du Levant*, vol. i, 1885, pp. 129–190; Beazley, *Dawn*, vol. ii, 1901, pp. 396–464.

[190] A brief account of this expedition with references to the Arabic sources will be found in Bernhard Moritz, *Arabien: Studien zur physikalischen und historischen Geographie des Landes*, Hanover, 1923, pp. 119–120.

[191] Heyd, *op. cit.*, pp. 163–176.

[192] *ibid.*, pp. 301–310. It is unnecessary to enter upon a detailed discussion of the geography of Asia Minor as given in the *De imagine mundi*, I, 19–20, and *Otia imperialia*, vol. ii, p. 762. This is no more than the dry repetition of information drawn from classical sources. The Jerome map of the Orient shows the classical divisions of Asia Minor with a good deal of detail; the river systems are also represented, but very poorly (Miller, *Mappaemundi*, vol. ii, 1895, pl. 11; vol. iii, 1895, pl. 1). Troy appears on the Psalter, Lambert, and Guido maps (*ibid.*, vol. iii, p. 56, and pls. 3 and 4). On the last-named it is the only detail in Asia Minor.

[193] Dreesbach, *Der Orient*, 1901.

[194] See above, pp. 176, 212, 238–239.

[195] *Historia*, XIII, 3; in medieval French translation in Paulin Paris' edit., vol. i, p. 480. The "Sur" of William of Tyre is Tyre. See also Dreesbach, *op. cit.*, pp. 24–28.

[196] *ibid.*, pp. 53–61.

[197] Miller, *op. cit.*, vol. iii, 1895, p. 93.

[198] Ambroise, *Estoire de la guerre sainte*, verses 9541–9542, in Gaston Paris' edit., col. 255. See also Dreesbach, *op. cit.*, p. 60.

[199] Dreesbach, *op. cit.*, pp. 36–49.

[200] *Historia*, XXI, 24; in medieval French translation, XXI, 22 (Paulin Paris' edit., vol. ii, pp. 397–398). See also Dreesbach, *op. cit.*, p. 41.

[201] Dreesbach, *op. cit.*, pp. 4–19.

[201a] *Historia*, XVII, 10, XIX, 13, 15, 21; in medieval French translation, XVII, 10, XIX, 12, 14, 20 (Paulin Paris' edit., vol. ii, pp. 153, 270, 272–274, 282–283); see also Dreesbach, *op. cit.*, pp. 10–11.

[202] Benjamin of Tudela, *Itinerary*, Adler's edit., p. 35.

[203] *ibid.*, p. 71.

[204] Dreesbach, *op. cit.*, pp. 13–19.

[204a] *Historia*, XIV, 19, XX, 29; in medieval French translation, XIV, 16, XX, 28 (Paulin Paris' edit., vol. ii, pp. 25 and 357–358).

[204b] *Estoire de la guerre sainte*, verses 8819–8846; in Gaston Paris' edit., cols. 236–237. Also quoted in Dreesbach, *op. cit.*, p. 17.

[205] See also Benjamin of Tudela, *Itinerary*, Adler's edit., pp. 53–54.

[206] "Hac in oriente Indii fluminis surgit, et per meridiem vergens in occidentem tendit" (*De imag. mundi*, I, 32). "Indii fluminis" as it occurs in the chapter on Africa, here, obviously refers to the Nile. See above, p. 304.

[207] The *Image du monde*, II, 4, on the other hand, confusedly includes Syria and Palestine in Africa.

[208] *Otia imper.*, vol. ii, p. 759.

[209] *De imag. mundi*, I, 18.

[210] *Etym.*, XIV, 3.

[211] The delta figures on many maps: Jerome map of Palestine (Miller, *Mappaemundi*, vol. iii, 1896, p. 14), St. Sever Beatus (*ibid.*, reproduction accompanying vol. i, 1895; Fig. 2, p. 69, above), Turin Beatus (*ibid.*, vol. ii, 1895, pl. 8), Cotton (*ibid.*, pl. 10), Henry of Mayence (*ibid.*, pl. 13; vol. iii, pl. 2), Psalter (*ibid.*, vol. iii, pls. 1 and 3).

[212] *De imag. mundi*, I, 36. See also Gervase of Tilbury, *Otia imper.*, vol. ii, p. 759. See above, pp. 260–261.

[213] Miller, *op. cit.*, vol. iii, p. 14. Also shown on the Osma Beatus map (*ibid.*, vol. ii, pl. 3; vol. iii, p. 35; Fig. 4, p. 123, above).

[214] Benjamin of Tudela, *Itinerary*, Adler's edit., pp. 75–77.

[215] *Historia*, XIX, 27; in medieval French translation, XIX, 28 (Paulin Paris' edit., vol. ii, pp. 298–299). See also Dreesbach, *Der Orient*, 1901, p. 32.

[216] Schaube, *Handelsgeschichte*, 1906, p. 146.

[217] *ibid.*, p. 181.

[218] Matthew Paris, *Chron. maiora*, Rolls Series edit., vol. v, p. 217, tells how "the indifferentist, Frederic II, nominal leader of a Crusade, main-

tains so close a friendship with the Sultan of Egypt that German merchants (it is said) were able to travel in the company of Egyptians to the Indies" (Beazley, *Dawn*, vol. ii, 1901, p. 461). Heyd, *Commerce du Levant*, vol. ii, 1886, pp. 153–156, refers to a Pisan claim to an expedition to India in 1175. This is very doubtful.

[219] *Historia*, XIX, 24, 27; in medieval French translation, XIX, 23, XIX, 28 (Paulin Paris' edit., vol. ii, pp. 288–289 and 298–299). See also Dreesbach, *op. cit.*, p. 29.

[220] *Historia*, XIX, 27; in medieval French translation, XIX, 28 (Paulin Paris' edit., vol. ii, 298–299). See also Dreesbach, *op. cit.*, p. 30.

[221] *Historia*, XIX, 28, XXI, 23; in medieval French translation, XIX, 29, XXI, 21 (Paulin Paris' edit., vol. ii, pp. 300 and 395). See also Dreesbach, *op. cit.*, p. 34.

[222] Benjamin of Tudela, *Itinerary*, Adler's edit., pp. 71–73. On the flood of the Nile, see also above, pp. 206–207.

[223] *De imag. mundi*, I, 32.

[224] Miller, *Mappaemundi*, vol. ii, 1895, pl. 13; vol. iii, 1895, pl. 2.

[225] *De imag. mundi*, I, 33.

[226] Miller, *op. cit.*, reproduction accompanying vol. i, 1895 (reduced in Fig. 2, p. 69, above).

[227] *ibid.*, vol. i, *passim;* vol. ii, pls. 2–9.

[228] *ibid.*, vol. i, p. 56.

[229] Schaube, *Handelsgeschichte*, 1906, pp. 276–277.

[230] *ibid.*, pp. 275–316.

[231] *ibid.*, pp. 289–290.

[232] Mas-Latrie, *Traités de paix*, 1866, p. 70.

[233] *ibid.*, pp. 71–72.

[234] *ibid.*, pp. 10, 124–125; Léon Godard, *Les évêques de Maroc*, in: Revue africaine, vol. ii, Algiers, 1857, pp. 124–130, 242–249, 433–440; vol. iii, 1858, pp. 1–8; vol. iv, 1859, pp. 259–273, 332–346.

[235] R. B. Merriman, *The Rise of the Spanish Empire*, 2 vols., New York, 1918, vol. i, pp. 303–304.

[236] Miller, *Mappaemundi*, vol. i, 1895, p. 56.

[237] *ibid.*, vol. iii, 1895, p. 42.

[237a] For a discussion of trade routes westward from Egypt and Nubia across the Sahara according to Benjamin of Tudela and Edrisi, see Paul Borchardt, *Die grossen Ost-West Karawanenstrassen durch die Libysche Wüste*, in Petermanns Mitteilungen, vol. lxx, Gotha, 1924, pp. 219–223.

[238] Miller, *op. cit.*, vol. ii, 1895, pl. 13; vol. iii, 1895, pl. 2 and p. 27.

[239] *ibid.*, vol. i, 1895, p. 56.

[240] *ibid.*, vol. iii, 1895, p. 14.

[241] *Otia imper.*, vol. ii, p. 759.

[242] *ibid.*, p. 760.

[243] *De imag. mundi*, I, 33.

[244] Miller, *op. cit.*, vol. i, 1895, p. 56.

[245] Miller, *op. cit.*, vol. ii, 1895, pl. 1, vol. iii, 1895, pl. 3 (Psalter); reproduction accompanying vol. v, 1896 (Ebstorf).

[246] Simar, *Afrique centrale*, 1912, pp. 15–23.

[247] *ibid.*, p. 10.

[248] Langenmaier, *Alte Kenntnis*, 1916, p. 47.

[249] *Hist. adv. pag.*, I, 2.

[250] *Otia imper.*, vol. i, p. 759.

[251] *Etym.*, XIII, 21, 7.

[252] *De imag. mundi*, I, 10.

[253] Miller, *Mappaemundi*, vol. i, 1895, *passim;* vol. ii, 1895, pls. 2–9.

[254] *ibid.*, vol. i, reproduction accompanying the volume, and also p. 57.

[255] *ibid.*, vol. ii, pl. 10; vol. iii, 1895, p. 34.

[256] *ibid.*, vol. iii, pp. 14, 18.

[257] *ibid.*, vol. ii, pl. 13; vol. iii, p. 27 and pl. 2.

[258] Simar, *op. cit.*, pp. 157–158.

[259] Solinus, *Collectanea*, 18, 1; 23, 13; Isidore, *Etym.*, XIII, 16, 1 (cited by Bunbury, *Ancient Geogr.*, 1879, vol. ii, pp. 678–679).

[260] *De imag. mundi*, I, 10, from Isidore, *Etym.*, XIV, 4; *Otia imper.*, vol. i, p. 920. On the other hand, during our period the term "mare mediterraneum" was not invariably applied to the sea between Africa and Europe. Bernard Sylvester says (*De mundi univ.*, pp. 34–35): "Neve rerum tranquillitas violentis passionibus temptaretur, contra fontem caloris solem quem linea medialis exportat, fontem humoris mediterraneum mare medio telluris infudi." "Nous," or the personification of Providence, is here speaking of the equatorial ocean girdling the earth. The same expression, *mare mediterraneum*, referring to the equatorial sea is used on the *mappaemundi* accompanying manuscripts of the *Liber floridus* of Lambert of St. Omer (Miller, *op. cit.*, vol. iii, 1895, p. 50; see also Rainaud, *Continent austral*, 1893, p. 162 and note 3).

[261] The term "Mediterranean Sea" in its present-day application is used on the Hereford map (see Miller, *op. cit.*, vol. iv, 1896, p. 23, and reproduction accompanying vol. iv). The St. Sever Beatus map represents the various parts of the sea by the following names: "Tirrenum Mare," "Mare Ligusticum," "Mare Balearicum," "Mare Libicum," "Mare Siculum," "Mare Creticum," "Mare Egeum," "Sinus Adriaticus," "Sinum Noricum," "Ellespontum," "Eusinus Pontus" (*ibid.*, vol. i, 1895, pp. 60–61 and reproduction accompanying vol. i; names barely legible on our Fig. 2, p. 69, above). The Jerome map of the East also designates portions of the Mediterranean as "Issicum," "Pamphilicum," "Ionicum" (*ibid.*, vol. iii, 1895, p. 12 and pl. 1). See also the discussion of the nomenclature of the Mediterranean and of the ocean in Frahm, *Das Meer*, 1914, pp. 73–77.

[262] *Otia imper.*, vol. i, p. 920.

[263] *De scientia stellarum*, Bologna edit., 1645, p. 25.

[264] [Benedict of Peterborough,] *Gesta regis Ricardi*, Rolls Series edit.,

vol. ii, pp. 198–199; Roger of Hoveden, *Chron.*, Rolls Series edit., vol. iii, p. 51.

[265] The usual route from the Tyrrhenian Sea to the east, however, was through the Strait of Messina. Burkhard, an official of Frederick Barbarossa, tells us that during the war of 1162–1179 between the Sicilians and Genoa, Genoese ships used to make their way to Egypt as follows: through the strait between Corsica and Sardinia, thence past the west coast of Sicily, Pantellaria, and Malta to the north coast of Africa, "until they came in sight of the great stone lighthouse of Alexandria by day or of its light by night" (Burkhard, in: *Mon. Germ. hist.*, Scriptores, vol. xxi, p. 236, cited by Schaube, *Handelsgeschichte*, 1906, p. 153).

[266] This would represent rapid, though probably not excessively rapid, sailing for the Middle Ages. The data which have come down to us on the speed of medieval sea journeys are so varied that it is impossible to determine a fair average. On the whole it is probable that better time was made by the Scandinavian seafarers than by those of the Mediterranean. A rate of fifty miles (English statute) a day was perhaps about all that could have been expected in the Mediterranean under ordinary circumstances, though on occasions one hundred to one hundred and fifty miles or even more may have been accomplished. The Icelanders, on the other hand, may well have covered as much as one hundred and fifty miles in twenty-four hours. See below, p. 486, note 440, and Ludwig, *Untersuchungen*, 1897, *passim*, especially pp. 131–132, 185–186.

To make the journey from Marseilles to Acre in fifteen days a rate of rather more than one hundred and twenty miles a day would have to be maintained throughout the entire passage. Schaube (*op. cit.*, pp. 153–154) brings together some interesting material on the speed of journeys in the Mediterranean. "The duration of the voyages naturally varied very much; we hear that it was reckoned from Messina or one of the Apulian harbors an average of forty days to Accon (Acre); obviously this would refer to a voyage in no way influenced by adverse circumstances. For galleys a somewhat longer time was necessary. The forty galleys of the Emperor Frederick II took in midsummer of 1228 twenty-four days for the journey from Brindisi to Limassol in Cyprus in the best of weather. Benjamin of Tudela assumed that the passage from Messina to Egypt took twenty days. At a somewhat later date Peter of Albeney went from Marseilles to Damietta in twenty-two days, though the ambassador of Barbarossa, Burkhard, who left Genoa on the 6th of September and followed the route by way of Pantellaria and Malta, took more than twice this long, or forty-seven days to reach Alexandria."

[267] [Benedict of Peterborough,] *Gesta regis Ricardi*, Rolls Series edit., vol. ii, pp. 192–199; Roger of Hoveden, *Chron.*, Rolls Series edit., vol. iii, pp. 47–53.

[268] Miller, *Mappaemundi*, vol. iii, 1895, p. 56.

[269] *ibid.*, reproduction accompanying vol. i, 1895 (our Fig. 2, p. 69, above).

[270] *ibid.*, vol. i, p. 35; vol. ii, 1895, pl. 3b (our Fig. 4, p. 123, above).

[271] *De imag. mundi*, I, 34–36; *Otia imper.*, vol. i, pp. 920–923.

[272] [Benedict of Peterborough,] *op. cit.*, vol. ii, p. 198.

[273] Wattenbach, *Guido von Bazoches*, 1891 (under Guy of Bazoches in the Bibliography), pp. 104–112.

[274] See above, pp. 221–222.

[275] Gaston Paris, *La Sicile*, 1876, pp. 108–113.

[276] "Mons ibi stat magnus qui dicitur esse Rolandus
Alter Oliverus simili ratione vocatus:
Haec monumenta truces consistere duces."
—*Pantheon*, pars. 17, in Pistorius' edit., 1726, p. 314.

Gaston Paris argues (*op. cit.*, p. 110) that place names of this origin are still to be found in Sicily.

[277] *Otia imper.*, vol. i, p. 921. On this legend see Graf, *Miti, leggende*, vol. ii, 1893, pp. 303–325.

[278] Gaston Paris, *op. cit.*, p. 112.

[279] See above, p. 221–222.

[280] Ganzenmüller, *Naturgefühl*, 1914, pp. 202, 207, 210–212.

[281] Conrad of Querfurt's letter, in: Arnold of Lübeck, *Chron. Slavorum*, V, 19.

[282] *Estoire de la guerre sainte*, verses 510–558, in: Gaston Paris' edit., cols. 14–16. See Gaston Paris, *La Sicile*, 1876, p. 111.

[283] See above, pp. 220–222 and p. 449, note 52.

[284] *De imag. mundi*, I, 22 (from Isidore, *Etym.*, XIV, 8) mentions the Rhipaean range. See Benl, *Frühere und spätere Hypothesen*, 1905, pp. 10–12. This doctrine may perhaps be traced back to Babylonian geography, according to which the high mountains at the headwaters of the Tigris and Euphrates were thought to bound the earth on the north. See Lutz, *Geographical Studies*, 1924, pp. 167–168.

[285] *Otia imper.*, vol. ii, p. 763.

[286] See, on Grosseteste, above, pp. 179–180. Roger Bacon's argument occurs in his *Opus majus*, Bridges' edit., vol. i, 1897, p. 359.

[287] Theodosia was on the coast of the Crimea, not far from the Strait of Azov (the Cimmerian Bosporus), which might well have been spoken of as the mouth of the Tanaïs, or Don.

[288] See above, p. 75.

[289] Nansen, *Northern Mists*, 1911, vol. ii, pp. 139–140. Adam of Bremen in the eleventh century wrote (*Gesta Hammenb. eccl. pont.*, IV, 13) of Russia as the last and largest province of the Wends, whose territory bounded the Baltic Sea on the east. He mentioned Ostrogard as an important Russian trading city in his time, situated on the Baltic (*ibid.*, II, 19; IV, 11); Chive, or Kiev, as the principal city of Russia (*ibid.*, II, 19), a rival to Constantinople and an honor to "Graecia"—the lands of the Greek church (Dietrich, *Geogr. Anschauungen*, 1885, p. 103). See Tiander, *Poyezdki*, 1906, pp. 47–48.

[290] Schaube, *Handelsgeschichte*, 1906, pp. 238–239.

[291] " . . . inter aquilonem et item orientem Pecenatorum et Falonum, maximam venationum copiam habente, sed vomere ac rastro pene experte campania" (*Gesta Frid.*, I, 31). In *Chron.*, VI, 10, Otto states that "Pecenati et hii qui Falones dicuntur, crudis et immundis carnibus, utpote equinis catinis, usque hodie vescuntur." "Falones" was the medieval German name for the Komans (see Hofmeister's edition of the *Chronicon*, p. 271, note 6). The eleventh-century chronicle of Nestor of Kiev speaks of the Komans as eaters of raw flesh (Zeuss, *Die Deutschen und die Nachbarstämme*, 1837, p. 744). On the Komans, Petchenegs, and other tribes of the Russian plains in the Middle Ages, see the exhaustive treatise of J. Marquart, *Über das Volkstum der Komanen*, forming chapter 2 of W. Bang and J. Marquart, *Osttürkische Dialektstudien*, in: Abhandlungen der königlichen Gesellschaft der Wissenschaften zu Göttingen, Philologisch-historische Klasse, vol. xiii (N. S.), 1912–1914, pp. 25–238.

[292] Hoff's edit., p. 52 (as cited by Dreesbach, *Der Orient*, 1901, pp. 82–83)

[293] See above, pp. 267–268.

[294] *Gesta Frid.*, III, 1.

[295] See above, pp. 330–331.

[296] Benjamin of Tudela, *Itinerary*, Adler's edit., p. 81.

[297] See above, p. 269.

[298] Petachia of Ratisbon, *Travels*, Benisch and Ainsworth's transl., 1856, pp. 3–5; Beazley, *Dawn*, vol. ii, 1901, pp. 266–268.

[299] *Otia imper.*, vol. ii, p. 764, from Orosius, *Hist. adv. pag.*, I, 2.

[300] *Gesta. Frid.*, I, 32.

[301] Karl, *La Hongrie dans les chansons de geste*, 1908.

[302] *ibid.*, pp. 20–21.

[303] *ibid.*, p. 29.

[304] *ibid.*, p. 36.

[305] *De imag. mundi*, I, 25–27.

[306] *Otia imper.*, vol. ii, pp. 764–766.

[307] Miller, *Mappaemundi*, vol. iii, 1895, p. 11 and pl. 1, vol. ii, 1895, pl. 11.

[308] *Chron. Slav.*, I, 3; IV, 9.

[309] Dietrich, *Geogr. Anschauungen*, 1885, p. 102, identifies this with the modern Cuprija (Tsupriya).

[310] Heyd, *Commerce du Levant*, vol. i, 1885, pp. 243–244.

[311] *ibid.*, p. 221.

[312] Benjamin of Tudela, *Itinerary*, Adler's edit., p. 12.

[313] Heyd, *op. cit.*, vol. i, 1885, p. 295. A brief of Innocent III of 1208 mentions the presence of Lombards, Danes, and English.

[314] Benjamin of Tudela, *Itinerary*, Adler's edit., pp. 12–14.

[215] *Gesta Frid.*, II, 13.

[316] Benjamin of Tudela traversed the length of Italy on his way to the Orient. He gives in his *Itinerary* (Adler's edit., pp. 5–10) some details

regarding the cities which he passed through. Genoa and Pisa, he said were governed "neither by king nor prince but only by the judges appointed by the citizens." Each was noted for its "turreted houses for battle in time of strife." Rome was "the head of the kingdoms of Christendom," but Benjamin dismissed with brief phrase her claims to glory as the seat of the Papacy. On the other hand, he wrote in some detail of the Jewish inhabitants of Rome and more especially of the ruins, among them "eighty palaces belonging to eighty kings who lived there, each called Imperator, commencing with King Tarquinius . . . and . . . ending with Pepin, who freed the land of Sepharad [Spain] from Islam, and was father of Charlemagne." The Colosseum, the Catacombs, statues of Samson and of Constantine the Great, and "many other edifices" and "remarkable sights beyond enumeration" aroused the admiration of the Hebrew traveler. Farther south he spoke of the great school of medicine at Salerno; of Amalfi, "the inhabitants of which are merchants engaged in trade, who do not sow or reap, because they dwell upon high hills and lofty crags, but buy everything for money;" of Benevento; of Trani, with a convenient port where pilgrims gather to take ship to Jerusalem; of Brindisi; and, finally, of Otranto, whence one crosses to Corfu.

Interesting details of a journey through Italy in the twelfth century are also supplied in Abbot Nikulás' *Itinerary* (Werlauff, *Symbolae*, 1821, pp. 29–35).

317 For a brief discussion of various regional divisions of Italy suggested by writers from the time of Augustus to that of Dante and of Flavio Biondo (fifteenth century) see Andriani, *La carta dialettologica*, 1923, and below, p. 484, note 418.

318 On another source of wealth of Northern Italy, its auriferous rivers, as listed in the *Honorantie civitatis papie*, a document of the second half of the ninth century, see F. Landogna, *Su alcuni fiumi auriferi nell' alto medio evo*, in: Rivista geografica italiana, vol. xxxi, Florence, 1924, pp. 77–86.

319 *Denumeratio*, p. 45.

320 *Gesta Frid.*, II, 13.

321 *Ligurinus*, II, 131–143.

322 *loc. cit.*

323 See above, pp. 180–181.

324 Gregorovius, *City of Rome* (Hamilton's translation), vol. iv, pt. II, 1896, p. 655. Gregorovius comments on the decided preference given in this book to the pagan as distinguished from the ecclesiastical city. He also commends the work as being fairly accurate in its details. On the interest in ruins that prevailed in our period, see Ganzenmüller, *Naturgefühl*, 1914, pp. 213–215.

325 One of the sources which Master Gregory used was a booklet entitled *De septem miraculis mundi*. The wonders as given in this

booklet were: (1) the Capitol at Rome; (2) the lighthouse at Alexandria; (3) the Colossus of Rhodes; (4) the statue of Bellerophon at Smyrna; (5) the theater at Heraclea; (6) the baths of Apollonius of Tyana; and (7) the temple of Diana at Ephesus. All of these, except the last, were included by Gregory in his account of Rome, though he did not believe that all were actually situated in Rome (James, *Magister Gregorius*, 1917, pp. 537–539).

[326] Conrad of Querfurt's letter, in: Arnold of Lübeck, *Chron. Slav.*, V, 19. See also Ganzenmüller, *Naturgefühl*, 1914, pp. 205–208.

[327] *Otia imper.*, vol. i, p. 916.

[328] *Hist. adv. pag.*, I, 2.

[329] *De imag. mundi*, I, 30.

[330] *Chron.*, Rolls Series edit., vol. iii, p. 48.

[331] *ibid.*, p. 176.

[332] *Gesta Frid.*, II, 13.

[333] *loc. cit.*

[334] Oehlmann, *Alpenpässe*, in: Jahrbuch, vol. iv, 1879, p. 304.

[335] *ibid.*, in: Jahrbuch, vol. iii, 1878, p. 181.

[336] *Mon. Germ. hist.*, Scriptores, vol. xvi, p. 340.

[337] Oehlmann, *op. cit.*, in: Jahrbuch, vol. iii, 1878, p. 180.

[338] Schaube, *Handelsgeschichte*, 1906, pp. 334–338. The Great St. Bernard Pass was the principal artery of trade between Northern Italy and the fairs of Champagne. The Septimer Pass, now little used, was much traveled in the Middle Ages and was a principal trade route between Lombardy and southern and western Germany (Schaube, *op. cit.*, p. 450; Oehlmann, *op. cit.*, in: Jahrbuch, vol. iv, 1879, pp. 305–323).

[339] Oehlmann, *op. cit.*, in: Jahrbuch, vol. iii, 1878, pp. 226–227.

[340] See especially Abbot Nikulás' description of the route over the Great St. Bernard Pass (Werlauff, *Symbolae*, 1821, pp. 18–19).

[341] Oehlmann, *op. cit.*, in: Jahrbuch, vol. iii, 1878, pp. 257–267.

[342] *ibid.*, vol. iv, 1879, pp. 304–323. The medieval history of the Alpine passes is discussed in detail by Oehlmann, *op. cit.;* see also, Reinhard, *Pässe und Strassen*, 1903; Schulte, *Geschichte*, 1900; Scheffel, *Verkehrsgeschichte*, vol. ii, 1914, pp. 167–286. For a more compact account of the Alpine passes in the Middle Ages and in later times, see Coolidge, *The Alps*, 1908, pp. 150–198.

It would seem that the passes of the Central Alps were relatively little known in our period in comparison with those farther east and west. The Simplon and St. Gotthard, now so important, were only just beginning to be frequented. Other routes across the main ranges of the Alps made use of in the twelfth and early thirteenth centuries were the Mont Genèvre and Little St. Bernard, leading from Italy into France and French-speaking Switzerland; the Grimsel and possibly the San Bernardino in the Central Alps; and farther east the Reschen-Scheideck and the Pontebba. Shortly before the opening of our period and during it many hospices were built to provide travelers with shelter and hospitality on the passes and along the routes leading to them.

[343] *Gesta Frid.*, II, 1, 24, 28. See also Dietrich, *Geogr. Anschauungen*, 1885, p. 99; Marinelli, *Scritti minori*, vol. i, [1908?], pp. 600–601.

[344] *Gesta Frid.*, III, 15a; IV, 3.

[345] *ibid.*, I, 8 (discussed in: Dietrich, *op. cit.*, p. 99). Ragewin used the term "Alemanni" to designate Germans in distinction from "Italici" (*Gesta Frid.*, III, 38).

[346] *De imag. mundi*, I, 24, 25.

[347] Notably by J. A. Endres, *Honorius Augustodunensis: Beitrag zur Geschichte des geistigen Lebens im 12. Jahrhundert*, Kempten and Munich, 1906, sect. 12. See Duhem, *Système*, vol. iii, 1915, p. 30.

[348] See above, p. 281.

[349] See above, p. 239.

[350] *Gesta Frid.*, II, 46.

[351] *Denumeratio*, pp. 49–50. For descriptive passages in Godfrey's *Pantheon* on various parts of Germany and Holland, especially on the regions of Nimwegen, Bamberg, and Würzburg, see *Mon. Germ. hist.*, Scriptores, vol. xxii, pp. 159–161, 240 (cited by Ganzenmüller, *Naturgefühl*, 1914, p. 194).

[352] *Ligurinus*, I, 377. See also Gaston Paris, *Dissertation critique*, 1872, pp. 85–86.

[353] Gunther (*Ligurinus*, *loc. cit.*) also describes in detail the frontier between the territory of Cologne and that of Mayence and mentions other local details of this region.

[354] *Subtilitates*, II, 3–10.

[355] See above, pp. 185 and 201–202.

[356] *Gesta Hammenb. eccl. pont.*, I, 1–5. This is taken from Einhard's *Vita Caroli magni* (Beazley, *Dawn*, vol. ii, 1901, p. 533). Beazley, *op. cit.*, pp. 514–548, gives an excellent résumé of the geography of Adam of Bremen. He asserts that Adam "possessed the geographical instinct; almost every mention he makes of persons, places, or nations is accompanied by some definition of their habitat or position" (*ibid.*, p. 516).

[357] Dietrich, *Geogr. Anschauungen*, 1885, p. 189. Adam gives, of course, much fuller detail regarding this and other regions; we have merely tried to bring out a few of his more important geographical ideas.

[358] *Gesta Danorum*, Praefacio, Holder's edit., p. 4.

[359] *ibid.*, pp. 4–5.

[359a] "Iulinum, Iumne, Iomsburg, 935/60–1043 a fort of the Jom Vikings" (Spruner-Menke, *Hand-Atlas für die Geschichte des Mittelalters und der neueren Zeit*, 3rd edit., Gotha, 1880, pl. 37)—the site of the present-day town of Wollin, according to some (Karl Baedeker, *Die deutsche Ostseeküste: Handbuch für Reisende*, Leipzig, 1922, p. 122) or of Swinemünde according to Dietrich, *op. cit.*, p. 189, note 8.

[360] Dietrich, *loc. cit.* Helmold (*Chron. Slav.*, I, 2) describes this city, but by his time it had been destroyed by a Danish king.

[361] *Gesta Hammenb. eccl. pont.*, IV, 18; Helmold, *Chron. Slav.* I, 1. See Dietrich, *op. cit.*, p. 192.

[362] *Chron. Slav.*, II, 216.

[363] Moritz, *Geogr. Kenntnis*, 1904, p. 26.

[364] *Gesta Hammenb. eccl. pont.*, IV, 10; IV, 15. In Adam of Bremen's work the designation "Baltic" probably appears for the first time. Adam says it was so called "because it extends in the form of a belt (baltei)" (Nansen, *Northern Mists*, 1911, vol. i, p. 185).

[365] Adam speaks of a bay trending northward at Birka (*Gesta Hammenb. eccl. pont.*, I, 62). See also Moritz, *op. cit.*, p. 21.

[366] Nansen, *op. cit.*, vol. i, p. 186. See also Marinelli, *Scritti minori*, vol. i, [1908?], pp. 301–302, esp. footnote 1 on p. 302.

[367] *Gesta Danorum*, Praefacio, Holder's edit., p. 8.

[368] Beazley, *Dawn*, vol. ii, 1901, pp. 516–520. For Adam of Bremen's conception of the geography of the North see the full treatment by Björnbo, *Adam af Bremen*, 1909. Björnbo's map showing his theory of Adam's geography is reproduced in Nansen, *Northern Mists*, 1911, vol. i, p. 186. See also Tiander, *Poyezdki*, 1906, pp. 46–51, for a Russian scholar's identification of places mentioned by Adam.

[369] *Gesta Hammenb. eccl. pont.*, IV, 30.

[370] Nansen, *op. cit.*, vol. i, pp. 203–232.

[371] *Gesta Danorum*, Praefacio, Holder's edit., p. 8.

[372] *Historia Norweg.*, I, Storm's edit., p. 83. See also Nansen, *op. cit.*, p. 204. A ski-runner is represented on the Hereford map of the thirteenth century (Miller, *Mappaemundi*, reproduction accompanying vol. iv, 1896; see also Nansen, *ibid.*, p. 157).

[373] *Gesta Hammenb. eccl. pont.*, IV, 31.

[374] Ragewin's continuation of Otto of Freising, *Gesta Frid.*, III, 1.

[375] *Ligurinus*, VI, 13–49.

[376] Traditions of cannibalism among the northern tribes of Europe and Scythia were widespread in the ancient world and date back at least to the time of Herodotus. Human sacrifice and cannibalism were undoubtedly practiced by the early Scandinavians (Nansen, *Northern Mists*, 1911, vol. 1, pp. 81, 148–149).

[377] *Chron.*, VI, 30.

[378] Wattenbach, *Guido von Bazoches*, 1891 (under Guy of Bazoches in the Bibliography), pp. 72–73.

[379] *Denumeratio*, pp. 47–48.

[380] *Otia imper.*, vol. i, pp. 914, 923.

[381] *ibid.*, p. 914.

[382] *Hist. adv. pag.*, I, 2.

[383] *Etym.*, XIV, 6, 38.

[384] *Otia imper.*, vol. i, p. 914.

385 *loc. cit.*

386 *De imag. mundi*, I, 29.

387 *Otia imper.*, vol. i, p. 922.

388 See above, pp. 172-173 and 175.

389 Benjamin of Tudela passed through the south of France. He gives a few details (for the most part concerning the Jewish population) about Narbonne, Béziers, Montpellier, Lunel, Posquières, Arles, and Marseilles. Apparently he went by sea from Marseilles to Genoa (*Itinerary*, Adler's edit., pp. 2-5).

William the Breton gives several striking descriptions of landscapes in France in his *Philippis*. His descriptions of Château Gaillard, of the vicinity of Tours, of Flanders, and of the region about Pontarlier are cited and in part translated into German by Ganzenmüller, *Naturgefühl*, 1914, pp. 196-197.

390 Miller, *Mappaemundi*, vol. i, 1895, p. 50 and reproduction accompanying the volume (reduced in Fig. 2, p. 69, above).

391 *Hist. adv. pag.*, I, 2.

392 *Hist. nat.*, IV, 16. Pliny gives Agrippa as authority for these figures. He states that the width of Britain is 300 miles, not 200 as according to Orosius (*loc. cit.*).

393 Miller, *op. cit.*, vol. ii, 1895, pl. 10; vol. iii, 1895, p. 33.

394 *De imag. mundi*, I, 31.

395 *Otia imper.*, vol. i, p. 916. Gervase quotes Orosius, *Hist. adv. pag.*, I, 2. 37, to the effect that Britain is 800 miles long by 200 broad, but adds that "more recent authorities" give its length as twenty days' journeys and its breadth as ten days' journeys. Elsewhere (*Otia imper.*, vol. i, pp. 936-938) Gervase copies extensively from Geoffrey of Monmouth's *Historia Britonum*, which contains a long account of various supernatural marvels of Britain.

396 *De laud. div. sap.*, V, 789-880.

397 *ibid.*, III, 825-938.

398 Giraldus Cambrensis, *Top. Hiber.*, I, 1.

399 *ibid.*, I, 2.

400 *ibid.*, I, 3.

401 See above, pp. 211-212.

402 *Top. Hiber.*, I, 5.

403 *ibid.*, I, 6.

404 *ibid.*, I, 8.

405 *ibid.*, I, 9.

406 *ibid.*, III, 2.

407 *ibid.*, III, 10.

408 *ibid.*, III, 11-15.

409 Giraldus Cambrensis, *Opera*, Rolls Series edit., vol. v, p. lxiii.

410 *Top. Hiber.*, I, 7.

411 "Gratianus Lucius" (Dr. John Lynch), *Cambrensis eversus*, edited

by Matthew Kelly, 3 vols., Dublin, 1848-1851. This work, a violent attack on Giraldus, was first published in 1662. Dr. Lynch believed that the Welsh traveler had uttered a terrible calumny against the good name of the Irish people and undertook to demolish practically everything he had said.

412 Kelly in his notes to the *Cambrensis eversus*, vol. i, 1848, pp. 117-119, shows how it would have been possible for Giraldus to have made this mistake. From near the Shannon Pot, or source of the River Shannon, other streams flow northward toward Ballyshannon; from Lough Clean (Allen), also very near the Shannon Pot, it is only four miles to the headwaters of the River Bennet, which flows westward into Sligo Bay. These facts might easily give an impression that the Shannon itself branches at its source in two directions, one branch running down towards Ballyshannon or the Bennet, and the other flowing to the southwest. The imperfect drainage development of Ireland would make such an impression seem natural. Lough Hoyle, for instance, is actually drained by two outlets at opposite ends of the lake.

413 *Desc. Kamb.*, 6.

414 *loc. cit.*

415 *ibid.*, 17.

416 See above, pp. 178-179, 197, 215, and 216.

417 *Desc. Kamb.*, 6.

418 An unusual treatment of linguistic geography is found, subsequent to our period, in the *De vulgari eloquentia* of Dante. Whereas Isidore of Seville on Biblical authority had divided the languages of the world into three main groups, the Japhetic, Hamitic, and Semitic, Dante recognized the fact that these groups are further divisible into secondary groups each consisting of several kindred languages. He believed that there were three original European tongues: Greek, spoken in the southeast and in Asia Minor; a language spoken in the southwest; and one spoken in the north and east. "Man being a most unstable and variable animal," these three original tongues became altered "according to the distances in place and time" with the result that certain "vulgar tongues" were formed. These tongues in turn underwent variations in different localities; the resultant forms were still further subdivided, until by Dante's time there were in existence in Italy alone more than a thousand local dialectic peculiarities. See Mori, *La geogr.*, 1922, pp. 289-292.

Andriani, *La carta dialettologica*, 1923, discusses Dante's study of the local dialects of Italy as elaborated in the *De vulgari eloquentia*. The poet divided the peninsula and Sardinia into fourteen major dialectic regions. These correspond essentially with the geographical regions established by Flavio Biondo in his *Italia illustrata* (fifteenth century). With the aid of the latter work Andriani constructs a tentative dialectic map of Italy as Dante probably would have conceived it. Modern research in the linguistic geography of that country has served in general to confirm Dante's assertions on the subject.

419 See Bibliography under William Fitzstephen.

420 See above, p. 331–332.

421 The preceding quotations from William Fitzstephen are taken from Morley's translation on pp. 22–26 of his edition of Stow's *A Survay of London . . . 1598*, 1908.

422 The quotations on the sports of the Londoners are from Stow's sixteenth-century translation in Morley's edition of Stow, *op. cit.*, pp. 117–125.

423 Miller, *Mappaemundi*, vol. iii, 1895, pp. 74–77.

424 *ibid.*, p. 75.

425 See above, p. 335 and p. 483, notes 392 and 395. For these and other legends quoted below, see Miller, *ibid.*, pp. 75–82.

426 "Pinlimon," "Montes Chivieti," "Mons Snaudun" (*ibid.*, pp. 78, 79).

427 "Regio montuosa et nemorosa, gentem incultam generans et pastoralem, quia pars eius mariscus est et harundinetum" (*ibid.*, p. 78).

428 "Regia invia et aquosa." "Patria palustris et invia, pecudibus et pastoribus apta" (*ibid*).

429 "Regio palustris, montuosa, nemorosa, invia, pastoribus accomoda, incolas habet agiles, incultos et bellicosos" (*ibid.*, p. 79). See above, p. 233.

430 "Sephe," "Thanet," "Vecta," "V̄eñ." (Alderney?), "Grenese" (Guernsey), "Purland," "Sulli," "Lundeth," "Engleseia insula," "Man," "Tyren insula" (this may be either Tiree or the peninsula of Kintyre, Miller, *ibid.*, p. 75), "insula Columkilli" (Icolmkill, or Iona), "Orkades Insule" (*ibid.*, p. 75).

431 *Top. Hiber.*, II, 15.

432 *ibid.*, II, 11.

433 *ibid.*, II, 13.

434 *ibid.*, II, 17.

435 C. H. Haskins, *The De Arte Venandi cum Avibus of the Emperor Frederick II*, in: English Historical Review, vol. xxxvi, London, 1921, p. 346, note 8; idem, *Studies*, 1924, p. 316, note 104. "Gallandia" here may mean Greenland, although in Ordericus Vitalis (*Hist. eccles.*, II, 5) "Gollanda" is probably Gotland (see below, p. 487, note 455). Abu-l-Hasan, a Moslem geographer of the thirteenth century, places the island of the white falcons to the west of Denmark. "Its length from west to east is about seven days and its breadth about four days." He reports that white falcons are brought from here for the Sultan of Egypt. He also speaks of a white bear in these regions, which goes out into the sea and swims and catches fish (Nansen, *Northern Mists*, 1911, vol. ii, pp. 208–209).

436 *Íslendingabók*, 1, 2–3; translation from Nansen, *op. cit.*, vol. i, p. 254.

The pre-Norse Christians in Iceland were Irish hermits, whose visits to Thule or Iceland are described by Dicuil, *De mens. orb. ter.*, 7 (Letronne's edit., p. 38). See also *ibid.*, pp. 165–166).

437 *Hist. de antiq. reg. norwag.*, 3, Storm's edit., p. 8; translation from Nansen, *op. cit.*, vol. i, p. 254. See above, p. 412, note 122.

438 *Hist. Norweg.*, I, Storm's edit., p. 92; translation from Nansen, *op. cit.*, vol. i, p. 255.

439 Translation from Nansen, *loc. cit.*

440 On Norse settlements and voyages on the coasts of Greenland, see Nansen, *op. cit.*, vol. i, pp. 258–311. The *Landnámabók*, I (transl. in Vigfusson and York Powell, *Orig. Island.*, vol. i, 1905, pp. 14–15) gives the distances in days' sailing from points on the coast of Iceland to points on the coasts of Norway, Greenland, Ireland, and to "Svalbard" (possibly Spitsbergen; see above, p. 349). It was said to have been a journey of seven *doegr* from Cape Stat in Norway to Cape Horn on the east coast of Iceland, of three (according to one version of the *Landnámabók*) or of five (according to another version) from Reykyanes to the Mare's Leap in Ireland, of four *doegr* from the northeasternmost cape of Iceland to Svalbard, and of one across to Greenland at what was probably the narrowest passage. These figures are difficult to interpret. The relative times given in no way correspond to the actual relative distances, and we are not absolutely certain what is meant by *doegr*. In fact Nansen writes that it is hopeless to look for any system in these data (*op. cit.*, vol. ii, p. 170). If we take *doegr* to be a journey of twelve hours (as would seem to be indicated by the *Heimskringla*, Morris and Magnússon's transl., vol. ii, p. 242; interpreted by Nansen, *op. cit.*, pp. 170, 171, and note) the passage from Norway to Iceland would require sailing at a rate of 155 sea miles in twenty-four hours, not altogether excessive under favorable conditions. On the other hand, the passage from Iceland to Ireland and to Greenland would necessitate a speed of either 475 or 385 sea miles in twenty-four hours respectively, which would be excellent speed for a modern liner. See Nansen, *loc. cit.*, and E. Magnússon's note on the sailing directions of the *Landnámabók* in: Transactions of the Cambridge Philological Society, vol. i, for 1872–1880, London, 1881, pp. 316–318.

441 *Konungs-Skuggsjá*, 16 (Brenner's edit.), pp. 47–48; translation from Nansen, *Northern Mists.*, 1911, vol. i, pp. 279–280.

442 *Gesta Hammenb. eccl. pont.*, IV, 39; translation from Nansen, *op. cit.*, vol. i, p. 195.

443 *Gesta Danorum*, VIII, Holder's edit., pp. 287–292.

444 *Hist. Norweg.*, I, Storm's edit., pp. 75–76; translation from Nansen, *op. cit.*, vol. ii, p. 167.

445 *Hist. Norweg.*, I, Storm's edit., pp. 78–79; translation from Nansen, *op. cit.*, vol. ii, p. 168. On the relation of this gulf with the mythical Ginungagap (see above, p. 147) see Nansen, *op. cit.*, vol. ii, p. 239–240.

[446] *Landnámabók*, I, 1 (transl. in Vigfusson and York Powell, *Orig. Island.*, vol. i, 1905, p. 15. See Nansen, *op. cit.*, vol. ii, p. 166.

[447] Nansen, *loc. cit.*

[448] It is of course not certain that Spitsbergen is meant by the "Svalbard" of the *Icelandic Annals*. See the discussion in Nansen, *op. cit.*, vol. ii, pp. 166–171.

[449] Reeves, *Wineland*, 1890, p. 10.

[450] *ibid.*, p. 81.

[451] English translation of these in Reeves, *op. cit.*, pp. 28–52, 64–78.

[452] See above, p. 405, note 90. This part of the geographical description is probably not the work of Abbot Nikulás Bergsson. See Nansen, *In Northern Mists*, 1911, vol. i, p. 313.

[453] Nikulás Bergsson's geographical description of the world, in: Werlauff, *Symbolae*, 1821, p. 14.

[454] *Gesta Hammenb. eccl. pont.*, IV, 38; translation from Reeves, *op., cit.*, p. 92.

[455] "Orcades insulae et Finlanda. Islanda quoque et Grenlanda, ultra quam ad Septentrionem terra non reperitur, aliaeque plures usque in Gollandam regi Noricorum subjiciuntur, et de toto orbe divitiae navigio illuc advehuntur" (*Hist. eccles.*, pt. III, bk. X, 5, in: Migne, *Pat. lat.*, vol. clxxxviii, col. 727). "Finlanda" here refers to Wineland (Rafn, *Antiq. americanae*, 1837, p. 337).

[456] See Rafn, *op. cit.*, p. 338, note g; Lappenberg, in his edition of Adam of Bremen in *Scriptores rerum germ.*, Hanover, 1876, p. xvii, maintained that this was a later interpolation made by Adam himself. See Nansen, *op. cit.*, vol. i, p. 195; vol. ii, pp. 147–155.

[457] *Gesta Hammenb. eccl. pont.*, IV, 38; translation from Reeves, *op. cit.* pp. 92–93.

[458] *De imag. mundi*, I, 36.

[459] E. Renan, *Essais de morale et de critique*, 3rd edit., Paris, 1868, p. 445, quoted by F. Michel, *Les voyages merveilleux de St. Brandan*, Paris, 1878, p. vii.

[460] Schröder, *Sanct Brandan*, 1871 (under Brandan in the Bibliography), p. vi.

[461] This résumé of the voyages of St. Brandan in the present text was made from the Latin text of the *Peregrinatio* given by Schröder, *op. cit.*, pp. 3–36. Reference has already been made to various aspects of the voyages; see above, pp. 197–198, 224–225, 230–231.

[462] *De mensura orbis terrae*, 7 (Letronne's edit., p. 40).

[463] The *Peregrinatio* (Schröder, *op. cit.*, p. 32) describes Paul's islet as being as long as it was broad and of equal height. This suggests the lonely Rockall, some 280 miles west of the Outer Hebrides. See J. B. Charcot, *Les croisières du "Pourquoi pas?" en 1921*, in: La Géographie, vol. xxxvi, Paris, 1922, pp. 475–476.

BIBLIOGRAPHY

SUPPLEMENTARY BIBLIOGRAPHICAL NOTE, 1964

The note that begins on the opposite page is reprinted as it appeared in the first edition of this book (1925).

Two basic sources of more recent bibliographical information are the *Research Catalogue of the American Geographical Society*, 15 vols., Boston (G. K. Hall), 1962 (available in large libraries), and the critical book reviews and bibliographies in *Isis*, of which the subtitle is now *International Review Devoted to the History of Science and its Cultural Influences* (see below, p. 493). By going through both of these the conscientious student might feel reasonably confident of being put on the track of the great majority of references to works of any consequence pertaining to the history of ancient and medieval geography. For further assurance, however, other up-to-date bibliographical reference works bearing on ancient and medieval history or civilization should be consulted.

See also: George Sarton, *Introduction to the History of Science*, vols. i and ii, Washington, 1927, 1931; G. H. T. Kimble, *Geography in the Middle Ages*, London, 1938; J. K. Wright and Elizabeth T. Platt, *Aids to Geographical Research*, 2nd edition, New York, 1947, pp. 100–111; A. C. Crombie, *Medieval and Early Modern Science*, 2 vols., Garden City, N.Y. (Doubleday Anchor Books), 1959 (revision of Crombie's *Augustine to Galileo: The History of Science, A.D. 400–1650*, London, 1952); A. C. Crombie, editor, *Scientific Change: Historical Studies in the Intellectual, Social and Technical Conditions for Scientific Discovery and Technical Invention, from Antiquity to the Present: Symposium of the History of Science, University of Oxford 9–15 July 1961*, New York, 1963, Part 3, "Science and Technology in the Middle Ages."

BIBLIOGRAPHICAL NOTE

Those who wish to carry out detailed investigations of the various topics discussed in the present volume will find in the Notes and Bibliography references to the original sources and to secondary works. Owing, however, to the scattered nature of the references in the Notes and to the alphabetical arrangement of the Bibliography it is impossible from them alone to gain a rapid introduction to the outstanding publications on the subject. To supply such an introduction is the purpose of the following note.

Titles are not as a rule here cited in full, and the reader should therefore turn to the Bibliography for the full titles, for indications of the place and manner of publication, and for other bibliographical details. The relatively few titles of publications mentioned here only are given in full and are followed by the words "(not in Bibliography)."

Bibliographies

The study of the geographical lore of the Middle Ages has been approached by scholars from many different points of view. This is reflected in the character of the bibliographies dealing specifically or incidentally with this field. We may group these bibliographies arbitrarily into three classes: (a) historical bibliographies; (b) geographical bibliographies; (c) bibliographies devoted to the history of science.

Historical Bibliographies

Among the historical bibliographies mention should first be made of Chevalier's *Répertoire des sources historiques du moyen âge*, 1894–1907. Two volumes of this work, with the subtitle *Bio-bibliographie*, list alphabetically a large number of personages of importance in the Middle Ages. Brief biographical notes are given, followed by extensive lists of references to publications by or in any way relating to these personages. A great difficulty in using the *Bio-bibliographie* lies in the fact that no clues are given regarding the type of publications to which reference is made. We are not told whether these publications are printed texts of medieval works, scholarly treatises, or merely passing and relatively unimportant allusions. In a third volume of Chevalier's *Répertoire* (with the subtitle *Topo-bibliographie*) the effort is made to list alphabetically a multitude of topics relating to medieval history and life and, as in the *Bio-bibliographie*, to give references to publications upon these topics. Here again, owing to the lack of critical evaluation of the references as well as to the somewhat arbitrary selection of the topical headings, the work is of very uneven utility.

Whereas Chevalier attempts to cover the entire range of medieval civilization, the writings of the historians and chroniclers of the age are dealt with in Potthast's indispensable *Bibliotheca historica medii aevi*, 1896.

The main part of these volumes consists of an alphabetical repertory of names and titles with references to manuscripts, editions, translations, and secondary works explanatory of the sources. There are also included highly useful synopses of the contents of the great collections of medieval sources (see below, pp. 493–495) and an appendix in which the titles of the original sources are given chronologically within regional divisions.

For a general guide to many of the more important books and articles on medieval history, L. J. Paetow's *Guide to the Study of Medieval History for Students, Teachers, and Librarians* (University of California Syllabus Series, no. 90), Berkeley, Cal., 1917 (not in Bibliography), is valuable. A large part of Paetow's book is devoted to medieval culture. Though by no means exhaustive, the *Guide* is excellent for orienting the student in an unfamiliar field.

We refrain from mentioning other historical bibliographies of regions and topics relating to the Middle Ages. References to many of these may readily be found in the first chapter of Paetow's *Guide* and in the various paragraphs entitled "Bibliographies" appended to the topical sections of that publication.

Geographical Bibliographies

The bibliography of ancient and medieval geography has been dealt with at some length in the summaries of the progress of geographical research that have appeared from time to time in the *Geographisches Jahrbuch* published by Justus Perthes, Gotha (not in Bibliography), which since 1880 has been edited by Professor Hermann Wagner of Göttingen. The ancient period has been covered by Professor Eugen Oberhummer in vols. xix (1896), xxii (1899), xxviii (1905), and xxxiv (1911); the medieval by Professors Sophus Ruge and Walther Ruge in vols. xviii (1895), xx (1897), xxiii (1900), xxvi (1903), and xxx (1907). These reports are running commentaries on the progress of current investigation, with references to the literature in the footnotes.

A section on the history of geography, with occasional references to publications in the medieval field, has appeared regularly in the *Bibliographie géographique annuelle* (not in Bibliography) of the periodical Annales de Géographie, published by Armand Colin, Paris, 1893–1914, and in its continuation, *Bibliographie géographique 1915–1919, 1920–1921, 1922* (not in Bibliography), published under the auspices of the Association de Géographes Français. References to secondary works in medieval geography are also given in the annual volumes of *Bibliotheca Geographica* (not in Bibliography), published by the Gesellschaft für Erdkunde Berlin, and covering 1891 to 1912.

Bibliographies of the History of Science

References to publications on medieval geography as a part of the history of science may be found in the critical bibliographies that have been included since its inception in 1913 in each number of the periodical Isis:

International Review Devoted to the History of Science and Civilization, Brussels.

DICTIONARIES

Research in the field covered by the present volume requires a working knowledge of medieval Latin, the language in which most of the original sources were written. Medieval Latin is not difficult—except in occasional passages—for one who has some knowledge of classical Latin. The great dictionary of C. D. Du Cange, *Glossarium ad scriptores mediae et infimae latinitatis* (not in Bibliography), first published at Paris in 1678 and subsequently in other editions (the latest at Niort, 1883–1887), is indispensable. For medieval French, consult F. E. Godefroy, *Dictionnaire de l'ancienne langue française*, 10 vols., Paris, 1881–1902 (not in Bibliography).

MANUSCRIPTS

Many of the works of medieval authors have never been printed. They can be consulted only in the collections of manuscripts of the libraries of Europe and, to a limited extent, of America. While research in manuscripts is not absolutely essential for a general study like the present, no detailed research can very well be conducted without direct recourse to unprinted documents.

The use of medieval manuscripts is an art in itself, requiring some familiarity with paleography. The handwritings of the twelfth and thirteenth centuries, however, are frequently not difficult to decipher. On this subject consult: E. M. Thompson, *An Introduction to Greek and Latin Palaeography*, Oxford, 1912 (not in Bibliography), and, for abbreviations commonly used in manuscripts, A. Cappelli, *Lexicon abbreviaturarum . . . : Dizionario di abbreviature latine ed italiene . . .* , Milan, 1899, 2nd edit., Milan, 1912 (not in Bibliography).

A list of catalogues of collections of manuscripts will be found in a publication of the Bibliothèque Nationale of Paris: *Collection alphabétique des livres imprimés mis à la disposition des lecteurs dans la salle de travail, suivi de la liste des catalogues usuels du département des manuscrits*, Paris, 1910 (not in Bibliography). Useful references to manuscripts of some of the writings on geography and natural science of the Middle Ages are included in Beazley, *Dawn of Modern Geography*, 1897–1906, in Thorndike, *History of Magic and Experimental Science*, 1923, and in Haskins, *Studies in the History of Mediaeval Science*, 1924. References to manuscript maps will be found in Miller, *Mappaemundi*, 1895–1898.

COLLECTIONS OF ORIGINAL SOURCES

The great printed collections of historical sources dealing with the Middle Ages are discussed in Paetow's *Guide* (see above, p. 492) and analyzed in Potthast's *Bibliotheca* (see above, p. 491). In the Bibliography of the present volume reference is made to printed texts of individual works. It will therefore not be necessary here to do more than indicate the titles of a few of the collections most important from the point of view of medieval geography.

The *Corpus scriptorum ecclesiasticorum latinorum*, 1866 ff., is a collection of critically edited texts of the writings of the Latin Church Fathers. Migne, *Patrologiae cursus completus . . . series latina* (referred to in the Notes as *Pat. lat.*), 1844–1864, contains texts, for the most part uncritical, not only of the writings of the Church Fathers but also of a vast assemblage of works bearing directly or indirectly on the medieval Church.

In nearly all the nations of Europe the publication has been carried through or is in progress of great collections of sources dealing with the national history during the Middle Ages. To mention briefly a few of these, we may refer first to the *Rerum britannicarum medii aevi scriptores*, 1858–1891, usually known as the "Rolls Series." This series includes not only the works of the historians and chroniclers of Britain of the Middle Ages but also those of many British writers on matters of geography and natural science. The *Monumenta Germaniae historica*, 1826–1874 and 1876 ff., contains in its magnificent volumes documents relating to all aspects of the history and life of the medieval Germans and incidentally of Europe as a whole. Many of the texts of the *Monumenta* have been more critically edited in the *Scriptores rerum germanicarum in usum scholarum ex Monumentis Germaniae historicis recusi*, 1840 ff. For France there are the *Rerum gallicarum et francicarum scriptores*, or *Recueil des historiens des Gaules et de la France*, Paris, 1738–1904 (not in Bibliography), and the publications of the Société de l'Histoire de France, Paris, 1835 ff. (not in Bibliography); for the Crusades the most important collection is the *Recueil des historiens des croisades*, 14 vols., Paris, 1841–1898 (not in Bibliography).

Collections dealing more especially with texts of geographical importance are, for ancient geography, Müller's *Geographi graeci minores*, 1882, and Riese's *Geographi latini minores*, 1878. Itineraries to and descriptions of the Holy Land will be found in Tobler, *Descriptiones terrae sanctae*, 1874, Tobler, *Itinera . . . saec. iv–xi*, 1877, Michelant and Reynaud, *Itinéraires à Jerusalem*, 1882, and Tobler, Molinier, and Kohler, *Itinera . . . bellis sacris anteriora*, 1880–1885. English translations of certain medieval travels in Palestine will be found in Thomas Wright, *Early Travels in Palestine*, 1848, and in the *Library* of the Palestine Pilgrims' Text Society, 1885–1897. Texts and English translations for the early exploration of Iceland will be found in Vigfusson and Yorke Powell, *Origines islandicae*, 1905. Documents relating to the Norse discovery of America are included in Rafn, *Antiquitates americanae*, 1837–1841; and Reeves, *The Finding of Wineland the Good*, 1890, gives English translations of the Vineland voyages. On the texts of the great Asiatic voyages of the thirteenth and fourteenth centuries, which do not fall within the scope of the present volume, see above, pp. 269–270, and p. 465, notes 70, 71, 74, 75.

The primary collection of facsimiles of medieval maps prior to the appearance of the portolan charts is Miller, *Mappaemundi*, 1895–1898; critical texts with references to manuscripts and discussions are here given. Reproductions of early medieval maps are also given in the atlases to Santarem, *Essai sur l'histoire de la cosmographie et de la cartographie*, 1849–1852, and to Lelewel, *Géographie du moyen âge*, 1852–1857.

A selection of medieval texts dealing with meteorology will be found in Hellmann, *Denkmäler mittelalterlicher Meteorologie*, 1904.

Secondary Works

We may divide our treatment of secondary works into two parts: first, a discussion of publications dealing with the broader background of medieval life and thus, incidentally, with the geographical lore of the period; second, a discussion of publications dealing directly with the geographical and related lore of antiquity and the Middle Ages or with the enlargement of geographical knowledge. The titles of secondary works relating to the specific writings or authors referred to in the present volume may readily be found by using the cross-references in the Bibliography.

Background of Medieval Intellectual Life

In order not to expand our discussion beyond due measure, we shall restrict ourselves in this section to mentioning a very few publications the majority of which have been of direct service in the preparation of the present volume.

For a broad and brilliantly written treatment of medieval intellectual activity in its many phases, we may refer to H. O. Taylor, *The Mediaeval Mind: A History of the Development of Thought and Emotion in the Middle Ages*, 2 vols., New York, 1911, revised edit., 1914 (not in Bibliography). Haskins' *Studies in the History of Mediaeval Science*, 1924, which appeared while the present volume was in press, is fundamental for the history of science in Western Europe in the twelfth and thirteenth centuries. Several of its chapters are revisions of articles which had previously appeared, but other parts of the work are entirely new contributions. The volume is based to a very large extent upon hitherto unpublished sources; many critical and interesting passages of Latin texts are published in it for the first time. Poole's *Illustrations of the History of Medieval Thought and Learning*, 1920, is a discussion of the work of a few selected exponents of typical modes of medieval thought. The original work of the scholars of Chartres in the Middle Ages is the subject of Clerval's *Écoles de Chartres*, 1895.

The Latin literature of the period as a whole is dealt with in Gröber, *Übersicht über die lateinische Literatur von der Mitte des 6. Jahrhunderts bis 1350*, 1888–1902, and medieval Latin literature prior to the middle of the eleventh century is treated in greater detail in M. Manitius, *Geschichte der lateinischen Literatur des Mittelalters*, vol. 1, 1911. On the Latin poetry of the twelfth and thirteenth centuries consult Francke, *Geschichte der lateinischen Schulpoesie*, 1879. For the French literature of the age there is the important volume of Gaston Paris, *La littérature française au moyen âge*, 1914, or the English translation.

Medieval philosophy is outlined in De Wulf, *Histoire de la philosophie médiévale*, 1900, or the English translation.

On the art of the twelfth and thirteenth centuries as expressing the thought of the time the student should read Mâle's two volumes, *L'art religieux du xiie siècle*, 1922, and *L'art religieux du xiiie siècle*, 1910, or the English translation of the volume dealing with the thirteenth century.

An old but highly suggestive treatise on the natural science of the early twelfth century is that of C. B. Jourdain, *Dissertation sur l'état de la philosophie naturelle*, 1838. Natural science, magic, and legendary lore of the first thirteen centuries of the Christian era form the topics of Thorndike's learned *History of Magic and Experimental Science*, 1923. Some of these subjects as they were embodied in medieval French encyclopedias compiled for the use of the layman are illustrated in C. V. Langlois, *La connaissance de la nature*, 1911. Legendary lore more especially is the theme of Denis' little *Monde enchanté*, 1843, of Berger de Xivrey's *Traditions tératologiques*, 1836, and, more recently, of Graf's *Miti, leggende e superstizioni*, 1892–1893.

The relation between theology and natural science in the Middle Ages has been a matter of controversy. From a point of view relatively favorable to medieval science the subject was discussed by Zöckler, *Geschichte der Beziehungen zwischen Theologie und Naturwissenschaft*, vol. i, 1877; from a more critical point of view, by Draper, *Conflict Between Religion and Science*, 1875, and in White's scholarly *Warfare of Science with Theology*, 1895.

The influence of classical scholarship upon medieval thought was potent. This topic as a whole is dealt with in much detail in Sandys' monumental *History of Classical Scholarship*, 3rd edit., vol. i, 1921. On the use of classical works in the Middle Ages see also the two monographs of M. Manitius, *Beiträge zur Geschichte der römischen Prosaiker*, 1890, and *Philologisches aus alten Bibliothekskatalogen*, 1892. In regard to medieval Latin translations from the Greek, Arabic, and Hebrew, the formerly authoritative treatises of Amable Jourdain, *Recherches critiques*, 1843, and Wüstenfeld, *Übersetzungen arabischer Werke*, 1877, have to a large extent been superseded by the researches of Steinschneider (*Hebräische Übersetzungen*, 1893; *Europäische Übersetzungen*, 1905–1906), Mandonnet (*Siger de Brabant*, 1908, 1911), Grabmann (*Forschungen über die lateinischen Aristotelesübersetzungen*, 1916), Haskins (*Studies in the History of Mediaeval Science*, 1924), and others (see above, pp. 95–102, and notes 32–70 on pp. 398–403.

The Geographical Lore of Antiquity and of the Middle Ages

The publications dealing with ancient and medieval geographical lore may be divided into three groups: those devoted to (a) the history of geography as a whole; (b) the history of geography in particular periods; (c) the history of particular aspects of geography.

The History of Geography as a Whole

With the exception of a few brief popular works, the writer knows of only three general histories of geography in which the attempt is made to cover the entire field. These are Louis Vivien de St. Martin, *Histoire de la géographie et des découvertes géographiques depuis les temps les plus reculés jusqu'à nos jours*, with atlas, Paris, 1873 (not in Bibliography); Peschel, *Geschichte der Erdkunde*, 1877; and Günther, *Geschichte der Erdkunde*, 1904. The first is concerned primarily with explorations and the expansion of regional knowledge; in its pages the medieval period receives but scant attention. Peschel aimed to cover both exploration and scientific geography, and his work, though old, is of great value: scholarly, well balanced, and clearly written. Whereas Peschel stopped with the early nineteenth century, Günther carries the record through that century; his book contains a wealth of detail and of useful bibliographical notes.

The History of Geography in Particular Periods

1. *Ancient Geography.* Bunbury's *History of Ancient Geography*, 1879, remains to the present day the only work of large scope on Greek and Latin geography as a whole. Tozer's delightful *History of Ancient Geography*, 1897, is a good introduction to the subject but is inadequate for detailed research. A scholarly treatment of the scientific geography of the Greeks is Berger's *Geschichte der wissenschaftlichen Erdkunde der Griechen*, 1903. The most extensive recent treatment of classical geography as a whole, with numerous references, is Gisinger's article "Geographie" in *Paulys Real-Encyclopädie*, 1924. The evolution of those theories of ancient geography which prepared the way toward the discovery of America is admirably outlined in the now somewhat out-of-date but nevertheless useful and stimulating chapter by Tillinghast, *Geographical Knowledge of the Ancients in Relation to the Discovery of America*, in the first volume of Winsor's *Narrative and Critical History*, 1889. Alexander von Humboldt in the first part of the *Examen critique de l'histoire de la géographie du nouveau continent et des progrès de l'astronomie nautique aux quinzième et seizième siècles*, Paris, 1st edit., 1814–1834 (not in Bibliography), probed deeply into the history of ancient geography. See also C. B. Jourdain, *De l'influence d'Aristote . . . sur la découverte du Nouveau-Monde*, 1861.

2. *Medieval Geography.* Santarem's *Essai sur l'histoire de la cosmographie et de la cartographie*, 1849–1852, marks one of the earliest attempts in modern times to open up the subject of medieval geography. It consists of a mass of detailed notes on the regional geographical theories of the cosmographers of the Middle Ages. Lelewel's *Géographie du moyen âge*, 1852–1857, is a work of erudition exasperating in the confusion of its arrangement, the difficulty of its style, and the untenability of many of

its theories. Lelewel, however, went beyond Santarem in his endeavor to take into consideration the work of Arabic as well as of Occidental geographical authors.

The most recent broad history of medieval geography is Beazley's important *Dawn of Modern Geography*, 1897–1906. These three volumes are the result of long and arduous research and will probably remain for many years to come on the whole the most satisfactory general treatment of the subject. They cover the period from 300 to 1420 A. D. Attention is given to the explorations and geographical science not only of the Christians but also of the Arabs and Chinese (the two latter subjects, however, having been studied through translations and secondary works only). Throughout, especial stress is laid upon the record of travel and exploration and upon the historical events that led to the acquisition of geographical information by travel and exploration. In the first two volumes, on the period until 1260, extensive chapters are devoted to "Geographical Theory," but in the third, covering 1260 to 1420, only 29 out of a total of 541 pages are given to geographical theory, and the chapter on geographical theory of the period from 900 to 1260 in the second volume barely touches upon the various topics discussed in Chapters V to X of the present book. To illustrate the theoretical "earth-knowledge" of the "Central Middle Age period" Beazley discusses three examples only, the work of Constantine Porphyrogenetos, that of Adam of Bremen, and the chief maps of the age. There is either the briefest passing mention or else no reference whatever to the writings of the highly characteristic authors the study of whose geographical opinions is the main purpose of the present volume—such writers as Peter Abelard, Peter Comestor, Hildegard of Bingen, Bernard and Theodoric of Chartres, Adelard of Bath, William of Conches, Gerard of Cremona, Michael Scot, Robert Grosseteste, Gervase of Tilbury, Otto of Freising, Gunther of Pairis, Giraldus Cambrensis, Saxo Grammaticus, Guy of Bazoches, and the various translators from the Arabic. Furthermore, Beazley makes no attempt to give a systematic analysis of the various elements that constituted the geographical lore of the scholar or educated reader of Western Europe in the age of the Crusades.

A scholarly account of the geography of the Church Fathers is Marinelli, *La geografia e i padri della chiesa*, 1882 (also translated into German). Very full references are here given in footnotes.

On the geography of the Moslems of the Middle Ages the first volume of Reinaud's *Géographie d'Aboulféda*, 1848, though now more than seventy years old, is still, to our knowledge, the only thoroughly scholarly work covering the whole field in detail. More recent, but much briefer treatments are those of Baron Carra de Vaux in the second volume of his *Penseurs de l'Islam*, 1921, and of Carl Schoy in various articles (cited in the Bibliography under his name), especially the article in the Geographical Review, 1924.

The History of Particular Aspects of Geography

1. *Cosmogony and Cosmology.* Duhem's great *Système du monde*, 1913–1917, is now the fundamental history of the evolution of cosmological doctrines from the time of Plato to the fourteenth century. To it the writer owes, to a large extent, his guidance to the original sources as well as much of the material which he has necessarily accepted at second hand in those parts of the present book which deal with the origins and the larger relations of the earth to the remainder of the universe. For the twelfth and thirteenth centuries Werner's two monographs, *Die Kosmologie . . . Wilhelm von Conches*, 1873, and *Die Kosmologie . . . des Roger Baco*, 1879, are important. On the development of Christian theories of the Creation one should also consult Zöckler, *Geschichte der Beziehungen zwischen Theologie und Naturwissenschaft*, 1877–1879, and Robbins, *Hexaemeral Literature*, 1912. See also A. C. McGiffert, *The God of the Early Christians*, New York, 1924 (not in Bibliography), for the theologians' view of the Creation in the early centuries of our era. An interesting monograph on the ancient theory of the periodic destruction and rebirth of the universe is that of Günther, *Die antike Apokatastasis*, 1916.

2. *Larger problems of terrestrial geography.* These problems are dealt with by Kretschmer in the monograph discussed in the following subsection (3).

Several important studies have been written on the medieval beliefs regarding the shape of the earth. Günther, in his *Studien zur Geschichte der mathematischen und physikalischen Geographie*, 1877–1879, treated the subject from the point of view shared by many Protestants; Schneid, *Die Lehre von der Erdrundung*, 1877, replied to Günther from the Catholic point of view. More recently the matter has been discussed by Betten (see above, p. 384, note 48). Proofs of the curvature of the earth adduced in antiquity and during the Middle Ages are the topic of a monograph by Günther, *Optische Beweisung für die Erdkrümmung*, 1920.

On the Eratosthenic measurement of the size of the earth and its subsequent influence the fundamental work is now the two volumes of Thalamas, *Étude bibliographique de la géographie d'Ératosthène*, 1921, and *La géographie d'Ératosthène*, 1921. Other interesting studies in this field are those of Mori, *La misurazione eratostenica*, 1911, Decourdemanche, *Note sur l'estimation de la longeur du degré terrestre*, 1913, and Miller, *Die Erdmessung im Alterthum*, 1919.

The problems of the antipodes and the austral continent are sketched historically by Rainaud, *Le continent austral*, 1893; the antipodes more particularly by Boffito, *La leggenda degli antipodi*, 1903.

Three important discussions of the evolution of ancient and medieval theories regarding the relative positions and extent of areas of land and water on the earth's surface and of the relations which obtain between the spheres of land and of water are Günther, *Ältere und neuere Hypothesen*

. . . . forming part iii of his *Studien zur Geschichte der mathematischen und physikalischen Geographie*, 1879; Boffito, *La controversia dell'acqua e della terra prima e dopo di Dante*, forming Memoria I of his *Intorno alla "Quaestio de aqua et terra,"* 1902; and Norlind, *Das Problem des gegenseitigen Verhältnisses von Land und Wasser*, 1918.

3. *Physical Geography.* An important monograph on the physical geography of the Christian Middle Ages is Kretschmer, *Die physische Erdkunde im christlichen Mittelalter*, 1889. After a discussion of the sources—both Greek and Latin—Kretschmer takes up systematically the problems of the size and shape of the earth, the question of the antipodes, medieval theories of the divergent centers of the spheres of earth and water, the compass, and the physical geography of the waters, the atmosphere, and the lands. The topics dealt with are similar to those treated in parts of Chapter VI and in Chapters VII, VIII, and IX of the present volume. On the other hand, Kretschmer neglects the interesting question of theories of the origin of the earth. In dealing with physical geography he gives little attention to the writers of the age of the Crusades. With the exception of William of Conches, he neglects the same authors of that age whom Beazley neglects (see above, p. 498).

Several works on particular phases of ancient and medieval physical geography deserve special mention. An elaborate study of the meteorological lore of the Greeks is that of Gilbert, *Die meteorologischen Theorien des griechischen Altertums*, 1907. A German doctoral dissertation is devoted to the theories of the Church Fathers in regard to meteorology: Hoffmann, *Die Anschauungen der Kirchenväter über Meteorologie*, 1907 (see also Günther, *Notiz zur Geschichte der Klimatologie*, 1887). Medieval wind-roses are discussed in Cusa, *Sulla denominazione dei venti*, 1884; Revelli, *Una "rosa dei venti,"* 1910; and Bertolini, *L'orologio solare di Aquileia e la sistemazione della rosa dei venti*, 1916. Dissertations by Frahm (*Das Meer und die Seefahrt in der altfranzösischen Literatur*, 1914) and Koch (*Das Meer in der mittelhochdeutschen Epik*, 1910) deal respectively with the sea as depicted in old French literature and in the Middle High German epic. The basic study of the history of theories of the tides in antiquity and during the Middle Ages is Almagià, *La dottrina della marea*, 1905. Material, pleasingly presented, on the history of geology, with, incidentally, some interesting observations on medieval physical geography, will be found in Geikie, *Founders of Geology*, 1905. Medieval beliefs regarding the interior of the earth, volcanoes, and earthquakes are outlined by Stegmann in a dissertation, *Die Anschauungen . . . über die endogenen Erscheinungen der Erde*, 1913. Classical and medieval ideas of the arrangement of the mountains of the earth's surface form the subject of Benl's dissertation, *Hypothesen über die regelmässige Anordnung der Erdgebirge*, 1905.

4. *Feeling for Nature.* The feeling for nature as expressed in the Latin literature of antiquity is the topic of a delightful book by Geikie, *The*

Love of Nature Among the Romans, 1912. On the feeling for nature in the medieval period we may refer to the works of Biese, *Die Entwicklung des Naturgefühls*, 1892 (or the English translation), and of Ganzenmüller, *Das Naturgefühl*, 1914. To the latter the writer is especially indebted for numerous references to source material that might otherwise have been overlooked. Interesting studies of early mountain climbing are those of Gribble, *The Early Mountaineers*, 1899; Günther, *Wissenschaftliche Bergbesteigungen*, 1896; and W. W. Hyde, *The Development of the Appreciation of Mountain Scenery in Modern Times*, in: Geographical Review, vol. iii, 1917, pp. 107–118 (not in Bibliography), though none of these devotes a great deal of attention to the period of the Crusades.

5. *Astronomical Geography*. On the history of the invention and use of methods of determining latitude, see Schoy, *Die geschichtliche Entwicklung der Polhöhenbestimmung*, 1911; on longitudes, Schoy's *Längenbestimmung und Zentralmeridian*, 1915. See also the various articles and monographs on Ptolemy cited in the cross-references under Ptolemy in the Bibliography. Knowledge of latitudes and longitudes in the Christian West in the Middle Ages is discussed by J. K. Wright, *Notes on the Knowledge of Latitudes and Longitudes*, 1923.

6. *Cartography*. The history of cartography is discussed in the works mentioned in the sections on the history of geography as a whole and in particular periods, pp. 497–498 above. To the cartography of the ancient period as a whole are devoted two important recent publications: Kubitschek's article "Karten" in *Paulys Real-Encyclopädie*, 1919, and Cebrian, *Geschichte der Kartographie*, 1923. The most complete single study of the medieval cartography of the period with which we have to deal is Miller, *Mappaemundi*, 1895–1898. Other publications which deal incidentally but significantly with the cartography of the pre-portolan period are the works of Pullé, Simar, and Langenmaier referred to in subsection 7, immediately below.

7. *Regional Geography*. The fundamental study of belief in the Terrestrial Paradise is that of Coli, *Il paradiso terrestre*, 1897, although the matter has also been discussed by Graf in his *La leggenda del paradiso terrestre*, 1878, and in his *Miti, leggende e superstizioni*, 1892–1893.

The growth of medieval knowledge of Asia is traced in the introduction to Yule, *Cathay and the Way Thither*, 1913–1916, and much important material on this topic may be gleaned from the notes in the third edition of Yule's *Marco Polo*, 1903, and from Cordier's *Ser Marco Polo*, 1920. India as depicted on medieval maps is the subject of an interesting treatise by Pullé, *La cartografia antica dell'India*, 1901–1905. Lowes, in *The Dry Sea*, 1905, deals with interesting problems in the geography of Central Asia in the Middle Ages (see also Pelliot, *Chrétiens d'Asie centrale et d'Extrême-Orient*, 1914). On the history of commercial connections between the Near East and Europe during our period, two highly important books are Heyd, *Commerce du Levant*, 1885–1886 (reprinted 1923), and

Schaube, *Handelsgeschichte der romanischen Völker des Mittelmeergebiets*, 1906. Dreesbach, *Der Orient in der altfranzösischen Kreuzzugsliteratur*, 1901, is a résumé of notices relating to the Near East as they appear in French literature of the Crusades.

Two scholarly works deal with the widening of Western knowledge of Central Africa in antiquity and during the Middle Ages. These are Simar, *La géographie de l'Afrique centrale*, 1912, and Langenmaier, *Alte Kenntnis . . . der Zentralafrikanischen Seenregion*, 1916. Schaube's *Handelsgeschichte* and Mas-Latrie, *Traités de paix et de commerce . . . , concernant les relations des Chrétiens avec les Arabes de l'Afrique septentrionale*, 1866, are also important for the relations between Europe and North Africa.

Not much has been written in modern times upon the geography of Europe as it was conceived in the period covered by the present book. Hungary as it figures in the *chansons de geste* is the subject of an article by Karl, *La Hongrie . . . dans les chansons de geste*, 1908, and there are other monographs of limited scope, but no general discussion. The progress of geographical knowledge of the North is outlined by Moritz, *Die geographische Kenntnis von den Nord- und Ostseeküsten*, 1904; Weinhold, *Die Polargegenden Europas*, 1871; and especially by Nansen, *In Northern Mists*, 1911. The history of Icelandic geography (both of historical geography and of geographical studies in Iceland) is treated by Thoroddsen, *Geschichte der isländischen Geographie*, 1897. European wanderings in the Atlantic and legends of fabulous islands in that ocean have been made the subject of a large library of books and monographs. We may mention here Westropp, *Brasil and the Legendary Islands of the Atlantic*, 1912, and the recent volume of Babcock, *Legendary Islands of the Atlantic*, 1922.

BIBLIOGRAPHY

This bibliography is intended merely as an aid to those who wish to carry on further studies of the topics covered by this book. It is in no sense complete. The publications listed are for the most part only those to which reference is made in the Notes. Enough, but only enough, additional information is given about each entry to enable the reader to identify it. In the case of original sources the attempt has been made to refer to modern critical editions, and only to manuscripts or early printed editions where modern critical editions are lacking. More complete bibliographical information may be obtained from the publications discussed on pp. 491–493 above.

The arrangement is alphabetical by authors and, in the case of anonymous works, by the first important word in the titles. (Collections of sources are in general placed under the editor's name.) The names of authors of original sources, or the titles in the case of anonymous original sources or collections of sources, are given in capital letters, the former in Roman, the latter in italic type. The names of authors of modern, secondary studies are set in small letters in Roman type. Different works by the same ancient, Arabic, or medieval author are listed together in the same entry and are indicated by Roman numerals. Different works by the same modern author are listed separately and are arranged chronologically.

Cross-references within the Bibliography are, as in the Notes, given in abbreviated form. The full titles of the works referred to will be found in the Bibliography in their proper places.

For a topical discussion of the bibliography of ancient and medieval geography, see the Bibliographical Note above.

ABDIAS, PSEUDO-. *Abdiae, Babyloniae primi episcopi, ab apostolis constituti, De historia certaminis apostolici libri X, Julio Africano interprete.* Paris, 1551, 1560, 1566, etc.

ABELARD, PETER. I. *Expositio in hexaemeron,* in: Migne, *Pat. lat.,* vol. clxxviii, cols. 731–784. II. *Sermones,* in: Migne, *op. cit.,* cols. 379–610. III. *Sic et non,* in: Migne, *op. cit.,* cols. 1329–1610.

ABŪ-L-FIDĀ. *Géographie d'Aboulféda, traduite de l'arabe en français.* Vol. i (Paris, 1848) of this work, by J. T. Reinaud, is a general introduction to Moslem geography. Vol. ii, pt. 1 (Paris, 1848), forms the first part of the French translation and is also by J. T. Reinaud. Vol. ii, pt. 2 (Paris, 1883), contains the second part of the translation and is by Stanislas Guyard.

ABŪ MA'SHAR (ALBUMASAR). *The Great Book of the Introduction.* This was translated into Latin by Hermann the Dalmatian and by John of Seville. The title of Hermann's translation reads in the manuscript *Liber introductorius in astrologiam* (see Haskins, *Studies,* 1924, p. 45); editions printed in Venice, 1489, 1495, 1506, bear the title *Introductorium in astronomiam* (see Duhem, *Système,* vol. iii, 1915, p. 174, note 6, and Haskins, *loc. cit.*)

ACTS OF THE APOSTLES, APOCRYPHAL. *Acta apostolorum apocrypha . . .* etc., edited by L. F. C. von Tischendorf, Leipzig, 1851. *Acta apostolorum apocrypha post Constantinum Tischendorf denuo ediderunt R. A. Lipsius et* [*A.*] *M. Bonnet*, Leipzig, 1891–1903. Acts of Thomas in vol. ii, pt. 2, of this edition. English translation by M. R. James, *The Apocryphal New Testament*, Oxford University Press, 1924.

ADAM OF BREMEN. *Gesta Hammenburgensis* (or *Hammaburgensis*) *ecclesiae pontificum* (also called *Historia ecclesiastica*, or *Bremensium praesulum historia*), edited by J. M. Lappenberg, in: *Mon. Germ. hist.*, Scriptores, vol. vii, 1846, pp. 280–389, and in: *Scriptores rerum germ. in usum scholarum*, Hanover, 1876.

See Björnbo, A. A.; Kohlmann, P. W.; Krabbo, *Nordeuropa*, 1909.

ADELARD OF BATH. I. *De eodem et diverso*, edited by Hans Willner, in: Beiträge zur Geschichte der Philosophie des Mittelalters, vol. iv, pt. 1, Münster, 1903. II. *Quaestiones naturales*. There is no modern edition of the text of this work. An English translation is found in Gollancz, *Dodi ve-Nechdi*, 1920, pp. 87–161. The references in the present work are to the chapters as numbered in the Louvain incunabulum, ap. 1484, Bibliothèque Nationale, Paris (shelf-mark "Rés. R. 900"). In parentheses are given references to the chapters as numbered in the twelfth-century manuscript, Bibliothèque Nationale, fonds latin, no. 6415. For further bibliographical references, see Haskins, *Adelard*, 1911, p. 493; the same, *Studies*, 1924, p. 26. III. Translation of *Khorazmian Tables*. In MSS. only. See Haskins, *loc. cit.*; KHWĀRIZMĪ, Al-, II.

Adler, M. N. See BENJAMIN OF TUDELA.

ADVENTU, DE, PATRIARCHAE INDORUM AD URBEM SUB CALISTO PAPA II. In: Zarncke, *Priester Johannes*, Erste Abhandlung, in: Abhandlungen, vol. vii, 1879, pp. 837–843 (also numbered 11–17).

AETHICUS OF ISTRIA. *Cosmographia Aethici Istrici*, edited by H. Wuttke, Leipzig, 1854.

AGRIPPA. Map of the world. See Detlefsen, D.; Lessert, C. P. de.

Ainsworth, W. F. See PETACHIA OF RATISBON.

ALAN OF LILLE. I. *De planctu naturae*, in: Migne, *Pat. lat.*, vol. ccx, cols. 430–482. English translation by D. M. Moffat, *The Complaint of Nature by Alain of Lille*, New York, 1908. II. *Anticlaudianus*, in: Migne, *op. cit.*, cols. 482–576.

Al-BATTĀNĪ, Al-FARGHĀNĪ, and other Arabic names beginning with the article Al. See under first letter of main part of name.

ALBERTUS MAGNUS (OF BOLLSTADT). *Opera omnia*, edited by Petrus Jammy, 21 vols., Lyons, 1651. Also an edition by Augustus Borgnet, 38 vols., Paris, 1890–1899 (not seen).

For brief discussion of the geographical works, see above p. 406, note 93.

ALBUMASAR. See ABŪ MA'SHAR.

ALEXANDER THE GREAT, ROMANCE OF. I. *Pseudo-Callisthenes*, edited by C. Müller and included in a volume with F. Dübner's edition of Arrian's *Anabasis* and *Indica*, Paris, 1846 (also 1877). II. Julius Valerius, *Res gesta Alexandri Macedoniae II*, edited by B. Kübler, Leipzig, 1888. III. *Epitoma Julii Valerii*, edited by J. Zacher in his *Pseudo-Callisthenes: Forschungen zur Kritik und Ge-*

schichte der ältesten Aufzeichnung der Alexandersage, Halle, 1867. See *De Julii Valerii epitoma oxoniense*, by G. G. Cillie (Dissertation, University of Strasburg, 1905). IV. *Epistola ad Aristotelem de mirabilibus Indiae*, edited by F. Pfister in his: *Kleine Texte zum Alexanderroman*, Heidelberg, 1910. See also Thorndike, *Magic*, 1923, vol. i, pp. 555–556, footnote 2. V. *Historia de praeliis* of Leo Archipresbyter. See Landgraf, G. VI. *Iter ad Paradisum*, edited by J. Zacher, Regimonti (Königsberg), 1859 (not seen). VII. The Romance in alexandrines: *Li romans d'Alixandre par Lambert li Tors et Alexandre de Bernay*, edited by Heinrich Michelant, in: Bibliothek des Literarischen Vereins in Stuttgart, vol. xiii, 1846; F. le Court de la Villethassetz and E. Talbot, *Alexandriade ou chanson de geste d'Alexandre le Grand, de Lambert le Court et Alexandre de Bernay*, Dinan, Huart, and Paris, 1861.

See Meyer, P. For further references to texts and secondary works on Oriental versions see Thorndike, *Magic*, 1923, vol. i, pp. 551–552.

ALEXANDER NECKAM. See NECKAM, ALEXANDER.

ALEXANDER III (Pope). See PRESTER JOHN, III.

ALEXANDRE DE BERNAI. See *ALEXANDER THE GREAT, ROMANCE OF*, VII.

ALEXANDRIADE. See *ALEXANDER THE GREAT, ROMANCE OF*, VII.

ALFRAGANUS. See FARGHĀNĪ, Al-.

ALFRED THE GREAT. See Geidel, H.

ALFRED OF SARESHEL. I. *De motu cordis*. Extracts were published by C. S. Barach in: Bibliotheca philosophorum mediae aetatis, vol. ii, Innsbruck, 1878. II. *Liber de congelatis*. Baeumker, *Alfred von Sareshel*, 1913, p. 27, note, states that this work was printed under the title *Avicennae de congelatione et conglutinatione lapidum*, in: *Theatrum chemicum, praecipuos selectorum auctorum tractatus de chemiae et lapidis philosophici* . . . etc., vol. iv, Argentorati (Strasburg), 1659, pp. 883–887 (not seen), and that it was also printed in: *Gebri, regis Arabum* . . . *summa perfectionis Magisterii, in sua natura* . . . *denique libri Investigationis Magisterii et Testamenti eiusdem Gebri ac aurei Trium Verborum libelli et Avicennae* . . . *mineralium additione castigatissimi*, "Gedani" (Danzig), 1682, pp. 245–253 (not seen).

See Baeumker, C.

Almagià, Roberto. *La dottrina della marea nell'antichità classica e nel medio evo*, in: Memorie della Reale Accademia dei Lincei, Classe di scienze fisiche, matematiche, e naturali, series 5, vol. v, Rome, 1905, pp. 375–514. (Also printed separately.)

The most authoritative study of the history of theories of the tides in ancient and medieval times.

ALPETRAGIUS. See BITRŪJĪ, Al-.

ALPHONSI, PETER (PETRUS ANFUSI). *Dialogus cum Judeo*. Bibliothèque Nationale MSS., fonds latin, no. 10722, fols. 3ff.; also in: Migne, *Pat. lat.*, vol. clvii, cols. 527–706.

Amari, M. *Storia dei Musulmani di Sicilia*, 3 vols., Florence, 1854–1872.

Contains material on Edrisi and earlier Moslem geographers of Sicily.

AMBROISE. *L'Estoire de la guerre sainte: Histoire en vers de la troisième croisade,* edited by Gaston Paris, Paris, 1897.

ANAXIMANDER. See Heidel, W. A.

Anderson, R. B. See SNORRI STURLUSON, II.

Andriani, Giuseppe. *La carta dialettologica d'Italia secondo Dante* in: Atti dell' VIII Congresso Geografico Italiano, vol. ii, Florence, 1923, pp. 255–263.

ANFUSI, PETRUS. See ALPHONSI, PETER.

ANONYMOUS. See under initial letter of first important word of title.

ANTIQUITATES AMERICANAE. See Rafn, C. C.

ARI FRODHI. *Íslendingabók.* For editions see Hermannsson, *Bibl. Icelandic Sagas,* 1908, pp. 56–59. English translation in: Vigfusson and York Powell, *Origines Islandicae,* vol. i, 1905, pp. 279–306.

ARISTARCHUS OF SAMOS. See Heath, T.

ARISTOTLE. *Aristoteles, graece (et latine, interpretibus variis), ex recensione Imm. Bekkeri, edidit Academia Regia Borussica,* 5 vols., Berlin, 1830–1870. This is the best general edition of the Greek text of the works of Aristotle and is known as the Berlin edition. It was reprinted with the title *Aristotelis opera, graece, ex recensione Imm. Bekkeri, accedunt indices sylburgiani,* 11 vols., Oxford, 1837. There is also the following useful edition with Latin translations: *Aristotelis opera omnia, graece et latine, cum indice nominum et rerum absolutissimo,* 5 vols., Paris (Firmin-Didot), 1848–1886. An English translation is appearing entitled: *The Works of Aristotle, Translated into English,* Oxford (Clarendon Press), 1908ff.; in this the *De caelo* (translated by J. L. Stocks), 1922, *De generatione et corruptione* (translated by H. H. Joachim), 1922, the spurious *De mundo* (translated by E. S. Forster), 1914, and the *Meteorologica* (translated by E. W. Webster), 1923, have appeared, together with other works of lesser geographical interest. The best Greek text of the *Meteorology* is that of F. H. Fobes, *Aristotelis meteorologicorum libri quattuor,* Cambridge, Mass., 1919.

See also Duhem, *Du temps, 1909;* Endrös, A.; Fobes, F. H.; Grabmann, M.; Hammer-Jensen, I.; Jourdain, A.; Jourdain, C. B., *Infl. d'Aristote,* 1861; von Lippmann, E. O.; Lones, T. E.; Mandonnet, P.

ARNOLD OF CHARTRES. *De sex dierum operibus,* in: Migne, *Pat. lat.,* vol. clxxxix, cols. 1513–1570.

ARNOLD OF LÜBECK. *Chronica Slavorum,* edited by J. M. Lappenberg, in: *Mon. Germ. hist.,* Scriptores, vol. xxi, pp. 115–250, and in: *Scriptores rerum germ. in usum scholarum,* Hanover, 1868.

ARNOLD THE SAXON. Encyclopedic work published in part by Valentin Rose, *Aristoteles de lapidibus und Arnoldus Saxo,* in: Zeitschrift für deutsches Altertum, vol. xviii (new series, vol. vi), Berlin 1875, pp. 424–454.

See Stange, E.

Asher, A. See BENJAMIN OF TUDELA.

ATHELHARD. See ADELARD OF BATH; KHWĀRIZMĪ, Al-, II.

AUGUSTINE, Saint. Works in Migne, *Pat. lat.,* vols. xxxii-xlvii. Also in part in *Corpus script. eccl. lat.*

AVERROËS. See IBN RUSHD.

Avezac, [Armand] d'. *Coup d'oeuil historique sur la projection des cartes de géographie,* in: Bulletin de la Société de Géographie de Paris, series

5, vol. v, 1863, pp. 257–361, 438–485. (Also printed separately, Paris, 1863.)

Still the classical and probably the most satisfactory treatment of the subject.

AVICENNA (IBN SINĀ). See ALFRED OF SARESHEL, II; IBN SINĀ; and above, p. 401, note 60.

Babcock, W. H. *Saint Brendan's Explorations and Islands*, in: Geographical Review, vol. viii, New York, 1919, pp. 37–46.

Babcock, W. H. *Legendary Islands of the Atlantic* (American Geographical Society Research Series, no. 8), New York, 1922.

BACON, ROGER. I. *The Opus majus of Roger Bacon*, edited by J. H. Bridges, 3 vols., Oxford, 1897–1900. II. *Opus minus, Opus tertium, Compendium philosophiae*, edited by J. S. Brewer, in: *Fr. Rogeri Bacon opera quaedam hactenus inedita* (Rolls Series, no. 15), London, 1859. III. *Communia naturalium*, edited by Robert Steele, in: *Opera hactenus inedita Rogeri Baconi*, fascs. ii, iii, iv, Oxford, 1905, 1911, 1913. IV. *Secretum secretorum*, edited by Robert Steele, *op. cit.*, fasc. v, Oxford, 1920.

See Bridges, J. H.; Little, A. G.; Steele, R.; Werner, *Kosm. Roger Baco*, 1879.

Baeumker, Clemens. *Die Stellung des Alfred von Sareshel (Alfredus Anglicus) und seiner Schrift De motu cordis in der Wissenschaft des beginnenden XIII. Jahrhunderts*, in: Koeniglich-bayerische Akademie der Wissenschaften, Sitzungsberichte, Philosophisch-philologische und historische Klasse, Munich, 1913, Abhandlung 9. (Also published separately, Munich, 1913.)

Barthold, W. *Die geographische und historische Erforschung des Orients mit besonderer Berücksichtigung der russischen Arbeiten* (Quellen und Forschungen zur Erd- und Kulturkunde herausgegeben von R. Strube, vol. viii), Leipzig, 1913.

Summary of the history of relations between Orient and Occident to the nineteenth century. Extensive bibliographies.

BARTHOLOMEW ANGLICUS. *De proprietatibus rerum*. There is no modern edition. Translations of extracts will be found in: Robert Steele, *Mediaeval Lore*, London, 1907.

BATTĀNĪ, Al-. *Astronomy*. Arabic text with Latin translation and commentary in C. A. Nallino, *Al-Battānī sive Albatenii opus astronomicum*, in: Pubblicazioni del Reale Osservatorio di Brera in Milano, no. xl, pts. 1–3, Milan, 1899–1907.

See PLATO OF TIVOLI.

Baur, L. *Der Einfluss des Robert Grosseteste auf die wissenschaftliche Richtung des Roger Bacon*, in: Little, *Roger Bacon Essays*, 1914, pp. 33–54.

Beazley, C. R. *The Dawn of Modern Geography*, 3 vols., London, 1897–1906.

This, the most extensive and satisfactory work on medieval geography as a whole, covers the period from 300 to 1420 A. D. The main emphasis is laid upon the history of discovery and exploration. The study of the geographical science of the latter part of the Middle Ages is relatively brief (see above, p. 498).

BEDE, The Venerable. I. *De natura rerum*, edited by J. A. Giles, *The Complete Works of the Venerable Bede* (*Bedae opera quae supersunt omnia*), vol. vi, London, 1843, pp. 99–138. Also in Migne, *Pat. lat.*,

vol. xc, cols. 187–278. II. *De temporum ratione*, edited by Giles, *op. cit.*, pp. 139–342. Also in Migne, *op. cit.*, vol. xc, cols. 293–578. III. *Hexaemeron, sive libri quatuor in principium Genesis*, in: Migne, *op. cit.*, vol. xci, cols. 9–190.
See above, p. 387, note 68.

[BENEDICT OF PETERBOROUGH.] I. *Gesta regis Henrici II;* II. *Gesta regis Ricardi;* both in: *The Chronicle of the Reigns of Henry II and Richard I, A. D. 1169–1192*, edited by William Stubbs (Rolls Series, no. 49), 2 vols., London, 1867.
These two works have been erroneously ascribed to Benedict of Peterborough.

Benini, R. *Origine, sito, forma e dimensioni del Monte del Purgatorio e dell'Inferno dantesco*, in: Rendiconti della Reale Accademia dei Lincei, Classe di scienze morali, storiche e filologiche, series 5, vol. xxv, Rome, 1917, pp. 1015–1129.
This important study of the cosmography of Dante came to the present writer's attention when this book was in press.

Benisch, A. See PETACHIA OF RATISBON.

BENJAMIN OF TUDELA. *The Itinerary of Rabbi Benjamin of Tudela*, text and English translation by A. Asher, 2 vols., London and Berlin, 1840–1841; *The Itinerary of Benjamin of Tudela*, critical text, English translation, and commentary, edited by M. N. Adler, London, 1907.
See Borchardt, P.; Zunz, —.

Benl, Oskar. *Frühere und spätere Hypothesen über die regelmässige Anordnung der Erdgebirge nach bestimmten Himmelsrichtungen* (Dissertation, University of Munich, 1905).

Berger, Hugo. *Geschichte der wissenschaftlichen Erdkunde der Griechen*, 2nd edit., Leipzig, 1903.
The fundamental work on the geographical science of antiquity.

Berger, Hugo. *Die Lehre von der Kugelgestalt der Erde im Altertum*, in: Geographische Zeitschrift., vol. xii, Leipzig, 1906, pp. 20–37.

Berger de Xivrey, [J.]. *Traditions tératologiques, ou récits de l'antiquité et du moyen-âge en Occident sur quelques points de la fable, du merveilleux et de l'histoire naturelle*, Paris, 1836.
Throws light on the marvels of India.

BERGSSON, NIKULÁS. See NIKULÁS BERGSSON.

BERNARD OF CLAIRVAUX, Saint. Works will be found in: Migne, *Pat. lat.*, vols. clxxxii-clxxxv. There are numerous other editions. See also: *The Life and Works of St. Bernard, Abbot of Clairvaux, Edited by Dom John Mabillon, Translated and Edited with Additional Notes* by Samuel J. Eales, 4 vols., London, vols. i and ii, 1889, vols. iii and iv, 1896. This translation is from the fourth edition of Mabillon, Paris, 1839.

BERNARD SYLVESTER. *De mundi universitate*, edited by C. S. Barach and J. Wrobel, in: Bibliotheca philosophorum mediae aetatis, vol. i, Innsbruck, 1876.
See Hauréau, *Mémoire*, 1883; Langlois, C. V., *Maître Bernard*, 1893; Poole, R. L., *Masters*, 1920.

Bertolini, G. L. *I quattro angoli del mondo e la forma della terra nel passo di Rabano Mauro*, in: Bollettino della Società Geografica Italiana, vol. xlvii, Rome, 1910, pp. 1433–1441.

Bertolini, G. L. *L'orologio solare di Aquileia e la sistemazione della rosa dei venti nel medio evo*, in: Bollettino della Reale Società Geografica Italiana, vol. liii, Rome, 1916, pp. 969–985.

BIBLE, THE. Citations are to the Vulgate; translations, except where otherwise stated, from the Douai and Rheims version.

Biese, A. *Die Entwicklung des Naturgefühls im Mittelalter und Neuzeit*, Leipzig, 1892. English translation with title *The Development of the Feeling for Nature in the Middle Ages and Modern Times*, London, 1905 (not seen).

Birkenmajer, Alexander. *Eine neue Handschrift des "Liber de naturis inferiorum et superiorum" des Daniel von Merlai*, in: Archiv für die Geschichte der Naturwissenschaften und Technik, vol. ix, Leipzig, 1920, pp. 45–51 (not seen).

BITRŪJĪ, Al- (ALPETRAGIUS). *On the Sphere*. This work was translated into Latin by Michael Scot in 1217 (on manuscripts see Haskins, *Michael Scot*, 1921–1922, p. 251, note 3; the same, *Studies* 1924, p. 273, note 9). It was also translated into Latin from the Hebrew version of Moses ben Samuel ben Tibbon (1259) by the Neapolitan Jew Calo Calonymos ben David under the title *Alpetragii Arabi planetarum theorica . . .* etc., Venice, 1528 (not seen; cited by Duhem, *Système*, vol. ii, 1914, p. 146).

Björnbo, A. A. *Adam af Bremens Nordensopfattelse*, in: Aarböger for nordisk Oldkyndighed og Historie, Copenhagen, 1909 (not seen).

Blázquez y Delgado Aguilera, Antonio. *San Isidoro de Sevilla: Mapa mundi*, in: Boletín de la Real Sociedad Geográfica, vol. 50, Madrid, 1908, pp. 207–272, 306–358.

Boffito, Giuseppe. *Intorno alla "Quaestio de aqua et terra" attribuita a Dante:* Memoria I, *La controversia dell'acqua e della terra prima e dopo di Dante*, in: Memorie della Reale Accademia delle Scienze di Torino, series 2, vol. li, Appr. nell'adunanza del 23 giugno 1901, Turin, 1902, pp. 73–159; Memoria II, *Il trattato dantesco*, in: *op. cit.*, series 2, vol. lii, Appr. nell'adunanza del giugno 1902, Turin, 1903, pp. 257–342. See also above, p. 410, note 98.

Boffito, Giuseppe. *La leggenda degli antipodi*, in: *Miscellanea di studi critici ed. in onore di Arturo Graf*, Bergamo, 1903, pp. 583–601.

Boncompagni, Baldassare. *Delle versione fatte da Platone Tiburtino, traduttore de secolo duodecimo: Notizie*, Rome, 1851.

Boncompagni, Baldassare. *Della vita e delle opere di Gherardo Cremonese, traduttore del secolo duodecimo, e di Gherardo da Sabbionetta, astronomo del secolo decimoterzo: Notizie raccolte da*—, in: Atti dell'Accademia Pontifica dei Nuovi Lincei, anno IV, sesione VII del 27 giugno, 1851, Rome, 1851. (Also published separately.)

Borchardt, Paul. *L'itinéraire de Rabbi Benjamin de Tudèle en Chine*, in: T'oung Pao, ou archives concernant l'histoire, les langues, la géographie et l'ethnographie de l'Asie orientale, vol. xxiii, Leiden, 1924, pp. 31–35.
See above, p. 414, note 156.

BRANDAN (BRENDAN), Saint. *Peregrinatio sancti Brandani abbatis*. Latin text and early German versions edited by Carl Schröder, *Sanct Brandan: Ein lateinischer und drei deutsche Texte*, Erlangen, 1871. Latin, Flemish, and French texts in: A. Jubinal, *La légende latine de Saint Brendaines*, Paris, 1836. Anglo-Norman text in: H. Suchier, *Brandans Seefahrt* (*anglonormannischer Text der*

Handschrift Cotton, Vesp. B. X.), in: Romanische Studien herausgegeben von E. Böhmer, vol. i, pt. 5, Strasburg, 1875, pp. 553–588.
See Babcock, W. H.; Goeje, M. J. de.

Brehaut, Ernest. *An Encyclopedist of the Dark Ages: Isidore of Seville* (Columbia University Studies in History, Economics, and Public Law, vol. xlviii, no. 1), New York, 1912.
Part I deals with Isidore's life, writings, relation to previous culture, his general view of the universe, and his attitude toward education. Part II consists of commentary and translation of selected passages from the *Etymologiae*, including extracts from Book XIV, "On the Earth and Its Parts."

Bréhier, Louis. *Les colonies d'orientaux en Occident au commencement du moyen-âge, v^{e}-viiie siècle*, in: Byzantinische Zeitschrift, vol. xii, no. i, Munich, 1903, pp. 1–39.

Bréhier, Louis. *L'Église et l'Orient au moyen âge: Les croisades*, Paris, 1911.

BRENDAN, Saint. See BRANDAN, Saint.

Bresslau, H. *Die Chroniken des Frutolf von Bamberg und des Ekkehard von Aura*, in: Neues Archiv der Gesellschaft für ältere deutsche Geschichtskunde, vol. xxi, Hanover, 1895, pp. 197–234.

Bridges, J. H. *The Life and Work of Roger Bacon: An Introduction to the Opus Majus*, edited by H. G. James, London, 1914.

Brown, J. Wood. *An Enquiry into the Life and Legend of Michael Scot*, Edinburgh, 1897.
Unreliable. See Haskins, *Michael Scot*, 1921–1922, p. 250; the same, *Studies*, 1924, p. 272.

BRUNETTO LATINO (or LATINI). See LATINO, BRUNETTO.

Bruun, P. *Die Verwandlungen des Presbiters Johannes*, in: Zeitschrift der Gesellschaft für Erdkunde zu Berlin, vol. xi, 1876, pp. 279–314.

Bubnov, Nicholaus. See GERBERT (SYLVESTER II).

Bunbury, E. H. *A History of Ancient Geography*, 2 vols., London, 1879.
Scholarly and accurate. Though old, the best work on the subject in English.

CALLISTHENES, PSEUDO–. See *ALEXANDER THE GREAT, ROMANCE OF*, I.

CAMBRENSIS, GIRALDUS. See GIRALDUS CAMBRENSIS.

CAPELLA, MARTIANUS. *De nuptiis Philologiae et Mercurii*, edited by F. Eyssenhardt, Leipzig (Teubner), 1866.
See Mori, *Misuraz. eratos.*, 1911.

Capelle, Wilhelm. *Berges- und Wolkenhöhen bei griechischen Physikern* (Στοιχεῖα: Studien zur Geschichte des antiken Weltbildes und der griechischen Wissenschaft herausgegeben von Franz Boll, vol. v), Leipzig and Berlin, 1916.

Carmoly, E., transl. and edit. *ITINÉRAIRES DE LA TERRE SAINTE DES XIIIe, XIVe, XVe, XVIe, ET XVIIe SIÈCLES traduits de l'hébreu, et accompagnés de tables, de cartes et d'éclaircissements*, Brussels, 1847.

Carra de Vaux, [Bernard.] *Les penseurs de l'Islam*, vols. i and ii, Paris, 1921; vol. iii, 1923 (to be complete in 5 vols.).
The first three chapters of vol. ii give an admirable popular account of the geographers of Islam and their work.

Cebrian, Konstantin. *Geschichte der Kartographie: Ein Beitrag zur Entwicklung des Kartenbildes und Kartenwesens. I. Altertum. 1. Von den ersten Versuchen der Länderabbildung bis auf Marinos und Ptolemaios (Zur Alexandrinischen Schule)*, (Geographische Bausteine, edited by Hermann Haack, vol. x), Gotha, 1923.

Useful general history, sometimes misleading in details. The author was killed in the World War, and hence the present part represents the only part published. Contains an appendix by Joseph Fischer, *Ptolemaios als Kartograph*, pp. 113–129, in which the endeavor is made to correct Cebrian's misapprehensions regarding Ptolemy.

Chevalier, Ulysse. *Répertoire des sources historiques du moyen âge:* (1) *Bio-bibliographie*, 2 vols., Paris, 1905–1907; (2) *Topo-bibliographie*, Montbéliard, 1894–1899, 1903.

See above, p. 491.

CHRONICLES AND MEMORIALS OF GREAT BRITAIN AND IRELAND. See "*ROLLS SERIES*."

Clarke, John. See SENECA.

CLEOMEDES. *De motu circulari corporum caelestium libri duo*, edited by Hermann Ziegler, Leipzig (Teubner), 1891.

Clerval, A. *Les écoles de Chartres au moyen âge du ve au xvie siècle.* (Mémoires de la Société Archéologique d'Eure-et-Loir, no. 11), Paris, 1895.

Important study of the scholars of the leading intellectual center of France in the early twelfth century.

Coli, Edoardo. *Il paradiso terrestre dantesco* (Pubblicazioni del R. Istituto di Studi Superiori Pratici e di Perfezionamento in Firenze, Sezione di filosofia e lettere, vol. ii, no. 28), Florence, 1897.

Columba, G. M. *La questione soliniana e la letteratura geografica dei Romani*, in: Atti della Reale Accademia di Scienze, vol. xi, Palermo, 1920 (not seen).

COMESTOR, PETER. *Historia scholastica*, in: Migne, *Pat. lat.*, vol. cxcviii, cols. 1045–1722.

See Masson, G.

CONRAD OF QUERFURT. Letter describing journey through Italy, in: Arnold of Lübeck, *Chronica Slavorum*, v, 19, in: *Mon. Germ. hist.*, Scriptores, vol. xxi, pp. 192–196.

Coolidge, W. A. B. *The Alps in Nature and History*, New York, 1908.

Contains compact, scholarly discussions of Alpine history and of the great passes.

Cordier, Henri. *Documents historiques et géographiques relatifs à l'Indochine*, 4 vols., Paris, 1910–1914.

Includes texts of Greek and Latin authors relating to the Far East from the fourth century before Christ to the fourteenth of our era. Also Oriental geographical texts.

Cordier, Henri, on Marco Polo. See POLO, MARCO.

CORPUS SCRIPTORUM ECCLESIASTICORUM LATINORUM, Vienna, 1866ff. 65 vols. have appeared (1924).

Great collection of critical texts of the Church Fathers until the seventh century.

Cousin, G. *Etudes de géographie ancienne*, Paris and Nancy, 1906.

Chapter 38 is on the geography of the East in the writings of Henri de Valenciennes and Villehardouin.

Cumont, Franz. *After Life in Roman Paganism*, New Haven, 1922.

Cusa, Salvatore. *Sulla denominazione dei venti e dei punti cardinali, e specialmente de Nord, Est, Sud, Ouest*, in: Terzo Congresso Geografico Internazionale tenuto a Venezia dal 15 al 22 settembre 1881, vol. ii, Rome, 1884, pp. 375–415.

Dahlmann, Joseph. *Die Thomas-Legende und die ältesten historischen Beziehungen des Christentums zum fernen Osten im Lichte der indischen Altertumskunde*, Freiburg-im-Breisgau, 1912.

DANIEL OF MORLEY. *De philosophia*, or *Liber de naturis inferiorum et superiorum*, edited by K. Sudhoff in: Archiv für die Geschichte der Naturwissenschaften und Technik, vol. viii, pts. 1–3, Leipzig, June, 1917, pp. 1–40.
See Birkenmajer, A.; Singer, *Daniel of Morley*, 1920.

DANTE. I. *Tutte le opere*, edited by Edward Moore, Oxford, 1894. A convenient edition of all the works. II. *The Convivio* [*Convito*] *of Dante Alighieri*, translated by P. H. Wicksteed, London, 1903. III. *Dante, De vulgari eloquentia*, translated by A. G. F. Howell, London, 1890. IV. *The Divine Comedy*. Among the numerous English translations note especially that of C. E. Norton, 3 vols., Boston, 1891–1892. V. *Quaestio de aqua et terra* [not certainly the work of Dante], edited by C. L. Shadwell, Oxford, 1909, with English translation. German translation by Josef Krejcik, *Dantes Quaestio de aqua et terra*, in: Kartographische und Schulgeographische Zeitschrift, vol. ix, Vienna, 1921, pp. 107–110, 136–140.
For further material on Dante's cosmology and geography see Andriani, G.; Benini, R.; Boffito, *Intorno alla "Quaestio de aqua et terra,"* 1902–1903; Coli, E.; Moore, E.; Mori, *La geogr.*, 1922; Schmidt, W.; and references in Krejcik, *op. cit.*

Daunou, P. C. F. *Discours sur l'état des lettres au xiiie siècle*, Paris, 1860. Also in: *Histoire littéraire de la France*, vol. xvi, Paris, 1824, pp. 1–254.
Chapter 17 is on geography and voyages.

DE, etc. For anonymous works title of which begins with *DE* see under initial letter of principal word of title.

Decourdemanche, J. A. *Note sur l'estimation de la longeur du degré terrestre chez les Grecs, les Arabes, et dans l'Inde*, in: Journal asiatique, series 11, vol. 1, Paris, 1913, pp. 427–444.
Presents a hazardous theory.

De Goeje, M. J. See Goeje, M. J. de.

Delaborde, H. F. See WILLIAM THE BRETON.

Delambre, J. B. J. *Histoire de l'astronomie du moyen âge*, Paris, 1819.
Old but still a standard work on medieval astronomy.

De La Roncière, Charles. See La Roncière, Charles de.

Delisle, Léopold. See GODFREY OF VITERBO.

Denis, Ferdinand. *Le monde enchanté: Cosmographie et histoire naturelle fantastiques du moyen âge*, Paris, 1843.
Popular, though scholarly, work on medieval marvels.

DESCRIPTIONES TERRAE SANCTAE. See Tobler, Titus.

Detlefsen, D. *Ursprung, Einrichtung und Bedeutung der Erdkarte Agrippas* (Quellen und Forschungen zur alten Geschichte und Geographie herausgegeben von W. Sieglin, no. 13), Berlin, 1906.

Detlefsen, D. *Die Geographie Afrikas bei Plinius und Mela und ihre Quellen* (Quellen und Forschungen zur alten Geschichte und Geographie herausgegeben von W. Sieglin, no. 14), Berlin, 1909.
See also PLINY.

DEVISION, LA, DE LA TERRE DE OULTREMER ET DES CHOSES QUI I SONT, edited by C. Hopf in: Chroniques gréco-romanes, Berlin, 1873, pp. 30–34.

De Wulf, Maurice. See Wulf, Maurice de.

DICUIL. *De mensura orbis terrae*, edited by A. Letronne, in his *Recherches*, 1814. Also by Gustav Parthey, Berlin, 1870.

Dietrich, ——. *Die geographischen Anschauungen einiger Chronisten des XI. und XII. Jahrhunderts*, in: Zeitschrift für wissenschaftliche Geographie, vol. v, Vienna, 1885, pp. 95–103, 187–207.

Dinse, Paul. *Die handschriftlichen Ptolemäus-Karten und die Agathodämonfrage*, in: Zeitschrift der Gesellschaft für Erdkunde zu Berlin, 1913, pp. 745–770.

DIONYSIUS PERIGETES. *Orbis descriptio*, in: C. Müller, *Geographi graeci minores*, 1882, vol. ii, pp. 103–176.

Doberentz, Otto. *Die Erd- und Völkerkunde in der Weltchronik des Rudolf von Hohen-Ems*, in: Zeitschrift für deutsche Philologie, vols. xii, Halle, 1880, pp. 257–301, 387–454, xiii, 1881, pp. 29–57, 165–223.
Important material in this monograph on the sources of the *De imagine mundi*.

DOMINICUS GONDISALVI (GUNDISSALINUS). I. *De divisione philosophiae*, edited by L. Baur, in: Beiträge zur Geschichte der Philosophie des Mittelalters herausgegeben von C. Baeumker, vol. iv, pts. 2–3, Münster, 1903. II. Translations of the *Physics* and *De caelo* of Aristotle. Unpublished. See Steinschneider, *Europäische Übersetzungen*, in: Sitzungsberichte, vol. cxlix, 1905, pp. 32, 42, 43.

Dozy, R. See IDRĪSĪ, Al-.

Draper, J. W. *History of the Conflict Between Religion and Science*, New York, 1875. (Also other editions.)
Endeavors to show the baneful influence of organized religion upon the development of science.

Dreesbach, Emil. *Der Orient in der altfranzösischen Kreuzzugsliteratur* (Dissertation, University of Breslau, 1901).
A compilation of references to the Near East in the French literature of the Crusades, with explanatory comment.

Duhem, Pierre. *Du temps où la scholastique latine a connu la physique d'Aristote*, in: Revue de philosophie, vol. xv, Paris, 1909, pp. 163–178.

Duhem, Pierre. *Le système du monde: Histoire des doctrines cosmologiques de Platon à Copernic*, 5 vols., Paris, 1913–1917.
A work of fundamental importance. From the geographical point of view significant for the data it contains on the history of cosmography, of astronomical geography, and of theories of the tides. Contains valuable bibliographical references, though not always complete (see criticism in Haskins, *Studies*, 1924, pp. 82–83).

Eales, S. J. See BERNARD OF CLAIRVAUX.

EDDAS, THE. I. *SAEMUNDAR EDDA*, or *POETIC EDDA*. Text in: R. C. Boer, edit., *Die Edda, mit historisch-kritischem Commentar*- Haarlem, 1922; Eduard Sievers, edit., *Die Eddalieder* (Abhandlungen der sächischen Akademie der Wissenschaften, Philologisch,

historische Klasse, vol. xxxvii, no. 3), Leipzig, 1923. English translation: H. A. Bellows, *The Poetic Edda, Translated from the Icelandic, With an Introduction and Notes*, 2 vols., New York, 1923.
II. *SNORRIS EDDA*, or *PROSE EDDA*. See SNORRI STURLUSON, II.
See also Hermannsson, *Bibl. Eddas*, 1920.

EDRISI. See IDRĪSĪ, Al-.

EKKEHARD OF AURA. See FRUTOLF OF MICHAELSBERG.

ELYSAEUS ACCOUNT. See PRESTER JOHN, II.

Endrös, A. *Die Gezeiten, Seiches und Strömungen des Meeres bei Aristoteles*, in: Bayerische Gesellschaft der Wissenschaften, Sitzungsberichte, Mathematisch-physikalische Klasse, Munich, 1915, pp. 355–385.

ERATOSTHENES. *Die geographischen Fragmente des Eratosthenes*, edited with commentary by Hugo Berger, Leipzig (Teubner), 1880.
See Mori, *Misuraz. eratos.*, 1911; Scala, R. von; Thalamas, A.

ERIGENA (or ERIUGENA), JOHN SCOT. See JOHN SCOT ERIGENA.

Esposito, M. *On Some Unpublished Poems Attributed to Alexander Neckam*, in: English Historical Review, vol. xxx, London, 1915, pp. 450–471.

Fant, C. *L'Image du monde, poème inédit du milieu du xiii*[e] *siècle, étudié dans ses diverses rédactions françaises d'après les manuscrits des bibliothèques de Paris et de Stockholm* (Dissertation, University of Upsala, 1886.)
Gives a summary of the contents of the poem.

FARGHĀNĪ, Al- (ALFRAGANUS). *On the Elements of Astronomy*. See GERARD OF CREMONA, I; JOHN OF SEVILLE, I.

FETELLUS (FRETELLUS). *Tractatus de distantiis locorum Terrae Sanctae*. Text in: Comte Melchior de Vogue, *Les églises de la Terre Sainte*, Paris, 1860, pp. 412–433; also in: Migne, *Pat. lat.*, vol. clv, cols. 1037–1054. English translation by J. R. Macpherson, *Fetellus (circa 1130 A. D.)*, London, 1892 (in: Palestine Pilgrims' Text Society, *Library*, 1897, vol. v).

Fischer, Joseph. *Ptolemäus und Agathodämon*, forming supplement (on pp. 71–93) to von Mžik, *Afrika*.

Fischer, Joseph. *Pappus und die Ptolemäuskarten*, in: Zeitschrift der Gesellschaft für Erdkunde zu Berlin, 1919, pp. 336–358.

Fischer, Joseph. *Ptolemaios als Kartograph*, forming supplement (on pp. 113–129) to Cebrian, *Geschichte der Kartographie*, 1923.

FITZSTEPHEN, WILLIAM. Description of London in Latin forming the preface to his Latin life of Thomas à Becket, in: J. C. Robertson, *Materials for the History of Thomas Becket, Archbishop of Canterbury* (Rolls Series, no. 67), vol. iii, London, 1877. Also in: Migne, *Pat. lat.*, vol. cxc, cols., 103–110; *A Survey of London by John Stow*, edited by C. T. Kingsford (2 vols., Oxford, 1908), vol. ii, pp. 219–223. English translation in: *John Stow, A Survay of London . . . 1598*, edited by Henry Morley, London, 1908, pp. 22–29, 117–119.

Fobes, F. H. *Mediaeval Versions of Aristotle's Meteorology*, in: Classical Philology, vol. x, Chicago, 1915, pp. 297–314.

Frahm, Wilhelm. *Das Meer und die Seefahrt in der altfranzösischen Literatur* (Dissertation, University of Göttingen, 1914).

Francke, Kuno. *Zur Geschichte der lateinischen Schulpoesie des XII. und XIII. Jahrhunderts*, Munich, 1879.

FRETELLUS. See FETELLUS.

Fritsche, Franz. *Untersuchung über die Quellen der Image du monde des Walther von Metz*, Halle, 1880.

FRODHI, ARI. See ARI FRODHI.

FRUTOLF OF MICHAELSBERG (or of BAMBERG). *Chronica.* Edited as if the work of Ekkehard of Aura, in: *Mon. Germ. hist.*, Scriptores, vol. vi, 1844, pp. 33–231. See Bresslau, H.

Ganzenmüller, Wilhelm. *Das Naturgefühl im Mittelalter* (Beiträge zur Kulturgeschichte des Mittelalters und der Renaissance herausgegeben von Walter Götz, vol. xviii), Leipzig and Berlin, 1914.

An attempt to interpret the medieval attitude toward nature "von innen heraus, aus der geistigen Eigenart des Mittelalters . . ." (p. 4). German translations of many descriptions of landscape and scenery are included.

Ganzenmüller, Wilhelm. *Die empfindsame Naturbetrachtung im Mittelalter*, in: Archiv für Kulturgeschichte, vol. xii, Berlin, 1916, pp. 195–228.

GAUTIER DE CHÂTILLON (or DE LILLE). See WALTER OF CHÂTILLON.

Geidel, Heinrich. *Alfred der Grosse als Geograph* (Münchener geographische Studien herausgegeben von Siegmund Günther, no. 15), Munich, 1904.

Geikie, Sir Archibald. *The Founders of Geology*, London, 1905.

Geikie, Sir Archibald. *The Love of Nature Among the Romans During the Later Decades of the Republic and the First Century of the Empire*, London, 1912.

GEOFFREY OF MONMOUTH. *Historia Britonum*, edited by J. A. Giles, Caxton Society, London, 1844. An English translation entitled *Geoffrey of Monmouth's British History* by J. A. Giles, in: *Monkish Historians of Great Britain*, vol. iv, London, 1844 (also in Bohn's Antiquarian Library, London, 1848).

GEOFFREY OF ST. VICTOR (GODEFROI DE BRETEUIL). I. *Fons philosophiae*, edited by M. A. Charma in his *Fons philosophiae: Poème inédit du xiie siècle, publié et annoté par* —, Caen, 1868. II. *Microcosmus.* Unpublished. See above, p. 428, note 135.

GEOGRAPHI GRAECI MINORES. See Müller, C.

GEOGRAPHI LATINI MINORES. See Riese, A.

GERALD OF BARRY. See GIRALDUS CAMBRENSIS.

GERARD OF CREMONA. I. *Liber de aggregationibus scientiae stellarum et principiis coelestium motum*, a translation of Al-Farghānī's *On the Elements of Astronomy.* See Woepcke, *Notice*, 1862, pp. 117–120. II. Translation of Az-Zarqalī's *Canons* on the *Toledo Tables.* See above, pp. 399–400, notes 44–45. III. Translations of Aristotle's *Meteorology* (first three books), *Physics*, *De caelo et mundo*, and *De generatione et corruptione.* Unpublished. On manuscripts see Thorndike, *Magic*, 1923, vol. ii, p. 87; see also above, pp. 401–402, notes 59, 60, 61, 62. IV. *Theorica planetarum.* MS. in Bibliothèque Nationale MSS., fonds latin, no. 7421. This work was also printed in the fifteenth and sixteenth centuries. The edition

referred to in the Notes of the present work as the "Renner edition" was printed in Venice "per Franciscū Renner de Hailbrun, MCCCC-LXXVIII." In the same volume is to be found the *De sphaera* of John of Holywood, q. v. For references to other editions see Duhem, *Système*, vol. iii, 1915, p. 219, note 3.
See Boncompagni, *Della vita*, 1851.

GERBERT (SYLVESTER II). *Gerberti postea Silvestri II papae opera mathematica*, edited by Nicholaus Bubnov, Berlin, 1899.

GERVASE OF CANTERBURY. I. *Chronica de tempore regum Angliae Stephani, Henrici II et Ricardi I*, edited by William Stubbs, in: *The Historical Works of Gervase of Canterbury* (Rolls Series, no. 71), vol. i, London, 1879. II. *Mappamundi*, edited by Stubbs, *op. cit.*, vol. ii, London, 1880, pp. 414–444.

GERVASE OF TILBURY. *Otia imperialia*, edited by G. G. Leibnitz, in: *Scriptores rerum brunsvicensium* (3 vols., Hanover, 1707–1711), vol. i, pp. 881–1004, vol. ii, pp. 754–784.
See Liebrecht, F.

Gilbert, Otto. *Die meteorologischen Theorien des griechischen Altertums*, Leipzig, 1907.
Fundamental study of ancient meteorology.

Giordano, Carlo. *Alexanderis, poema di Gautier da Châtillon*, Naples, 1917.

GIRALDUS CAMBRENSIS (GERALD OF BARRY). I. *Topographia Hiberniae et* (II) *Expugnatio Hiberniae*, edited by J. F. Dimock, in: *Giraldi Cambrensis opera* (Rolls Series, no. 21), vol. v, London, 1867. English translation by Thomas Foster, *The Historical Works of Giraldus Cambrensis Containing the Topography of Ireland and the History of the Conquest of Ireland*, revised by Thomas Wright, in Bohn's Antiquarian Library, London, 1863. III. *Itinerarium Kambriae et* (IV) *Descriptio Kambriae*, edited by J. F. Dimock, *op. cit.*, vol. vi, London, 1868. Sir R. C. Hoare's English translation of 1806 appeared under the title *The Itinerary Through Wales and the Description of Wales by Giraldus Cambrensis* in Everyman's Library, London and New York, 1908. V. *Symbolum electorum*, edited by J. S. Brewer, in: *Giraldi Cambrensis opera* (Rolls Series, no. 21), vol. i, London, 1861, pp. 199–395.
See Lynch, J.

Gisinger, F. "Geographie," article in: *Paulys Real-Encyclopädie der classischen Altertumswissenschaft: Neue Bearbeitung, begonnen von Georg Wissowa*, edited by Wilhelm Kroll, supplementary vol. iv, Stuttgart, 1924, cols. 521–685.

GODFREY OF VITERBO. I. *Pantheon seu universitatis libri, qui chronici appellantur, XX, . . . ab O. C.–1186.* Edited by B. J. Herold, Basel, 1559. and by J. Pistorius (3rd edition, edited by B. G. Struve, vol. ii, Ratisbon, 1726, pp. 2–392); also edited (in part only) in: Migne, *Pat. lat.*, vol. cxcviii, cols. 875–1044, and in: *Mon. Germ. hist.*, Scriptores, vol. xxii, 1872, pp. 107–307. II. *Denumeratio regnorum imperio subjectorum*, edited by Léopold Delisle in his *Littérature latine et histoire du moyen âge*, Paris, 1890, pp. 41–50.

Goeje, M. J. de. *La légende de St. Brandan*, in: Actes du Huitième Congrès Internationale des Orientalistes, 1889, Leiden, 1891, pp. 43–76. (Also printed separately, Leiden, 1890.)

Goeje, M. J. de, on Edrisi. See IDRĪSĪ, Al-.

Gollancz, Hermann. *Dodi ve-Nechdi (Uncle and Nephew), the Work of Berachya Hanakdan*, Oxford, etc., 1920. Pp. 87–161 consist of a translation of the *Quaestiones naturales* of Adelard of Bath, q. v.

GONDISALVI, DOMINICUS. See DOMINICUS GONDISALVI.

GOSSOUIN OF METZ. Possibly author or co-author of the *Image du monde*. See above, p. 105 and p. 405, note 89.

Grabmann, Martin. *Forschungen über die lateinischen Aristotelesübersetzungen des XIII. Jahrhunderts*, in: Beiträge zur Geschichte der Philosophie des Mittelalters herausgegeben von C. Baeumker, vol. xvii, pts. 5–6, Münster, 1916.

Graf, Arturo. *La leggenda del paradiso terrestre*, Turin, 1878.

Graf, Arturo. *Roma nella memoria e nelle immaginazioni del medio evo*, 2 vols., Turin, 1882–1883.

Graf, Arturo. *Miti, leggende e superstizioni del medio evo*, 2 vols., Turin, 1892–1893.

Much material and a wealth of references on legendary geography. Vol. i, pp. 1–193, deals with the legend of the terrestrial paradise.

GREGORIUS, MAGISTER. See GREGORY, MASTER.

Gregorovius, Ferdinand. *Geschichte der Stadt Rom im Mittelalter*, 8 vols., 1st edit., Stuttgart, 1859–1872. Translation from fourth German edition by Annie Hamilton, *History of the City of Rome in the Middle Ages*, 8 vols. in 13, London, 1894–1912.

GREGORY, MASTER. *Magister Gregorius de mirabilibus urbis Romae*, edited with introduction by M. R. James in his *Magister Gregorius*, in: English Historical Review, vol. xxxii, London, 1917, pp. 531–554.

Gribaudi, Pietro. *La geografia di S. Isidoro di Siviglia* (Memorie della Reale Accademia delle Scienze di Torino, series 2, vol. lv), Turin, 1905.

Gribaudi, Pietro. *Per la storia della geografia, specialmente nel medio evo*, Turin, 1906. Fasc. I of this contains: *L'autorità de S. Isidoro de Siviglia, come geografo, nel medio evo.*

Gribble, Francis. *The Early Mountaineers*, London, 1899.

Gröber, G. *Übersicht über die lateinische Literatur von der Mitte des 6. Jahrhunderts bis 1350*, in his *Grundriss der romanischen Philologie* (2 vols., Strasburg, 1888–1902), vol. ii, pt. i, pp. 97–432.

GROSSETESTE, ROBERT (ROBERT OF LINCOLN). (I) *De sphaera*, (II) *De impressionibus aëris seu de prognosticatione*, (III) *De luce seu de inchoatione formarum*, (IV) *Quod homo sit minor mundus*, (V) *De lineis angulis et figuris seu de fractionibus et reflexionibus radiorum*, (VI) *De natura locorum*, (VII) *De impressionibus elementorum*, (VIII) *De finitate motus et temporis*, all edited by Ludwig Baur in his *Die philosophischen Werke des Robert Grosseteste, Bischofs von Lincoln* (Beiträge zur Geschichte der Philosophie des Mittelalters herausgegeben von C. Baeumker, vol. ix), Münster, 1912. (IX) *Summa super libros octo Physicorum* (commentary on the *Physics* of Aristotle), first printed in Venice in 1498, and subsequently frequently printed in the sixteenth century; no modern critical edition. On early editions and manuscripts see Baur, *op. cit.*, pp. 19*–20*. (X) *Hexaemeron*. Unpublished. Baur, *op. cit.*, p. 24*, note 1, cites MS. Brit. Mus. Bibl. reg. 6 E. V. (XI) *Summa philosophiae*. Ascribed probably erroneously to Grosseteste. Edited by Baur, *op. cit.*, pp. 275–643.

See also Baur, L.; Little, A. G.

GUI DE BAZOCHES. See GUY OF BAZOCHES.

GUIDO. Encyclopedic compilation in six books containing geographical passages which in part are edited by M. Pinder and G. Parthey, *Ravennatis anonymi Cosmographia et Guidonis Geographica*, Berlin, 1860, pp. 449–556.

GUILELMUS, GUILLAUME, etc. See WILLIAM.

GUNDISSALINUS, DOMINICUS. See DOMINICUS GONDISALVI.

Günther, Siegmund. *Studien zur Geschichte der mathematischen und physikalischen Geographie*, 3 vols., Halle, 1877–1879. Parts i and ii consist of *Die Lehre von der Erdrundung und Erdbewegung im Mittelalter;* part iii, of *Ältere und neuere Hypothesen über die chronische Versetzung des Erdschwerpunktes durch Wassermassen.*
See Marinelli, *Scritti minori*, vol. i, [1908?].

Günther, Siegmund. *Die kosmographischen Anschauungen des Mittelalters*, in: Deutsche Rundschau für Geographie und Statistik, vol. iv, Vienna, 1882, pp. 249–254, 313–317, 345–352.

Günther, Siegmund. *Notiz zur Geschichte der Klimatologie*, in: Bibliotheca mathematica, no. 3, Stockholm, 1887.

Günther, Siegmund. *Wissenschaftliche Bergbesteigungen in älterer Zeit*, in: Jahresberichte der Geographischen Gesellschaft in München für 1894 und 1895, Munich, 1896, pp. 51–67.

Günther, Siegmund. *Geschichte der Erdkunde*, Leipzig and Vienna, 1904.
A dry and compact summary of the history of geographical science and exploration from antiquity to modern times. Contains many valuable references.

Günther, Siegmund. *Die antike Apokatastasis auf ihre astronomischen und geophysischen Grundlagen geprüft*, in: Bayerische Akademie der Wissenschaften, Sitzungsberichte, Mathematisch-physikalische Klasse, Munich, 1916, pp. 83–112.

Günther, Siegmund. *Optische Beweisung für die Erdkrümmung sonst und jetzt*, in: Bayerische Akademie der Wissenschaften, Sitzungsberichte, Mathematisch-physikalische Klasse, Munich, 1920, pt. 2, pp. 371–385.

GUNTHER OF PAIRIS. *Ligurinus*, edited by C. G. Dümge, Heidelberg, 1812; also in: Migne, *Pat. lat.*, vol. ccxii, cols. 327–476. German translation by T. Vulpinus, *Der Ligurinus Gunthers von Pairis im Elsass . . . etc.*, Strasburg, 1889.
See Pannenborg, A.; Paris, G., *Dissertation critique*, 1872.

GUY OF BAZOCHES. Selections from the letters in: W. Wattenbach, *Aus den Briefen des Guido von Bazoches*, in: Neues Archiv der Gesellschaft für Ältere Deutsche Geschichtskunde, vol. xvi, Hanover, 1891, pp. 69–113.
See above, p. 414, note 152.

Haag, Heinrich. *Die Geschichte des Nullmeridians* (Dissertation, University of Giessen, 1913).
The discussion of the prime meridians used in the Middle Ages appears to be based mainly on the now antiquated work of Lelewel.
See Schoy, *Längenbestimmung*, 1915.

Hammer-Jensen, Ingeborg. *Das sogennante IV. Buch der Meteorologie des Aristoteles*, in: Hermes: Zeitschrift für classische Philologie, vol. 50, Berlin, 1915, pp. 113–136.

Haskins, C. H. *Adelard of Bath*, in: English Historical Review, vol. xxvi, London, 1911, pp. 491–498.
See below, Haskins, *Studies*, 1924.

Haskins, C. H. *The Reception of Arabic Science in England*, in: English Historical Review, vol. xxx, London, 1915, pp. 56–69.
See below, Haskins, *Studies*, 1924.

Haskins, C. H. *Michael Scot and Frederick II*, in: Isis: International Review Devoted to the History of Science and Civilization, vol. iv, Brussels, 1921–1922, pp. 250–275.
See below, Haskins, *Studies*, 1924.

Haskins, C. H. *Science at the Court of the Emperor Frederick II*, in: American Historical Review, vol. xxvii, New York, 1922, pp. 669–694.
See below, Haskins, *Studies*, 1924.

Haskins, C. H. *Studies in the History of Mediaeval Science*, Cambridge, Mass., 1924.
A profound contribution, based largely on research in manuscript sources, to the history of science in the twelfth and thirteenth centuries. Traces the work of translators from the Arabic and Greek and deals with science at the court of the Emperor Frederick II. All the studies by Haskins referred to above appear in this volume in revised form.

Haskins, C. H., and D. P. Lockwood. *The Sicilian Translators of the Twelfth Century and the First Latin Version of Ptolemy's Almagest*, in: Harvard Studies in Classical Philology, vol. xxi, Cambridge, Mass., 1910, pp. 75–102. See also: Haskins, C. H., *Further Notes on the Sicilian Translators of the Twelfth Century*, in *ibid.*, vol. xxiii, 1912, pp. 155–166.
Important for material on early translations of the *Almagest.*
See above, Haskins, *Studies*, 1924.

Hauptmann, E. *Die Erdvermessung der Römer* [*im*] *Raum des heutigen Kriegsschauplatzes bis zur Rheingrenze . . . , Zugleich Lehrbuch der antiken Erdmesskunst*, Bonn, 1915.

Hauréau, B. *Singularités historiques et littéraires*, Paris, 1861.

Hauréau, B. *Mémoire sur quelques chanceliers de l'église de Chartres*, Paris, 1883. Also in: Mémoires de l'Institut Nationale de France, Académie des Inscriptions et Belles-Lettres, vol. xxxi, pt. 2, Paris, 1884, pp. 63–122.

Hauréau, B. *Les oeuvres de Hugues de Saint-Victor: Essai critique*, new edit., Paris, 1886.

Hauréau, B. *Thierry de Chartres, De sex dierum operibus*, in his *Notices et extraits de quelques manuscrits latins de la Bibliothèque Nationale.* Paris, vol. i, 1890, pp. 48–68 (commentary, pp. 48–51; text, pp, 52–68).

Heath, Sir Thomas. *Aristarchus of Samos*, Oxford, 1913.

Heidel, W. A. *Anaximander's Book, the Earliest Known Geographical Treatise*, in: Proceedings of the American Academy of Arts and Sciences, vol. lvi, Boston, 1921, pp. 239–288.

HEIMSKRINGLA. See SNORRI STURLUSON, I.

Hellmann, G., edit., *DENKMÄLER MITTELALTERLICHER METEOROLOGIE* (Neudrucke von Schriften und Karten über

Meteorologie und Erdmagnetismus herausgegeben von G. Hellmann, no. 15), Berlin, 1904.
Collection of texts dealing with meteorology from medieval authors.

HELMOLD. *Chronica Slavorum*, edited by J. M. Lappenberg, in: *Mon. Germ. hist.*, Scriptores, vol. xxi, 1869, pp. 11–99. Also in: *Script. rer. germ. in usum scholarum*, Hanover, 1868. German translation by J. C. M. Laurent, Berlin, 1852; 2nd edit., Leipzig, 1888 (not seen).

HENRY OF HUNTINGDON. *Historiae Anglorum libri VIII*, edited by Thomas Arnold (Rolls Series, no. 72), London, 1879.

HERMANN THE DALMATIAN (HERMANN THE CARINTHIAN, HERMANN THE SLAV, HERMANNUS SECUNDUS). I. *Liber de essentiis*. Unpublished. See Haskins, *Studies*, 1924, pp. 48–49, 56–66. On pp. 62–65 Haskins publishes for the first time the text of two interesting geographical passages. II. Translation of *The Great Book of the Introduction* of Abū Ma'shar under the title *Liber introductorius in astrologiam*. See ABU MA'SHAR. III. Translation of the *Khorazmian Tables* of Al-Khwārizmī. No text of this is known. See above p. 95.

Hermannsson, Halldór. *Bibliography of the Icelandic Sagas and Minor Tales*, in: Islandica, vol. i, Ithaca, N. Y., 1908.

Hermannsson, Halldór. *The Northmen in America (982–c.1500): A Contribution to the Bibliography of the Subject*, in: Islandica. vol, ii, Ithaca, N. Y., 1909.

Hermannsson, Halldór. *Bibliography of the Sagas of the Kings of Norway and Related Sagas and Tales*, in: Islandica, vol. iii, Ithaca, N. Y., 1910.

Hermannson, Halldór. *Bibliography of the Eddas*, in: Islandica, vol. xiii, Ithaca, N. Y., 1920.

HERRAD OF LANDSPERG. *Hortus deliciarum*, edited by A. Straub and G. Keller, Strasburg, 1879–1899.
See Le Noble, A.

Heyd, W. *Histoire du commerce du Levant au moyen âge*, translated from the German into French by F. Raynaud, 2 vols., Leipzig, 1885–1886. French translation reprinted, Leipzig, 1923.
The French translation contains material not to be found in the German original. Still a fundamentally important work on medieval trade with the East.

HILDEGARD OF BINGEN. (I) *Scivias sive visionum ac revelationum libri tres*, (II) *Liber divinorum operum simplicis hominis*, (III) *Liber vitae meritorum*, (IV) *Subtilitates diversarum naturarum creaturarum*, and (V) *Solutiones quaestionum XXXVIII*, all in: Migne, *Pat. lat.*, vol. cxcvii. (VI) *Causae et curae*, edited by Paul Kaiser, Leipzig (Teubner), 1903.
For references to other editions, manuscripts, and secondary works, see Thorndike, *Magic*, 1923, vol. ii, pp. 125–126. See also Singer, *Visions of Saint Hildegard*, 1917.

Histoire littéraire de la France, 35 vols., Paris, 1733ff. 35 vols. had appeared by 1921.
A great collection of bio-bibliographical notices, printed texts, and critical discussions of the literature of Gaul and France. Publication was begun by the Benedictines of the Congregation of St. Maur in the eighteenth century and continued by the Académie des Inscriptions et Belles-Lettres early in the nineteenth.

HISTORIA DE PRAELIIS. See Landgraf, G.

HISTORIA NORWEGIAE, edited by P. A. Munch, in: *Symbolae ad historiam antiquiorem rerum Norvegicarum*, Christiania, 1850. A more critical edition in: Storm, *Mon. hist. Norveg.*, 1880, pp. 69–124.

Hoffmann, Immanuel. *Die Anschauungen der Kirchenväter über Meteorologie* (Dissertation, University of Munich, 1907). (Also as: Münchener geographische Studien herausgegeben von Siegmund Günther, no. 22.)

Hofmeister, Adolf. *Studien über Otto von Freisingen*, in: Neues Archiv der Gesellschaft für Ältere Deutsche Geschichtskunde, vol. xxxvii, Hanover, 1911–1912, pp. 99–161, 663–768.

HONORIUS AUGUSTODUNENSIS, HONORIUS INCLUSUS, HONORIUS OF AUTUN. See *IMAGINE MUNDI, DE.*

HUGH OF ST. VICTOR. I. *Adnotationes elucidatoriae in Pentateuchon*, in: Migne, *Pat. lat.*, vol. clxxv, cols. 29–114. II. *De arca Noë morali*, in: Migne, *op. cit.*, vol. clxxvi, cols. 617–680. III. *De arca Noë mystica*, in: Migne, *op. cit.*, vol. clxxvi, cols. 681–704. IV. *De vanitate mundi*, in: Migne, *op. cit.*, vol. clxxvi, cols. 703–740; also edited by Karl Müller, *Hugo von St. Victor soliloquium De arrha animae und De vanitate mundi* (Kleine Texte für Vorlesung und Übungen, no. 123), Bonn, 1913. V. *De sacramentis*, in: Migne, *op. cit.*, vol. clxxvi, cols. 173–618. VI. *De situ terrarum* (not certainly the work of Hugh of St. Victor), forming bk. III of *Tractatus excerptionum*, in: Migne, *Pat. lat.*, vol. clxxvii, cols. 209–216.
See Hauréau, *Oeuvres*, 1886.

IBN RUSHD (AVERROËS). Commentaries on the works of Aristotle. See [Bernard] Carra de Vaux, article "Ibn Rushd," in: *The Encyclopaedia of Islam*, vol. ii, Leiden and London, 1918, pp. 410–413.
See also Renan, E.

IBN SINĀ (AVICENNA). Commentaries on the works of Aristotle. See ALFRED OF SARESHEL, II; T. J. de Boer, article "Ibn Sina," in: *The Encyclopaedia of Islam*, vol. ii, Leiden and London, 1918, pp. 419–420; and above, p. 401, note 60.

IBN YŪNUS. *Hākimī Tables.* Portions of these tables and the commentaries which accompanied them were published and translated by J. J. A. Caussin de Perceval in: *Notices et extraits des manuscrits de la Bibliothèque Nationale*, vol. vii, Paris, An XII [1803–1804], pp. 16–240; for the description of the measurement of the circumference of the earth, see especially pp. 94, 96, footnote (2).

IDRĪSĪ, Al- (EDRISI). *Geography* (or *Roger Book*, or *Rogerian Description*), in: *Géographie d'Édrisi, traduite de l'Arabe en français*, by P. A. Jaubert (Recueil de voyages et de mémoires publié par la Société de Géographie, vols. v and vi), 2 vols., Paris, 1836–1840. This is the only translation of the whole of Edrisi's *Geography*. More recent and more critical translations of parts are (1) *Description de l'Afrique et de l'Espagne par Edrîsî*, Arabic text with French translation and notes by R. Dozy and M. J. de Goeje, Leiden, 1866; (2) *L'Italia descritta nel "Libro del Re Ruggero" compilato da Edrisi*, Arabic text with Italian translation and notes by M. Amari and C. Schiaparelli, Rome, 1883 (not seen).
See also Pardi, G.

IMAGE DU MONDE, L'. Metrical versions unedited. For text of prose version, see O. H. Prior, *L'Image du monde de Maître Gossouin*, Lausanne, 1913. For Caxton's English translation of 1485, see the same, *Caxton's Mirrour of the World*, London, 1913. On sources see Fant, C.; Fritsche, F.; Le Clerc, V.

See also Langlois, C. V., *Connaissance*, 1911, ch. 5.

IMAGINE MUNDI, DE. In: Migne, *Pat. lat.*, vol. clxxii, cols. 115–188, where it is attributed to Honorius of Autun. See above, p. 403, note 73; pp. 325–326, and p. 481, note 347.
See Doberentz, O.

ISIDORE OF SEVILLE. I. *Etymologiae sive originum libri XX*, edited by W. M. Lindsay, 2 vols., Oxford, 1911. Also in: Migne, *Pat. lat.*, vol. lxxxii, cols. 73–728. See Brehaut, E.; Philipp, H. II. *De natura rerum*, in: Migne, *op. cit.*, vol. lxxxiii, cols. 963–1018. See also above, p. 387, note 79.
See Blázquez y Delgado Aguilera, A.; Brehaut, E.; Gribaudi, P.

ITER AD PARADISUM. See *ALEXANDER THE GREAT, ROMANCE OF*, VI.

ITINERA ET DESCRIPTIONES TERRAE SANCTAE. See Tobler, Titus.

ITINERA HIEROSOLYMITANA. See Tobler, T., and A. Molinier.

ITINÉRAIRES À JERUSALEM. See Michelant, H., and G. Reynaud.

ITINÉRAIRES DE LA TERRE SAINTE . . . traduits de l'hêbreu. See Carmoly, E.

JACQUES DE VITRY. *Historia hierosolymitana*, in: J. Bongars, *Gesta Dei per Francos*, vol. i, Hanover, 1611, pp. 1047–1125. English translation by Aubrey Stewart, *The History of Jerusalem, A. D. 1180, by Jacques de Vitry*, London, 1896 (in: Palestine Pilgrims' Text Society, *Library*, 1897, vol. xi).

James, M. R. See GREGORY, MASTER.

JEROME. *De situ et nominibus locorum Hebraicorum* (or *De Palestinae locis*), in Migne, *Pat. lat.*, vol. xxiii, cols. 859–928.

JERUSALEM ITINERARIES. See Carmoly, E.; Michelant, H., and G. Reynaud; Tobler, T.; Tobler, T., and A. Molinier.

JOHANNES. See JOHN.

JOHANNES, PRESBYTER. See PRESTER JOHN.

JOHANNES HISPANENSIS. See JOHN OF SEVILLE.

JOHN, PRESTER. See PRESTER JOHN.

JOHN OF HOLYWOOD (SACROBOSCO). *De sphaera*, or *Sphaera mundi*, in: *Johannes de Sacrobusto anglici viri clarissimi Spera mundi, impressa Venetiis per Franciscũ Renner de Hailbrun, MCCCCLXXVIII.* This text of the *De sphaera* was printed in the same volume with the *Theorica planetarum* of Gerard of Cremona, q. v. See also Duhem, *Système*, vol. iii, 1915, p. 239, note 4, and p. 240, note 1.

JOHN OF LUNA. See JOHN OF SEVILLE.

JOHN OF SALISBURY. *Opera omnia*, edited by J. A. Giles, Oxford, 1848, and reprinted in Migne, *Pat. lat.*, vol. cxcix, cols. 1–1039. The *Policraticus, sive de nugis curialium et vestigiis philosophorum*, was edited by C. C. J. Webb, 2 vols., Oxford, 1909.

JOHN SCOT ERIGENA. *De divisione naturae*, in: Migne, *Pat. lat.*, vol. cxxii, cols. 439–1022.
See Rand, E. K.

JOHN OF SEVILLE (JOHANNES HISPANENSIS, JOHN OF LUNA). I. Translation of the *On the Elements of Astronomy* of Al-Farghānī was published by Johannes Petreius in Nuremberg, 1537, under the title *Brevis ac perutilis compilatio Alfragani, quod ad rudimenta astronomica est opportunum*. For references to manuscripts, see Woepcke, *Notice*, 1862, pp. 115–117. II. Translation of Abū Ma'shar's *The Great Book of the Introduction*. See Haskins, *Studies*, 1924, p. 45.

JOHN OF WÜRZBURG. *Descriptio terrae sanctae*, in: Tobler, *Descriptiones terrae sanctae*, 1874, pp. 108–192, 415–448. Also in: Migne, *Pat. lat.*, vol. clv, cols. 1054–1090. English translation by Aubrey Stewart, *Description of the Holy Land by John of Würzburg (A. D. 1160–1170)*, London, 1890 (in Palestine Pilgrims' Text Society, *Library*, 1897, vol. v).

Jourdain, Amable. *Recherches critiques sur l'âge et l'origine des traductions latines d'Aristote et sur des commentaires grecs ou arabes employés par les docteurs scholastiques*, 2nd edit., Paris, 1843.

Jourdain, C. B. *Dissertation sur l'état de la philosophie naturelle en Occident et principalement en France pendant la première moitié du XIIe siècle*, Paris, 1838.

Jourdain, C. B. *De l'influence d'Aristote et de ses interprètes sur la découverte du Nouveau-Monde*, Paris, 1861.

Jowett, Benjamin. See PLATO.

Jubinal, A. See BRANDAN, Saint.

JULIUS VALERIUS. See *ALEXANDER THE GREAT, ROMANCE OF*, II, III.

Karl, L. *La Hongrie et les Hongrois dans les chansons de geste*, in: Revue des langues romanes, vol. li, Montpellier, 1908, pp. 5–38.

Khvostov, M. *Istoriya vostochnoi torgovli Greko-Rimskago Egipta (History of the Eastern Trade of Greco-Roman Egypt)*, Kazan, 1907.

KHWĀRIZMĪ, Al-. I. *Kitāb ṣūrat al-arḍ*, edited by C. A. Nallino, with commentary, under title *Al-Ḫuwârizmî e il suo rifacimento della Geografia di Tolomeo*, in: Memorie della Reale Accademia dei Lincei, series 5, Classe di scienze morali, storiche, e filologiche, vol. ii, pt. 1, Rome, 1894 (published 1896). See also von Mžik, *Ptolemaeus*, 1915; the same, *Afrika*, 1916; Nallino, *Al-Khuwarizmi*, 1896; Spitta, W. II. Astronomical tables known as *Khorazmian Tables*, in: H. Suter, *Die astronomischen Tafeln des Muḥammed ibn Mūsā al-Khwārizmī in der Bearbeitung des Maslama ibn Aḥmed al-Madjrīṭī und der latein. Übersetzung des Athelhard von Bath*, etc. (Mémoires de l'Académie Royale des Sciences et des Lettres de Danemark, series 7, Section des lettres, vol. iii, no. 1), Copenhagen, 1914. As to the *Little Sindhind* of Al-Khwārizmī, to which these tables were related, see above, p. 394, note 20.

KING'S MIRROR. See *KONUNGS-SKUGGSJÁ*.

Klotz, Alfred. *Quaestiones Plinianae geographicae* (Quellen und Forschungen zur alten Geschichte und Geographie herausgegeben von W. Sieglin, no. 11), Berlin, 1906.

Koch, Joseph. *Das Meer in der mittelhochdeutschen Epik* (Dissertation, University of Münster, 1910).

Kohlmann, P. W. *Adam von Bremen: Ein Beitrag zur mittelalterlichen Textkritik und Kosmographie* (Leipziger historische Abhandlungen, vol. x), Leipzig, 1908.

KONUNGS-SKUGGSJÁ. *Speculum regale, ein altnorwegischer Dialog*, edited by Oscar Brenner, Munich, 1881. English translation by L. M. Larson, American Scandinavian Foundation, New York, 1917.

Krabbo, Hermann. *Bischof Virgil von Salzburg und seine kosmologischen Ideen*, in: Mitteilungen des Institut für Österreichische Geschichtsforschungen, vol. xxiv, Vienna, 1903, pp. 1–28.

Krabbo, Hermann. *Nordeuropa in der Vorstellung Adams von Bremen*, in: Hansische Geschichtsblätter, vol. xv, Leipzig, 1909, pp. 37–51.

Krejcik, J. See DANTE, V.

Kretschmer, Konrad. *Die physische Erdkunde im christlichen Mittelalter*, in: Geographische Abhandlungen herausgegeben von Albrecht Penck, vol. iv, pt. 1, Vienna and Olmütz, 1889.

The best general summary of medieval theories of physical geography. See the critical review in Marinelli, *Scritti minori*, vol. i, [1908?], pp. 439–448.

Krumbacher, K. *Geschichte der byzantinischen Literatur von Justinian bis zum Ende des Oströmischen Reiches (527–1453)*, Munich, 1890, 2nd edit. 1897 (forming vol. ix, pt. 1 of Iwan von Müller, *Handbuch der klassischen Altertumswissenschaft*).

Kubitschek, Wilhelm. "Karten," article in: *Paulys Real-Encyclopädie der classischen Altertumswissenschaft: Neue Bearbeitung, begonnen von Georg Wissowa*, edited by Wilhelm Kroll, vol. x, pt. 2 (20th half vol.), Stuttgart, 1919, cols. 2022–2149.

LACTANTIUS. *Divinae institutiones*, edited by Samuel Brandt, in: *Corpus script. eccl. lat.*, vol. xix, pt. 1, 1890.

La Marche, R. A. Lecoy de. See Lecoy de La Marche, R. A.

LAMBERT LI TORS. See *ALEXANDER THE GREAT, ROMANCE OF*, VII.

LAMBERT OF ST. OMER. *Liber floridus*. There is no modern edition. For a synopsis, see Migne, *Pat. lat.*, vol. clxiii, cols. 1003ff. For references to manuscripts see Miller, *Mappaemundi*, vol. iii, 1895, pp. 43–46, and Beazley, *Dawn*, vol. ii, 1901, pp. 621–624.

Landgraf, Gustav. *Die Vita Alexandri Magni des Archipresbyters Leo (Historia de preliis)*, Schweinfurt, 1885 (not seen).

LANDNÁMABÓK. For editions see Hermannsson, *Bibl. Icelandic Sagas*, 1908, pp. 70–72. English translations by T. Ellwood, *The Book of the Settlement of Iceland*, Kendal, 1898, and by Vigfusson and York Powell, *Origines Islandicae*, vol. i, 1905, pp. 2–236, 266–274. For corrections of renderings given in the latter, see review by E. Magnússon, in: Saga Book of the Viking Club, vol. iv, pt. 2, London, 1905–1906, pp. 415–467.

Langenmaier, Theodor. *Alte Kenntnis und Kartographie der zentralafrikanischen Seenregion*, in: Mitteilungen der Geographischen Gesellschaft in München, vol. xi, Munich, 1916, pt. 1, pp. 1–144. Also published separately as a dissertation, University of Erlangen, 1916.

An elaborate and detailed study covering the period from Ptolemy to the beginning of the eighteenth century. Extensive bibliography and lists of maps.

Langlois, C. V. *Maître Bernard,* in: Bibliothèque de l'École des Chartes, vol. liv, Paris, 1893, pp. 225–250.

Langlois, C. V. *La connaissance de la nature et du monde au moyen âge d'après quelques écrits français à l'usage des laïcs,* Paris, 1911.
Chapters on popular medieval encyclopedias in French. Throws light on medieval geographic ideas as expressed in these works. A useful bibliography is given (pp. 394–400) of eighty-eight titles of secondary works on references to natural phenomena in the Middle Ages.

Langlois, E. *Tables des noms propres de toute nature compris dans les chansons de geste imprimées,* Paris, 1904.
Includes geographic names.

La Roncière, Charles de. *Histoire de la marine française,* 5 vols., Paris, 1899–1920. Vol. i, 2nd edit., 1909.

LATINO, BRUNETTO. *Le livre du trésor.* Edited by P. Chabaille, *Li livres dou trésor, publié pour la première fois,* Paris, 1863. See the references in C. V. Langlois, *Connaissance,* 1911, pp. 328–337.

Le C[lerc], V[ictor]. *L'Image du monde et autres enseignements,* in: *Histoire littéraire de la France,* vol. xxiii, 1856, pp. 294–335, 836–837.

Lecoy de La Marche, R. A. *Les connaissances géographiques au moyen âge,* in: Revue du monde catholique, vol. lxxix, July-Sept., 1884.

Lelewel, Joachim. *Géographie du moyen âge,* 5 vols. and atlas, Brussels, 1852–1857.
Poorly arranged and written in often incomprehensible French (the author was a Pole). A work of great erudition marred by the hazardous character of the theories put forth. For the most part on Moslem geography.

Le Noble, Alexandre. *Notice sur le Hortus deliciarum, encyclopédie manuscrite composée au douzième siècle par Herrade de Landsberg, abbesse du monastère de Hohenbourg (Sainte Odile) en Alsace, et conservée à la Bibliothèque de Strasbourg,* in: Bibliothèque de l'École des Chartes, vol. i, Paris, 1839, pp. 239–261.

Lenormant, François. *Magog: Fragments d'une étude sur l'ethnographie du chapitre X de la Genèse,* in: Le Muséon: Revue des sciences et des lettres, publiée par la Société Internationale des Lettres et des Sciences, vol. i, Louvain, 1882, pp. 9–48.

LEO ARCHIPRESBYTER. See Landgraf, G.

Lessert, C. Pallu de. *L'oeuvre géographique d'Agrippa et d'Auguste,* in: Mémoires de la Société Nationale des Antiquaires de France, vol. lxviii, pp. 215–298, Paris, 1909. (Also published separately.)

Letronne, A. *Recherches géographiques et critiques sur le livre De mensura orbis terrae, composé en Irlande au commencement du neuvième siècle par Dicuil, suivi du texte restitué,* Paris, 1814.

Letronne, [A.] *Des opinions cosmographiques des pères de l'église, rapprochées des doctrines philosophiques de la Grèce,* in: Revue des deux mondes, series 3, vol. i, Paris, 1834, pp. 601–633.

LIBER DE PROPRIETATIBUS ELEMENTORUM (or *LIBER DE ELEMENTIS*). Latin translation of an Arabic work falsely attributed to Aristotle in the Middle Ages. Duhem, *Système,* vol. ii, 1914, p. 226, note 3, refers to a text to be found on fols. 464 vo–469 vo in an edition of the works of Aristotle published in Venice, 1496, "per Gregorium de Gregoriis expensis Benedicti Fontanae." On manuscripts, see Haskins, *Studies,* 1924, p. 24.

Liebrecht, Felix. *Des Gervasius von Tilbury Otia imperialia*, Hanover, 1856.
Selections from the *Otia imperialia* with commentary to illustrate the development of Germanic mythology.

Lippmann, E. O. von. *Chemisches und Alchemisches aus Aristoteles*, in: Archiv für die Geschichte der Naturwissenschaften und der Technik, vol. ii, Leipzig, 1910, pp. 233–300.

Little, A. G., edit. *Roger Bacon Essays, Contributed by Various Writers on the Commemoration of the Seventh Centenary of His Birth*, Oxford, 1914.

Lloyd, J. E. *A History of Wales from the Earliest Times to the Edwardian Conquest*, 2 vols., London, 1911.

LOMBARD, PETER. *Libri quattuor sententiarum*, in: Migne, *Pat. lat.*, vol. cxcii, cols. 519–962. Critical text in the edition of the *Opera* of Saint Bonaventura, Quaracci, 1882–1889, vols. i–iv.

Lones, T. E. *Aristotle's Researches in Natural Science*, London, 1912.
A useful introduction.

Lowes, J. L. *The Dry Sea and the Carrenare*, in: Modern Philology, vol. iii, Chicago, 1905, pp. 1–46.
On the origins of Chaucer's "Dry Sea" in the history of Prester John and elsewhere.

LUCIDARIUS, edited from the Berlin manuscript by Felix Heidlauf, in: Deutsche Texte des Mittelalters herausgegeben von der Königlich Preussischen Akademie der Wissenschaften, vol. xxviii, Berlin, 1915.
See also above, p. 404, note 82.

Ludwig, Friedrich. *Untersuchungen über die Reise- und Marschgeschwindigkeit im XII. und XIII. Jahrhundert*, Berlin, 1897.
Important investigation of an interesting phase of medieval travel.

Lutz, H. F. *Geographical Studies Among Babylonians and Egyptians*, in: American Anthropologist, vol. xxvi, N. S., Menasha, Wis., 1924, pp. 160–174.

Lynch, Dr. John ("Gratianus Lucius"). *Cambrensis eversus, seu potius historica fides in rebus hibernicis Giraldo Cambrensi abrogata, 1662*, edited and translated by Matthew Kelly for the Irish Celtic Society, 3 vols., Dublin, 1848–1851.

MACROBIUS. *In somnium Scipionis commentarius*, edited by [J. M. N. D.] Nisard in *Macrobe* (*Oeuvres complètes*), *Varron* (*De la langue latine*), *Pomponius Mela* (*Oeuvres complètes*), *avec la traduction en français* (Collection des auteurs latins, avec la traduction en français, publiée sous la direction de M. Nisard), Paris, 1883, pp. 9–116. Also edited by F. Eyssenhardt, Leipzig, 1893.

MAGISTER GREGORIUS. See GREGORY, MASTER.

Magnússon, E. See *LANDNÁMABÓK*.

Mâle, Émile. *L'art religieux du xiiie siècle en France: Étude sur l'iconographie du moyen âge et sur ses sources d'inspiration*, Paris, 1898, 3rd edit., 1910. English translation by Dora Nussey, *Religious Art in France*, London, 1913.
Explains, among other matters, the representation of geographic and cosmographic ideas in medieval sculpture, architecture, stained glass, and other forms of artistic expression.

Mâle, Émile. *L'art religieux du xiie siècle en France: Étude sur les origines de l'iconographie du moyen âge*, Paris, 1922 (not seen).

Mandonnet, Pierre. *Les idées cosmographiques d'Albert le Grand et de St. Thomas d'Aquin et la découverte de l'Amérique*, in: Revue thomiste, vol. i, St. Maximin, 1893.

Mandonnet, Pierre. *Siger de Brabant et l'Averroïsme latin au xiiie siècle*, Fribourg, 1899; 2nd edit.: vol. i, constituting: Les philosophes belges: Textes et études, vol. vi, Louvain, 1911; vol. ii, pt. 1, chs. 1–2, constituting *op. cit.*, vol. vii, Louvain, 1908 (*sic*).

MANEGOLD. *Magistri Manegaldi contra Wolfelmum Coloniensem opusculum*, in: L. Muratori, *Anecdota quae ex Ambrosianae Bibliothecae codicibus nunc primum eruit* —, vol. iv, Padua, 1713, pp. 163–208.

Manitius, Karl. See PTOLEMY, CLAUDIUS, I.

Manitius, M. *Beiträge zur Geschichte der römischen Prosaiker im Mittelalter*, in: Philologus: Zeitschrift für das classische Alterthum, vol. xlix, Göttingen, 1890, pp. 380–384.

Manitius, M. *Philologisches aus alten Bibliothekskatalogen (bis 1300)*, in: Rheinisches Museum, Ergänzungs-Heft, Frankfurt-a-M., 1892.

Manitius, M. *Geschichte der lateinischen Literatur des Mittelalters*, vol. i, Munich, 1911 (forming vol. ix, pt. 2, section 1, of Iwan von Müller, *Handbuch der klassischen Altertumswissenschaft*).

MARCO POLO. See POLO, MARCO.

Marinelli, Giovanni. *La geografia e i padri della chiesa*, in: Bollettino della Società Geografica Italiana, vol. xix, Rome, 1882, pp. 472–498, 532–573. (Also printed separately, Rome, 1882.) Reprinted with additional footnotes by Carlo Errera in *Scritti minori di Giovanni Marinelli*, vol. i, [1908?], pp. 281–383 (see next title). German translation, with an introduction by Siegmund Günther, by Ludwig Neumann entitled *Die Erdkunde bei den Kirchenväter*, Leipzig, 1884.

Marinelli, Giovanni. *Scritti minori di Giovanni Marinelli:* vol. i, *Metodo e storia della geografia*, Florence, [1908?]; vol. ii, *Corografia italiana e questioni didattiche*, Florence, [1920?].

Collection of reprints of important monographs, all of which had appeared previously. Additional editorial notes and bibliographical references are given by the editors in the footnotes. The following are the titles of the most interesting monographs from the point of view of medieval geography, with references to the publications in which they were first published: (vol. i, pp. 63–98) *Note straboniane*, in: Cosmos di Guido Cora, vol. vi, Turin, 1880, pp. 161–180 (also printed separately); (vol. i, pp. 181–279) *Intorno agli studi del Dott. Günther sulla storia della geografia matematica e fisica*, in: Bollettino della Società Geografica Italiana, vol. xvii, Rome, 1880, pp. 309–332, 469–487, 534–543, 585–596 (also printed separately; forms an extensive review and analysis of Günther, *Studien*, 1877–1879); (vol. i, pp. 281–383) *La geografia e i padri della chiesa* (see preceding entry); (vol. i, pp. 385–438) *Gog e Magog: Leggenda geografica*, in: Cosmos di Guido Cora, vol. vii, Turin, 1882–1883, pp. 155–180, 199–207; (vol. i, pp. 439–448) *Un nuovo lavoro sulla storia della geografia medioevale*, in: Bollettino della Società Geografica Italiana, vol. xxvii, Rome, 1890, pp. 232–238 (also printed separately; a review of Kretschmer, *Die physische Erdkunde*, 1889).

Marquart, Josef. *Über das Volkstum der Komanen*, in: Koenigliche Gesellschaft der Wissenschaften zu Göttingen, Abhandlungen, Philologisch-historische Klasse, vol. xiii (N. S.), 1912–1914, pp. 25–238.

MARTIANUS CAPELLA. See CAPELLA, MARTIANUS.

Mas-Latrie, L. de. *Traités de paix et de commerce et documents divers concernant les relations des Chrétiens avec les Arabes de l'Afrique septentrionale au moyen âge*, Paris, 1866.

The introduction deals with the relations between Europe and North Africa in the Middle Ages and incidentally with the extent of European knowledge of North African geography.

Masson, Gustave. *Biblical Literature in France During the Middle Ages: Peter Comestor and Guiart Desmoulins*, in: Journal of Sacred Literature, vol. viii (N. S.), London, 1865, pp. 81–106.

MASTER GREGORY. See GREGORY, MASTER.

MATTHEW PARIS. I. *Chronica maiora*, edited by H. R. Luard (Rolls Series, no. 57), 7 vols., London, 1872–1883. II. On maps see Miller, *Mappaemundi*, vol. iii, 1895, pp. 68–94.

MAUR, RABAN. See RABAN MAUR.

MELA, POMPONIUS. See POMPONIUS MELA.

METHODIUS, PSEUDO–. See Sackur, E.

Meyer, Paul. *Alexandre le Grand dans la littérature française du moyen âge*, 2 vols., Paris, 1886.

Thorough study of the Romance in French literature. Also, in vol. ii, a general treatment of the Latin versions.

MICHAEL PSELLOS. See Zervos, C.

MICHAEL SCOT. I. *Liber introductorius*. Unpublished. On manuscripts see Haskins, *Michael Scot*, 1921–1922, p. 262, note 6; the same, *Studies*, 1924, p. 287, note 95. II. *Liber particularis*. Unpublished. On manuscripts see Haskins, *Michael Scot*, 1921–1922, p. 266, note 7; the same, *Studies*, 1924, p. 290, note 117. III. Translation of Al-Biṭrūjī's *On the Sphere*, unpublished. On manuscripts see Haskins, *Michael Scot*, 1921–1922, p. 251, note 3; the same, *Studies*, 1924, p. 273, note 9. IV. Translation of Aristotle's *De caelo*. Unpublished. On manuscripts see Haskins, *Michael Scot*, 1921–1922, p. 256; the same, *Studies*, 1924, p. 278, note 39.

See Brown, J. W.; Haskins, *Michael Scot*, 1921–1922; the same, *Studies*, 1924, pp. 272–298.

Michelant, H. See *ALEXANDER THE GREAT, ROMANCE OF*, VII.

Michelant, H., and Gaston Reynaud, edits. *ITINÉRAIRES À JERUSALEM ET LA DESCRIPTION DE LA TERRE SAINTE REDIGÉS EN FRANÇAIS AUX XI*e*, XII*e*, ET XIII*e *SIÈCLES*, Geneva, 1882.

Migne, J. P., edit. *PATROLOGIAE CURSUS COMPLETUS, SIVE BIBLIOTHECA . . . . OMNIUM SS. PATRUM, DOCTORUM SCRIPTORUMQUE ECCLESIASTICORUM, QUI AB AEVO APOSTOLICO AD USQUE INNOCENTII III TEMPORA FLORUERUNT . . . : SERIES LATINA*, 221 vols., Paris, 1844–1864. (Referred to in the present work as Migne, *Pat. lat.*)

Great collection of the writings of the Church Fathers and other medieval authors. The texts in many cases are not critical.

Miller, Konrad. *Die Weltkarte des Castorius, genannt die Peutinger'sche Tafel*, Ravensburg, 1888. Colored facsimile and explanatory text.

More complete commentary in the same author's *Itin. Romana*, 1916.

Miller, Konrad. *Mappaemundi, die ältesten Weltkarten*, 6 vols., Stuttgart, 1895–1898.
A series of critical discussions of medieval maps of the world with transliterations of the texts. Profusely illustrated with facsimiles.

Miller, Konrad. *Itineraria Romana: Römische Reisewege an der Hand der Tabula Peutingeriana*, Stuttgart, 1916.
An elaborate commentary on the Peutinger Table, its sources and influence.

Miller, Konrad. *Die Erdmessung im Alterthum und ihr Schicksal*, Stuttgart, 1919.
Summary and synthesis of recent investigations regarding ancient and Moslem estimates of the circumference of the earth. See, however, critical review in Petermanns Mitteilungen, vol. lxviii, Gotha, 1922, p. 27.

MIRABILIA URBIS ROMAE, edited by G. Parthey, Berlin, 1869; also edited by H. Jordan in his: *Topographie der Stadt Rom im Altertum*, vol. ii, Berlin, 1871. English translation by F. M. Nichols, *Mirabilia Urbis Romae: The Marvels of Rome, or a Picture of the Golden City, an English Version of the Mediaeval Guidebook*, London, 1889.

Molinier, A. See Tobler, T.; and A. Molinier.

Mommsen, Theodor. See SOLINUS.

MONUMENTA GERMANIAE HISTORICA, folio series, Hanover, later Berlin, 1826–1874; quarto series, Hanover, later Berlin, 1876ff.
Great collection of historical sources in many volumes relating to the history of Germany and incidentally of Europe as a whole. Divided into five sections: (1) Scriptores; (2) Leges; (3) Diplomata; (4) Epistolae; (5) Antiquitates.
Certain texts published in the *Monumenta* are also edited in *Scriptores rerum germ. in usum scholarum.*

MONUMENTA HISTORICA NORVEGIAE. See Storm, G.

Moore, Edward. *Studies in Dante: Second Series*, Oxford, 1899. Contains *The Genuineness of the Quaestio de aqua et terra*, pp. 303–374.

Moore, Edward. *Studies in Dante: Third Series*, Oxford, 1903. Contains *The Astronomy of Dante*, pp. 1–108; *The Geography of Dante*, pp. 109–143. The last-named is translated into Italian and reviewed at length by G. Boffito and E. Sanesi, *La geografia di Dante secondo Edoardo Moore*, in: Rivista geografica italiana, vol. xii, Florence, 1905, pp. 92–101, 204–215.

Mori, Assunto. *La misurazione eratostenica del grado ed altre notizie geografiche della "Geometria" di Marciano Capella*, in: Rivista geografica italiana, vol. xvii, Florence, 1911, pp. 177–191, 382–391, 584–603.

Mori, Assunto. *La geografia nell'opera di Dante*, in: Atti dell' VIII Congresso Geografico Italiano, vol. i, Florence, 1922, pp. 271–299.
Deals with the traditional geography of Dante's period and with the poet's original contributions in the field of geography.

Moritz, Eduard. *Die geographische Kenntnis von den Nord- und Ostseeküsten bis zum Ende des Mittelalters*, pt. 1, in: Wissenschaftliche Beilage zum Jahresbericht der Sophienschule zu Berlin, Berlin, 1904.

Müller, Carl (Carolus Müllerus), edit. *GEOGRAPHI GRAECI MINORES*, 2 vols., Paris, 1882.
Important collection of the texts of the lesser Greek geographers, with Latin translations.

Mžik, Hans von. *Ptolemaeus und die Karten der arabischen Geographen*, in: Mitteilungen der Kaiserlich-koeniglichen Geographischen Gesellschaft in Wien, vol. lviii, Vienna, 1915, p. 152–176.

Mžik, Hans von. *Afrika nach der arabischen Bearbeitung der Γεωγραφικὴ ὑφήγησις des Claudius Ptolemaeus von Muhammad ibn Mūsā al-Ḫwārizmī*, edited and translated with commentary by —— (Kaiserliche Akademie der Wissenschaften in Wien, Denkschriften, Philosophisch-historische Klasse, vol. lix, Abhandlung 4) Vienna, 1916.

Nallino, C. A. *Al-Khuwarizmi et son remaniement de la Géographie de Ptolémée*, in: Bulletin de la Société Khédiviale de Géographie, series 4, no. 8, Cairo, Feb. 1896, pp. 525–543.
See BATTĀNĪ, Al-; KHWĀRIZMĪ, Al-, I.

Nansen, Fridtjof. *In Northern Mists: Arctic Exploration in Early Times*, 2 vols., New York, 1911.
Elaborate history of theories and explorations. References to the sources and many translations.

NECKAM, ALEXANDER. I. *De naturis rerum libri duo*, edited by Thomas Wright (Rolls Series, no. 34), London, 1863, pp. 1–354. II. *De laudibus divinae sapientiae*, edited by Thomas Wright (Rolls Series, no. 34), London, 1863, pp. 356–503.
See Esposito, M.

Neubauer, A. *Where Are the Ten Tribes?* in: Jewish Quarterly Review, vol. i, London, 1888–1889, pp. 14–28, 95–114, 185–201, 408–423.

Nichols, F. M. See *MIRABILIA URBIS ROMAE*.

NIKULÁS BERGSSON OF THVERÁ, Abbot. Geographical description of the world and itinerary to Rome and the Holy Land (probably in part only the work of Abbot Nikulás). Icelandic text with Latin translation from MS. no. 194 in the Arne Magnússon collection at Copenhagen, in: Werlauff, *Symbolae*, 1821, pp. 9–34. Also in: C. C. Rafn and others, edits., *Antiquités russes d'après les monuments historiques des Islandais et des anciens Scandinaves*, published by the Société Royale des Antiquaires du Nord, 2 vols., Copenhagen, 1850–1852, vol. ii, pp. 394–415.
See above, p. 405, note 90.

Norlind, Arnold. *Das Problem des gegenseitigen Verhältnisses von Land und Wasser und seine Behandlung im Mittelalter* (Lunds Universitets Arsskrift, N. S., pt. 1, vol. xiv, no. 12), Lund and Leipzig, 1918.
On the evolution of ancient and medieval theories regarding the relative positions of earth and water and the interpenetration of the land by channels of water.

Oberhummer, Eugen. *Bericht über Länder- und Völkerkunde der antiken Welt*, in: Geographisches Jahrbuch, Gotha, vols. xix, 1896, xxii, 1899, xxviii, 1905. (See also vol. xxxiv, 1911.)
See above, p. 492.

ODO OF RHEIMS. *Epistola ad Thomam comitem de quodam miraculo S. Thomae Apostoli*, in: Zarncke, *Priester Johannes*, Erste Abhandlung, in: Abhandlungen, vol. vii, 1879, pp. 845–846 (also numbered 19–20).

Oehlmann, E. *Die Alpenpässe im Mittelalter*, in: Jahrbuch für schweizerische Geschichte, Zurich, vol. iii, 1878, pp. 165–289, vol. iv, 1879, pp. 163–324.

Oppert, Gustav. *Der Presbyter Johannes in Sage und Geschichte*, 2nd edit., Berlin, 1870.

ORDERICUS VITALIS. *Historia ecclesiastica*, edited by Auguste le Prévost and Léopold Delisle (Société de l'Histoire de France, [publ.] no. 6), 5 vols., Paris, 1838–1855. Also in Migne, *Pat. lat.*, vol. clxxxviii, cols. 47–984.

ORIGINES ISLANDICAE. See Vigfusson, G., and F. York Powell.

OROSIUS. *Historiarum adversus paganos libri VII*, edited by C. Zangemeister, Leipzig (Teubner), 1889. Also in: *Corpus script. eccles. lat.*, vol. v, 1882. The geographical chapter alone in: Riese, *Geogr. lat. min.*, 1878, pp. 56–70.

OTTO OF FREISING. I. *Chronicon*, edited by Adolf Hofmeister, in: *Scriptores rerum germ. in usum scholarum*, Hanover and Leipzig, 1912. This edition supersedes that in: *Mon. Germ. hist.*, Scriptores, vol. xx, pp. 116–301. II. *Gesta Friderici I imperatoris cum continuatione Rahewini*, edited by G. Waitz, in: *Scriptores rerum germ. in usum scholarum*, Hanover, 1884. This edition supersedes that in: *Mon. Germ. hist.*, Scriptores, vol. xx, pp. 347–491.
See Hofmeister, A.

Palestine Pilgrims' Text Society. *THE LIBRARY OF THE PALESTINE PILGRIMS' TEXT SOCIETY*, 13 vols. and index vol., London, 1897. The individual texts, which were combined under this title, had been issued separately between 1885 and 1897.
English translations of medieval pilgrims' descriptions of the Holy Land.

Pannenborg, A. *Über den Ligurinus*, in: Forschungen zur deutschen Geschichte, vol. xi, Munich, 1871, pp. 163–300.

Pannenborg, A. *Magister Guntherus und seine Schriften*, in: Forschungen zur deutschen Geschichte, vol. xiii, Munich, 1873, pp. 227–331.

Pannenborg, A. *Der Verfasser des Ligurinus: Studien zu den Schriften des Magister Gunther*, Göttingen, 1884.

Paraskévopoulos, J. S. *The Etesiens*, in: Monthly Weather Review, vol. 50, Washington, 1922, pp. 417–422.

Pardi, G. *L'Italia nel XII secolo descritta da un geografo arabo* (Memorie geografiche di Giotto Dainelli pubblicate come supplemento alla "Rivista geografica italiana," no. 38), Florence, 1919.
A discussion of Edrisi's geography of Italy.

Paris, Gaston. *Dissertation critique sur le poème latin du Ligurinus attribué à Gunther*, Paris, 1872.

Paris, Gaston. *La Sicile dans la littérature francaise du moyen âge*, in: Romania, vol. v, Paris, 1876, pp. 108–113.
Aims to suggest possibilities of research rather than to stand as a finished study.

Paris, Gaston. *La littérature française au moyen âge*, 3rd edit., Paris, 1905; 5th edit., 1914. English translation by H. Lynch entitled *Medieval French Literature* in Temple Primer Series, London, 1902.
Covers the eleventh to the fourteenth centuries. A useful summary and interpretation by a foremost authority.

PARIS, MATTHEW. See MATTHEW PARIS.

Parker, H. *The Seven Liberal Arts*, in: English Historical Review, vol. v, London, 1890, pp. 417–461.

PAUL THE DEACON. *Historia gentis Langobardorum*, in: *Mon. Germ. hist., Scriptores rerum langobardicarum*, Hanover, 1878. Also in: *Scriptores rerum germ. in usum scholarum*, Hanover, 1878.

Pelliot, Paul. *Chrétiens d'Asie centrale et d'Extrême-Orient*, in: T'oung Pao, ou archives concernant l'histoire, les langues, la géographie et l'ethnographie de l'Asie orientale, vol. xv, Leiden, 1914, pp. 623–644.
Summary of recent researches. Includes data on the origins of the legend of Prester John.

Peschel, Oscar. *Geschichte der Erdkunde bis auf Alexander von Humboldt und Karl Ritter*, 2nd edit., edited by Sophus Ruge, Munich, 1877.

Peschel, Oscar. *Abhandlungen zur Erd- und Völkerkunde*, 3 vols., Leipzig, 1877–1879.

PETACHIA OF RATISBON. *The Travels of Rabbi Petachia of Ratisbon.* English translation by A. Benisch and W. F. Ainsworth, London, 1856.

PETER ABELARD. See ABELARD, PETER.

PETER ALPHONSI. See ALPHONSI, PETER.

PETER COMESTOR. See COMESTOR, PETER.

PETER LOMBARD. See LOMBARD, PETER.

PEUTINGER TABLE. See Miller, *Weltkarte des Castorius*, 1888; the same, *Itin. Romana*, 1916.

Philipp, Hans. *Die historisch-geographischen Quellen in den Etymologiae des Isidorus von Sivillia* (Quellen und Forschungen zur alten Geschichte und Geographie herausgegeben von W. Sieglin, nos. 25–26), 2 pts., Berlin, 1912–1913.

Philipps, W. R. *The Connection of St. Thomas the Apostle with India*, in: The Indian Antiquary, vol. xxxii, Bombay, 1903, pp. 1–15, 145–160.

PLATO. *Dialogues*, English translation by Benjamin Jowett, *The Dialogues of Plato*, 5 vols., London, 1892.

PLATO OF TIVOLI. Translation of the *Astronomy* of Al-Battānī. Manuscript in: Bibliothèque Nationale MSS., fonds latin, no. 7266, fols. 47–112vo. Also published under the title *Mahometis Albatenii de scientia stellarum liber, cum aliquot additionibus Joannis Regiomontani, ex Bibliotheca Vaticana transcriptus*, Bologna, 1645.
See BATTĀNĪ, Al-; Boncompagni, *Delle versione*, 1851.

PLINY. *Historia naturalis.* Edited by C. Mayhoff, *C. Plinii Secundi Naturalis historiae libri XXXVII*, 6 vols., Leipzig, 1892–1909. The references in the present work are to chapters of this edition. English translation by John Bostock and H. T. Riley, 6 vols. (Bohn's Classical Library), London, 1855–1857. For the geographical books see D. Detlefsen, *Die geographischen Bücher (II, 242–VI Schluss) der Naturalis Historia des C. Plinius Secundus, mit vollständigem kritischen Apparat* (Quellen und Forschungen zur alten Geschichte und Geographie herausgegeben von W. Sieglin, no. 9), Berlin, 1904.
See Detlefsen, *Geographie Afrikas*, 1909; Klotz, A.; Rück, K.

POLO, MARCO. *The Book of Ser Marco Polo the Venetian Concerning the Kingdoms and Marvels of the East*, translated and edited with notes by Sir Henry Yule, 3rd edit. revised by Henri Cordier, 2 vols., London, 1903. Supplemented by: Henri Cordier, *Ser Marco Polo: Notes and Addenda to Sir Henry Yule's Edition, Containing the Results of Recent Research and Discovery*, London and New York, 1920.

POMPONIUS MELA. *De situ orbis*, edited by [J. M. N. D.] Nisard, in: *Macrobe* (*Oeuvres complètes*), *Varron* (*De la langue latine*), *Pomponius Mela* (*Oeuvres complètes*), *avec la traduction en français* (Collection des auteurs latins avec la traduction en français, publiée sous la direction de M. Nisard), Paris, 1883. Also edited by G. Parthey, Berlin, 1867.

Poole, R. L. *Illustrations of the History of Medieval Thought and Learning*, 2nd edit., revised, London, 1920.

Poole, R. L. *The Masters of the Schools at Paris and Chartres in John of Salisbury's Time*, in: English Historical Review, vol. xxxv, London, 1920, pp. 321–342.

Potthast, August. *Bibliotheca historica medii aevi: Wegweiser durch die Geschichtswerke des europäischen Mittelalters bis 1500*, 2nd edit., 2 vols., Berlin, 1896.
See above, pp. 491–492.

Powell, F. York. See SAXO GRAMMATICUS; Vigfusson, G., and F. York Powell.

PRECEPTUM CANONIS PTOLEMEI. Manuscript in Chartres, Bibliothèque Publique, MS. no. 214.

PRESBYTER JOHANNES. See PRESTER JOHN.

PRESTER JOHN. Letters and documents relating to Prester John or supposedly written by him: I. *Letter of Prester John*, in: Friedrich Zarncke, *Der Priester Johannes*, Erste Abhandlung, in: Koeniglich-saechsische Gesellschaft der Wissenschaften, Abhandlungen, Philologisch-historische Classe, vol. vii, Leipzig, 1879, pp. 909–924 (also numbered 83–98). For medieval German translations, see Zarncke, *ibid.*, pp. 947–1028 (also numbered 121–202); for other medieval Latin and English versions, see Zarncke, in: Koeniglich-saechisische Gesellschaft der Wissenschaften, Berichte, vol. xxix, Leipzig, 1877, pp. 111–156; vol. xxx, pt. 1, 1878, pp. 41–46. II. *Elysaeus Account*, in: Zarncke, *Der Priester Johannes*, Zweite Abhandlung, in: Königlich-sächische Gesellschaft der wissenschaften, Abhandlungen, Philologisch-historische Classe, vol. viii, Leipzig, 1876 (*sic*), pp. 122–128. III. *Letter from Pope Alexander III to Prester John*, in: Zarncke. *op. cit.*, Erste Abhandlung, in: Abhandlungen, vol. vii, 1879, pp. 941–944 (also numbered 115–118).
See Bruun, P.; Oppert, G.

Prior, O. H. See *IMAGE DU MONDE, L'*.

PRISCIAN. *Periegesis*, edited by C. Müller, *Geogr. graeci min.*, vol. ii, Paris, 1882, pp. 190–199.

PSELLOS, MICHAEL. See Zervos, C.

PSEUDO-ABDIAS. See ABDIAS, PSEUDO-.

PSEUDO-CALLISTHENES. See *ALEXANDER THE GREAT, ROMANCE OF*, I.

PSEUDO-METHODIUS. See Sackur, E.

PTOLEMY, CLAUDIUS. I. Μαθεματικῆς συντάξεως βιβλία ιγ (*Mathematical Composition* or *Almagest*), edited by J. L. Heiberg, *Claudii Ptolemaei opera quae exstant omnia*, vol. i, pts. 1 and 2, *Syntaxis mathematica*, Leipzig (Teubner), 1898–1903. French translation: *Composition mathématique de Claude Ptolemée traduite pour la première fois du grec en français sur les manuscrits originaux de la Bibliothèque imperiale par M. Halma* (*avec le texte grec*) *et suivie des notes de M. Delambre*, 2 vols., Paris, 1813–1816. German translation: Karl

Manitius, *Des Claudius Ptolemäus Handbuch der Astronomie*, Leipzig (Teubner), 1912. The introduction of the last named gives a brief account of the influence of the *Almagest* in later times. See also above, p. 398, note 32. II. Γεωγραφικὴ ὑφήγησις (*Geography*). Books i-v edited, with Latin translation, by Carolus Müllerus, *Claudii Ptolemaei Geographia*, vol. i, pts. i and 2, and atlas, Paris, 1883–1901. Complete Greek text edited by C. F. A. Nobbe, *Cl. Ptolemaei Geographia*, 3 vols., Leipzig, 1888–1913. Also numerous fifteenth- and sixteenth-century editions.

See Dinse, *Ptolemäus-Karten*, 1913; Fischer, J.; Haskins, C. H., and D. P. Lockwood; Rose, V.; Schütte, G.; Tudeer, L. O. T.

Pullé, F. L. *La cartografia antica dell' India*, pt. 2: *Il medio-evo europeo e il primo rinascimento*, in: Studi italiani di filologia indo-iranica, vol. v, Florence and Pisa, 1905. (Pt. 1, in vol. iv of the Studi italiani, etc., is entitled *Disegno della cartografia antica dell' India*, Florence, 1901, and deals with the period "dai principi fino ai Bizantini e egli Arabi").

RABAN MAUR. *De universo*, in: Migne, *Pat. lat.*, vol. cxi, cols. 9–614. See Bertolini, *I quattro angoli*, 1910.

Rafn, C. C., edit. *ANTIQUITATES AMERICANAE, SIVE SCRIPTORES SEPTENTRIONALES RERUM ANTE-COLUMBIANARUM IN AMERICA*, Societas Regia Antiquariorum Septentrionalium, Copenhagen, 1837; Supplement, 1841.

Collection of sources of Norse voyages to America with commentary.

RAGEWIN. See OTTO OF FREISING, II.

Rahn, J. R. *Die Glasgemälde in der Rosette der Kathedrale von Lausanne: Ein Bild der Welt aus dem XIII. Jahrhundert*, in: Mittheilungen der Antiquarischen Gesellschaft in Zürich, vol. xx, 1878–1879, pp. 31(3)–58 (30).

Deals with medieval geography as displayed on a stained glass window. A facsimile of the window is given.

Rainaud, Armand. *Le continent austral: Hypothèses et découvertes*, Paris, 1893.

History of the evolution of theories regarding the antipodes and austral continent and of explorations to the south from early times to the voyages of Cook.

Rand, E. K. *Johannes Scottus* (Quellen und Forschungen zur lateinischen Philologie des Mittelalters herausgegeben von Ludwig Traube, vol. i, pt. 2), Munich, 1906.

RAVENNA GEOGRAPHER, Anonymous. *Cosmographia*, edited by M. Pinder and G. Parthey, *Ravennatis anonymi Cosmographia et Guidonis Geographica*, Berlin, 1860, pp. 1–445.

RAYMOND OF MARSEILLES. *Marseilles Tables*. Unpublished. On manuscripts see Haskins, *Studies*, 1924, pp. 96–98, and also above, p. 399, note 41. On a geographical table accompanying the Paris manuscript see J. K. Wright, *Knowledge of Latitudes and Longitudes*, 1923, pp. 87–88.

Reeves, A. M. *THE FINDING OF WINELAND THE GOOD: THE HISTORY OF THE ICELANDIC DISCOVERY OF AMERICA*, London, 1890.

Translations of the sources with critical commentary.

Reinhard, R. *Pässe und Strassen in den schweizer Alpen: Topographisch-historische Studien*, Lucerne, 1903.

Reinaud, J. T. *Mémoire géographique, historique, et scientifique sur l'Inde antérieurement au milieu du xie siècle*, etc., Paris, 1849.

Reinaud, J. T., on Moslem geography. See ABŪ-L-FIDĀ.

Renan, Ernest. *Averroès et l'Averroïsme*, 1st edit., Paris, 1852; 3rd edit., Paris, 1866; 4th edit., Paris, 1882.

RERUM BRITANNICARUM MEDII AEVII SCRIPTORES. See "*ROLLS SERIES.*"

Revelli, P. *Una "rosa dei venti" del secolo ix*, in: Bollettino della Società Geografica Italiana, vol. xlvii, Rome, 1910, pp. 269–279.

Rey, E. *Les colonies franques de Syrie aux xiie et xiiie siècles*, Paris, 1883.

On society, economic conditions, and life.

Rey, E. *Géographie historique de la Syrie au temps des croisades: Formation des noms de lieux avec index des localités occupées en Syrie par les Francs au xiie et xiiie siècles*, Geneva. n. d.

Reynaud, G. See Michelant, H., and G. Reynaud.

Riese, Alexander, edit. *GEOGRAPHI LATINI MINORES*, Heilbronn, 1878.

Important collection of texts of the writings of the lesser Latin geographers.

Robbins, F. E. *The Hexaemeral Literature: A Study of the Greek and Latin Commentaries on Genesis* (Doctoral Dissertation, University of Chicago, 1912).

Includes useful material on classical and medieval theories of cosmogony.

ROBERT DE CLARI. *La prise de Constantinople*, edited by Charles Hopf, in his *Chroniques gréco-romanes inédites ou peu connues*, Berlin, 1873, pp. 1–85.

ROBERT GROSSETESTE. See GROSSETESTE, ROBERT.

ROBERT OF RETINES (ROBERT OF KETENE, ROBERT OF CHESTER). I. Translation of the *Astronomy* of Al-Battānī. No text of this is known. See above p. 398, note 36. II. Adaptation to the meridian of London of tables of Az-Zarqalī and Al-Battānī. Unpublished. See Haskins, *Reception*, 1915, p. 64; the same, *Studies*, 1924, p. 122. III. Adaptation of Adelard of Bath's translation of the *Khorazmian Tables* to the meridian of London. Unpublished. See Haskins, *Reception*, 1915, pp. 64–65; the same, *Studies*, 1924, p. 123.

ROGER OF HEREFORD. I. *Theorica planetarum*. Unpublished. II. Tables for the meridian of Hereford based on tables for Toledo and Marseilles. Unpublished.

On manuscripts see Haskins, *Reception*, 1915, p. 66; the same, *Studies*, 1924, p. 125.

ROGER OF HOVEDEN (HOWDEN). *Chronica*, edited by William Stubbs (Rolls Series, no. 51), 4 vols., London, 1868–1871.

Röhricht, Reinhold. *Bibliotheca geographica Palaestinae*, Berlin, 1890.

"*ROLLS SERIES.*" Customary designation of *RERUM BRITANNICARUM MEDII AEVI SCRIPTORES, OR CHRONICLES AND MEMORIALS OF GREAT BRITAIN AND IRELAND DURING THE MIDDLE AGES*, published by authority of Her Majesty's Treasury, under direction of the Master of the Rolls, London, 1858–1891.

Roscher, W. H. *Omphalos*, in: Koeniglich-saechsische Gesellschaft der Wissenschaften, Abhandlungen, Philologisch-historische Klasse, vol. xxix, Leipzig, 1913, pp. 1–140.

Roscher, W. H. *Neue Omphalosstudien*, in: Koeniglich-saechsische Gesellschaft der Wissenschaften, Abhandlungen, Philologisch-historische Klasse, vol. xxi, Leipzig, 1915, pp. 1–90.

Rose, Valentin. *Ptolemäus und die Schule von Toledo*, in: Hermes: Zeitschrift für classische Philologie, vol. viii, Berlin, 1874, pp. 327–349.

Rose, Valentin, on Arnold the Saxon. See ARNOLD THE SAXON.

Rück, Karl. *Auszüge aus der Naturgeschichte des C. Plinius Secundus in einem astronomisch-komputistischen Sammelwerke des achten Jahrhunderts*, Programm des Ludwigsgymnasiums in München, Munich, 1888.

Rück, Karl. *Die Naturalis Historia des Plinius im Mittelalter: Exzerpte aus der Naturalis Historia auf den Bibliotheken zu Lucca, Paris und Leiden*, in: Koeniglich-bayerische Akademie der Wissenschaften zu München, Sitzungsberichte, Philosophisch-philologische und historische Classe, vol. ii, Munich, 1898, pp. 203–318.

Rück, Karl. *Das Exzerpt der Naturalis Historia des Plinius von Robert von Cricklade*, in: Koeniglich-bayerische Akademie der Wissenschaften zu München, Sitzungsberichte, Philosophisch-philolologische und historische Classe, Munich, 1902, pp. 195–285.

RUDOLF OF HOHEN-EMS. See Doberentz, O.

Ruge, Sophus, and Walther Ruge. *Die Litteratur zur Geschichte der Erdkunde vom Mittelalter an*, in: Geographisches Jahrbuch, Gotha, vols. xviii, 1895, pp. 1–60; xx, 1897, pp. 217–248; xxiii, 1900, pp. 173–212; xxvi, 1903, pp. 175–218; xxx, 1907, pp. 329–380.
See above, p. 492.

RUPERT OF DEUTZ. *De sancta trinitate et operibus eius*, in: Migne, *Pat. lat.*, vol. clxvii, cols. 199–1828.

Sackur, Ernst. *Sibyllinische Texte und Forschungen*, Halle, 1898.
Data on early medieval prophecies of the end of the world, including the *Pseudo-Methodius*.

SACROBOSCO. See JOHN OF HOLYWOOD.

SAEWULF. *De situ Hierusalem*, edited by A. d'Avezac (Recueil de voyages et de mémoires publiées par la Société de Géographie, vol. iv, pp. 817–854), Paris, 1839. English translation in Thomas Wright, *Early Travels*, 1848, pp. 31–50. Also translation by Canon Brownlow in Palestine Pilgrims' Text Society, *Library*, vol. iv, London, 1897.

SAGAS, THE. For editions, see Hermannsson, *Bibl. Icelandic Sagas*, 1908; the same, *Bibl. Sagas Kings*, 1910.

Sandys, Sir J. E. *A History of Classical Scholarship*, 3rd edit., vol. i, *From the Sixth Century B.C. to the End of the Middle Ages*, Cambridge, 1921.

Santarem, [M. F.] Le Vicomte de. *Essai sur l'histoire de la cosmographie et de la cartographie pendant le moyen âge*, etc., 3 vols. and atlas, Paris, 1849–1852.
An elaborate study. Vol. i contains a general summary of the development of cartography and geographic theories during the early Middle Ages. Though largely out of date in details, this great work is still one of the primary approaches to medieval geography.

SAXO GRAMMATICUS. *Gesta Danorum*, edited by Alfred Holder, Strasburg, 1886. English translation: *The First Nine Books of the Danish History of Saxo Grammaticus*, translated by Oliver Elton, with some considerations on Saxo's sources, historical methods, and folk lore, by Frederick York Powell, London, 1894.

Scala, R. von. *Das Fortleben der eratosthenischen Masse*, in: Verhandlungen des achtzehnten deutschen Geographentages zu Innsbruck, Berlin, 1912, pp. 206–217.

Schaube, Adolf. *Handelsgeschichte der romanischen Völker des Mittelmeergebiets bis zum Ende der Kreuzzüge*, Munich and Berlin, 1906.

Valuable from the geographic point of view for the light it throws on the extent of travel of Mediterranean peoples during the Middle Ages.

Scheffel, P. H. *Verkehrsgeschichte der Alpen*: vol. i, *Bis zum Ende des Ostgotenreiches Theodorichs des Grossen;* vol. ii, *Das Mittelalter;* Berlin, 1908, 1914.

Schmidt, W. *Über Dante's Stellung in der Geschichte der Kosmographie*, Graz, 1876 (not seen).

Schneid, M. *Die Lehre von der Erdrundung und Erdbewegung im Mittelalter*, in: Historisch-politische Blätter für das katholische Deutschland, vol. lxxx, no. 6, Munich, 1877, pp. 433–451.

Reply from Catholic point of view to a paper of same title in S. Günther's *Studien*, 1877–1879.

Schneider, Artur. *Die abendländische Spekulation des zwölften Jahrhunderts in ihrem Verhältnis zur aristotelischen und jüdisch-arabischen Philosophie*, in: Beiträge zur Geschichte der Philosophie des Mittelalters herausgegeben von C. Baeumker, vol. xvii, pt. 4, Münster, 1915.

Schoy, Carl. *Die geschichtliche Entwicklung der Polhöhenbestimmung bei den älteren Völkern* (Dissertation, University of Munich, 1911).

Schoy, Carl. *Längenbestimmung und Zentralmeridian bei den älteren Völkern*, Mitteilungen der Kaiserlich-koeniglichen Geographischen Gesellschaft in Wien, vol. lviii, Vienna, 1915, pp. 27–62.

Schoy, Carl. *Erdmessungen bei den Arabern*, in: Zeitschrift der Gesellschaft für Erdkunde zu Berlin, 1917, pp. 431–445.

Schoy, Carl. *Aus der astronomischen Geographie der Araber: Originalstudien aus "Al-Qânûn al-Mas'ûdî" des arabischen Astronomen Muḥ. b. Aḥmed Abû'l-Rîḥân al-Bîrûnî (973–1048)*, in: Isis: International Review Devoted to the History of Science and Civilization, vol. v, pt. 1, Brussels, 1923, pp. 51–74.

Schoy, Carl. *The Geography of the Moslems of the Middle Ages*, in: Geographical Review, vol. xiv, New York, 1924, pp. 257–269.

Schröder, Carl. See BRANDAN, Saint.

Schulte, A. *Geschichte des mittelalterlichen Handels und Verkehrs zwischen Westdeutschland und Italien mit Ausschluss von Venedig*, 2 vols., Leipzig, 1900.

Includes data on the Alpine passes in the Middle Ages.

Schütte, Gudmund. *Ptolemy's Maps of Northern Europe*, Copenhagen, 1917.

SCOT, MICHAEL. See MICHAEL SCOT.

SCOTUS ERIGENA. See JOHN SCOT ERIGENA.

SCRIPTORES RERUM GERMANICARUM IN USUM SCHOLARUM EX MONUMENTIS GERMANIAE HISTORICIS RECUSI, Hanover, 1840 ff. The volumes of this series are not numbered, only dated.

Important collection of sources based on *Mon. Germ. hist.* In some cases the texts are revisions and improvements over those of the *Monumenta*.

SCRIPTURE. See *BIBLE.*

SENECA. *Quaestiones naturales*, edited by Alfred Gercke, *Naturalium quaestionum libri VIII*, Leipzig (Teubner), 1907. English translation: John Clarke, *Physical Science in the Time of Nero, Being a Translation of the Quaestiones Naturales of Seneca*, with notes by Sir Archibald Geikie, London, 1910.

Shadwell, C. L. See DANTE, V.

SIGURD THE CRUSADER. *The Saga of Sigurd the Crusader*, in Snorri Sturluson's *Heimskringla*. See Hermannsson, *Bibl. Sagas Kings*, 1910, pp. 19–30. English translation in Thomas Wright, *Early Travels*, 1848, pp. 50–62.

Simar, T. *La géographie de l'Afrique centrale dans l'antiquité et au moyen âge*, Brussels, 1912. Also published in: Revue Congolaise, vol. iii, Brussels, 1912, pp. 1–23, 81–102, 145–169, 225–252, 289–310, 440–441.

A thorough and well-documented study of the evolution of ancient and medieval knowledge of Central Africa.

Singer, Charles. *The Scientific Views and Visions of Saint Hildegard*, in: Charles Singer, edit., *Studies in the History and Method of Science*, vol. i, Oxford, 1917, pp. 1–55.

Singer, Charles. *Daniel of Morley, An English Philosopher of the XIIth Century*, in: Isis: International Review Devoted to the History of Science and Civilization, vol. iii, Brussels, 1920, pp. 263–269.

SITU ORBIS, DE. M. Manitius, edit., *Anonymi de situ orbis*, Stuttgart, 1884.

A compilation dating from the end of the ninth century.

SITU TERRARUM, DE. See HUGH OF ST. VICTOR, VI.

SNORRI STURLUSON. I. *Heimskringla*. On editions see Hermannsson, *Bibl. Sagas Kings*, 1910, pp. 19–30. English translation by William Morris and Eiríkr Magnússon in: *The Saga Library*, vols. iii–vi, London, 1893–1905. II. *Snorra Edda* (*Snorri's Edda*). On editions see Hermannsson, *Bibl. Eddas*, 1920, pp. 74–79. English translations: R. B. Anderson, *The Younger Edda, Also Called Snorre's Edda, or the Prose Edda: An English Version of the Foreword; the Fooling of Gylfe; the Afterword; Brage's Talk; the Afterword to Brage's Talk; and Important Passages of the Poetical Diction* (*Skaldskaparmal*), Chicago, 1880; A. G. Brodeur, *The Prose Edda by Snorri Sturluson*, New York, 1916 (not seen).

SOLINUS. *C. Iulii Solini collectanea rerum memorabilium*, edited by Theodor Mommsen, Berlin, 1895.

See Columba, G. M.

SPECULUM REGALE. See *KONUNGS-SKUGGSJÁ*.

Spitta, Wilhelm. *Die Geographie des Ptolemaeus bei den Arabern*, in: Verhandlungen des fünften internationalen Orientalisten-Congresses, pt. 2, Abhandlungen und Vorträge, vol. i, Berlin, 1882, pp. 19–28.

Stange, Emil. *Arnoldus Saxo, der älteste Enzyklopädist des XIII. Jahrhunderts* (Dissertation, University of Halle, 1885).

Stange, Emil. On Arnold the Saxon, in: Programm des königlichen Gymnasiums zu Erfurt, 1905–1907 (not seen).

Steele, Robert. *Roger Bacon and the State of Science in the Thirteenth Century*, in: Charles Singer, edit., *Studies in the History and Method of Science*, vol. ii, Oxford, 1921, pp. 121–150.

Steele, Robert. See BARTHOLOMEW ANGLICUS.

Stegmann, Otto. *Die Anschauungen des Mittelalters über die endogenen Erscheinungen der Erde* (Dissertation, University of Tübingen, 1913). Also in: Archiv für die Geschichte der Naturwissenschaften und der Technik, vol. iv, Leipzig, 1913, pp. 243–269.

Steinschneider, Moritz. *Études sur Zarkali, astronome arabe du xie siècle, et ses ouvrages*, in: Bollettino di bibliografia e di storia della scienze matematiche e fisiche pubblicato da B. Boncompagni, Rome, vols. xiv, 1881, pp. 171–182; xvi, 1883, pp. 493–527; xvii, 1884, pp. 765–794; xviii, 1885, pp. 343–360; xx, 1887, pp. 1–36, 575–604.

Steinschneider, Moritz. *Die hebräischen Übersetzungen des Mittelalters und die Juden als Dolmetscher: Ein Beitrag zur Literaturgeschichte des Mittelalters*, 2 vols., Berlin, 1893.

Steinschneider, Moritz. *Die europäischen Übersetzungen aus dem Arabischen bis Mitte des 17. Jahrhunderts*, in: Kaiserlich-koenigliche Akademie der Wissenschaften in Wien, Sitzungsberichte, Philosophisch-historische Klasse, Vienna, vol. cxlix, 1905, pp. 1–84; vol. cli, 1906, pp. 1–108.

This and the preceding are arranged alphabetically by authors' or translators' names and by titles.

Storm, Gustav, edit. *MONUMENTA HISTORICA NORVEGIAE: LATINSKE KILDESKRIFTER TIL NORGES HISTORIE I MIDDELALDEREN*, Christiania, 1880.

Collection of texts of several medieval histories of Norway, including *Historia Norwegiae* and Theodricus Monachus, *Historia de antiquitate regum norwagensium.*

Stubbs, William. See BENEDICT OF PETERBOROUGH; GERVASE OF CANTERBURY; ROGER OF HOVEDEN.

STURLUSON, SNORRI. See SNORRI STURLUSON.

Suchier, H. See BRANDAN, Saint.

SULPICIUS SEVERUS. *Dialogus*, in: Migne, *Pat. lat.*, vol. xx, cols. 183–222.

Suter, Heinrich. *Die Mathematiker und Astronomen der Araber und ihre Werke*, in: Abhandlungen zur Geschichte der mathematischen Wissenschaften, etc., vol. x and vol. xiv, pp. 155–185, Leipzig, 1900, 1902.

Suter, Heinrich, on the Kharazmian Tables. See KHWĀRIZMĪ, Al-, II.

SYLVESTER, BERNARD. See BERNARD SYLVESTER.

SYLVESTER II (Pope). See GERBERT.

TABULA PEUTINGERIANA. See Miller, *Weltkarte des Castorius*, 1888; the same, *Itin. Romana*, 1916.

Thalamas, A. *Étude bibliographique de la géographie d'Ératosthène*, Versailles, 1921.

Thalamas, A. *La géographie d'Ératosthène*, Versailles, 1921.

THEODERIC (Pilgrim). *Libellus de locis sanctis*, edited by T. Tobler, St. Gall and Paris, 1865. English translation by Aubrey Stewart, *Theoderich's Description of the Holy Places (circa 1172 A. D.)*, London, 1891 (in: Palestine Pilgrims' Text Society, *Library*, vol. v, London, 1897).

THEODORIC OF CHARTRES. *De sex dierum operibus*, edited by B. Hauréau, in his *Notices et extraits de quelques manuscrits latins de la Bibliothèque Nationale*, vol. i, Paris, 1890, pp. 52–68.

THEODRICUS MONACHUS. *Historia de antiquitate regum norwagiensium*, edited by G. Storm, in his *Mon. hist. Norveg.*, 1880, pp. 1–68.

THIERRY DE CHARTRES. See THEODORIC OF CHARTRES.

THOMAS, Saint (The Apostle). See ACTS OF THE APOSTLES, APOCRYPHAL; Dahlmann, J.; Philipps, W. R.

Thorndike, Lynn. *A History of Magic and Experimental Science During the First Thirteen Centuries of Our Era*, 2 vols., New York, 1923.
Fundamental work on the subject. Contains many valuable bibliographical indications. The researches whose results are embodied in these volumes were largely made in manuscript sources.

Thoroddsen, Thorvaldur. *Geschichte der isländischen Geographie.* Translated into German by A. Gebhart. Vol. i, *Die isländische Geographie bis zum Schlusse des 16. Jahrhunderts*, Leipzig, 1897.
The outstanding work on the historical geography of Iceland. Contains section (pp. 53–92) on the oldest descriptions of Iceland and on Iceland on medieval maps.

Tiander, K. *Poyezdki Skandinavov v Byeloe More (The Voyages of the Scandinavians to the White Sea)*, in: Zapiski Istoriko-Filologicheskago Fakulteta Imperatorskago S. Peterburgskago Universiteta (Journal of the Historical-Philological Faculty of the Imperial University of St. Petersburg), vol. lxxix, 1906.

Tillinghast, W. H. *The Geographical Knowledge of the Ancients Considered in Relation to the Discovery of America*, in: Justin Winsor, edit., *Narrative and Critical History of America*, vol. i, Boston and New York, 1889, ch. i.
Particularly valuable for its bibliographical references.

Tobler, Titus, edit. *DESCRIPTIONES TERRAE SANCTAE EX SAECULO VIII, IX, XII, ET XV*, Leipzig, 1874.
See also THEODERIC (Pilgrim).

Tobler, Titus, edit. *ITINERA ET DESCRIPTIONES TERRAE SANCTAE, LINGUA LATINA SAEC. IV–XI EXARATA*, vol. i (constituting Publications de la Société de l'Orient Latin: Série géographique, no. 1), Geneva, 1877.

Tobler, Titus, and A. Molinier, edits. *ITINERA HIEROSOLYMITANA ET DESCRIPTIONES TERRAE SANCTAE BELLIS SACRIS ANTERIORA ET LATINA LINGUA EXARATA*, vol. i, pt. 2 (constituting Publications de la Société de l'Orient latin: Série géographique, no. 2) Geneva, 1880; vol. ii, edited by A. Molinier and C. Kohler, (constituting *op. cit.*, no. 4), Geneva, 1885.

TOLEDO TABLES. Unpublished. On manuscripts of Latin translations, see Steinschneider, *Études sur Zarkali*, in: Bollettino, vol. xx, 1887, pp. 1–36, 575–604.

Tozer, H. F. *A History of Ancient Geography*, Cambridge, 1897.
Brief, attractively written introduction.

Tudeer, L. O. T. *On the Origin of the Maps Attached to Ptolemy's Geography*, in: Journal of Hellenic Studies, vol. xxxvii, pt. 1, London, 1917, pp. 62–76.

VALERIUS, JULIUS. See *ALEXANDER THE GREAT, ROMANCE OF*, II, III.

Van der Linden, Herman. *Virgile de Salzbourg et les théories cosmographiques au VIIIe siècle*, in: Académie royale de Belgique, Bulletin de la Classe des lettres, Brussels, 1914, pp. 163–187.

Vaux, Carra de. See Carra de Vaux, B.

Vidier, A. *La mappemonde de Théodulfe et la mappemonde de Ripoll (ixe-xie siècle)*, in: Bulletin de géographie historique et descriptive, Paris, 1911, pp. 285–313.

Vigfusson, Gudbrand, and F. York Powell, edits. and transls. *ORIGINES ISLANDICAE: A COLLECTION OF THE MORE IMPORTANT SAGAS AND OTHER NATIVE WRITINGS RELATING TO THE SETTLEMENT AND EARLY HISTORY OF ICELAND*, 2 vols., Oxford, 1905.

VINCENT OF BEAUVAIS. I. *Speculum naturale* and (II) *Speculum historiale*, in: *Bibliotheca mundi Vincentii Burgundii . . . episcopi Bellovacensis speculum quadruplex, opere et studio theologorum Benedictinorum collegii Vedastini*, 4 vols., Douai, 1624. This is the latest complete edition. For bibliographical notes, see J. C. Brunet, *Manuel du libraire*, vol. v, Paris, 1864, cols. 1253–1257. On *Speculum historiale*, see Potthast, *Bibliotheca*, vol. ii, 1896, p. 1095.

VITALIS, ORDERICUS. See ORDERICUS VITALIS.

von Mžik; von Scala; etc. See Mžik, von; Scala, von; etc.

Vulpinus, T. See GUNTHER OF PAIRIS.

WALTER OF CHÂTILLON (WALTER OF LILLE). *Alexandreis*, edited by F. A. W. Müldener, Leipzig (Teubner), 1863. For commentary and bibliography, see Giordano, *Alexandreis*, 1917.

Wattenbach, W. See GUY OF BAZOCHES.

Weinhold, Karl. *Die Polargegenden Europas nach den Vorstellungen des deutschen Mittelalters*, in: Kaiserliche Akademie der Wissenschaften in Wien, Sitzungsberichte, Philosophisch-historische Klasse, vol. lxviii, Vienna, 1871, pp. 783–808.

Data on the voyages northward described by Adam of Bremen, Saxo Grammaticus, and other Germanic writers.

Werlauff, E. C. *Symbolae ad geographiam medii aevi ex monumentis islandicis*, Copenhagen, 1821.

A brief summary of the status of Icelandic geographical knowledge in the Middle Ages together with texts dating from the twelfth century and later.

Werner, Karl. *Die Kosmologie und Naturlehre des scholastischen Mittelalters mit specieller Beziehung auf Wilhelm von Conches*, in: Kaiserliche Akademie der Wissenschaften in Wien, Sitzungsberichte, Philosophisch-historische Classe, vol. lxxv, Vienna, 1873, pp. 309–403.

Werner, Karl. *Die Kosmologie und allgemeine Naturlehre des Roger Baco*, in: Kaiserliche Akademie der Wissenschaften in Wien, Sitzungsberichte, Philosophisch-historische Classe, vol. xciv, Vienna, 1879, pp. 489–612.

Westropp, T. J. *Brasil and the Legendary Islands of the Atlantic*, in: Proceedings of the Royal Irish Academy, vol. xxx, sect. C, no. 8, Dublin, 1912, pp. 223–260.

White, A. D. *A History of the Warfare of Science with Theology in Christendom*, 2 vols., New York, 1895 (reprinted 1920).

A wealth of material is here brought together in an attempt to demonstrate the almost universally adverse influence that theology (as distinguished from religion) has exerted on the development of scientific thought.

WILLIAM OF AUVERGNE. *De universo*, in: *Guillelmi Alverni, episcopi parisiensis, opera*, etc. . . . *curante Blasio Ferronio*, 2 vols., Orléans, 1674 (not seen).

WILLIAM THE BRETON. *Philippidos libri XII*, or *Gesta Philippi regis Franciae*, edited by H. F. Delaborde, in: *Oeuvres de Rigord et de Guillaume le Breton*, vol. ii, Paris, 1885, pp. 1–385. Also in part in: *Mon. Germ. hist.*, Scriptores, vol. xxvi, pp. 319–389.

WILLIAM OF CONCHES. I. *De philosophia mundi* (or *Philosophicarum et astronomicarum institutionum libri, tres* or Περὶ διδαξέων *sive elementorum philosophiae libri quattuor*), edited in: Migne, *Pat. lat.*, vol. clxxii, cols. 39–102, among the works of Honorius of Autun (the references in the present work are to books and chapters of this edition); also in: Migne, *op. cit.*, vol. xc, cols. 1127–1182, among the works of Bede. See above, p. 398, note 28. Book III, chs. 1–11 and 15, dealing with meteorology, are printed in Hellmann, *Denkmäler* 1904, pp. 62–74. II. *Dragmaticon philosophiae.* This is the title given in the manuscripts. This work, which corresponds closely in content to the *De philosophia mundi*, was published at Strasburg, 1567, under the title *Dialogus de substantis physicis, ante annos ducentos confectus a Vuilhelmo Aneponymo philosopho. Item libri tres incerti authoris eiusdem aetatis. I. De calore vitalis. II. De mari aquis. III. De fluminum origine. Industria Guilelmi Grataroli medici* . . . etc. The portion of *Dragmaticon philosophiae* dealing with meteorology is published in Hellmann, *Denkmäler*, 1904, pp. 42–45.

See Werner, *Kosm. Wilhelm von Conches*, 1873.

WILLIAM FITZSTEPHEN. See FITZSTEPHEN, WILLIAM.

WILLIAM OF TYRE. *Historia rerum in partibus transmarinis gestarum*, or *Belli sacri historia*, in: *Recueil des historiens des croisades*, Historiens Occidentaux, vol. i, Paris, 1844. Also in: Migne, *Pat. lat.*, vol. cci, cols. 209–892. Medieval French translation edited by Paulin Paris, *Guillaume de Tyr et ses continuateurs*, 2 vols., Paris, 1879–1880.

Wisotzki, Emil. *Zeitströmungen in der Geographie*, Leipzig, 1897.

Important study of tendencies of geographical thought in the sixteenth to nineteenth centuries, with occasional references to the earlier periods.

Woepcke, Franz. *Notice sur quelques manuscrits arabes . . . relatifs aux mathématiques et récemment acquis par la Bibliothèque Impériale*, in: Journal asiatique, series 5, vol. xix, Paris, 1862, pp. 101–127.

Wolkenhauer, W. *Aus der Geschichte der Kartographie*, in: Deutsche geographische Blätter, vol. xxxiv, Bremen, 1911, pp. 120–129 (on the cartography of the Greeks and Romans), vol. xxxv, 1912, pp. 29–47 (on medieval and Moslem cartography).

A useful summary. Maps are listed and bibliographical data appended.

Wright, J. K. *Notes on the Knowledge of Latitudes and Longitudes in the Middle Ages*, in: Isis: International Review Devoted to the History of Science and Civilization, vol. v, pt. 1, Brussels, 1923, pp. 75–98.

Wright, Thomas, edit. *Popular Treatises on Science Written During the Middle Ages in Anglo-Saxon, Anglo-Norman, and English,* London, 1841.

Wright, Thomas. *EARLY TRAVELS IN PALESTINE* (Bohn's Antiquarian Library), London, 1848.
Translations of medieval books of travel.

Wulf, Maurice de. *Histoire de la philosophie médiévale, précédée d'un aperçu sur la philosophie ancienne,* Louvain, 1900 (4th edit., Louvain, 1912). English translation by P. Coffey entitled *History of Medieval Philosophy,* London and New York, 1909.

Wüstenfeld, F. *Die Übersetzungen arabischer Werke in das Lateinische seit dem XI. Jahrhundert,* in: Abhandlungen der königlichen Gesellschaft der Wissenschaften zu Göttingen, Philologisch-historische Klasse, vol. xxii, no. 2, 1877.
Now superseded by Steinschneider, *Europ. Übersetz.,* 1905–1906.

Xivrey, Berger de. See Berger de Xivrey, J.

York Powell, F. See SAXO GRAMMATICUS; Vigfusson, G., and F. York Powell.

Yule, Sir Henry. *Cathay and the Way Thither,* 2nd edit., edited by Henri Cordier, 4 vols., Hakluyt Society [publs.], series 2, vols. xxxiii, xxxvii, xxxviii, xli, London, 1913–1916.
The best general account of the development of Western knowledge of the Far East in ancient and medieval times. Translations of the sources are given with commentaries. The introduction is an excellent outline of the entire subject.
See also POLO, MARCO.

Zarncke, Friedrich. See PRESTER JOHN.

ZARQALĪ, Az-. *Canons on the Toledo Tables.* Unpublished. On manuscripts, see Steinschneider, *Études sur Zarkali,* in: Bollettino, vol. xx, 1887, pp. 1–36, 575–604.
See GERARD OF CREMONA, II.

Zervos, Charles. *Un philosophe néoplatonicien du XIe siècle, Michel Psellos: Sa vie, son oeuvre, ses luttes philosophiques, son influence,* Paris, 1919.

Zeuss, Kaspar. *Die Deutschen und die Nachbarstämme,* Munich, 1837.
Many quotations from chronicles and medieval historians. Useful in determining changes in the names of tribes.

Zimmer, Heinrich. *Über die frühesten Berührungen der Iren mit den Nordgermanen,* in: Koeniglich Preussiche Akademie der Wissenschaften, Sitzungsberichte, Berlin, 1891, pp. 279–317.

Zöckler, O. *Geschichte der Beziehungen zwischen Theologie und Naturwissenschaft mit besondrer Rücksicht auf Schöpfungsgeschichte,* 2 vols., Gütersloh, 1877–1879: vol. i, *Von den Anfängen der christlichen Kirche bis auf Newton und Leibniz;* vol. ii, *Von Newton und Leibniz bis zur Gegenwart.*
A thorough study of the development of natural science in its relation to theology. The author attempts to show that medieval theology was not adverse to the growth of natural science. Analyses given of theories of the Creation.

Zunz, ——. *Essay on the Geographical Literature of the Jews from the Remotest Times to the Year 1841,* in: *The Itinerary of Rabbi Benjamin of Tudela,* edited by A. Asher, vol. ii, London and Berlin, 1841, pp. 230–317.

INDEX

INDEX

Matter in the Notes (pp. 365–487) that can readily be found from references in the text is omitted in the index.

Titles in the Bibliography (pp. 503–543), as such, are also omitted in the index.

CATALOGUE OF DOVER BOOKS

PHILOSOPHY OF SCIENCE AND MATHEMATICS

FOUNDATIONS OF SCIENCE: THE PHILOSOPHY OF THEORY AND EXPERIMENT, N. R. Campbell. A critique of the most fundamental concepts of science in general and physics in particular. Examines why certain propositions are accepted without question, demarcates science from philosophy, clarifies the understanding of the tools of science. Part One analyzes the presuppositions of scientific thought: existence of the material world, nature of scientific laws, multiplication of probabilities, etc.: Part Two covers the nature of experiment and the application of mathematics: conditions for measurement, relations between numerical laws and theories, laws of error, etc. An appendix covers problems arising from relativity, force, motion, space, and time. A classic in its field. Index. xiii + 565pp. 5⅝ x 8⅜.
S372 Paperbound **$2.95**

THE NATURE OF PHYSICAL THEORY, P. W. Bridgman. Here is how modern physics looks to a highly unorthodox physicist—a Nobel laureate. Pointing out many absurdities of science, and demonstrating the inadequacies of various physical theories, Dr. Bridgman weighs and analyzes the contributions of Einstein, Bohr, Newton, Heisenberg, and many others. This is a non-technical consideration of the correlation of science and reality. Index. xi + 138pp. 5⅜ x 8.
S33 Paperbound **$1.25**

THE VALUE OF SCIENCE, Henri Poincaré. Many of the most mature ideas of the "last scientific universalist" covered with charm and vigor for both the beginning student and the advanced worker. Discusses the nature of scientific truth, whether order is innate in the universe or imposed upon it by man, logical thought versus intuition (relating to math, through the works of Weierstrass, Lie, Klein, Riemann), time and space (relativity, psychological time, simultaneity), Hertz's concept of force, interrelationship of mathematical physics to pure math, values within disciplines of Maxwell, Carnot, Mayer, Newton, Lorentz, etc. Index. iii + 147pp. 5⅜ x 8.
S469 Paperbound **$1.35**

SCIENCE AND HYPOTHESIS, Henri Poincaré. Creative psychology in science. How such concepts as number, magnitude, space, force, classical mechanics were developed, and how the modern scientist uses them in his thought. Hypothesis in physics, theories of modern physics. Introduction by Sir James Larmor. "Few mathematicians have had the breadth of vision of Poincaré, and none is his superior in the gift of clear exposition," E. T. Bell. Index. 272pp. 5⅜ x 8.
S221 Paperbound **$1.35**

PHILOSOPHY AND THE PHYSICISTS, L. S. Stebbing. The philosophical aspects of modern science examined in terms of a lively critical attack on the ideas of Jeans and Eddington. Discusses the task of science, causality, determinism, probability, consciousness, the relation of the world of physics to that of everyday experience. Probes the philosophical significance of the Planck-Bohr concept of discontinuous energy levels, the inferences to be drawn from Heisenberg's Uncertainty Principle, the implications of "becoming" involved in the 2nd law of thermodynamics, and other problems posed by the discarding of Laplacean determinism. 285pp. 5⅜ x 8.
T480 Paperbound **$1.65**

THE PHILOSOPHICAL WRITINGS OF PEIRCE, edited by Justus Buchler. (Formerly published as THE PHILOSOPHY OF PEIRCE.) This is a carefully balanced exposition of Peirce's complete system, written by Peirce himself. It covers such matters as scientific method, pure chance vs. law, symbolic logic, theory of signs, pragmatism, experiment, and other topics. Introduction by Justus Buchler, Columbia University. xvi + 368pp. 5⅜ x 8.
T217 Paperbound **$2.00**

LANGUAGE, TRUTH AND LOGIC, A. Ayer. A clear introduction to the Vienna and Cambridge schools of Logical Positivism. It sets up specific tests by which you can evaluate validity of ideas, etc. Contents: Function of philosophy, elimination of metaphysics, nature of analysis, a priori, truth and probability, etc. 10th printing. "I should like to have written it myself," Bertrand Russell. Index. 160pp. 5⅜ x 8.
T10 Paperbound **$1.25**

MATHEMATICS AND SCIENCE: LAST ESSAYS (DERNIÈRES PENSÉES), Henri Poincaré. Translated by J. W. Bolduc. A posthumous volume of articles and lectures by the great French mathematician, philosopher, scientist. Here are nine pieces, never before translated into English, on such subjects as The Evolution of Laws, Space and Time, Space and 3 Dimensions, The Logic of infinity in Mathematics (discussing Russell's theory of types), Mathematics and Logic, The Quantum Theory and its Modern Applications, Relationship Between Matter and Ether, Ethics and Science and The Moral Alliance. First English translation of Dernières Pensées. New index. viii + 128pp. 5⅜ x 8½.
S1101 Paperbound **$1.25**

THE PSYCHOLOGY OF INVENTION IN THE MATHEMATICAL FIELD, J. Hadamard. Where do ideas come from? What role does the unconscious play? Are ideas best developed by mathematical reasoning, word reasoning, visualization? What are the methods used by Einstein, Poincaré, Galton, Riemann? How can these techniques be applied by others? Hadamard, one of the world's leading mathematicians, discusses these and other questions. xiii + 145pp. 5⅜ x 8.
T107 Paperbound **$1.25**

EXPERIMENT AND THEORY IN PHYSICS, Max Born. A Nobel laureate examines the nature and value of the counterclaims of experiment and theory in physics. Synthetic versus analytical scientific advances are analyzed in the work of Einstein, Bohr, Heisenberg, Planck, Eddington, Milne, and others by a fellow participant. 44pp. 5⅜ x 8. S308 Paperbound **75¢**

THE PHILOSOPHY OF SPACE AND TIME, H. Reichenbach. An important landmark in the development of the empiricist conception of geometry, covering the problem of the foundations of geometry, the theory of time, the consequences of Einstein's relativity, including: relations between theory and observations; coordinate and metrical properties of space; the psychological problem of visual intuition of non-Euclidean structures; and many other important topics in modern science and philosophy. The majority of ideas require only a knowledge of intermediate math. Introduction by R. Carnap. 49 figures. Index. xviii + 296pp. 5⅜ x 8.
S443 Paperbound **$2.00**

OBSERVATION AND INTERPRETATION IN THE PHILOSOPHY OF PHYSICS: WITH SPECIAL REFERENCE TO QUANTUM MECHANICS, Edited by S. Körner. A collection of papers by philosophers and physicists arising out of a symposium held at Bristol, England in 1957 under the auspices of the Colston Research Society. One of the most important contributions to the philosophy of science in recent years. The discussions center around the adequacy or inadequacy of quantum mechanics in its orthodox formulations. Among the contributors are A. J. Ayer, D. Bohm, K. Popper, F. Bopp, S. Körner, J. P. Vigier, M. Polanyi, P. K. Feyerabend, W. C. Kneale. W. B. Gallie, G. Ryle, Sir Charles Darwin, and R. B. Braithwaite. xiv + 218pp. 5⅜ x 8½.
S131 Paperbound **$1.60**

SPACE AND TIME IN CONTEMPORARY PHYSICS: AN INTRODUCTION TO THE THEORY OF RELATIVITY AND GRAVITATION, Moritz Schlick. Exposition of the theory of relativity by the leader of the famed "Vienna Circle." Its essential purpose is to describe the physical doctrines of special and general relativity with particular reference to their philosophical significance. Explanations of such topics as the geometrical relativity of space, the connection with inertia and gravitation, the measure-determination of the space-time continuum, the finite universe, etc., with their philosophical ramifications. Index. xii + 89pp. 5⅜ x 8½.
T1008 Paperbound **$1.00**

SUBSTANCE AND FUNCTION, & EINSTEIN'S THEORY OF RELATIVITY, Ernst Cassirer. Two books bound as one. Cassirer establishes a philosophy of the exact sciences that takes into consideration newer developments in mathematics, and also shows historical connections. Partial contents: Aristotelian logic, Mill's analysis, Helmholtz & Kronecker, Russell & cardinal numbers, Euclidean vs. non-Euclidean geometry, Einstein's relativity. Bibliography. Index. xxi + 465pp. 5⅜ x 8.
T50 Paperbound **$2.25**

PRINCIPLES OF MECHANICS, Heinrich Hertz. This last work by the great 19th century physicist is not only a classic, but of great interest in the logic of science. Creating a new system of mechanics based upon space, time, and mass, it returns to axiomatic analysis, to understanding of the formal or structural aspects of science, taking into account logic, observation, and a priori elements. Of great historical importance to Poincaré, Carnap, Einstein, Milne. A 20-page introduction by R. S. Cohen, Wesleyan University, analyzes the implications of Hertz's thought and the logic of science. Bibliography. 13-page introduction by Helmholtz. xlii + 274pp. 5⅜ x 8.
S316 Clothbound **$3.50**
S317 Paperbound **$1.85**

THE ANALYSIS OF MATTER, Bertrand Russell. How do our senses concord with the new physics? This volume covers such topics as logical analysis of physics, prerelativity physics, causality, scientific inference, physics and perception, special and general relativity, Weyl's theory, tensors, invariants and their physical interpretation, periodicity and qualitative series. "The most thorough treatment of the subject that has yet been published," THE NATION. Introduction by L. E. Denonn. 422pp. 5⅜ x 8. T231 Paperbound **$1.95**

FOUNDATIONS OF GEOMETRY, Bertrand Russell. Analyzing basic problems in the overlap area between mathematics and philosophy, Nobel laureate Russell examines the nature of geometrical knowledge, the nature of geometry, and the application of geometry to space. It covers the history of non-Euclidean geometry, philosophic interpretations of geometry—especially Kant—projective and metrical geometry. This is most interesting as the solution offered in 1897 by a great mind to a problem still current. New introduction by Prof. Morris Kline of N. Y. University. xii + 201pp. 5⅜ x 8.
S232 Clothbound **$3.25**
S233 Paperbound **$1.75**

IDENTITY AND REALITY, Emile Meyerson. Called by Einstein a "brilliant study in the theory of knowledge," this book by the renowned Franco-German thinker is a major treatise in the philosophy of science and epistemology. Thorough, critical inquiries into causality, scientific laws, conservation of matter and energy, the unity of matter, Carnot's principle, the irrational, the elimination of time. Searches out the solutions of epistemological questions that form the bases of the scientific method. Authorized translation by Kate Loewenberg. Author's prefaces. Editor's preface. Appendices. Index. 495pp. 5⅜ x 8½.
T65 Paperbound **$2.25**

ESSAYS IN EXPERIMENTAL LOGIC, John Dewey. This stimulating series of essays touches upon the relationship between inquiry and experience, dependence of knowledge upon thought, character of logic; judgments of practice, data and meanings, stimuli of thought, etc. Index. viii + 444pp. 5⅜ x 8.
T73 Paperbound **$1.95**

GEOLOGY, GEOGRAPHY, METEOROLOGY

PRINCIPLES OF STRATIGRAPHY, A. W. Grabau. Classic of 20th century geology, unmatched in scope and comprehensiveness. Nearly 600 pages cover the structure and origins of every kind of sedimentary, hydrogenic, oceanic, pyroclastic, atmoclastic, hydroclastic, marine hydroclastic, and bioclastic rock; metamorphism; erosion; etc. Includes also the constitution of the atmosphere; morphology of oceans, rivers, glaciers; volcanic activities; faults and earthquakes; and fundamental principles of paleontology (nearly 200 pages). New introduction by Prof. M. Kay, Columbia U. 1277 bibliographical entries. 264 diagrams. Tables, maps, etc. Two volume set. Total of xxxii + 1185pp. 5⅜ x 8.
S686 Vol I Paperbound **$2.50**
S687 Vol II Paperbound **$2.50**
The set **$5.00**

TREATISE ON SEDIMENTATION, William H. Twenhofel. A milestone in the history of geology, this two-volume work, prepared under the auspices of the United States Research Council, contains practically everything known about sedimentation up to 1932. Brings together all the findings of leading American and foreign geologists and geographers and has never been surpassed for completeness, thoroughness of description, or accuracy of detail. Vol. 1 discusses the sources and production of sediments, their transportation, deposition, diagenesis, and lithification. Also modification of sediments by organisms and topographical, climatic, etc. conditions which contribute to the alteration of sedimentary processes. 220 pages deal with products of sedimentation: minerals, limestones, dolomites, coals, etc. Vol. 2 continues the examination of products such as gypsum and saline residues, silica, strontium, manganese, etc. An extensive exposition of structures, textures and colors of sediments: stratification, cross-lamination, ripple mark, oolitic and pisolitic textures, etc. Chapters on environments or realms of sedimentation and field and laboratory techniques are also included. Indispensable to modern-day geologists and students. Index. List of authors cited. 1733-item bibliography. 121 diagrams. Total of xxxiii + 926pp. 5⅜ x 8½.
Vol. I: S950 Paperbound **$2.50**
Vol. II: S951 Paperbound **$2.50**
Two volume set Paperbound **$5.00**

THE EVOLUTION OF THE IGNEOUS ROCKS, N. L. Bowen. Invaluable serious introduction applies techniques of physics and chemistry to explain igneous rock diversity in terms of chemical composition and fractional crystallization. Discusses liquid immiscibility in silicate magmas, crystal sorting, liquid lines of descent, fractional resorption of complex minerals, petrogenesis, etc. Of prime importance to geologists & mining engineers, also to physicists, chemists working with high temperatures and pressures. "Most important," TIMES, London. 3 indexes. 263 bibliographic notes. 82 figures. xviii + 334pp. 5⅜ x 8. S311 Paperbound **$2.00**

INTERNAL CONSTITUTION OF THE EARTH, edited by **Beno Gutenberg.** Completely revised. Brought up-to-date, reset. Prepared for the National Research Council this is a complete & thorough coverage of such topics as earth origins, continent formation, nature & behavior of the earth's core, petrology of the crust, cooling forces in the core, seismic & earthquake material, gravity, elastic constants, strain characteristics and similar topics. "One is filled with admiration . . . a high standard . . . there is no reader who will not learn something from this book," London, Edinburgh, Dublin, Philosophic Magazine. Largest bibliography in print: 1127 classified items. Indexes. Tables of constants. 43 diagrams. 439pp. 6⅛ x 9¼.
S414 Paperbound **$3.00**

HYDROLOGY, edited by **Oscar E. Meinzer.** Prepared for the National Research Council. Detailed complete reference library on precipitation, evaporation, snow, snow surveying, glaciers, lakes, infiltration, soil moisture, ground water, runoff, drought, physical changes produced by water, hydrology of limestone terranes, etc. Practical in application, especially valuable for engineers. 24 experts have created "the most up-to-date, most complete treatment of the subject," AM. ASSOC. of PETROLEUM GEOLOGISTS. Bibliography. Index. 165 illustrations. xi + 712pp. 6⅛ x 9¼. S191 Paperbound **$3.25**

SNOW CRYSTALS, W. A. Bentley and W. J. Humphreys. Over 200 pages of Bentley's famous microphotographs of snow flakes—the product of painstaking, methodical work at his Jericho, Vermont studio. The pictures, which also include plates of frost, glaze and dew on vegetation, spider webs, windowpanes; sleet; graupel or soft hail, were chosen both for their scientific interest and their aesthetic qualities. The wonder of nature's diversity is exhibited in the intricate, beautiful patterns of the snow flakes. Introductory text by W. J. Humphreys. Selected bibliography. 2,453 illustrations. 224pp. 8 x 10¼. T287 Paperbound **$2.95**

PHYSICS OF THE AIR, W. J. Humphreys. A very thorough coverage of classical materials and theories in meteorology . . . written by one of this century's most highly respected physical meteorologists. Contains the standard account in English of atmospheric optics. 5 main sections: Mechanics and Thermodynamics of the Atmosphere, Atmospheric Electricity and Auroras, Meteorological Acoustics, Atmospheric Optics, and Factors of Climatic Control. Under these headings, topics covered are: theoretical relations between temperature, pressure, and volume in the atmosphere; composition, pressure, and density; circulation; evaporation and condensation; fog, clouds, thunderstorms, lightning; aurora polaris; principal ice-age theories; etc. New preface by Prof. Julius London. 226 illustrations. Index. xviii + 676pp. 5⅜ x 8½. S1044 Paperbound **$3.00**

URANIUM PROSPECTING, H. L. Barnes. For immediate practical use, professional geologist considers uranium ores, geological occurrences, field conditions, all aspects of highly profitable occupation. Index. Bibliography. x + 117pp. 5⅜ x 8. T309 Paperbound **$1.00**

SELECTED PAPERS IN THE THEORY OF THERMAL CONVECTION: WITH SPECIAL APPLICATION TO THE EARTH'S PLANETARY ATMOSPHERE, Edited by Barry Saltzman. An indispensable volume for anyone interested in the motions of the earth's atmosphere. 25 basic theoretical papers on thermal convection by major scientists, past and present: Helmholtz, Overbeck, Jeffreys, Rayleigh, G. I. Taylor, Chandrasekhar, A. R. Low, Rossby, Davies, Charney, Eady, Phillips, Pellew and Southwell, Elbert, Fjortoft, and H.-L. Kuo. Bibliography. x + 461pp. 6⅛ x 9¼. S171 Paperbound **$3.00**

THE FOUNDERS OF GEOLOGY, Sir Archibald Geikie. Survey of the high moments and the work of the major figures of the period in which the main foundations of modern geology were laid—the latter half of the 18th century to the first half of the 19th. The developments in the science during this era centering around the lives and accomplishments of the great contributors: Palissy, Guettard, Demarest, Pallas, Lehmann, Füchsel, Werner, Hutton, Playfair, Sir James Hall, Cuvier, Lyell, Logan, Darwin, Agassiz, Nicol, and others. Comprehensive and readable. Index. xi + 486pp. 5⅜ x 8½. T352 Paperbound **$2.25**

THE BIRTH AND DEVELOPMENT OF THE GEOLOGICAL SCIENCES, F. D. Adams. Most thorough history of the earth sciences ever written. Geological thought from earliest times to the end of the 19th century, covering over 300 early thinkers & systems: fossils & their explanation, vulcanists vs. neptunists, figured stones & paleontology, generation of stones, dozens of similar topics. 91 illustrations, including medieval, renaissance woodcuts, etc. Index. 632 footnotes, mostly bibliographical. 511pp. 5⅜ x 8. T5 Paperbound **$2.25**

A HISTORY OF ANCIENT GEOGRAPHY, E. H. Bunbury. Standard study, in English, of ancient geography; never equalled for scope, detail. First full account of history of geography from Greeks' first world picture based on mariners, through Ptolemy. Discusses every important map, discovery, figure, travel, expedition, war, conjecture, narrative, bearing on subject. Chapters on Homeric geography, Herodotus, Alexander expedition, Strabo, Pliny, Ptolemy, would stand alone as exhaustive monographs. Includes minor geographers, men not usually regarded in this context: Hecataeus, Pythea, Hipparchus, Artemidorus, Marinus of Tyre, etc. Uses information gleaned from military campaigns such as Punic wars, Hannibal's passage of Alps, campaigns of Lucullus, Pompey, Caesar's wars, the Trojan war. New introduction by W. H. Stahl, Brooklyn College. Bibliography. Index. 20 maps. 1426pp. 5⅜ x 8.
T570-1, clothbound, 2 volume set **$12.50**

DE RE METALLICA, Georgius Agricola. 400-year old classic translated, annotated by former President Herbert Hoover. The first scientific study of mineralogy and mining, for over 200 years after its appearance in 1556, it was the standard treatise. 12 books, exhaustively annotated, discuss the history of mining, selection of sites, types of deposits, making pits, shafts, ventilating, pumps, crushing machinery; assaying, smelting, refining metals; also salt, alum, nitre, glass making. Definitive edition, with all 289 16th century woodcuts of the original. Biographical, historical introductions, bibliography, survey of ancient authors. Indexes. A fascinating book for anyone interested in art, history of science, geology, etc. Deluxe edition. 289 illustrations. 672pp. 6¾ x 10¾. Library cloth. S6 Clothbound **$10.00**

GEOGRAPHICAL ESSAYS, William Morris Davis. Modern geography & geomorphology rest on the fundamental work of this scientist. 26 famous essays presenting most important theories, field researches. Partial contents: Geographical Cycle, Plains of Marine and Subaerial Denudation, The Peneplain, Rivers and Valleys of Pennsylvania, Outline of Cape Cod, Sculpture of Mountains by Glaciers, etc. "Long the leader & guide," ECONOMIC GEOGRAPHY. "Part of the very texture of geography . . . models of clear thought," GEOGRAPHIC REVIEW. Index. 130 figures. vi + 777pp. 5⅜ x 8. S383 Paperbound **$2.95**

Prices subject to change without notice.

Dover publishes books on art, music, philosophy, literature, languages, history, social sciences, psychology, handcrafts, orientalia, puzzles and entertainments, chess, pets and gardens, books explaining science, intermediate and higher mathematics, mathematical physics, engineering, biological sciences, earth sciences, classics of science, etc. Write to:

Dept. catrr.
Dover Publications, Inc.
180 Varick Street, N.Y. 14, N.Y.